Agricultural

Iowa State University Press
Ames, Iowa, U.S.A.

AGRICULTURAL FINANCE

Fifth Edition

Finance

FIFTH EDITION

AARON G. NELSON

UNIVERSITY OF ARIZONA

WILLIAM G. MURRAY

IOWA STATE UNIVERSITY

ABOUT THE AUTHORS

AARON G. NELSON joined the Economic Research Service, USDA, as agricultural economist in May, 1967. Prior to that time he was professor of agricultural economics at the University of Arizona, and he continues to hold this title. He holds the B.S. degree from Utah State University and the M.S. and Ph.D. degrees from Iowa State University. He has been assistant professor in the Department of Agricultural Economics at South Dakota State University; agricultural economist, USDA; and director of research and education, Farm Credit Banks, Omaha, Nebraska. Dr. Nelson is a consultant for the Arizona Bankers Agricultural Credit Conference and for the Wellton-Mohawk Irrigation and Drainage District, and a director of the Inter-American Life Insurance Company. He is a member of the American Farm Economic Association and currently is serving as a member of the Published Research Awards Committee. He also is a member of the Western Farm Economics Association and a past recipient of a Certificate of Merit for outstanding accomplishment in Agricultural Economics. In addition, he is a member of the International Association of Agricultural Economists, the American Society of Farm Managers and Rural Appraisers, the Arizona Society of Farm Managers and Rural Appraisers, Gamma Sigma Delta, Alpha Zeta, and Pi Gamma Mu. Besides this book he has to his credit numerous bulletins and articles.

WILLIAM G. MURRAY, professor of economics and former head of the Department of Economics and Sociology at Iowa State University, holds the B.A. degree from Coe College, the M.A. degree from Harvard University, and the Ph.D. degree from the University of Minnesota. In 1965 he received the Iowa State University Faculty Citation. He has served as chief economist of the Farm Credit Administration and research director of the Iowa Taxation Study Committee. He has been a member of the board of directors of the University Bank and Trust Company since 1946. Dr. Murray is a member and 1948 past president of the American Farm Economic Association. He is also a member of the American Economics Association, the National Tax Association, the American Society of Farm Managers and Rural Appraisers, American Institute of Real Estate Appraisers, Phi Beta Kappa, Phi Kappa Phi, and Gamma Sigma Delta. Besides this book he is the author of *Farm Appraisal and Valuation*.

© 1941, 1947, 1953, 1960, 1967 The Iowa State University Press, Ames, Iowa, U.S.A. All rights reserved. Printed in the U.S.A. First edition, 1941; Second edition, 1947; Third edition, 1953; Fourth edition, 1960; Fifth edition, 1967; Revised printing, 1968. Library of Congress Catalog Card Number: 67–26063. Stock #0050.

PREFACE

THIS EDITION of *Agricultural Finance* is a major revision of the fourth edition (1960), which was an even more substantial revision of the 1953 edition. The basic organization of the text remains the same, with Part I containing an emphasis on principles and Part II an analysis of lending institutions and a portrayal of their loan policies and procedures. Much new material has been added, however. Since agricultural finance is given as a "service course" in many colleges and universities, a chapter on basic economic principles has been included to provide economic background needed in the course. Two other new chapters have been added: one on farm financial management to introduce students to this important area in financing the farm business, and a concluding summary in Part II to help the student obtain a proper perspective of the various types of lenders. Selected financial tables are included in the Appendix to facilitate an understanding of concepts and to help in solving problems presented in the body of the text.

A number of chapters in the 1960 fourth edition were substantially revised and in some cases completely rewritten. The first chapter was broadened to portray an overall framework of agricultural finance, including both macro- and microfinance aspects. The chapter on basic concepts involved in analyzing returns as a guide in use of credit was largely rewritten to base the analysis more specifically on economic principles. The chapter on income statement analysis was completely rewritten and the one on balance sheet analysis partly rewritten to incorporate a new farm illustration

v

and to relate the analysis more directly to returns produced and to risk-bearing ability. Much of the material on interest rates also is new. New information on the Uniform Commercial Code was added in the chapter on legal aspects of using credit. New material was included in the discussion of merchant and dealer credit, and the material on the other types of lenders was completely up-dated.

This fifth edition (and to a somewhat lesser extent the fourth edition) focuses attention on basic finance principles, referred to as the Three R's of Credit: (1) *Returns produced*, (2) *Repayment capacity*, and (3) *Risk-bearing ability*. Much of the material in Part I has been organized to bear directly on these three basic principles. In the final chapter the various types of lending institution are analyzed in terms of this framework.

The authors gratefully acknowledge the assistance of a number of professional people who contributed to this work. Robert S. Firch read most of the manuscript for the fifth edition and gave helpful suggestions, advice, and counsel. V. F. Bowland, Jr., read and gave helpful suggestions on Chapters 2, 3, and 5. H. B. Howell provided data for the farm used as an example in Chapters 6, 9, and 13, and also reviewed the manuscript for these chapters. Lyle M. McIff gave suggestions on setup and analysis of the income statement and balance sheet, and also reviewed the related manuscript. John R. Brake reviewed Chapter 7 and gave pertinent comments and suggestions. Ray J. Davis reviewed the chapter related to legal aspects of use of credit, giving special attention to the new material pertaining to the Uniform Commercial Code. M. L. Upchurch read the chapter on financial management and contributed a number of helpful suggestions. Robert H. Marshall read parts of the chapters related to commercial banks. Marshall Burkes, LeRoy F. Rogers, Odell Walker, G. A. Peterson, and Donald S. Moore provided material or data useful in preparation of the text. Russell C. Engberg, M. M. Kelso, John D. Lyons, E. J. Brown, Martin Planting, and Nicholas A. Jamba reviewed selected chapters at the time the fourth edition was prepared, which contributed to the current edition.

In addition, various governmental agencies and lenders provided data, material, and assistance. Norman J. Wall and his associates in the Agricultural Finance Branch, Farm Production Economics Division, ERS, were, as always, very helpful in providing data, charts, and material. The major part of the load was shouldered by Carson D. Evans for the fifth edition. Lawrence A. Jones also provided data and gave suggestions on manuscript dealing with hail insurance. C. H. Grainger, Agricultural Stabilization and Conservation Service, provided data and suggestions on text material pertaining to the Commodity Credit Corporation. John N. Luft, Federal Crop Insurance Corporation, provided data and material on operations of the Corporation. Wilellyn Morelle, Board of Governors, Federal Reserve System; John A. Hopkin, Bank of America; Dean E. McKee, Deere and Company; and E. S. Rumely, Ford Motor Company, provided material on merchant and dealer credit.

Major revisions were not needed in the material dealing with commercial banks. Consequently, appreciation is again expressed to Lawrence E. Kreider, ABA; R. J. Doll, Federal Reserve Bank of Kansas City; and Ernest T. Baughman and associates, Federal Reserve Bank of Chicago, for their review and suggestions on these chapters for the fourth edition. Similarly, major changes were not called for in chapters on insurance companies and, therefore, we renew our thanks to Vern A. Englehorn, Western Farm Management Company; Robert G. Parvin, The Equitable Life Assurance Society; F. E. Ferguson, The Northwestern Mutual Life Insurance Company; and H. W. Anway, Mutual of New York, for providing information on insurance company loan policies and procedures.

Robert B. Tootell and associates in the Farm Credit Administration reviewed the four chapters on the Farm Credit System and provided material and suggestions to update this part of the text. David W. Angovine and associates, Farmer Cooperative Service, reviewed material on financing cooperatives and Norman M. Clapp and associates, Rural Electrification Administration, gave suggestions on material relating to that agency. Philip S. Brown provided current data and material on policies and operations of the Farmers Home Administration, and reviewed the chapter which was prepared on FHA. The assistance of these and other individuals and organizations is sincerely appreciated and acknowledged. However, the authors alone are responsible for the material presented and the views expressed.

AARON G. NELSON
WILLIAM G. MURRAY

CONTENTS

Part 1

PRINCIPLES OF AGRICULTURAL FINANCE

"THERE is no magic about credit. It is a powerful agency for good in the hands of those who know how to use it. So is a buzz saw. They are about equally dangerous in the hands of those who do not understand them."

T. N. CARVER

Chapter 1

NATURE AND SIGNIFICANCE
OF AGRICULTURAL FINANCE

IN MODERN FARMING, as in other business, the key to a satisfactory money income is a proper combination of productive assets such as land, live-stock, and machinery, with available labor and managerial ability. Capital for acquiring productive assets is essential for success. Where a man used to "earn his bread by the sweat of his brow," he now earns a living by use of capital. The amount of capital a farm family controls, the terms and conditions under which it is obtained, and the way it is used determine, in large degree, the level of income.

A knowledge of fundamental principles and analytical procedures facilitates obtaining capital and using it effectively. The study of agricultural finance helps provide such knowledge. Economic analysis, coupled with income statement and loan cost analysis, helps the farmer determine how much capital it will pay to use. Analysis relating to repayment capacity and risk-bearing ability indicates the amount of credit a farmer can safely use. Supplemental information pertaining to legal aspects of borrowing, the lender's analysis and servicing of loans, and the like, add efficiency and confidence in "shopping" for credit. A knowledge of the various types of lenders and their characteristics helps the farmer select the one which will contribute most to his business operation.

3

MEANING AND SCOPE OF AGRICULTURAL FINANCE

Agricultural finance is an economic study of financing agriculture. It includes those parts of the field of agricultural economics which pertain to finance. It relates to both the macrofinance and microfinance aspects of the agricultural segment of the economy.

Macrofinance

The macrofinance aspects pertain to financing agriculture in the aggregate. Since the amount of capital available in the economy is limited, macrofinance is concerned primarily with (1) the amount of capital to be allocated to agriculture, (2) the terms and conditions under which it is made available, and (3) the way in which it is used in the aggregate sense of balanced production, economic efficiency, and the like. Lending institutions play a dominant role in macrofinance, particularly in the first two of these aspects. The Government plays a direct role by establishing lending institutions (the Farm Credit System and the Farmers Home Administration are examples) and other loan programs, and by farm programs in general. Both Federal and State governments play an indirect role through legislation and, in turn, through supervisory agencies such as the Federal Reserve System, state banking departments, and state departments of insurance which give overall guidance to lending institutions with reference to the amount loaned, quality of loans which are acceptable, and loan terms.

Microfinance

Microfinance aspects of agricultural finance pertain to the individual farm.[1] It includes those parts of farm management which relate to *acquisition* and *use* of capital in the farm business. The *acquisition* phase involves determining the sources of capital and the amount to be obtained from each source. It also involves the terms and conditions under which the capital is obtained. The *use* phase involves allocating the limited supply of capital available

---

[1] The term "farm" will be used to include both "farm" and "ranch," and the term "farm management" will include "ranch management" unless otherwise indicated.

between the farm household and the business; i.e. determining the amount of capital available for use in the business. The problem then is to determine where and how to use the capital available to the business so as to maximize income.

Dominant Role of Credit

Credit plays a dominant role in agricultural finance.[2] The amount of credit extended, and the terms and conditions under which it is extended, have a significant influence on agriculture. From the viewpoint of the individual farmer, credit plays a relatively important role since it constitutes the additional (marginal) units of capital employed in the business. In other words, credit is used to supplement equity capital, and capital which may be rented. Therefore, the amount of credit to use, the terms and conditions involved in its acquisition, and the management of finances to meet associated contractual commitments are major considerations involved in management of the business.

The role of credit in agricultural finance can be visualized by considering the kinds of decisions involved for the farmer and the lender. For example, a dairy farmer owns a small farm and rents an adjoining 80 acres. He thinks he can increase his net returns by expanding the size of his business, but he does not have enough funds without borrowing. First of all, he has to decide where he should expand, whether expanding the dairy herd would pay as much as using the borrowed funds to expand some other enterprise such as hogs or crops. Assuming expanding the dairy herd is most promising, the farmer must decide how much to expand the herd. The question includes not only an estimate of net returns for different sized herds but also consideration of the repayment schedule and the amount of risk which will be encountered as the size of the herd increases. Finally, the farmer has to decide whether this is the time to expand. What is the outlook? Would it be better to wait another year before borrowing to carry out the expansion of his dairy herd?

Assuming the farmer decides to go ahead and approaches his banker for a loan, the banker must consider the situation to see whether he should make the loan. He must determine whether he has the funds available to loan. In making this decision the banker

---

[2] The term "credit" will be used synonymously with "borrowed funds" throughout this text.

must decide whether he should use some of his limited supply of funds to make this loan, or whether it would be better, from his own standpoint and from the standpoint of the community, to use the funds to make other loans or investments. The banker must also consider whether the loan would be in line with policies of federal or state supervisory authority; i.e. whether the loan would meet the standards of the bank examiners. Assuming he decides to make the loan, the banker and the farmer must then agree upon the interest rate, the terms of repayment, the security to be pledged, and other loan terms.

Note that, as was pointed out above, credit constitutes the marginal units of capital employed in the business. Credit was used in the above example to supplement equity and rented capital. The decision as to how much capital it would pay to use was in fact a question of how much credit it would pay to use. Moreover, when credit is used in conjunction with equity capital, risk increases at a faster rate than the amount of credit employed. Thus, the risk involved hinges in large measure on the use of credit.

Classification of Credit

There are two main purposes for which farmers borrow money, for *business* and for *consumption*. We are concerned here with business credit. However, there are many different types or uses of business credit, and a proper classification will facilitate communication, and also financial analysis. Unfortunately, no one classification is completely satisfactory for all purposes. Therefore, four primary classifications are summarized here. The one based upon time or term of loan is probably used most frequently.

TIME CLASSIFICATION

In the time classification, credit is classified in three groups— *short, intermediate,* and *long*—according to the term of the loan. The following general classification is customary, together with the further division into monthly, seasonal, and annual loans.

A. Short-term credit (production credit)
   1. Monthly (0–3 months)
   2. Seasonal (3–9 months)
   3. Annual (9 months–1 year)

B. Intermediate-term credit (1–5 years)

C. Long-term credit (real estate credit)

Long-term loans fall definitely into a separate grouping, being as the name implies, credit extended on real estate security for periods longer than one year—usually five, ten, twenty, or more years, depending on the terms offered by the mortgage lenders. An equally specific classification is not possible, however, for short- and intermediate-term credit.

Intermediate credit is usually defined as credit extended for purposes which will provide full payment, not in one season, but in several seasons. The term intermediate credit has been used to designate those loans maturing in a year but renewed from year to year if the security and the income of the borrower warranted. Loans on dairy herds, beef cattle herds, improvements, and machinery come in this category. Moreover, the so-called "barnyard" loans—loans which are written for one year but which the lender does not expect the borrower to repay completely in that time— sometimes are also included in this class.

Such an overlapping in classifying short-term and intermediate credit makes for confusion, as the following example will illustrate. A farmer raising crops borrowed $500 each year to finance his crop expenses. A livestock farmer borrowed $500 on his herd, renewing the note each year when it came due. The short-term loan to the crop farmer enabled him to produce a cotton crop, while the intermediate-term loan on the beef cattle herd enabled the livestock farmer to produce a crop of beef calves each year. It may be argued that the crop loan was a separate transaction each year while the livestock loan was continuous over several years. But each farmer had to have the $500 to finance his business, year after year, the only important difference being that the cotton farmer needed the credit a few months of the year while the livestock farmer needed it the entire year. This is a difference largely of degree, depending on the number of months required to raise crops or produce livestock.

A bona fide intermediate loan is one used for investments which mature over a period longer than a year. Orchards, livestock equipment, feeding floors, drainage or irrigation systems, machinery, and the like, are good examples of investments in this intermediate category.

The distinction between short-, intermediate-, and long-term credit coincides with a difference in loan purpose. Short-term loans are generally used for the production of farm crops and livestock;

intermediate-term loans are generally for working-capital assets like machinery; and long-term loans are frequently for the purchase of a farm. A classification of credit according to purpose brings out this close relationship between time and purpose.

The purpose classification appears to be the easiest to understand because each loan is labeled according to the use made of the proceeds. This classification generally groups loans according to the purpose of the loan, with subclasses based upon specific uses of the funds. Among the common uses made of credit the following are the most important.

A. Production loans (short- and intermediate-term loans) to:
  1. Buy seed, feed, and fertilizer
  2. Pay operating expenses
  3. Buy livestock feeders
  4. Carry or buy range livestock
  5. Buy dairy cattle
  6. Buy machinery—equipment or tractor
  7. Finance commodity storage
  8. Refinance any one or combination of above including "barnyard" loans
B. Real estate loans (long-term loans) to:
  1. Purchase a farm
  2. Purchase additional land
  3. Finance buildings, drainage, irrigation, and other improvements
  4. Refinance any one or combination of above
C. Farmer cooperative borrowing to:
  1. Pay operating expenses
  2. Finance patrons
  3. Finance commodity storage
  4. Finance buildings, equipment, or real estate purchase
  5. Refinance any one of above

The purpose classification has the advantage of facilitating analysis to determine profitability of a specific loan if other records essential to such an analysis are kept. It also gives information on which loans are for investment purposes and which are for operating credit. Long-term loans for purchase of land usually are primarily for investment since the land is not "used up" in the production process. On the other hand, funds put into operation of the farm are used up in one or a few years. Production expenses, such as for seed, are completely used in one year, while a tractor lasts for several years. These things are important from the viewpoint of using credit since they influence the repayment capacity of farmers. Where items are used up in the production process, their value enters the gross cash farm income flow, assuming operations are profitable, and are available to apply on repayment of the loan. Funds put into a tractor which lasts for ten years, for example, enter the cash income flow over the ten-year period and can be used to apply on the tractor loan. In contrast, where investments are not used up, only the return on the investment enters the cash flow, with the result that principal payments on loans thus invested must be taken from net income or savings. This limits the amount of debt a farm family can incur for investment purposes.

A common difficulty incurred with the purpose classification arises when a loan is used for a number of different purposes. The "barnyard," or "combination," loan often encountered in diversified farming areas, is an example of a loan which is difficult to classify.

SECURITY CLASSIFICATION

The grouping of credit by security provides a third classification often used. The two major classifications are secured and unsecured loans, as the following outline indicates.

A. Secured loans
  1. Short- and intermediate-term loans
    a. Chattel mortgage loans
      (1) Crop
      (2) Livestock
      (3) Machinery, equipment or tractor
      (4) Commodity
      (5) Mixed, or "barnyard" loans
    b. Warehouse receipt loans
    c. Loans made on collateral securities (government bonds, and the like)
  2. Long-term loans
    a. Real estate mortgage loans
B. Unsecured loans
  1. Short- and intermediate-term loans
    a. Crop

    b. Livestock
    c. Machinery, equipment or tractor
    d. Commodity
    e. Mixed, or "barnyard" loans

Short- and intermediate-term loans may be either secured or unsecured. When secured, they usually are secured by chattel (usually movable) property. As a result, loans for short- and intermediate-term purposes are often referred to as "chattel" loans. Long-term loans generally are secured by a mortgage on real estate. When the term "farm-mortgage loans," or debt, is used (as it frequently is in USDA publications) it generally refers to loans secured by farm real estate.

LENDER CLASSIFICATION

Credit often is classified by the lender because the policies of lenders vary greatly. Quite often this classification is used in conjunction with the time grouping, as the following summary classification illustrates.

A. Short- and intermediate-term (nonreal-estate) loans
    1. Banks
    2. Production Credit Associations
    3. Other financing institutions, discounting with Federal Intermediate Credit Banks
    4. Farmers Home Administration
    5. Commodity Credit Corporation
    6. Individuals and others
B. Long-term (real estate) loans
    1. Commercial and savings banks
    2. Insurance companies
    3. Federal Land Banks
    4. Farmers Home Administration
    5. Individuals and others

This type of classification is used in the latter part of the text in the discussion of lenders.

Lending Institutions

The important role played by lending institutions in macrofinance was outlined above. They also play a significant role in microfinance. Selecting the proper lender is of paramount importance in success of a farm business. If a farmer selects a top-notch lender and cooperates fully with him, he has materially improved his odds for success. A well-educated lender with adequate experience who keeps informed on current developments can be of immeasurable value to a farmer. Through wide and varied contacts and study, such a lender develops an understanding and basis for judgment which the individual farmer working within confines of his own business cannot hope to develop. Such a lender serves as a balance wheel, cautioning the farmer against excesses or overenthusiasm, and limits expansion to safe bounds dictated by repayment capacity and risk-bearing ability. At the same time he encourages the farmer to accept fruitful opportunity, stimulates expansion which is profitable and sound, and counsels with the farmer on adjustments in the business so that every dollar will be used where it will produce the maximum return. Financing plans developed in cooperation with such a lender have real value to the farmer.

In order to make an intelligent choice among lenders, the farmer must know the lender's "pedigree" and record. The "pedigree" of a lender is indicated by such things as the type of financing institution, personnel who operate the institution, and its loan and service policies. The record of a lender is indicated by the way he has helped others in the community. The farmer should obtain information about each lender and, on the basis of facts learned, decide which can give him the credit service best fitted to his particular needs. A study of the various types of lending institutions comprises a basic part of the study of agricultural finance and becomes of increasing importance as capital and credit requirements of agriculture expand.

SIGNIFICANCE OF AGRICULTURAL FINANCE

Tremendous strides in technology have enabled United States farmers to increase agricultural production about 40 per cent in the past two decades. Never in the history of agriculture has there been such a revolution in agricultural technology as experienced since World War II. New machines, new methods, and new materials all have combined to increase production per acre, per animal, and per man-hour of labor. Output per man-hour has doubled in the past 12 years (see Fig. 1.1). As a result, the total number of man-hours worked on farms continues to decline despite expansion in farm production.

Growth of Farm Capital Requirements

The large increases which have occurred in agricultural production and labor efficiency are in large degree the product of
additional capital employed in agriculture. Increased productivity
of land and livestock is the result of added capital in the form of:
(a) improved seeds, feeds, and breeding livestock; (b) more and
better fertilizers, insecticides, herbicides, and other agricultural
chemicals; together with (c) increased use of fuel and electricity.
More and better power, machinery, and equipment increase the
number of acres and animal units a man can handle.

FARM LABOR
Use and Productivity

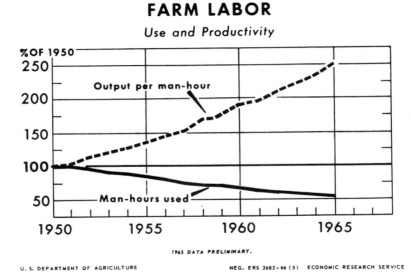

U. S. DEPARTMENT OF AGRICULTURE   NEG. ERS 2682-66 (5)   ECONOMIC RESEARCH SERVICE

Fig. 1.1—Farm output per man-hour and man-hours worked. (Courtesy
of the Economic Research Service, USDA.)

Technological advances and associated capital investments introduce a time factor that makes it possible to minimize many of the
hazards of nature that formerly cut production. For example, an
insect infestation that formerly would have destroyed a crop can
now be controlled by using efficiently equipped tractors or an air-
plane. Timeliness of operations made possible by added use of
capital in the form of mechanical power and equipment often averts
serious loss in crop production.

Increasing amounts of capital are required per unit of output to meet production expenses. Whereas cropland (a noncash outlay) employed per unit of farm output is gradually declining, farmers are now using much more fertilizer, machinery, and other purchased materials per unit of production than they did formerly (see Fig. 1.2). All together, purchased inputs increase more than output, creating an increased demand for cash operating funds.

Greater investment in mechanical power and machinery not

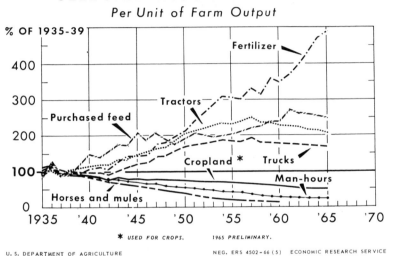

SELECTED RESOURCES USED
Per Unit of Farm Output

Fig. 1.2—Purchased inputs per unit of farm output. (Courtesy of the Economic Research Service, USDA.)

only facilitates handling more land but it also stimulates the farmer to acquire a larger acreage to "spread" his fixed costs in machinery and equipment. Established farmers strive to buy additional land to enlarge their present farms. During 1965 nearly two-thirds of the land purchases in the Corn Belt and western cotton areas were for farm enlargement. About four-fifths of the land purchases in the wheat area were for this purpose. Even in the Northeast—an established dairy area—one-third of the land purchases were for farm enlargement (see Fig. 1.3).

The aggregate effect of increasing capital requirements in agriculture is shown by the balance sheet of agriculture, portrayed graphically in Figure 1.4. The balance sheet brings together assets

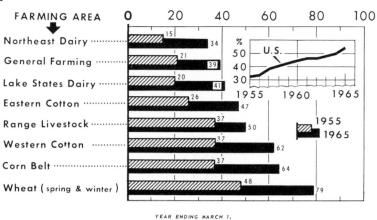

Fig. 1.3—Land purchases for farm enlargement as a per cent of all transfers. (Courtesy of the Economic Research Service, USDA.)

THE BALANCE SHEET OF AGRICULTURE

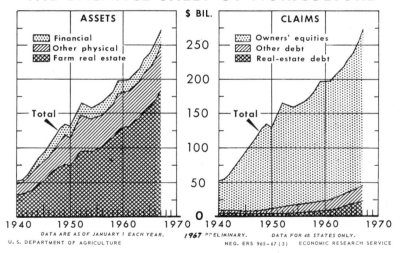

Fig. 1.4—Farm assets and claims of agriculture, 48 contiguous states,
1940–67. (Courtesy of the Economic Research Service, USDA.)

and liabilities of agriculture as though it were one large farm. In
using and interpreting the figure, it should be recognized that this
portrays aggregates and, therefore, does not portray assets and debts
as they would appear for owner-operators, tenants, and landlords.

Moreover, the data back of the balance sheet do not permit full separation of the farm business from the farm household. For these and other reasons, caution should be exercised in interpreting this balance sheet, but the trends serve to show the continuing advance in overall capital requirements of agriculture. Part of the increase is caused by the generally rising price level, but a major part is due to advances in technology and related developments. The combined result is that capital requirements of agriculture are growing at a rapid pace, and farmers who do not "keep up" will soon be operating on a subsistence basis. Farm units fairly adequate a decade or so ago have become inadequate units today. A challenge facing students of agricultural finance is how farmers can provide adequate capital for farms of the future.

Capital Used Per Farm

The large amount of capital employed by typical commercial family-operated farms is evident from data given in Table 1.1. For the types of farms shown, total capital requirements ranged from $48,000 to $315,000 in 1965. If the trend of the past decade continues, by 1975 total capital requirements will range from $60,000 to $487,000.

Large amounts of capital are also required for farm operating expenses, as indicated by data in Table 1.1. Where income is received throughout the year, such as in dairying, current income will cover part or all operating costs, so a smaller amount of capital funds is required for that purpose. In other types of agriculture, such as ranching, the largest part of income is received once a year, and the amount of capital funds which must be provided to meet current expenses is practically equal to total operating costs.

In addition to these requirements, capital is needed for home furnishings and for living expenses. Capital used for these purposes varies widely, but the amounts are fairly large. Where income is received once a year, capital funds for living expenses alone may total $2,500 to $5,000 or more.

It should be recognized that figures given in Table 1.1 show the amount of capital *used* by commercial family-operated farms—not the *optimum* amount of capital which could be employed. Since most farmers could successfully use more capital, the figures given probably are on the low side considered in terms of the optimum combination of resources for maximum income and satis-

TABLE 1.1

ACTUAL CAPITAL INVESTMENTS AND CASH OPERATING EXPENSES PER FARM
IN 1955 AND 1965, AND PROJECTIONS TO 1975, BY TYPE OF FARM

Type of Farm, Location, Item	1955*	1965*	Projected † 1975
	(dollars)	(dollars)	(dollars)
Dairy Farms, Central Northeast			
Land and buildings	15,200	27,200	49,000
Other capital	13,000	20,700	33,000
Total capital	28,200	47,900	82,000
Operating expenses	6,012	12,089	24,000
Hog-Beef Fattening, Corn Belt			
Land and buildings	56,170	91,790	150,000
Other capital	25,890	39,650	61,000
Total capital	82,060	131,440	211,000
Operating expenses	15,294	29,918	59,000
Cash Grain, Corn Belt			
Land and buildings	71,070	158,710	354,000
Other capital	10,730	17,500	29,000
Total capital	81,800	176,210	383,000
Operating expenses	6,819	12,429	23,000
Egg Producing, New Jersey			
Land and buildings	30,880	38,800	49,000
Other capital	7,990	9,580	11,000
Total capital	38,870	48,380	60,000
Operating expenses	24,256	24,869	25,000
Tobacco-Cotton, North Carolina			
Land and buildings	23,390	29,980	38,000
Other capital	3,530	17,740	46,000
Total capital	26,920	47,720	85,000
Operating expenses	4,667	6,542	9,000
Cotton-General Crop, California (Medium sized, irrigated)			
Land and buildings	167,620	264,740	418,000
Other capital	37,500	50,830	69,000
Total capital	205,120	315,570	487,000
Operating expenses	30,587	50,337	83,000
Winter Wheat, Southern Plains			
Land and buildings	59,260	99,600	167,000
Other capital	13,850	19,190	27,000
Total capital	73,110	118,790	194,000
Operating expenses	4,782	8,133	14,000
Cattle Ranches, Intermountain Region			
Land and buildings	28,660	43,310	65,000
Other capital	36,610	47,230	61,000
Total capital	65,270	90,540	126,000
Operating expenses	5,907	8,170	11,000
Sheep Ranches, Northern Plains			
Land and buildings	53,120	76,930	111,000
Other capital	28,290	34,430	42,000
Total capital	81,410	111,360	153,000
Operating expenses	12,229	14,131	16,000

* Source: *Farm Costs and Returns, Commercial Farms by Type, Size and Location*, ERS, USDA.

† Straight-line projection of 1955–65 trend; rounded to thousands.

faction. Large-scale cotton farms, for example, had a capital investment of over $1 million in 1965—far more than the average.

Significance of Credit

Use of capital in agriculture has been an important factor contributing to improvement in farm income and the standard of living, and a continuation of this trend is dependent in no small measure upon a continued rise in farm investment. The question is, however, Where are the funds coming from to permit the continued growth of investment? The individual farmer has a number of alternatives such as saving (increase in net worth, less gifts and inheritance), borrowing, renting, partnerships, and purchase contracts. However, all of these except saving and borrowing merely represent a transfer of capital from one farmer to another. Renting, for example, merely represents a transfer of use of assets and not a net increase in capital in agriculture. Net worth acquired by gifts, inheritance, and the like, fall largely in this same category. Thus, new additions to capital in agriculture stem basically from savings and credit. Savings are very important in this capital accumulation process. But the continuing increase in capital requirements certainly will call for use of more credit. ". . . survival in the agricultural economy of the future will depend largely upon the individual farmer's management and ability and whether he has sufficient credit of the right type."[3]

Farming has become big business and farm financing needs to be handled on a business basis, both by farmers and by lenders, for credit to make its maximum contribution to capital requirements. A farm operation should be recognized as an integrated business in credit analysis and extension. While long-, intermediate-, and short-term financing is needed, extension of the maximum amount of credit requires that it be based upon the earning, repayment, and risk-bearing ability of the farm unit as a whole, and not on separate parts of the business or on adequacy of collateral, as has often been the case. This calls for more business planning in projecting (a) capital requirements for current operations, needed expansion, and improvements; and (b) earnings expected to result from such expenditures. This planning should be based upon analysis of overall financial resources and credit requirements of the business.

[3] Robert B. Tootell, Governor of the Farm Credit Administration, in *The Co-op Bank Messenger*, Omaha Bank for Cooperatives, Mar., 1959, p. 4.

Growth of Credit Utilization

Growth in credit utilization has been proceeding at a fairly rapid rate for a number of years. The farm real estate mortgage debt has more than doubled in the past decade (see Table 1.2). Even though land values have been advancing at a fairly rapid rate, farm mortgage debt as a per cent of the value of land and buildings has been increasing. The increase in land values has served to "sweeten" many loans. The ratio of debt to real estate value is relatively low. It should be kept in mind, however, that these data refer to U.S. agriculture as a whole. The situation of individual farmers varies greatly.

Since payments on real estate debt must be derived primarily from net income, the ratio of farm mortgage debt to net farm income from agriculture portrays an important relationship. This ratio has increased very sharply over the past decade (see Table 1.2, column 6). Currently, the real estate debt is approximately equal to net farm income from agriculture. This is not a high ratio, in fact by some standards it is low. However, an increase in debt relative to net income means that, other things being equal, meeting principal payments will be more difficult.

A disturbing aspect of the finance situation is the relatively low rate of return on capital employed in agriculture. When an allowance (5 per cent of the annual value of cash receipts from farm marketings and Government payments) is made for the operators' management, the rate of return on farm real estate capital usually is less than 5 per cent, and often less than 3 per cent (see Table 1.2, column 9). Before deducting a charge for management, the rate of return on real estate capital often is lower than the average interest rate on the outstanding farm mortgage debt (compare columns 8 and 11). As indicated above, capital is essential for success in agriculture. A low rate of return on capital in agriculture tends to discourage the flow of capital to agriculture. The paradox is: Why do land values continue to rise in view of this situation?

The rate of increase in nonreal-estate debt has been about the same as for real estate debt. During the past decade the amount outstanding January 1 more than doubled (see Table 1.3). The amount of short-term credit used during the year is much larger, of course, than is reflected by the January 1 data.

Dividing nonreal-estate capital by nonreal-estate debt indicates the liquidity position of agriculture over an intermediate

TABLE 1.2

FARM MORTGAGE DEBT AND INTEREST CHARGES RELATED TO VALUE OF FARM REAL ESTATE, NET FARM INCOME FROM AGRICULTURE AND RETURN ON REAL ESTATE CAPITAL, UNITED STATES.*

Year	Farm Mortgage Debt	Value of Land and Buildings	Debt as Pct. of Value	Net Farm Income From Agric.	Debt as Pct. of Income	Return to Real Estate Capital	Rate of Return on Real Estate Capital Before Management Allowance	Rate of Return on Real Estate Capital After Management Allowance	Farm Mortgage Interest Charges Amount	Farm Mortgage Interest Charges Av. Rate
(1)	(2)	(3)	(4)	(5)	(6)	(7)	(8)	(9)	(10)	(11)
	(mil. dol.)	(mil. dol.)		(mil. dol.)		(mil. dol.)	(per cent)	(per cent)	(mil. dol.)	(per cent)
1955	8,245	98,172	8.4	15,399	54	3,401	4.0	2.2	402	4.7
1956	9,012	102,934	8.8	15,441	58	3,655	4.0	2.3	442	4.7
1957	9,822	110,421	8.9	15,483	63	4,077	4.2	2.6	482	4.7
1958	10,382	115,934	8.9	17,946	58	6,420	6.3	4.6	521	4.8
1959	11,091	124,393	8.9	15,891	70	3,735	3.4	1.8	572	4.9
1960	12,082	129,929	9.3	16,568	73	5,022	4.3	2.8	627	5.0
1961	12,820	131,363	9.8	17,692	72	6,373	5.4	3.9	685	5.1
1962	13,899	137,436	10.1	18,066	77	6,863	5.4	4.0	758	5.2
1963	15,168	142,820	10.6	18,307	83	7,067	5.6	4.0	845	5.3
1964	16,804	150,712	11.1	17,235	97	6,012	5.5	3.0	951	5.3
1965	18,894	159,441	11.8	20,521	92	9,256	4.4	5.0	1,075	5.4
1966	21,200	171,100	12.4	21,888	97	9,814	6.4	5.0	1,214	5.4
1967	23,500	184,200	12.8				6.3	4.8		

* **Source:** *Agricultural Finance Review Supplement*, Feb., 1966, and data obtained from ERS. Data for column (2) are from page 11; column (3), page 67; column (5), column (7), (8), and (9), page 69; column (10), page 24; and column (11), page 47. Explanatory footnotes on these pages give details as to what each of the items includes or how it was derived. Debt data in column (2) are as of January 1. Data for 1966 and 1967 are preliminary.

TABLE 1.3

NONREAL-ESTATE FARM DEBT RELATED TO NONREAL-ESTATE FARM
CAPITAL, GROSS FARM INCOME, AND IMPUTED RETURNS TO NON-
REAL-ESTATE CAPITAL, UNITED STATES*

Year	Nonreal-estate Debt	Nonreal-estate Capital	Capital Divided by Debt	Gross Farm Income From Agric.	Debt as Pct. of Gross Inc. From Agric.	Imputed Returns to Non-real-estate Capital	Av. Rate of Return on Non-real-estate Capital
(1)	(2)	(3)	(4)	(5)	(6)	(7)	(8)
	(mil. dol.)	(mil. dol.)		(mil. dol.)		(mil. dol.)	(per cent)
1955	9,415	53,800	5.7	33,353	28	1,495	2.8
1956	9,780	52,900	5.4	33,818	29	1,542	2.9
1957	9,523	54,000	5.7	34,619	28	1,674	3.1
1958	10,029	56,300	5.6	38,736	26	1,821	3.2
1959	12,558	64,300	5.1	37,560	33	2,061	3.2
1960	12,686	59,600	4.7	38,257	33	2,016	3.4
1961	13,351	58,800	4.4	39,927	33	1,941	3.3
1962	14,768	60,900	4.1	41,664	35	2,027	3.3
1963	16,549	62,700	3.8	42,687	39	2,154	3.4
1964	18,111	63,100	3.5	41,355	44	2,107	3.3
1965	18,675	62,800	3.4	44,900	42	2,172	3.5
1966	20,400	68,700	3.4	49,322	42	2,599	3.8
1967	21,400						

* Source: USDA data, primarily from *Agricultural Finance Review Supplement*, Feb., 1966. Nonreal-estate capital in column (3) is the total of nonreal-estate and financial assets, less "Household furnishings and equipment" and "Investments in Cooperatives," given in the Balance Sheet of Agriculture, page 79 of the Feb., 1966 Supplement. Data in column (5) are from page 80, and those in column (7) from page 69. Nonreal-estate debt and nonreal-estate capital are as of Jan. 1. Data for 1966 and 1967 are preliminary.

period of time. While still relatively strong, the liquidity position of agriculture deteriorated during the past decade (see Table 1.3, column 4). In the mid-fifties current and working assets were around 5.5 times short- and intermediate-term debt. By the mid-sixties the ratio had dropped below 3.5 to 1. A ratio of less than 2 to 1 is generally considered hazardous. The situation undoubtedly varies considerably from farm to farm, with some farms probably being in a precarious position.

Nonreal-estate debts—short- and intermediate-term loans—are repaid in large part from gross income and, therefore, the relationship of these two is pertinent in analyzing growth in use of credit. Nonreal-estate debt as a per cent of gross farm income from agriculture has increased considerably in recent years (see Table 1.3, column 6). In other words, the proportion of gross income required to meet short- and intermediate-term debt payments has increased substantially. This may be due at least in part to the increase in purchased inputs employed in agriculture.

The average rate of return on nonreal-estate capital is also low (see Table 1.3, column 8). It is only slightly over one-half the rate paid on production loans. One wonders why capital continues to flow to agriculture in view of this relationship. One explanation is that commercial farms realize a higher return on capital than the average for U.S. agriculture, so it is profitable to borrow. Another explanation is that only variable costs are considered in bidding for capital. This point is developed in a later chapter.

HISTORICAL PERSPECTIVE

U.S. agriculture as a whole is in a strong position financially. Individual farms may be in a hazardous position, but from an overall standpoint more credit can be safely used in agriculture. However, it is well to maintain perspective. The past quarter of a century has been a "golden age" for agricultural credit. Farm income has been relatively good and the already strong equity position of agriculture has been consistently bolstered by the long rise in land values. Under such circumstances one may become overly optimistic. Figure 1.5 helps to give the needed perspective. Land values have not always risen. Farm foreclosures have not always been low.

Following a long period of prosperity, rising land values and practically no foreclosures, lenders and borrowers find it difficult in many cases to give adequate consideration to repayment and risk-

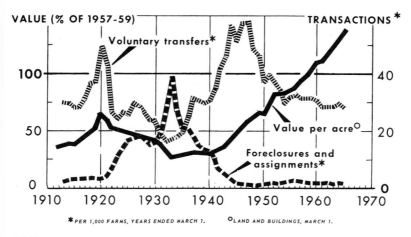

*PER 1,000 FARMS, YEARS ENDED MARCH 1.   °LAND AND BUILDINGS, MARCH 1.

U. S. DEPARTMENT OF AGRICULTURE   NEG. ERS 3487-65 (7)   ECONOMIC RESEARCH SERVICE

Fig. 1.5—Volume of foreclosures and assignments, voluntary transfers, and index numbers of value per acre of farm real estate, United States, 1912–66. (Courtesy of the Economic Research Service, USDA.)

bearing ability, even though they recognize that debt distress usually originates with large loans made under these conditions. Officers of lending institutions generally are eager to make a good showing and to keep the personnel busy. Local field personnel may be conscious of the trends, but they often are unable to resist pressure from the home office to meet loan quotas; or, when compensation is partially or entirely on a commission basis, they are hesitant to reject loan increases, which would work against their own financial interests. Hindsight is, to be sure, always clearer than foresight. Hindsight indicates that the trend of land values has not always been up, and that foreclosures are the inevitable result of excessive loans. History tells us that repayment capacity and risk-bearing ability should be given full consideration in loan analysis and credit extension.

Summary

What, then, is the meaning and significance of agricultural finance? Agricultural finance is an economic study of financing agriculture. It relates to both the macrofinance and microfinance aspects of agriculture. The farmer is concerned with the aggregate flow and utilization of capital in agriculture. Lending institutions and the Government play important roles in this phase of agricultural finance. The microfinance aspect deals with the economics of acquiring and using financial resources in the business. Since credit often provides the marginal financial resources, a study of the amount of credit that can be *profitably* and *safely* used comprises a major part of the field of agricultural finance. Terms and conditions under which credit is acquired are also important, and for this reason considerable emphasis is placed upon a study of agricultural lenders, including their basic organization, objectives in making agricultural loans, loan policies and procedures, and source of loan funds. These factors portray the "pedigree" and "production record" of the lender, indicating the credit service and treatment a borrower could expect.

The significance of agricultural finance is twofold. First, as a part of the study of economics it sets out the principles of analysis so the farmer, lender, or any student of finance can make a choice or decision with full awareness of the implications of the choice or decision. There is nothing in the study of agricultural finance which will give a specific answer as to how much to borrow, or where to borrow, but it provides the principles by which the individual can arrive at a decision to these questions. Agricultural finance provides the economic principles for analysis of how much it would be profitable and safe to borrow, and the principles or type of information needed to select a lender which will best suit the needs of the borrower. However, the final choice or decision on both questions must be made by the individual borrowing the money.

The second area of significance of agricultural finance is the importance of finance in the farm business and the increasing role of credit in the expanding capital requirements of agriculture. Many do not realize the rapid expansion of capital demanded by the technological revolution going on in agriculture nor the consequences which face the farmer who does not "keep up." Adequate units become inadequate in half a generation if the family does not continue to add capital. Must farm families throughout their lifetime deny themselves comforts considered essential for urban families in order to amass a small or moderate fortune required to capitalize an efficient farm unit? Burdened with the load of acquiring the minimum of capital needed to start farming, what chance does the beginning farmer have of ever developing an adequate unit if capital requirements keep growing at a faster rate than he can save?

One solution to these questions may lie in knowing how to use credit and how to get it extended on proper terms. Farmers use credit and will continue to do so, but the significance rests in how much they use, how they use it, and where they obtain it. Where will they obtain credit—from lenders who can help them help themselves, or from lenders who are not interested in their efforts to make progress? Or will they forfeit a portion of their managerial freedom and turn to vertical integration as a means of acquiring capital with which to work? The supply of credit, the terms on which it is made available to agriculture, and the knowledge farmers have about how to use it, have great significance for the future. These things might very well determine the future of the family farm.

QUESTIONS AND PROBLEMS

1. Explain the meaning of macrofinance and microfinance as related to agricultural finance.
2. Why does credit play a dominant role in agricultural finance?
3. Why is it desirable to have a classification for agricultural

credit? Outline the four classifications given in the chapter and discuss the use of each.

4. Why is the study of lending institutions included as a part of agricultural finance?
5. Why is selecting a lender important to a farmer?
6. How much capital does it take in your community to start farming as a tenant? As an owner? How much capital does a typical middle-aged farmer use in your community? Should a farmer attempt to become free of debt or continue to use credit? Discuss.
7. Discuss the increase in capital requirements of agriculture. What has caused the increase? Is the trend likely to continue? Estimate the capital requirements of your typical middle-aged farmer (question 6) in ten years; in twenty years.
8. What is the significance of credit in agriculture? Is it changing? How is it likely to change in the next decade?
9. What are the consequences of improper use of credit? Illustrate these by referring to history. Do you expect history will "repeat itself" in this regard?
10. Analyze the trend of the farm mortgage debt in the United States to the value of land and buildings, and to net farm income from agriculture. Does the trend give cause for alarm?
11. Considering the rate of return earned on farm real estate capital (see Table 1.2, column 9) do you think the Government should encourage use of more capital in agriculture by sponsoring the Federal Land Bank system and the Farmers Home Administration?
12. Analyze the trend of the nonreal-estate debt in the United States to the value of nonreal-estate capital and to gross farm income from agriculture. Does the trend give cause for alarm?
13. Why do farmers continue to borrow if the rate earned on capital in agriculture is lower than the rate of interest charged on loans, as is indicated by Table 1.2, column 9, and by Table 1.3, column 8?
14. Find figures showing farm mortgage and nonreal-estate (short-term) loans in your state for recent years. Discuss changes which have occurred.

REFERENCES

Allen, Philip T., *Farm Real-Estate Credit, An Analysis of Borrowers and Lenders,* USDA, Econ. Res. Serv. Agr. Econ. Rept. No. 104, Nov., 1966.
American Bankers Association, "The Changing Face of Farming: Economic and Operational Implications for Bankers," *Banking,* April, 1963, issue.
Atkinson, J. H., *A New Look at the Farm Debt Picture,* Fed. Res. Bul., Dec., 1962, pp. 1571–88.
Baum, E. L., Diesslin, H. G., and Heady, E. O. (eds.), *Capital and Credit Needs in a Changing Agriculture,* Iowa State Univ. Press, Ames, 1961.
Bivens, Gordon E., Ball, A. Gordon, and Miller, Frank, *Use of Credit by*

Farm Families in Southern Iowa and Northern Missouri, Iowa Agr. Exp. Sta. Spec. Rept. 35, 1963.

Boyne, David H., *Changes in the Real Wealth Position of Farm Operators, 1940–60,* Mich. Agr. Exp. Sta. Tech. Bul. 294, 1964.

Butler, G. E., and Sinclair, R. O., *Capital Requirements of Vermont Dairy Farmers,* Vt. Agr. Exp. Sta. Bul. 637, 1963.

Cotner, M. L., Wirth, M. E., and Brake, J. R., *Credit Experience of Commercial Crop and Livestock Farmers in Purchasing Land in Michigan,* Mich. Agr. Exp. Sta. Quarterly Bul. Reprint, Vol. 45, No. 4, May, 1963.

Davidson, J. R., and Mighell, R. L., "Tracing Farmers' Reactions to Uncertainty," *Jour. Farm Econ.,* Aug., 1963, pp. 577–86.

Doll, Raymond J., *Farm Debt as Related to Value of Sales,* Fed. Res. Bul., Feb., 1963, pp. 140–48.

Farm Finance in This Modern Era, Monthly Review, Fed. Res. Bank of Kansas City, July, 1959.

Garlock, Fred L., *Farmers and Their Debts, The Role of Credit in the Farm Economy,* USDA, ERS, Agr. Econ. Rept. 93, June, 1966.

Heady, Earl O. *Economics of Agricultural Production and Resource Use,* Prentice-Hall, Inc., Englewood Cliffs, N.J., 1952, Chaps. 18 and 19.

Hesser, Leon F., *The Market for Farm Mortgage Credit,* Purdue Agr. Exp. Sta. Res. Bul. 770, 1963.

———, Doll, Raymond J., and Sullivan, Gary F., *Farm Debt as Related to Economic Class of Farm,* Res. Dept., Fed. Res. Bank of Kansas City, 1964.

Jones, Lawrence A., *What Young Farm Families Should Know About Credit,* USDA Farmers' Bul. 2135, 1959.

Ortel, Dennis D., *The Transfer of Large Farms,* Cornell Univ. Agr. Exp. Sta. Bul., A. E. Res. 180, 1965.

Robbins, Lionel, *An Essay on the Nature and Significance of Economic Science,* Macmillan and Co., Ltd., London.

Saunders, A. D., *Financing Alaska's Farms,* Alaska Agr. Exp. Sta. Bul. 35, 1964.

Structural Changes in Commercial Agriculture, Proceedings of a conference held in Chicago, Ill., Apr. 12–14, 1965, sponsored by Iowa State Univ., Univ. of Wisc., and Farm Foundation, Chicago, CAED Report 24.

Chapter 2

BASIC ECONOMIC PRINCIPLES
INVOLVED IN FINANCE[1]

ECONOMIC PRINCIPLES form a basis for making decisions relative to financing the farm business. They provide a framework for deciding the enterprises to be included in the business, the relative amounts of various factors of production to be employed in each enterprise, and the total amount of capital to be used in the business. A knowledge of economic principles also helps in comparing the various sources of finance and in determining the amount of capital to be utilized from each source.

These principles are not peculiar to finance or to any other particular aspect of the farm business. They are universally applicable in all aspects of management. Only the application varies.

The objective of this chapter is to review briefly the basic economic principles involved in finance. A few illustrations will be used to help clarify the principles. Their application and importance in financial analysis will become evident in the following chapters.

---

[1] This chapter is intended to provide an introduction to basic economic principles essential to an understanding of principles of finance. Students who have a good understanding of basic economic principles, including marginal analysis, may skip this chapter.

THE PRINCIPLE OF DIMINISHING RETURNS

The principle of diminishing returns is of prime importance in economic analysis. The level to which a farmer should push yield per acre, marketing weight per animal, milk production per cow, and size of farm all revolve around this principle. It comprises the basis for the entire framework of marginal analysis, the most comprehensive and powerful tool in economics. Based on physical relationships, it has economic significance whenever the physical goods involved have value.

The principle of diminishing returns refers to the amount of additional output obtained as additional inputs of variable factors of production are added to a fixed amount of other factors. The principle may be expressed in its simplest form as follows: With the quantity of one factor of production held constant or fixed, the additional output derived from each additional unit of a variable factor declines after a certain level of variable factor use has been attained.

One Variable Factor

Fertilizer application in crop production provides a good illus-

TABLE 2.1

GRAIN PRODUCTION RELATED TO VARIOUS LEVELS OF FERTILIZER APPLICATION
(Hypothetical data)

Inputs		Output: Grain Production		
Fixed factor	Variable factor: nitrogen fertilizer	Total	Average per unit of fertilizer	Additional per unit of fertilizer
	(number of units)	(cwt.)	(cwt.)	(cwt.)
1	0 (no nitrogen)	24	. . .	
				16
1	1 (20 lbs.)	40	40.0	
				10
1	2 (40 lbs.)	50	25.0	
				6
1	3 (60 lbs.)	56	18.7	
				3
1	4 (80 lbs.)	59	14.8	
				1
1	5 (100 lbs.)	60	12.0	
				0
1	6 (120 lbs.)	60	10.0	

tration of the principle of diminishing returns. Table 2.1 portrays grain production with various amounts of fertilizer applied to a "bundle" of fixed factors. The term "bundle" is used for the fixed factors (land, seed, labor, tractor fuel, machine services, and the like) to emphasize that the proportions as well as the absolute quantities of these factors are held constant. As the amount of fertilizer applied is increased, *total* production increases, but at a decreasing (diminishing) rate. This is reflected in the decrease in additional production per unit of fertilizer added. The first unit of fertilizer applied increased production 16 hundredweight. However, the second unit applied increased production only 10 hundred-weight. Additional (incremental) production associated with increased applications of fertilizer continues to decline until, finally, the sixth unit of fertilizer produced no increase in output.

More Than One Variable Factor

The degree to which production of a product per unit of input diminishes depends in large measure on the number of factors involved in producing the product—the number which are allowed to vary and the number which are fixed. The above example illustrates diminishing returns with only one variable factor and all others fixed. If greater amounts of other factors of production also were applied as more fertilizer were added, incremental grain production would decline less sharply. Assume, for example, applications of labor, power and machinery, herbicides, and the like, were increased along with fertilizer. Total production likely would increase to a considerably greater extent; that is, additional production associated with successive applications of the "bundle" of variable inputs would not decline so much.

Constant Returns

Diminishing productivity usually occurs in per acre yields, per animal gains, or per animal production. However, many situations are found in agriculture where productivity is constant, perhaps leading one to question the universal application of the law of diminishing returns. Constant productivity may be possible under two circumstances:

1. Where there are no fixed resources and all factors of production are increased simultaneously. In our fertilizer example it was

assumed a "bundle" of fixed resources—one acre of land and associated seed, labor, machinery services, and the like—was used. Grain production declined since, as fertilizer applications were increased, there was relatively less of the fixed factor with which the fertilizer could "work," or combine, in the production process. If the resources which were assumed to be fixed had been increased along with fertilizer, the increase in production would have been at a constant rate. However, as the size of business grows, increasing all factors of production together becomes difficult, with the result that sooner or later diminishing returns become evident.

2. Where factors which are fixed have "reserve" or "excess" capacity. For example, livestock enterprises often can be expanded with existing facilities without adversely affecting the level of production. Excess capacity of the fixed improvements is sufficient to permit the expansion. Also, farmers buy or rent additional land to increase the size of their farming operation without any significant reduction in yields. In this example, as well as in the preceding one, there is sufficient "excess" or "reserve" managerial ability to facilitate the expansion. However, constant returns will be realized only so long as there is excess capacity in the fixed factors. When any one of the factors is fully utilized, further expansion of production will be accompanied by diminishing returns.

Diminishing Economic Returns

The principle of diminishing returns has economic significance since most of the factors of production and products produced have economic value. By converting the physical data to monetary terms, diminishing economic returns are portrayed. Comparing these returns with the costs involved provides the basis for determining whether production is profitable and, if so, the level of production which will maximize returns.

The fertilizer example discussed above is expanded in Table 2.2 to portray costs and returns in addition to the physical data. It was estimated that the "bundle" of fixed factors cost $100 and that each 20-pound unit of fertilizer cost $2.50. The grain produced was priced at $2.00 per hundredweight.

The total value of output (column 11) obviously increases at a decreasing rate, the same as total physical output (column 7).

TABLE 2.2

COSTS AND RETURNS RELATED TO DIMINISHING RETURNS IN GRAIN PRODUCTION (Hypothetical data)

Inputs		Cost of Inputs				Output			Value of Output			
Fixed factor	Variable factor: nitrogen	Fixed factor	Variable factor	Total cost	Added (marginal) cost	Total	Average per unit of fert.	Additional (marginal)	Per cwt.	Total	Av. per unit of fert.	Additional (marginal)
(1)	(2)	(3)	(4)	(5)	(6)	(7)	(8)	(9)	(10)	(11)	(12)	(13)
	(no. of units)	(dol.)	(dol.)	(dol.)	(dol.)	(cwt.)	(cwt.)	(cwt.)	(dol.)	(dol.)	(dol.)	(dol.)
1	0	100	0	100		24	…		2.00	48	…	
1	1	100	2.50	102.50	2.50	40	40.0	16	2.00	80	80.00	32
1	2	100	5.00	105.00	2.50	50	25.0	10	2.00	100	50.00	20
1	3	100	7.50	107.50	2.50	56	18.7	6	2.00	112	37.33	12
1	4	100	10.00	110.00	2.50	59	14.8	3	2.00	118	29.50	6
1	5	100	12.50	112.50	2.50	60	12.0	1	2.00	120	24.00	2
1	6	100	15.00	115.00	2.50	60	10.0	0	2.00	120	20.00	0

Similarly, value of the additional (marginal) output (column 13) follows the same pattern as the additional (marginal) physical output (column 9). Similar relationships prevail with constant returns.

Marginal Concepts

The term "marginal" is widely used in economics and should be clearly understood. It means the same as "added" or "additional," and also is used synonymously with "incremental."

When reference is to inputs, marginal means the last unit of a factor of production or resource applied, and marginal factor cost refers to the cost of that input. For example, in Table 2.2, the marginal input is one unit of fertilizer, arbitrarily taken to be 20 pounds of nitrogen. The marginal factor cost is $2.50 (column 6).

When reference is to output or products, marginal means the amount of product produced with the last unit of a factor or resource applied. For example, in Table 2.2, the marginal physical product is shown in column 9. The marginal physical product of the first unit of fertilizer applied is 16 hundredweight, the marginal physical product of the second unit of fertilizer is 10 hundredweight, and so on. The value of the marginal product, shown in column 13, is obtained by multiplying the marginal product by its price. The value of the marginal product is commonly referred to as "marginal returns."

FIXED AND VARIABLE COST CONCEPTS

An understanding of the distinction between fixed and variable costs, together with the reasons for the difference, is essential in economic analysis. Profit maximization is determined by marginal analysis, an essential ingredient of which is variable costs. Thus, one needs to be able to distinguish between fixed and variable costs, and to do this an understanding is needed of what makes costs variable or fixed. The problem is not simply one of setting up two lists, one of fixed costs and the other of variable costs. The classification is complicated by the fact that the same item of cost may be fixed under certain circumstances and variable under others.

Fixed Costs

Fixed costs, as the term indicates, are fixed; they are constant, not subject to change. They are the result of past commitments, of costs already "sunk," of overhead costs.

Costs ordinarily thought of as being fixed include property taxes, insurance on improvements, building depreciation, interest payments on farm real estate debts, cash rent, and the like. If a hired man is employed on an annual basis, his wage is a fixed cost. Depreciation on machinery is generally considered as a fixed cost on the basis that the machines usually become obsolete before they are worn out. Such costs are not influenced by what is produced or by the level of production.

Variable Costs

Variable costs, as the term indicates, vary with the level of production, and with what is produced. In contrast to fixed costs, they have not been "sunk"—management is free to determine whether or not the expense should be incurred.

Costs usually classified as variable include such inputs as seed, tractor fuel, fertilizer, repairs, and feed. Labor hired by the day or week as needed is a variable cost. Interest payments on operating loans usually are classified as a variable cost.

The Influence of Time on the Nature of Costs

In the above examples of fixed and variable costs, the classifications are hedged since costs which are fixed under certain circumstances are variable under others, and vice versa. Time is the culprit involved.

In the long run there are no fixed costs; all costs are variable. This concept may strike one as impossible at first, but a moment's reflection shows that it is feasible. Consider cash rent, for example. Once a cash lease has been signed, the farmer is obligated to pay the rent. When the farmer signs the lease, the payment specified becomes a fixed cost. However, it is fixed only for the term of the lease. When the lease expires, the farmer is free to determine whether or not he wants to rent the property again. Similarly, building depreciation is a fixed cost in the short run since it occurs regardless of whether the farmer uses the building. However, depreciation will occur only as long as the building lasts. When the building is gone there are no "sunk" costs remaining. The farmer is free to make decisions which will best suit his production plans. Property taxes probably come closest to being a truly fixed cost since they are ever present. Moreover, since they are determined by society, the individual farmer has little control over them. However, in the long run, taxes are subject to change, and they are changed as changes in the level of production and in products produced affect the assessed value of the resource.

All costs are variable in the long run since a sufficient period of time is involved so that each factor employed in production is completely used. Obviously, the period of time involved is not the same for all factors of production. The long run associated with each factor is the lifetime of the factor. Therefore, there are no "sunk" costs remaining at the end of a long-run period.

Since no "sunk" costs are involved, the long run also connotes managerial freedom to decide whether or not a cost should be incurred. Fixed costs stem from past commitments by management. For example, interest payments stem from a past commitment by management to borrow money. Building depreciation is the result of a past commitment by management to construct a building, which, in turn, gives rise to "sunk" costs until such time as the building is fully depreciated. The long run pertinent to each factor of production is that period required for all committed costs to be fully retired or expended, leaving management free of costs associated with past commitments.

A critical point in the distinction between fixed and variable costs is managerial freedom to determine whether or not a cost should be incurred. Whenever the manager does not have this choice the funds already have been "sunk" and, therefore, the cost is fixed. Thus, costs generally classified as variable become fixed as the production period progresses. For example, the cost of seed, fertilizer, tractor fuel, and the like, are variable costs up to the time they are utilized. But once they have been applied in land preparation and growing the crop, they are fixed—they are "sunk" costs over which management has no control.

These concepts are of great significance in determining whether it will pay to produce and, if so, how far to go in use of variable factors.

WILL IT PAY TO PRODUCE?

The usual objective in undertaking a business venture is to produce income at least sufficient to cover all costs. Over the long pull, both fixed and variable costs must be covered if the business is to be profitable. When this objective is realized there is no question as to whether it will pay to produce. However, there is a question when gross income is less than the total of fixed and variable costs.

In the short run it will pay to produce whenever gross income is greater than variable costs. Since fixed costs do not change even though production is nil, one will be ahead financially by producing as long as sufficient income is forthcoming to cover costs related directly to producing the crop or product. When gross income is greater than the total of fixed and variable costs, the objective is to maximize profit by expanding production to the point where marginal factor costs are equal to marginal returns. When gross income exceeds variable costs but is insufficient to also cover fixed costs, losses are minimized by again applying the principle of marginal cost equals marginal return; that is, by using more resources until added factor costs equal added returns. These points will be further analyzed in the next section.

The fact that it will pay to produce if gross income is greater than variable costs can be illustrated by data for a 240-acre grain-livestock farm given in Table 2.3. Referring to the first column, gross income is sufficient to more than cover total costs, leaving net farm income of $6,760. Thus, it is profitable to operate the farm. However, would it be profitable if prices received for farm products were one-third lower? Gross income would then be only $21,044, which is less than total costs of $24,805. A net loss of $3,761 would be realized. It would still pay to operate the farm, however. Gross income of $21,044 is $3,344 greater than variable costs, and this amount would cover part of the fixed costs. Thus, the farmer's loss would be minimized by operating the farm even though total costs were not covered.

HOW FAR WILL IT PAY TO EXPAND PRODUCTION?

Once a farmer has determined that production is profitable, the next question is, How much in the way of resources will it pay to use? The principle of marginal cost equals marginal return is the

TABLE 2.3

COSTS AND RETURNS FOR A 240-ACRE GRAIN-LIVESTOCK FARM WITH THREE
LEVELS OF FERTILIZER APPLICATION (Hypothetical data)

Item	No fertilizer	Costs and Returns With: 40 lbs. of N per acre of corn	80 lbs. of N per acre of corn
	(dollars)	(dollars)	(dollars)
Gross Income........................	31,565	33,350	33,785
Variable Costs			
Seed.............................	325	325	325
Fuel and machine repairs..............	1,895	1,945	1,990
Hired labor, including prerequisites......	885	960	985
Fertilizer.........................	None	490	980
Crop supplies......................	995	995	995
Custom work......................	215	215	215
Livestock purchased.................	7,800	7,800	7,800
Other livestock expense..............	875	875	875
Feed purchased....................	4,420	4,420	4,420
Other............................	290	290	290
Total Variable...................	17,700	18,315	18,875
Fixed Costs			
Property taxes.....................	1,230	1,230	1,230
Insurance........................	275	275	275
Interest..........................	2,500	2,500	2,500
Building depreciation and repairs........	875	875	875
Machinery and equipment depreciation...	1,750	1,750	1,750
Other............................	475	475	475
Total Fixed......................	7,105	7,105	7,105
Total Costs........................	24,805	25,420	25,980
Net Income........................	6,760	7,930	7,805
Added Costs.......................	...	615	560
Added Gross Income.................	...	1,785	435

proper measure to use in answering this question. Net income is at a
maximum when

$$\text{Marginal Cost (MC)} = \text{Marginal Return (MR).} \qquad (2.1)$$

Budgets for the 240-acre grain-livestock farm referred to in the
preceding section (see Table 2.3) indicate that income from corn
can be increased by adding commercial fertilizer. Applying 40
pounds of nitrogen added $615 to variable costs but increased gross
income $1,785. Thus, the budget analysis indicates it would be
profitable to apply 40 pounds of nitrogen. The second 40 pounds of
nitrogen applied per acre increased costs $560, but gross income
increased only $435. Thus, the analysis indicates it would not pay to
apply the second 40-pound unit of fertilizer since the added cost was
greater than the added return. The most profitable amount of

fertilizer to apply probably would be somewhere between 40 and 80 pounds of nitrogen per acre.

The illustration of the principle of marginal cost equals marginal return just presented is based upon analysis of the whole farm. The analysis also can be applied to an individual enterprise or segment of the farm business by preparing a "partial" budget for the enterprise or part being studied. It also can be used to determine how far to go in applying variable inputs on a per acre, per cow, and per animal basis. As indicated above, the illustration presented in Table 2.2 assumes a bundle of fixed factors consisting of one acre of land and associated seed, labor, machinery services, and the like, to which was added varying amounts of commercial fertilizer. Marginal income (column 13) from the fourth unit of nitrogen applied was $6.00, which is greater than the marginal factor cost of $2.50 (column 6). Thus, adding the fourth unit of nitrogen increased net income. Marginal income from the fifth unit of fertilizer was only $2.00, however, which is less than the marginal factor cost of $2.50. Therefore, applying four units of fertilizer gave the highest profit per acre. Observe that net income per acre ($8.00) is at a maximum with this level of fertilizer application.

In the discussion of the principle of marginal cost equals marginal return given in the preceding paragraph, the approach was to add additional units of the variable factor until marginal returns had declined to the point where they were equal to the unit price of the factor. Another approach is to add additional units of the variable factor until marginal costs have risen to the point where they are equal to the price of the product. This approach is illustrated in Table 2.4, which is based upon the physical and cost data given in Table 2.2. Marginal cost per unit of output (column 6) is derived by dividing added costs by added production.

Keeping in mind that the price of grain produced was $2.00 per hundredweight (see Table 2.2, column 10), one finds that the principle of marginal cost equals marginal return indicates it will pay to apply four 20-pound units of nitrogen. At this rate of application the marginal cost per unit of output is $.83, considerably less than the unit product price of $2.00. However, the added product produced with the fifth unit of nitrogen would cost $2.50 per hundredweight, $.50 more than the price of the product. Thus, returns are maximized by applying somewhere between 80 and 100 pounds of nitrogen, the same conclusion indicated by the former approach.

Note that the significant comparison involved in maximizing

TABLE 2.4

MARGINAL AND AVERAGE COSTS PER UNIT OF OUTPUT

Inputs of Nitrogen	Grain Output	Fixed Costs	Variable Cost	Total Costs	Marginal Cost Per Unit of Output	Average Fixed Costs Per Unit of Output	Average Variable Cost Per Unit of Output	Average Total Costs Per Unit of Output
(1)	(2)	(3)	(4)	(5)	(6)	(7)	(8)	(9)
(no.)	(cwt.)	(dol.)	(dol.)	(dol.)	(dol.)	(dol.)	(dol.)	(dol.)
0	24	100	0	100.00		4.17	0	4.17
1 (20 lbs.)	40	100	2.50	102.50	.16	2.50	.06	2.56
2 (40 lbs.)	50	100	5.00	105.00	.25	2.00	.10	2.10
3 (60 lbs.)	56	100	7.50	107.50	.42	1.79	.13	1.92
4 (80 lbs.)	59	100	10.00	110.00	.83	1.69	.17	1.86
5 (100 lbs.)	60	100	12.50	112.50	2.50	1.67	.21	1.88
6 (120 lbs.)	60	100	15.00	115.00	Infinity	1.67	.25	1.92

net income is marginal cost versus marginal return. Some people are misled by the value of average output, thinking that if average returns are greater than costs it will pay to produce the additional product. The error of this reasoning is demonstrated by the fifth application of fertilizer in Table 2.2. Average income is $24.00 (column 12), much more than the marginal cost of $2.50. However, as was pointed out above, adding the fifth unit of fertilizer actually reduced net income.

Minimizing Costs

The principle of diminishing returns indicates how production or income will vary as additional resources are applied per acre, per animal, or per farm. It provides an analytical framework for determining whether it will pay to use a given "bundle" of resources in production and, if so, the amount of resources to use. However, nothing is said about the composition of the "bundle" of resources. What combination of fertilizer nutrients will be most economical? What combinations of machines and men will cost the least? How much protein supplement should be included in the livestock ration to be most economical? These are the types of questions with which we are concerned in this section. In each case the question is, In what proportions should two competing resources or practices be used in producing a given amount of product to maximize profit?

Diminishing Rates of Substitution

Consider, first, the situation in which diminishing rates of substitution are involved as one factor or practice is substituted for another with a given level of output. A diminishing rate of substitution occurs whenever addition of successive units of one factor replaces less and less of a second factor used in production of a product. For example, the initial application of protein in beef-fattening rations replaces a substantial amount of grain. However, the second unit added to the ration replaces less grain than the first, the third unit less than the second, and so on. Thus, successive additions of protein replace less and less grain or, in other words, protein substitutes at a diminishing rate for grain in rations for fattening cattle. The problem is to determine the most profitable grain-protein supplement combination.

Analysis involved in solving the problem is illustrated in Table 2.5. It is assumed that 1,000 units of product Y are produced with factors A and B. The letter Y is used to represent any product produced under conditions of diminishing rates of substitution, and the letters A and B are used to represent two factors used in production of product Y that substitute for each other at diminishing rates. Beef production with protein and grain already has been indicated as an example. The quantity of Y produced remains

TABLE 2.5

COMBINATIONS OF VARIABLE FACTORS OF PRODUCTION, A AND B, IN PRODUCING
1,000 UNITS OF PRODUCT, Y (Hypothetical data)

Factor Combination	Factor A	Factor B	Marginal Rate of Substitution of A for B*	Cost of Producing 1,000 Units of Y With		
				A @ $6.00 B @ $1.00	A @ $4.00 B @ $1.00	A @ $2.50 B @ $1.00
(1)	(2)	(3)	(4)	(5)	(6)	(7)
	(units)	(units)		(dol.)	(dol.)	(dol.)
1	20	300		420.00	380.00	350.00
			7			
2	25	265		415.00	365.00	327.50
			5			
3	30	240		420.00	360.00	315.00
			4			
4	35	220		430.00	360.00	307.50
			3			
5	40	205		445.00	365.00	305.00
			2			
6	45	195		465.00	375.00	307.50
			1			
7	50	190		490.00	395.00	315.00

* Units of factor B replaced by 1 unit of factor A at the given level of production.

constant at 1,000 units, while the quantities of the two factors required vary inversely; that is, the quantity of factor A increases, while the quantity of factor B decreases. In changing from factor combination (1) to factor combination (2), five units of factor A replace 35 units of factor B. At the other extreme, five units of factor A replace only five units of factor B. Thus, a diminishing marginal rate of substitution of factor A for factor B is evident. The marginal rate of substitution for each of the factor combinations is shown in the fourth column.

The costs of producing 1,000 units of product Y with three sets of prices for factors A and B are given in columns 5, 6, and 7. With factor A priced at $6.00 and factor B at $1.00 per unit, costs are at a minimum with factor combination (2); that is, when 25 units of factor A and 265 units of factor B are used. Changing the price ratio changes the relative amounts of the factors it will pay to use, of course. With factor A priced at $4.00 and factor B at $1.00, costs are at a minimum somewhere between factor combinations (3) and (4). With factor A priced at $2.50 and factor B at $1.00 the least cost combination is realized by using 40 units of factor A and 205 units of factor B to produce the 1,000 units of product Y.

Costs are at a minimum when the factor substitution ratio is equal to the inverse of the price ratio. The substitution ratio is the number of units of the "replaced" factor divided by the number of units of the "added" factor. The price ratio is the price of the "added" factor divided by the price of the "replaced" factor. In algebraic form

$$\frac{\Delta A}{\Delta B} = \frac{Pb}{Pa} \tag{2.2}$$

where ΔA represents a small change in the amount of factor A, ΔB represents a small change in factor B, and Pb and Pa represent the prices per unit of factors B and A, respectively. If the substitution ratio is greater than the price ratio, costs can be reduced by using more of the "added" factor. On the other hand, if the substitution ratio is smaller than the price ratio, costs can be lowered by using less of the "added" factor. Costs are at a minimum when the cost of the factor "replaced" is equal to the cost of the factor "added."

In applying this principle to the example given in Table 2.5, ΔA represents the change in factor A, which is five units in all cases. The changes in factor B, or ΔB, can vary from 35 units to five units. With factor A priced at $4.00 and factor B at $1.00, we substitute the known quantities in the equation and solve for the unknown, ΔB, as follows:

$$\frac{5}{\Delta B} = \frac{1}{4} \quad \text{or} \quad \Delta B = 20.$$

Thus, costs are at a minimum somewhere between factor combinations (3) and (4). With the data given, this is as close as we can come to the optimum combination of factors.

Constant Rates of Substitution

Not all factors of production or practices substitute for one another at diminishing rates. In some cases the rate of substitution is constant. Use of machines versus manual labor illustrates this type of relationship. For example, two cotton pickers or two corn pickers will substitute for twice as many men as one picker. When constant substitution rates are involved, the problem of minimizing costs is simply one of determining which practice, or factor, is least expensive and using that in the production process. The one which is most economical ordinarily will be used exclusively, there being no reason to use a combination of the two.

Combining Enterprises

The two preceding sections have dealt with the amount of resources it will pay to use in production (factor-product relationships), and the combination of factors which will be most economical (factor-factor relationships). In this section we are concerned with the third major problem facing managers: the combination of enterprises which will produce the greatest net income (product-product relationships). The objective is to outline concepts involved in combining enterprises and to present guiding principles which are helpful in making decisions.

The problem of combining enterprises arises primarily because of limitations on capital available. If capital were not limited, a farmer could expand his acreage and improvements as far as he wished. There would be no need to choose among enterprises. He could produce all the crops and livestock enterprises adapted to his area of operation, and expand output of each to the point where marginal costs and returns were equal. Some farmers own or have access to large amounts of capital, running into millions of dollars, which permits them considerable flexibility. However, in most cases the amount of capital available limits the enterprise combinations which can be included in the farm business, and also their size.

The problem involved in combining enterprises depends in part on the interrelationships between enterprises; that is, whether they are independent, competitive, supplementary, or complementary. Under conditions of limited capital, few, if any, enterprises are completely independent. Primary concern is with the three latter enterprise relationships.

Competitive Enterprises

Competitive enterprises compete with each other for use of resources. This raises two questions: Which enterprises should be included in the business, and How large should each enterprise be? With limited resources the number of enterprises which can be included will be limited and, since expansion of one enterprise will necessitate contraction of another, the sizes of the enterprises included will be limited.

Enterprises which compete for use of resources may substitute for each other either at increasing or at constant rates. The rate of substitution of one enterprise for another refers to the amount of one enterprise displaced as another is added to the business or as an existing enterprise is increased in size. Enterprises substitute at increasing rates when an increase in one requires larger and larger reductions in the other. They substitute at constant rates when a uniform increase in one requires a uniform reduction in the other. Increasing rates of substitution always occur when diminishing marginal productivity takes place in producing either or both of the two competing products. Constant rates of substitution always occur when constant marginal productivity prevails in production of the products.

An example of two products substituting at increasing rates is given in Table 2.6. It is assumed that six units of resources are available which can be used to produce either product Y_1 or Y_2. One unit of resources produces 11 units of Y_1; the second unit of resources

TABLE 2.6

COMBINATIONS OF PRODUCTS Y_1 AND Y_2 WHICH CAN BE PRODUCED WITH SIX UNITS OF FACTOR X (Hypothetical data)

Product Combination	Product Y_1	Product Y_2	Marginal Rate of Substitution of Y_2 for Y_1*	Income With: $P_{y_1} = \$1.00$ $P_{y_2} = \$3.00$	$P_{y_1} = \$1.00$ $P_{y_2} = \$6.00$
(1)	(2)	(3)	(4)	(5)	(6)
	(units)	(units)		(dollars)	(dollars)
1	42	0		42	42
			.33		
2	40	6		58	76
			.80		
3	36	11		69	102
			1.50		
4	30	15		75	120
			3.00		
5	21	18		75	129
			5.00		
6	11	20		71	131
			11.00		
7	0	21		63	126

* $-\Delta Y_1/\Delta Y_2$; i.e. reduction in production of Y_1 associated with an increase of 1 unit in Y_2.

adds 10 units of product, making a total of 21; the third unit of resources adds nine units of product, making a total of 30; and so on until the sixth unit of resources adds two units of product, making a total of 42. Note that each successive unit of resources adds less to the total product; that is, diminishing marginal productivity takes place in producing product Y_1.

Diminishing marginal productivity also occurs when the six units of resources are used to produce Y_2. The first unit of resources produces six units, the second unit of resources adds five units, the third four units, and so on until the sixth unit of resources adds only one unit of product, making a total of 21.

The various combinations of products Y_1 and Y_2 which can be produced with the six units of resources are shown in columns 2 and 3. For example, 40 units of Y_1 and six units of Y_2 can be produced. If one more unit of resources is used in the Y_2 enterprise, production is increased to 11 units but production of Y_1 is reduced to 36 units.

The marginal rate of substitution of Y_2 for Y_1 is shown in column 4. In changing from product combination (1) to (2), the marginal rate of substitution is .33; that is, a reduction of two units of Y_1 releases sufficient resources to produce six units of Y_2. As additional resources are shifted, the sacrifice in production of Y_1 increases relative to the increase in Y_2, until 11 units of Y_1 are required to substitute for one unit of Y_2.

Determining the most profitable combination of enterprises depends upon the rate of substitution of one enterprise for another and the prices of the products. Referring again to Table 2.6, with Y_1 priced at $1.00 and Y_2 at $3.00, the highest income is realized by producing either 30 units of Y_1 and 15 units of Y_2, or 21 units of Y_1 and 18 units of Y_2. Profits are at a maximum somewhere between these two combinations. With Y_1 priced at $1.00 and Y_2 at $6.00, income is at a maximum when 11 units of Y_1 and 20 units of Y_2 are produced. Increasing the price of Y_2 relative to the price of Y_1 made it profitable to produce relatively more of Y_2.

With a fixed amount of resources, maximum income is obtained when the marginal rate of product substitution is equal to the inverse of the price ratio. In algebraic form

$$\frac{\Delta Y_1}{\Delta Y_2} = \frac{Py_2}{Py_1} \qquad (2.3)$$

where ΔY_1 represents a small change in the quantity of product Y_1,

ΔY_2 represents a small change in the quantity of product Y_2, and Py_2 and Py_1 represent the prices of the two products.

Applying this principle to the situation portrayed in Table 2.6, ΔY_1 represents the change in production of Y_1 associated with a change (increase or decrease) of one unit in the amount of resources. ΔY_2 has a similar meaning with reference to production of Y_2. With Y_1 priced at \$1.00 and Y_2 at \$3.00, income is at a maximum where ΔY_1 is 9 and ΔY_2 is 3. Thus, the marginal rate of product substitution is equal to the inverse price ratio, indicating as is evident in the table that the optimum combination of enterprises Y_1 and Y_2 is between product combinations (4) and (5).

When competitive enterprises substitute for each other at a constant rate, income generally is maximized by specializing in one enterprise and excluding the other. In such cases it is very infrequent that price and substitution ratios are equal. Thus, it is unlikely that income can be maximized if both products are produced.

Supplementary Enterprises

Enterprises are supplementary when they jointly permit more complete use of resources than when only one enterprise is included in the business. Supplementarity arises due to existence of unused resources which are fixed as far as the farm is concerned but which are variable between enterprises. Supplementary enterprises do not compete with other enterprises for resources, neither do they contribute anything to other enterprises—such as is the case with complementary enterprises. A small garden or fruit orchard, a small flock of sheep, and hogs following fattening cattle are examples of enterprises which are primarily supplementary enterprises on many farms.

Since truly supplementary enterprises have no relationship to other enterprises in the farm business, the discussion of enterprise relationships given above does not apply. The decision to be reached is whether the price of the product is sufficient to make production profitable.

Complementary Enterprises

Enterprises are complementary when one adds to the production of another. A complementary enterprise does not cause a sacrifice in production of another product as is the case with competitive enterprises. Neither does it stand alone as pure supplementary enterprises do. Given a fixed amount of resources, enterprises which are complementary will produce more product as a pair than the sum of their products produced independently. Alfalfa and grain production are examples of complementary enterprises. Alfalfa complements grain as a result of a by-product, nitrogen, which it produces.

Quite a number of complementary relationships exist in agriculture. Enterprises are never complementary over all possible combinations of the two, however. Complementarity always gives way to competition as one enterprise is expanded relative to the other.

Income is increased by resource combinations which encourage complementarity since a greater total product is produced. Price comparisons are not needed when allocation of resources between complementary enterprises is being considered. However, as soon as the complementary relationship gives way to a competitive relationship, price relationships become of immediate importance.

THE INFLUENCE OF TIME ON COSTS AND RETURNS

Time has a significant influence on costs and returns, and as a result involves considerations which should be recognized in managerial decisions. Two aspects of the problem are considered: growth of a cash outlay over time, and discounting of future income.

Growth of a Cash Outlay

A cash outlay grows over time due to the compounding of interest charges or opportunity costs involved in using the capital. If $100 are put in a savings account with interest at 5 per cent, compounded annually, it will increase, or grow, to $127.63 by the end of five years. A cash outlay or investment made in a farm business grows over time in a similar manner. Farm improvements, machinery, breeding stock, milk cows, and alfalfa stands are examples. While such items depreciate over time, growth of the remaining capital invested should be considered in analysis of whether the investment likely will be profitable. Assume, for example, that it cost $30.00 per acre to establish an alfalfa stand which would be in production for three years, with one-third of the capital outlay charged off each year. Thus, one-third of the $30.00, or $10.00, would be invested for one year, another $10.00 for two years, and the third $10.00 for three years. Under these conditions, with interest at 5 per cent, compounded annually, the initial $30.00 investment would grow to $33.10 by the end of the three-year period. In other words, with the assumptions given, $33.10 would be the appropriate cost to use in determining whether it would pay to plant alfalfa.

The rate of growth of a cash outlay over time depends primarily on the interest rate. With interest at 10 per cent, compounded annually, $100.00 will grow to $161.05 at the end of five years, compared with $127.63 with interest at 5 per cent. The frequency of compounding also influences the rate of growth; the more frequent the compounding the faster the growth. With interest at 10 per cent compounded semiannually, $100.00 will grow to $162.90 by the end of five years, compared with $161.05 when the interest was compounded annually.

Since costs grow as a result of interest or opportunity cost accumulations, the equation for compounding interest

$$S = s(1 + i)^n \qquad\qquad (2.4)$$

may be used to show growth in a cash outlay. S represents the sum at the end of n periods; s, the amount which is invested for n periods; and i, the interest rate. Applying this equation to $1.00 invested at 5 per cent interest compounded annually for three years we have $S = 1\,(1.05)^3 = \$1.16$. Note that in this example "n periods" is three years, since interest is compounded annually. If interest had been compounded semiannually for three years, the annual interest rate would have been divided by two and n increased to six, since six periods would have been involved.

The amount of $1 at compound interest is given in Appendix Table 1. As in the equation, the letter n at the top of the first column refers to the number of periods; and the numbers at the top of the other columns refer to the interest rate i applicable to the period being used. For example, when n refers to years, the annual interest rate should be used; when n refers to three-month periods, i equals the annual interest rate divided by four.

Equation 2.4 is appropriate when resource services are given off in their entirety at the end of a given number of periods. However, in most cases capital investments gradually depreciate. In other words, a portion of the initial investment is given off each year. The appropriate equation to use in such cases is

$$S = s_1(1 + i) + s_2(1 + i)^2 + s_3(1 + i)^3 + \cdots + s_n(1 + i)^n \qquad (2.5)$$

where s_1, s_2, s_3, and s_n refer to the amount of the initial investment given off at *the end* of the first, second, third, and nth years.

Applying Equation 2.5 to the investment in an alfalfa stand, given above, we have $S = 10\,(1.05) + 10\,(1.05)^2 + 10\,(1.05)^3 = 33.10$, the same compound cost figure given above.

Equation 2.5 corresponds to accounting procedures customarily applied to capital investments which embody stocks of services which must be purchased at one point in time but are given off over several production periods. Depreciation—the charge for services given off during the production period—customarily is charged at the end of the year, or accounting period. In other words, the portion of the initial investment given off during the year (the amount of depreciation) is assumed to be in use the entire year.

A slightly modified approach may be more appropriate in circumstances where services are given off *during* a production period, if costs are not compounded for a fraction of a production period. In such cases the following equation is appropriate:

$$S = s_1 + s_2(1 + i) + s_3(1 + i)^2 + \cdots + s_n(1 + i)^{n-1}. \qquad (2.6)$$

Compounded costs derived by use of Equation 2.6 generally are slightly on the low side while use of Equation 2.5 generally gives a figure slightly on the high side.

The above discussion has considered situations in which a single capital investment is made and services are forthcoming in several production periods. In contrast, a number of agricultural enterprises involve investments in several periods prior to production. A citrus orchard, for example, requires several years to come into production; several years are required to produce a milk cow; and more than one year ordinarily is required to raise and fatten a steer for slaughter. In such cases the sum of costs compounded up to a specified date can be arrived at by using the equation

$$S = s_1(1 + i)^n + s_2(1 + i)^{n-1} + s_3(1 + i)^{n-2} + \cdots + s_n(1 + i). \qquad (2.7)$$

In using this equation it is assumed that the product is sold (or comes into production) at the end of n years, with s_1, s_2, s_3, and s_n representing investment outlays at the *beginning* of the first, second, third, and nth years. If the investment outlay is made during each year, and interest is not charged for a fraction of a year, the following equation should be used:

$$S = s_1(1 + i)^{n-1} + s_2(1 + i)^{n-2} + s_3(1 + i)^{n-3} + \cdots + s_n. \qquad (2.8)$$

This equation generally understates compounded costs slightly, while Equation 2.7 generally slightly overstates them.

As is indicated by the above discussion, compounding costs is a method whereby interest costs on a capital investment, or other outlay, are accumulated over time. This permits comparison of two costs in time. It also permits comparison of costs with future income. Each of the above equations links present resource costs to their future products and revenue. Thus, by using the compounding cost approach, costs are directly comparable with income at some point of time in the future. Another approach, considered in the next section, is to discount income so it is comparable to costs in the present.

Discounting Income

Discounting income is the procedure whereby the present value of future income is determined. The concept is the converse of growth in value due to accrued interest. Thus, with interest at 5 per cent, \$1.00 today grows to \$1.05 in a year and, conversely, \$1.05 a year from now is worth only \$1.00 today.

The present value of a given income in a future year is derived by using the equation

$$V = \frac{I}{(1+i)^n} \tag{2.9}$$

where V is present value, I is future income, i is the discount (or capitalization) rate, and n is the number of years before the income will be received. This is the equation to use when future income is discounted on an annual basis. If the income is discounted m times per year, i should be divided by m, and n multiplied by m.

This equation can be derived directly from Equation 2.4, given above, for compounding costs. Equation 2.4 was

$$S = s(1+i)^n. \tag{2.4}$$

Dividing both sides by $(1+i)^n$ we have

$$\frac{S}{(1+i)^n} = s \frac{(1+i)^n}{(1+i)^n} \tag{2.10}$$

or

$$s = \frac{S}{(1+i)^n}. \tag{2.11}$$

In Equation 2.4, s represented the principal sum invested, which is the unknown amount, V, in Equation 2.9. S represented the sum of the compounded costs, which in Equation 2.9 is the amount of income, I, to be received at the end of a future year. Thus, Equations 2.9 and 2.11 are identical, the letters used having been changed to better represent the terminology.

Application of Equation 2.9 can be illustrated by determining the present value of $127.63 to be received at the end of five years, assuming the discount rate is 5 per cent. (This odd amount is used since it is the end product of an example used above in compounding costs.) Substituting the known quantities in Equation 2.9 gives

$$V = \frac{\$127.63}{(1 + .05)^5}$$

$$V = \frac{\$127.63}{1.2763} = \$100.$$

The present value of $1 at compound interest is given in Appendix Table 2. As in the equation, the letter n at the top of the first column refers to the number of years involved, and the numbers at the top of the other columns refer to the discount or capitalization rate, i.

Using this table in solving the above example, first find the column headed with 5 per cent, move down to n equals 5 and read .78352617. This amount multiplied by $127.63 gives $100.00.

The present value of a sequence of annual incomes is given by the equation

$$V = \frac{I_1}{1 + i} + \frac{I_2}{(1 + i)^2} + \frac{I_3}{(1 + i)^3} + \cdots + \frac{I_n}{(1 + i)^n}. \quad (2.12)$$

In this equation I represents annual (net) income, which may or may not be the same each year. When annual income varies from year to year, Equation 2.12 is used to compute present value. However, when annual income is constant and continues in perpetuity, Equation 2.12 may be reduced to

$$V = \frac{I}{i}. \quad (2.13)$$

The discount (capitalization) rate, i, has a very significant influence on present value. For example, a perpetual annual income of $100 discounted at 5 per cent gives a present value of $2,000. Lowering the discount (capitalization) rate to 4 per cent increases the present value to $2,500. Thus, in deriving and using the present value, one should always be cognizant of the importance of the discount (capitalization) rate. Moreover, it should be recognized that the discount (capitalization) rate will vary, depending upon circumstances. This point will be considered further in later chapters.

QUESTIONS AND PROBLEMS

1. Explain the principle of diminishing returns.
2. Is the principle of diminishing returns a physical or economic law? Discuss.
3. Explain how increasing the number of factors of production which are permitted to vary affects diminishing returns.
4. Are "constant returns" possible? If so, doesn't this negate the principle of diminishing returns? Discuss.
5. Using the data in Table 2.2, prepare a chart or figure showing total output, average output, and additional (marginal) output.
6. Explain what is meant by the term marginal.
7. Distinguish between fixed and variable costs. What considerations may cause costs to change from fixed to variable and vice versa?
8. How can one determine whether or not it will pay to produce?
9. How can one determine how much to produce?
10. Using the data in Table 2.4, prepare a chart or figure showing the following costs per unit of output: marginal, average variable, average fixed, and average total costs. What is the relationship of average variable, average fixed, and average total costs per unit of output? What is the relationship between marginal costs per unit of output and average total costs per unit of output?
11. Theoretically, how can one determine whether or not his costs are as low as they should be?
12. Using data in Table 2.5, prepare a chart showing the combinations of factors A and B which can be used to produce 1,000 units of product. Using the prices given, show graphically the least cost combination of the two factors.
13. What is meant by "diminishing marginal rate of substitution"? What is its significance in economic analysis?
14. What guides do economic principles provide in combining enterprises? Explain.
15. Using the data in Table 2.6, prepare a chart showing the production functions for products Y_1 and Y_2. (Use the X axis for the six inputs of factor X and the Y axis for the amounts produced.) Prepare another chart showing the combinations of products Y_1 and Y_2 which can be produced with the six units of factor X. Using the product prices given, show graphically the optimum combination of the two enterprises.

16. What is the significance of time in analyzing costs and returns in agriculture?
17. Explain what is meant by "compounding costs."
18. Explain what is meant by "discounting returns."
19. What is the relationship of compounding costs to discounting returns? When should each be applied?

Chapter 3

FARM FINANCIAL MANAGEMENT

THE LARGE and increasing amounts of capital required in agriculture, as outlined in Chapter 1, serve to emphasize the need for more attention to management of finances. When farms were smaller and not so highly developed, finances were relatively less important in the overall picture. However, as farms have developed into substantial businesses, a definite need has arisen for astute handling of financial affairs. Earnings of capital, both absolutely and in one use as compared to another, are crucial to the farm business since (1) capital requirements are extremely large and (2) a high proportion of gross income is required to pay for purchased inputs.

Financial management and farm management are synonymous in many respects. This overlapping is natural since farm management is the primary activity, with financial management contributing to overall management of the farm firm. However, financial management includes some things not ordinarily included in farm management. While it is well for the student of finance to be cognizant of this situation, outlining a specific field is considered unnecessary. For purposes of this discussion, farm financial management may be thought of as including financial aspects involved in management as they relate to the individual farm.

Financial management in its broadest sense has two aspects. Macrofinancial management pertains to overall aspects of finance from the viewpoint of society, the agricultural industry, lending institutions, and the like. Microfinancial management is concerned with finances from the viewpoint of managing the individual farm or business firm. Primary attention is devoted to the latter aspect in this chapter. This should not be interpreted as meaning that macro-financial management is unimportant; it is of equal or greater importance than microfinancial management since it deals with aspects of finance which provide the overall framework within which the individual firm functions. For example, most commercial farmers are dependent upon lending institutions for part of their finances. In most cases the individual farmer has relatively little influence on policies and procedures of his lender. Yet, the way in which he manages his finances depends to a great degree on how his lender operates. In other words, the lending institution—along with society generally—sets the overall framework within which the individual farmer must manage his finances. It is evident, therefore, that macro aspects of financial management are of great importance. However, since the primary focus in the first part of this text is on the individual farm, attention will be directed here to microfinancial management. Some aspects of macrofinancial management will be considered in the analysis of lending institutions in the latter part of the book.

Aspects of financial management analyzed in this chapter pertain to (1) determination of goals or objectives, (2) determination of the amount of capital or funds available, (3) allocation of capital between the farm business (firm) and alternative uses, (4) the effect of time on use of funds, and (5) procedures which facilitate effective control and management of finances. Aspects of financial management related to internal phases of the farm business are included as an integral part of the analysis in subsequent chapters.

DEFINING GOALS

Financial management is not an end in itself but a means of accomplishing goals or objectives. The first step in financial management, therefore, is to determine the goals. Individual and family goals grow out of needs and interests, past experiences, and values. Goals are the ends toward which individuals and families work.

Goal setting is a continuous process. In every family there are several goals, some of which may conflict. Thus, establishing goals involves weighing interests and needs and modifying either the goals or the methods of attaining them. Not all goals are equally important and some may be stepping-stones to achieving subsequent or more ultimate goals.

Goals of the family may be classified into two groups: those involving consumption and those pertaining to production. Goals involving consumption relate to the home itself, its furnishings, food and clothing of the family, vacation, and the like. Goals pertaining to production involve the farm business and any non-farm investments the farmer may own. Such goals relate to the size and type of farm to be operated, the type and quality of livestock, the level of production to be achieved, and the like. We are concerned with the latter group of goals in this chapter.

Function of Goals

Goals ordinarily define specific objectives. Some are immediately attainable and often imperative, others may be reached in months, while some may take years or perhaps a lifetime. The short-term goal may be to rent a farm; the intermediate goal, owner operation with the aid of considerable borrowed funds; the more distant goal, owner operation with a reasonably safe equity. An immediate goal may be a specific cropping system; the long-term goal may be to bring additional land into cultivation by drainage or irrigation, and to improve production through soil conservation, improved rotations, and fertilization. The present ranch may accommodate 200 cows and appurtenant young stock; the long-term goal may call for expanding the unit to a 500-cow unit.

Goals are important in financial management since they indicate investments which will be called for, expenses to be met, and income to be realized. Thus, goals should be formulated with these things in mind. They should be sufficiently explicit and nonduplicating so that associated finances can be estimated. Timing of the goal should be recorded to indicate when funds will be needed for their fulfillment and/or when income will be forthcoming.

FINANCIAL PLANS

Establishment of goals has limited merit unless these goals are organized and coordinated in financial plans for the farm business.

It has been said that "when we fail to plan, we plan to fail." When we fail to plan, almost certainly some of our most valued goals go begging because available funds will have been spent on the less important. Plans serve as guides in achieving goals, as blue prints and specifications serve as guides in the engineering and construction field.

A minimum of two basic financial plans should be made: a short-time plan or budget covering the period immediately ahead—year, quarter, or whatever period is most pertinent—and a long-time plan. These two basic plans should be supplemented with other plans as necessary to provide a well-organized basis for achieving goals. For example, if a major purchase is contemplated, a special analysis might be helpful in determining the influence of the outlay on the business and farm family. Moreover, the basic short- and long-term plans should be rebuilt or revised from time to time to keep them up-to-date.

Building financial plans is not a simple task. While they need not be made a matter of drudgery, creating more dissatisfaction than satisfaction, plans must be based upon a sound foundation and proper business procedures to provide reliable guidance for decisions.

How Much Capital Is Available?

A basic requirement for developing farm financial plans is a general indication of how much capital is available. For example, does the farmer have access to $50,000, $100,000, or $500,000? With this general indication, plans can then be developed for specific uses of the funds. The specific amount to be used will depend upon the profitability of using capital, the terms and conditions involved in acquiring capital, and the amount of risk the family can carry. These aspects of capital acquisition and utilization by the farm business are considered in some detail in subsequent chapters.

Many farmers do not take an overall look at finances and, therefore, do not realize the amount of capital to which they have access. Two reasons probably are: (1) They have not investigated the various sources of capital, and (2) they have not developed a pattern of analysis to help them determine the amount of capital they should use. The sources of capital available, together with an analysis of the advantages and disadvantages of each, are discussed in the next chapter. The objective of this section is to outline a pattern of analysis which may be helpful in determining the amount of capital to acquire from various sources.

The Amount of Capital It Will Pay To Use

The economic model presented in Chapter 2 for determining the amount of resources it will pay to employ may be used in analyzing the amount of capital to be acquired. In the absence of capital rationing, the amount of capital to be used is indicated by equating the marginal cost of acquiring capital, including an allowance for risk, with the marginal returns it produces.

Consideration of the overall amount of capital it will pay to employ in the business usually is approached within a long-run planning framework. Most factors of production, therefore, are subject to modification. Management may be relatively fixed, but most commercial farmers have sufficient surplus ability to permit considerable expansion of the business before diminishing returns become serious. Under such circumstances marginal returns decline very little with increased use of capital, while marginal costs gradually increase until they equal marginal returns.

The increase in marginal costs associated with use of capital may arise from three sources: increased operating costs associated with size of unit, increased risk involved in using larger amounts of credit, and nonmonetary "costs" involved in acquiring and using capital. The long-run average cost curve indicates the relative level of costs associated with different sizes of farms. Theoretically, costs eventually will increase as the size of farm increases, due to inefficiencies associated with size, limitations of management, and the like. Quite a number of studies of the cost structures of various sizes of farms indicate, however, that increasing costs generally do not occur within the size range of most commercial farms. While this generalization may not hold for all farms and farmers, it appears that relatively little of the increase in marginal costs typically is associated with size as such. The increase in marginal costs associated with use of larger amounts of capital stems primarily from risk aversion and nonmonetary "costs" involved in acquiring and using capital. These costs are responsible for what is commonly referred to as "internal capital rationing" in the farm business.

Risk of loss of equity capital increases as the relative amount of borrowed capital used in a typical farm business increases. As the analysis of risk-bearing ability in subsequent chapters will show, risk of loss of equity capital due to crop failure, low prices, or other adverse conditions—the possibility of loss of the farm business—generally limits the amount of credit used in the business to less than it would pay to use under normal conditions. Even when the consequences may not be so serious, using more credit often has adverse effects. Worry over not being able to meet the loan payments increases. The lender may ask more questions and require more information on the business.

For several reasons nonmonetary costs increase as the amount of capital acquired for use in the business increases. As the amount of capital saved in a given period increases, dissatisfaction or negative satisfaction associated with foregoing current consumption increases. More difficulty may be encountered in finding capital to rent or borrow. The "cost" of management may increase due to the added time, effort, worry, and the like, involved in managing a larger amount of capital.

Thus, in approaching the problem of determining the overall amount of capital available to the business, a farmer should keep in mind that the end objective is to equate marginal costs and returns. He should also recognize that diminishing returns may be involved. However, his primary problem consists of determining the "cost" associated with his risk aversion and the nonmonetary "costs" involved in acquisition and use of varying amounts of capital, and balancing these along with marginal monetary costs against marginal returns. Since both monetary and nonmonetary costs are involved, the problem is one of equating marginal negative satisfaction with marginal positive satisfaction involved in acquiring and using increasing amounts of capital in the farm business.

Choosing Among Sources of Capital

The model presented in Chapter 2 for determining the minimum cost combination of factors of production is the appropriate model to use in determining the amount of capital to obtain from various sources. In applying this model, capital obtained from each source is considered as a different factor of production.

Capital obtained from one source substitutes for capital from another source on a dollar-for-dollar basis. In other words, the rate of substitution is constant. Under such circumstances, as was pointed out in Chapter 2, the problem is one of determining the most economical source of capital and obtaining the needed capital from that source. The problem is not quite that simple, however, due to (1) limitations on capital available from various sources, (2) increasing costs (monetary plus nonmonetary) of capital derived from a given source, and (3) "lumpiness" of capital acquired by renting. Capital available from savings or equity may be the most economical source, but the amount of such capital generally is limited. The rate of savings may be increased but only at a higher "cost." Similarly, the amount of capital which can be obtained by borrowing tends to be limited. Larger amounts may be obtained by using second mortgages, and the like, but again the cost is increased. Thus, all the capital used in a business usually will not be obtained from one source. Several sources will be used, with the amount obtained from each being increased until the marginal cost of each source is equal and, in turn, equal to marginal returns from use of capital. Since nonmonetary costs are involved, the equality will be determined in terms of satisfaction rather than dollars.

ALLOCATION OF CAPITAL TO ALTERNATIVE USES

Allocation of capital to alternative uses involves both internal and external aspects of the farm business. Allocation of capital among enterprises within the farm business is considered in subsequent chapters. Consideration here is directed to allocation of capital between the farm business and external competitors for funds: primarily the farm household and nonfarm business ventures. The capital being considered is owned capital (savings, gifts, inheritances, and the like) and current income received during a given period, say one year.

Farm Business Versus Farm Household Use of Funds

The farm business and the farm household compete for funds in the same manner as do competitive enterprises. Pressure exerted by the farm business for more and more capital, together with interest of the family in expanding the size of business so as to increase income, effectively encourages allocation of capital to the business on most farms. On the other hand, a certain amount of funds is required for even minimum living standards, and farm people are becoming more "comfort conscious." As a result, the farm household is becoming an increasingly keen competitor for available funds.

With limited capital (there would be no problem if capital were unlimited) a family must choose among alternatives in production and consumption. They must decide how much of their capital to invest in the farm business and how much to use for consumption. In other words, the question of farm business versus farm household use of funds is basically a question of determining the allocation of capital between savings and current consumption.

ALLOCATION POSSIBILITIES

During a period of time the family has a given amount of capital at its disposal. The family has the choice of spending this capital for current consumption, of saving it for consumption at a later time, or of allocating part of it to each use. The model for determining the optimum allocation of capital between the two uses is portrayed in Figure 3.1.

Consumption in the current time period, t_1, is registered on the horizontal axis, and savings, or consumption in a later time period, t_2, is measured on the vertical axis. The amount of capital available is represented by oa, which is equal to ob. The various alternatives for allocating capital between consumption in time period t_1 and in time period t_2 are indicated by the allocation possibility (iso-capital) line, ab. The family may go on a "spending spree" and spend all their capital, ob, in the current period. On the other hand, they might live very frugally and save their accumulated capital plus a part of their current income. Their savings for consumption in period t_2 would then approach oa. The allocation chosen by most families falls somewhere between these two extremes.

The optimum allocation of capital between current and future consumption depends upon the amount of satisfaction associated with each use. Thus, satisfaction is the appropriate choice indicator to use in this case rather than product prices, as was outlined in Chapter 2. The methodology outlined there for analysis of product-product relationships may be applied; however, the indifference concept is used in place of prices.

INDIFFERENCE CONCEPT

The indifference concept may be illustrated by the indifference curves shown in Figure 3.1. Each of the indifference curves, I_1, I_2, I_3, and I_4, is comprised of a continuous line of points, each point on a given indifference curve representing combinations of consumption in the current time period, C_1, and consumption in a future time

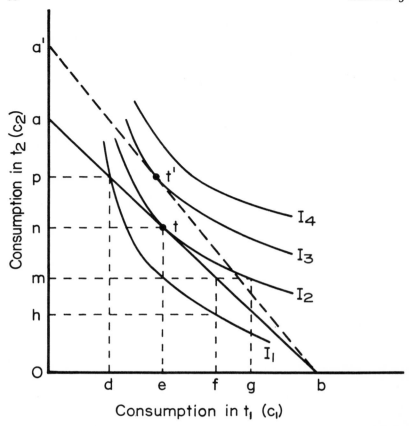

Fig. 3.1—Basic relationships involved in allocation of capital to consumption and savings.

period (savings), C_2, which give equal satisfaction or utility. Thus, *od* of C_1 and *op* of C_2, *oe* of C_1 and *om* of C_2, and *of* of C_1 and *oh* of C_2 each has the same utility to the farm family. It is a matter of indifference to the family which of the three combinations of C_1 and C_2 they have.

The indifference curves shown in Figure 3.1, being convex to the origin, indicate that an increasing amount of savings, C_2, consumption in t_2 is needed to compensate for loss of each successive unit of current income, C_1. For example, a gain of *hm* in C_2 adds as much utility as is lost by a sacrifice of *ef* of C_1. However, if a second unit of C_1, *de* (equal to *ef*), is sacrificed, a larger amount of C_2, *mp*, is needed to replace it.

Indifference curves higher in the plane of a diagram represent higher levels of satisfaction. Thus, indifference curve I_2 represents a higher level of satisfaction than indifference curve I_1. Similarly, indifference curve I_3 represents a higher level of satisfaction than curve I_2. For any indifference curve, all points represent the same level of satisfaction and the curves which constitute one person's, or one group's, indifference map never cross each other.

THE OPTIMUM ALLOCATION

The point of tangency, t, of allocation opportunity curve, ab, and indifference curve I_2, represents the optimum allocation of capital to current consumption and savings. Any other allocation of capital yields less total satisfaction (satisfaction from current consumption plus satisfaction from savings). An allocation of od dollars to current consumption and op dollars to savings would be possible, of course. However, this combination lies on indifference curve I_1, which indicates total satisfaction is less than at point t. In other words, by shifting some capital from savings to current consumption, the farmer could raise the level of total satisfaction to indifference curve I_2.

While total satisfaction would remain the same by shifting from point t to any other point on indifference curve I_2, such a shift is not possible with the amount of capital available. An allocation of om dollars to C_2 and og dollars to C_1, for example, would produce the same level of total satisfaction as at point t. However, capital available is inadequate for such a combination. With om dollars allocated to C_2, only of dollars remain for C_1, fg dollars short of the amount required for total satisfaction to be equivalent to point t. It follows, therefore, that the optimum allocation of capital to current consumption and to savings is the one represented by point t. At this point

$$\frac{\Delta C_1}{\Delta C_2} = \frac{\Delta Sc_2}{\Delta Sc_1} \tag{3.1}$$

where ΔC_1 represents the marginal unit of capital allocated to current consumption, ΔC_2 represents the marginal unit of capital allocated to savings (consumption in time period t_2), and ΔSc_1 and ΔSc_2 represent the change in satisfaction the family derives from use of one unit of capital for current consumption and for savings. Or expressed in another form

$$\Delta C_1 \, \Delta Sc_1 = \Delta C_2 \, \Delta Sc_2 \tag{3.2}$$

which indicates the optimum allocation of capital to consumption and to savings is achieved when the satisfaction from the last (marginal) unit of capital allocated to consumption is equal to the satisfaction derived from an equivalent unit of capital allocated to savings.

EFFECT OF THE RATE OF RETURN

In the foregoing discussion nothing has been said about the effect of the rate of return on the rate of savings. A small amount may be saved when the return is low; in fact, people typically will save a minimum amount even if the monetary return is negative. But what happens to the rate of savings as the rate of return increases? Two opposing forces are at work. One force encourages extra savings since the rate of return is higher. Each dollar spent for current consumption is more expensive—hence, one is inclined to *substitute* extra savings for current consumption. However, working against this so-called "substitution effect" is the second force called the "income effect."[1] With a higher rate of return one is better off and is likely to be inclined to spend more for current consumption. Thus, the net effect of a change in the rate of return on the rate of savings depends upon which is the more powerful, the substitution effect or the income effect.

With most people of modest means the substitution effect of a higher rate of return is assumed to outweigh the income effect. The rate of savings will, therefore, be positively correlated with the rate of return. As the rate of return increases, other things being equal, the amount saved will increase. This is true particularly of younger farmers who generally have great need for more capital in their business. Thus, the rate of return anticipated on savings affects the allocation of capital between consumption and savings. This point may be illustrated by reference to Figure 3.1.

The distance aa' in Figure 3.1 represents the return expected on the capital, oa, which may be saved. Assuming this return is realized, capital available for consumption in time period t_2 will be the original capital saved plus the return realized; that is, oa plus

---

[1] The income effect of an increase in the rate of return is defined as the tendency for a person to feel more affluent and able to afford more consumption goods. The related substitution effect is the tendency for a person to want to react to the higher cost of current consumption, due to the higher rate of return which must be foregone to enjoy current consumption, by substituting savings for the additional consumption goods which could be purchased with the higher return.

aa' equals *oa'*. As a result, the allocation of capital between current consumption and savings will be based on curve *a'b*. Since we have assumed that the substitution effect is stronger than the income effect, the point of tangency, *t'*, is farther to the left than point *t*. In other words, a smaller amount of capital will be used for current consumption and a larger amount will be saved. The higher the anticipated rate of return on savings, the greater will be the shift of capital from current consumption to savings, and vice versa.

The amount of capital saved will depend to a large degree upon the nature (shape) of the indifference curves which, in turn, depends upon the goals of the family. Indifference curves which are more nearly horizontal than those portrayed in Figure 3.1 mean that the family has a relatively high preference for savings, and more capital, therefore, will be allocated to savings. Indifference curves which are steeper than those portrayed indicate the opposite result.

EFFECT OF TIME

Time also affects the allocation of capital to consumption and to savings. Savings "grow" over time when earnings they produce are allowed to accumulate. As was pointed out in Chapter 2, $100 at 5 per cent interest, compounded annually, will grow to $127.63 in five years. On the other hand, the $127.63 five years in the future is not worth $127.63 today. The amount it is worth today depends upon the rate of discount. If it is discounted at 5 per cent, the $127.63 five years from now is worth only $100 today.

It is evident that the effect of time on the allocation of capital to consumption and to savings depends upon the relationship of the rate of earnings on savings to the rate of discount on consumption in a future time period. If the rate of earnings is large relative to the rate of discount, time will serve to encourage savings. Under such circumstances line *a'b* in Figure 3.1 will be considerably steeper than line *ab*. The point of tangency will be to the left of point *t*, indicating that relatively more capital will be allocated to savings. However, if the rate of earnings is less than the rate of discount, time will tend to discourage savings. Under such circumstances curve *a'b* would fall below *ab;* that is, it would be flatter than line *ab*, with the result that the point of tangency in the indifference map would move to the right of point *t*, indicating relatively less capital would be saved.

The rate of discount varies from one person to another, and

particularly from one age to another. Older people generally discount future consumption more than younger people. This fact, coupled with changes which age brings in goals and indifference curves, explains in large measure the pattern of consumption and savings. A young family with limited resources has great need for machinery, livestock, and the like. Earnings on capital invested in such items usually are relatively high. The rate of discount on future earnings usually is relatively low. Thus, the margin between earnings and discount is large; that is, aa' in Figure 3.1 is relatively large. The line $a'b$ is relatively steep, causing the point of tangency to move to the left, indicating greater relative emphasis on savings. As the family accumulates capital and develops a farm unit which enables it to have a reasonably comfortable income, the rate earned on capital often declines. More machinery may be purchased than is actually needed because of the satisfaction it gives. Quality livestock may be acquired more for the boost they give to prestige and satisfaction than to income. As the family becomes older, goals continue to change not only with age but also with the level of income. The shape of their indifference curves may change (become steeper in Figure 3.1), indicating relatively less preference for savings. Similarly, their rate of discount of future consumption may increase and, along with a lower rate of earnings on savings, cause the line $a'b$ to fall below line ab in Figure 3.1. Thus, with steeper indifference curves than those shown in Figure 3.1, and with line $a'b$ more nearly horizontal than line ab, the point of tangency would shift substantially to the right, indicating that relatively little capital would be allocated to savings. In fact, capital allocated to savings may be less than accumulated capital; that is, capital saved in earlier years, or inherited. In other words, the family may use some of its accumulated savings for current consumption. This is often reflected by run-down machinery and improvements, limited attention to conservation, and the like.

Farm Business Versus Nonfarm Business Use of Funds

In the preceding section consideration has been directed to allocation of a given (limited) supply of capital between production (savings) and consumption. The problem considered in this section is the allocation of a given amount of capital used for production between farm and nonfarm business ventures. The problem is pertinent regardless of whether or not the farmer has surplus capital. The farmer short of capital for operating his farm must decide whether he could make more money (or derive more satisfaction) by using part or all of his capital in nonfarm business ventures. The farmer with surplus capital faces this same question plus the problem of whether the surplus capital will earn more or less in the farm business than in nonfarm business ventures. It is assumed that the farm business can be expanded to make use of the funds if that alternative is determined to be most profitable.

PRODUCTION POSSIBILITIES WITH INCREASING RATES OF SUBSTITUTION

The economic model for allocating capital between competing enterprises may be applied directly to this problem. Consider, for example, the situation portrayed in Table 3.1. A farmer has 10 units of capital available which he may use in the farm business, in enterprise Y_1, or in a nonfarm investment, enterprise Y_2. If the capital is used in enterprise Y_1, products shown in column 2 will be produced. A corresponding production function for enterprise Y_2 is shown in column 3. Production possibilities with the 10 units of capital are shown in columns 4 and 5. Since diminishing returns occur in the production function for Y_1, Y_2 substitutes for Y_1 at an increasing rate.

As indicated in Chapter 2, the most profitable combination of enterprises is when

$$\frac{\Delta Y_1}{\Delta Y_2} = \frac{Py_2}{Py_1} \tag{3.3}$$

with ΔY_1 representing a small change in output of product Y_1; ΔY_2, a small change in output of product Y_2; and Py_2 and Py_1 representing prices per unit of product. With Py_1 at \$2.00 and Py_2 at \$1.00, income is at a maximum when

$$\frac{\Delta Y_1}{\Delta Y_2} = .5.$$

This solution may be confirmed by reference to column 7 of Table 3.1, which shows the maximum income of \$106.40 falls between marginal rates of substitution 0.48 and 0.68. Thus, the actual maximum income slightly exceeds \$106.40—but with the units of capital given, this is as close as we can come. Maximum income is realized by allocating seven units of capital to the farm enterprise and three units of capital to the nonfarm enterprise.

In allocating capital between two enterprises, only variable

TABLE 3.1

PRODUCTION FUNCTIONS, PRODUCTION POSSIBILITIES, MARGINAL RATE OF PRODUCT SUBSTITUTION, AND INCOME UNDER INCREASING RATES OF SUBSTITUTION (Hypothetical data)

Inputs of Capital	Output		Production Possibilities With 10 Units of Capital		Marginal Rate of Substitution of Y_2 for Y_1 ($\Delta Y_1/\Delta Y_2$)	Income With P_{y_1} @ \$2 P_{y_2} @ \$1	Production Possibilities With 10 Units of Capital		Marginal Rate of Substitution of Y_2 for Y_3 ($\Delta Y_3/\Delta Y_2$)	Income With P_{y_3} @ \$2 P_{y_2} @ \$1
	Y_1	Y_2	Y_1	Y_2			Y_3	Y_2		
(1)	(2)	(3)	(4)	(5)	(6)	(7)	(8)	(9)	(10)	(11)
0	0	0	50.0	0		\$100.00	33.3	0		\$66.60
1	9.0	5.0	49.5	5.0	.10	104.00	33.0	5.0	.06	71.00
2	18.0	10.0	48.1	10.0	.28	106.20	32.1	10.0	.18	74.20
3	25.8	15.0	45.7	15.0	.48	106.40	30.5	15.0	.32	76.00
4	32.4	20.0	42.3	20.0	.68	104.60	28.2	20.0	.46	76.40
5	37.9	25.0	37.9	25.0	.88	100.80	25.3	25.0	.58	75.60
6	42.3	30.0	32.4	30.0	1.10	94.80	21.6	30.0	.74	73.20
7	45.7	35.0	25.8	35.0	1.32	86.60	17.2	35.0	.88	69.40
8	48.1	40.0	18.0	40.0	1.56	76.00	12.0	40.0	1.04	64.00
9	49.5	45.0	9.5	45.0	1.70	64.00	6.0	45.0	1.20	57.00
10	50.0	50.0	0	50.0	1.90	50.00	0	50.0	1.20	50.00

costs of production are considered in determining the quantities of the two products to produce. Fixed costs of production are not involved. This fact is of considerable significance in allocation of capital. It means that relatively more capital will be allocated to established farm enterprises which can be expanded within the framework of existing fixed costs than to nonfarm enterprises (investments) being considered. In nonfarm enterprises (investments) in which farmers usually invest (savings accounts, bonds, stocks, and the like), all costs are variable from the farmer's viewpoint. Income realized by the farmer on his investment is based upon income of the company after all costs—both fixed and variable— have been deducted from gross income. Thus, the income per dollar of capital put in nonfarm investments tends to be relatively low compared with returns from capital used in established farm enterprises. This point can be illustrated by further reference to Table 3.1.

Enterprises Y_1 and Y_3 are assumed to be identical with the exception that Y_1 is an established enterprise whereas Y_3 is still in the planning stage; that is, no fixed costs have been incurred, all costs are variable. Variable costs for enterprise Y_1 are assumed to be two-thirds of total costs. Since variable costs for enterprise Y_3 equal total costs, variable costs for enterprise Y_1 are only two-thirds of variable costs for Y_3. As a result, output of enterprise Y_3 per unit of capital is only two-thirds of the output for enterprise Y_1. This relationship can be observed by comparing columns 4 and 8 in Table 3.1. As a result of the smaller output, enterprise Y_3 competes less favorably for capital than enterprise Y_1. With enterprises Y_1 and Y_2 competing for the 10 units of capital, the optimum allocation was 7 units to Y_1 and three units to Y_2. With enterprises Y_3 and Y_2 competing, only six units of capital are allocated to Y_3, with four units being allocated to Y_2.

Since substantial fixed costs are involved in agriculture, and since many farm businesses can expand substantially without a proportionate increase in fixed costs, agriculture is a strong contender for capital in the short run. In the long run, however, the situation is quite different. Since all costs are variable in the long run, production per unit of capital is relatively low on many farms. In some cases, income (output multiplied by price) is less than total costs (capital used in production of the output). When such a situation prevails it does not pay to invest more capital in the farm business. Income would be maximized by liquidating the business and investing the capital elsewhere.

PRODUCTION POSSIBILITIES WITH CONSTANT RATES OF SUBSTITUTION

The illustration presented in Table 3.1 and the related discussion pertain to a situation where an increasing marginal rate of product substitution occurs. When the farm and nonfarm products substitute at constant rates the same principles apply, but it is unlikely that a combination of products will be produced. Production of one or the other of the products will be most profitable and, therefore, maximum returns will be realized by using all of the capital available to produce that product.

BUSINESS PROCEDURES FACILITATE EFFECTIVE MANAGEMENT

Phases of financial management sometimes overlooked or slighted are keeping adequate records, providing legal documents and related instructions for transfer of the estate in case of death, and providing a place where these records and documents can be used and safely kept. Adequate farm records are essential to effective management; their importance will become evident in subsequent chapters. Having important papers in order will contribute not only to success and satisfaction in the business operation but will materially lighten the load (negative satisfactions) and possibly the expense of transferring the business and property in case of death.

Farm Records

Records of the farm business should be kept and used as an integral part of good business and tax management. On commercial farms, farm records are practically a necessity for income tax purposes and if properly designed will contribute materially to financial management. Records should provide as a minimum:

1. A complete annual inventory of assets and liabilities in sufficient detail and with adequate description to make them understandable. The number and description of livestock; items of machinery; method of depreciation; names, addresses, and explanation of accounts receivable and payable will be helpful.
2. A complete listing and description of income and expense items during the year, preferably by enterprise. This part of the record

should also show production, purchases, births, debt payments, funds borrowed, and the like, to permit bringing the inventory up to date.

3. A summary giving information for analysis of the business and management decisions on each of the farm enterprises, and for tax purposes.

Documents for Transfer of Property

While not a particularly pleasant task, every family should make plans for transfer of property in case of death. When farm owners die without making legal arrangements for disposition of their property, the property is divided among the heirs according to the state law of intestate succession. While these laws vary from state to state, they generally provide that heirs of like relationship be treated alike.

Major disadvantages are inherent in allowing farm property to be transferred in this way. Unnecessary hardship may result. For example, in some states should a farmer die and leave a wife and two children without a will, the wife would inherit only one-third of the farm property and the other two-thirds would go to the children. If the children were minors, their property would be subject to management by a court-appointed guardian. This arrangement might materially complicate affairs for the wife. In other cases the wife might be left without adequate support.

In an attempt to be equitable, legislators in most states have established laws providing for all children to be treated alike. If no other provision is made, the son who has helped run the farm would receive no more than any of his brothers or sisters. A son would have little incentive to stay on the home farm under such circumstances. Or he may let the farm run down, since, otherwise, he may have to pay for improvements when made and again when he buys the shares of other family members. Should the price be too high or the other family members refuse to sell, the son who had operated the farm would have to give it up when the parents die. Hardships and family conflicts are much more probable when adequate provision has not been made for transferring the farm to the next generation. Moreover, outlays for taxes and administration of the estate are frequently higher when property is left to be transferred according to provisions of the law.

If interstate laws of succession are not adequate for transfer of property to the next generation, what better possibilities or legal arrangements may be employed? Consideration should be given to wills, joint tenancy, life estates, and incorporation of the business. Each method has strong points and weaknesses. The method best suited to one family may not be well suited to another. Family circumstances and farm characteristics should be considered in selecting the method of transfer. Often a combination of methods is employed. Moreover, as the family grows older and children become independent, an entirely different method may be employed than when the family is younger.

WILLS

Every farm owner should have a will prepared by a qualified lawyer. The expense involved is relatively small, usually amounting to only a few dollars unless the provisions are unusual or complicated. From time to time the will should be reviewed and amended or rewritten so as to fully meet the needs of the family as circumstances change.

Wills have a number of advantages and disadvantages as a means of transferring property. The will enables the owner to distribute his property to the family members as he desires. By creation of life estates as part of the will, the owner can partially direct use of the property for a period after his death. The will also enables the owner to retain absolute control of the property as long as he lives. These features are advantages to the owner but may be disadvantages to the one receiving the property.

Wills have other serious disadvantages from the viewpoint of transferring the farm to the next generation. Since wills can be changed they provide no real security for a son who contemplates eventual ownership of the farm.[2] With average family development and life expectancy the son taking over the farm will have reached or passed middle age before he acquires the farm and is able to start paying off other heirs. Moreover, since wills become effective only on death of the maker, there is no opportunity for changes or modifications if things do not work out satisfactorily. In preparing a will it is difficult to visualize all contingencies and ramifications

---

[2] The laws of New York and of some other states provide that a parent can enter into a legally binding contract not to change a will. Such a contract is enforceable in court. While such a contract may eliminate the uncertainty associated with transfer of property by will, it complicates things and the parent loses control of the property. The parent, therefore, might just as well have transferred the property by a more direct method.

which might result. Furthermore, it is very easy to let a well-drawn will become out of date. These things may result in the will failing to carry out the wishes of the owner at a time when nothing can be done to improve things. The intended distribution of the property might not even be achieved should property be left to the spouse. For example, a farm owner might will all his property to his wife. Should she remarry and predecease her second husband, he will acquire as much of the farm as is provided by law or by her will, which may not conform to the wishes of her first husband.

JOINT TENANCY

Where property is owned in joint tenancy, two or more people share equally the ownership and right to use and enjoy the property. Joint tenants have what is known as a "right of survivorship," which means that when one joint tenant dies his interest in the jointly held property is divided equally among the surviving joint tenants. In contrast, if land is owned by two or more persons as "tenants in common," when one of the tenants in common dies his interest is passed to his heirs according to state law or as he otherwise provides.

Property is often owned jointly with the right of survivorship as a method of transferring ownership in case of death. State laws governing joint ownership of property vary, however, and persons owning property together should make sure who will have ownership in case of death. Strict statutory requirements have been established in many states regarding creation of joint tenancies or "tenancy by the entireties." Therefore, it is important to know what the law provides if joint tenancy is to do the job intended.

Joint tenancy should not be considered as a substitute for a will. Should a husband and wife own property jointly with right of survivorship and both should die simultaneously, without a will their property is transferred according to the intestate laws of succession, which may not be according to their desires.

LIFE ESTATES

Life estates, usually created by a deed or a will, provide that the holder of such an estate can use the property during his life or the life of someone else. For example, a farmer may deed or will the farm to his wife for her lifetime, with the provision that after her death it shall go to his children. The widow thus has a life estate in the farm which entitles her to possession and use of the property, and to the income produced, during her lifetime.

Life estates are often used to transfer ownership to the next generation. A farmer wanting his son to have the farm may deed the farm to him, reserving a life estate for himself and his wife. Thus, life estates can be used to insure ownership for the younger generation while the farm income is retained by the parents to provide support during their lifetime.

While life estates have advantages as a means of providing support for parents and transferring the farm, they also have a number of disadvantages. The life tenant may not improve the farm and may even exploit the land and buildings in an effort to secure maximum income during his lifetime. He may be held responsible by the remainderman (the one entitled to the property at the life tenant's death) for destruction of permanent improvements, trees, and the like, but the life tenant cannot be forced to keep up the farm. Even if such provision were made in the law, it is very doubtful that a family member who is to inherit the property would bring legal action against aged parents. Moreover, the parents may not want to neglect the farm, but conditions may have changed so that more income is needed than was contemplated. Since economic and social changes both inside and outside the family cannot be foreseen, the life estate may work a hardship both on the parents and the son. Moreover, the son has no specific commitment as to when he will become owner and able to put his plans for the farm and a home into effect.

INCORPORATION

Incorporation of the farm business is increasing in popularity as a means of owning and operating the farm, and interest in it as an aid in transferring the farm to the next generation is increasing. In states where fees and legal expense of establishing a corporation are not prohibitive, incorporation has some advantages, particularly for larger farms. Since ownership is represented by shares of stock, ownership is flexible and can be divided among family members in any manner desired. Partial ownership in the whole farm business can be transferred to each son as he becomes old enough to share in management of the farm. Incorporation provides a means whereby several members of the family can share ownership, operation, and management of a large farm business. Moreover, when the parents approach retirement, ownership and management of the farm can be gradually relinquished by transferring stock to the children.

Incorporation should not be looked upon, however, as a perfect method for transferring ownership, or as a cure-all for financial difficulties and family squabbles. Incorporation involves red tape and some extra bookkeeping. Proper management of finances of the corporation is necessary to take advantage of possible tax savings, and to avoid higher taxes. Some added legal expense also will be involved. As with all affairs involving legal aspects, competent legal counsel should be employed. Tax savings and other advantages may far outweigh the disadvantages involved if the farm business and income are relatively large.

A Home Business Office

A business office in the home facilitates keeping adequate records, and knowing where documents can be found when they are needed. An office provides a place to work on business affairs; keep records up to date; and file bills, important papers, checks, and the like. Readily replaceable business papers and those currently used can be kept in the home business office. However, important records, papers, and documents such as wills, leases, mortgages, stock certificates, bonds, and insurance policies are best kept in a safe-deposit box or fireproof safe. The duplicate copy of income tax reports should be kept for at least five years.

A record, in duplicate, should be made of all important documents telling where they are kept. One copy should be kept with the documents in the safe-deposit box, and the duplicate can be maintained in the business center at home for handy reference.

QUESTIONS AND PROBLEMS

1. Explain what is meant by macrofinancial management, by microfinancial management, by goals.
2. What is the role of goals in financial management?
3. Explain the relationship of goals and financial plans.
4. Outline the principle involved:
   a. In inventorying the amount of capital available to the farm business.
   b. In choosing among various sources of capital.

5. Outline and explain the economic model a family may use in allocating capital to the farm business and the household.
6. Should farmers put any of their capital in nonfarm investments? Explain the economic principles involved.
7. Explain how fixed and variable costs influence the allocation of capital to farm business and nonfarm business investments.
8. Explain the effect of the rate of return on savings on allocation of capital.
9. Does time have an effect on the allocation of capital to consumption and to savings? Explain.
10. List the business procedures which will facilitate effective management. Discuss each.

REFERENCES

Fitzsimmons, C., and Holmes, E. G., *Factors Affecting Farm Family Goals,* Ind. Agr. Exp. Sta. Res. Bul. 663, July, 1958.

Heady, Earl O., *Economics of Agricultural Production and Resource Use,* Prentice-Hall, Inc., Englewood Cliffs, N.J., Chap. 14, 1952.

——, Back, W. B., and Peterson, G. A., *Interdependence Between the Farm Business and the Farm Household With Implications on Economic Efficiency,* Iowa Agr. Exp. Sta. Res. Bul. 398, June, 1953.

Hesser, Leon F., "Conceptual Models of Capital Rationing Among Farmers," *Jour. Farm Econ.,* Vol. 42, No. 2, pp. 325–34, May, 1960.

Hillman, C. H., and Steward, D. D., *Financial Management Practices of Farm Families in Southeastern Ohio Agriculture,* Ohio Agr. Exp. Sta. Res. Bul. 940, June, 1963.

Irwin, G. D., and Baker, C. B., *Effects of Lender Decisions on Farm Financial Planning,* Ill. Agr. Exp. Sta. Bul. 688, Nov., 1962.

Krausz, N. G. P., and Allen, A. R., *Family Planning of Titles and Taxes in the Transfer of Farm Property,* Ill. Ext. Serv. Circ. 885, Apr., 1964.

Technical Committee for NC-32, *Family Financial Security,* N. Cen. Reg. Res. Publ. 131, Iowa Agr. Exp. Sta. Spec. Rept. 36, Mar., 1964.

Chapter 4

ACQUIRING CAPITAL TO FARM

DATA GIVEN in Chapter 1 indicate the probable capital requirements to meet goals of the farm family. The question then arises, Where can the needed capital be acquired?

There are seven methods by which farmers may obtain the capital which they use in their business. The first three listed below represent equity capital, and the last three might be considered different methods of borrowing.

1. Savings
2. Family arrangements
3. Incorporation
4. Leasing
5. Purchase contracts
6. Vertical integration
7. Borrowing

Some capital may also be acquired by gifts or inheritance, but we are not concerned with such sources in this chapter.

SAVINGS

Capital accumulated through savings (defined as net worth, less gifts and inheritance) forms the foundation of the farm financial structure. Except for gifts and inheritance, savings provide the backbone for farm and ranch capital. Savings provide not only capital, as such, but risk-bearing ability (reserves) and demonstrated capacity to earn and save, two very essential components of a strong credit rating.

Farming is big business and big business requires a large amount of capital and a sound financial foundation and framework which savings alone can provide. Few people who are unable to save will be successful in commercial farming. The farmer is the one to whom profit derived from farming accrues and, therefore, he must stand the risk of loss. Funds also are needed for sickness, education, and other family uses. Savings must be accumulated by the successful farm family to provide a financial base for all such purposes.

Accumulating any amount of savings takes time for most people. Living standards tend to be upgraded as income increases, which leaves little for saving. However, it is surprising how rapidly wisely invested savings "grow." Even a small amount saved regularly produces a surprisingly large sum in a fairly short period. Save $5.00 per week and in ten years it will grow to $3,050 when invested at 3 per cent, and to $3,270 when invested at 5 per cent. Larger amounts saved accumulate to larger totals, of course. Many young men or families serious about wanting to farm, probably could save $1,500 per year, which in five years would grow to $8,200, invested at 3 per cent, and to $8,700, invested at 5 per cent.

Attitude of Farmers Toward Savings

Farmers save large amounts during their lifetimes. It is doubtful if any other occupational group in the economy saves as large a proportion of its income. Much of these savings are "forced" by the nature of the business. The farmer must have capital to be successful and this practically forces the farm family to save. Would farmers save as much if it were not for this "forced savings" aspect of agricultural production? The recommendation is often made that larger loans be made to farmers so they will not have to save so much. On the other hand, it is apparent that well-established farmers continue to save when additional capital is not a necessity in the business. What are farmers' attitudes on savings?

An Iowa study (see Table 4.1) gives information on how farmers thought farm income should be allocated between farm investments and consumption. Note the large proportion that farm-

TABLE 4.1

FARMER ATTITUDES TOWARD USE OF FARM INCOME AT DIFFERENT OPERATOR AGES, BY STAGES OF THE LIFE CYCLE *

Operator Stage †	Suggested Percentage Divisions of Income at Operator Ages									
	25 yrs.		35 yrs.		45 yrs.		55 yrs.		65 yrs.	
	(Farm bus.)	(House-hold)	(Farm bus.)	(House-hold)	(Farm bus.)	(House-hold)	(Farm bus.)	(House-hold)	(Farm bus.)	(House-hold)
I........	56	44	55	45	52	48	50	50	36	65
II.......	49	51	47	53	46	54	43	57	34	66
III......	56	44	54	44	52	48	45	55	34	66
IV......	56	44	56	44	54	46	49	51	37	63
Weighted Average........	54.1	45.9	52.1	47.9	50.8	49.2	46.7	53.3	35.2	64.8

* Source: Earl O. Heady, Back, U. B., and Peterson, G. A., *Interdependence Between the Farm Business and the Farm Household With Implications on Economic Efficiency*, Iowa Agr. Exp. Sta. Res. Bul. 398, June, 1953, p. 426.
† I. Beginning operator. II. To middle age. III. Middle age to retirement. IV. Retirement.

ers felt should be invested in the farm business. Another significant point is the importance of the family cycle in the activities and plans of farm people. All age groups thought it desirable to increase consumption at the expense of investment near the end of the family cycle.

FAMILY ARRANGEMENTS

Family arrangements are of considerable importance in acquiring capital to farm, particularly for beginning farmers. Where parents or family members are able, gifts or loans are made to the beginning farm family to assist in providing capital. In other cases assistance in acquiring capital to farm is provided through formalized agreements, such as father-son partnerships, and rental arrangements.

The importance of family agreements is increasing. Extension of Social Security to farmers encourages many to reduce their farming activities so as to gain full Social Security benefits. Family arrangements to accomplish this objective are becoming more frequent. Moreover, with larger and fewer farms the beginner is becoming increasingly dependent upon family assistance in acquiring a farm to operate.

Father-and-son agreements are the most common form of family arrangements. They provide a means whereby a son or son-in-law with limited capital can work into the farm business. From the father's viewpoint such an arrangement often is desirable since he is able to "ease up" a bit. With the decrease in the amount of manual labor an older farmer can perform comes an almost certain decline in farm upkeep and income. An agreement with a son, therefore, may be welcomed by the father not only to help out with the work but to help maintain a vigorous and profitable business.

The agreement also has advantages for the younger man, offering him an opportunity to start farming with less capital than is possible with any other method. By working with his father, he can profit from mature advice and can develop gradually his knowledge of agriculture and business and his management ability. Where the father is nearing retirement and other heirs are not involved, an agreement facilitates transfer of the farm to the son, enabling him to start farming "on his own" with a more adequate unit than might otherwise be possible.

Essentials of Successful Family Partnership Agreements

Various studies of father-and-son partnership agreements have shown that certain characteristics are associated with the most successful arrangements. A Michigan study[1] gives ten essentials for successful father and son farm partnerships. These and related statements are summarized as follows:

1. *Desire of the son and his wife to farm.* The best accomplishments in life are made by individuals who like their work. Farming is not easy, and to be successful a farmer and his wife must enjoy their profession as an offset to the hard work and long hours involved.
2. *Satisfactory living conditions for two families.* Separate living accommodations should be provided if at all possible, to allow individual freedom and to eliminate a source of possible friction.
3. *Ability to get along with each other.* The elder couple should have a determination to recognize that the younger couple will do things differently and have different ways. The young folks should respect their elders and their judgment.
4. *Belief that a farm partnership is desirable.* Do all parties concerned believe the partnership will enable the two families to make better progress and be happier than if they operated independently?
5. *Adequate size of farm business.* Is the farm large enough to provide employment and an adequate living for the two families? If not, can it be enlarged sufficiently through more intensive operation, or by renting or buying additional land?
6. *Good farm management.* If good farm management is not followed, the agreement probably will not succeed.
7. *Knowledge of farm business by son.* The son should have a knowledge of the business of farming and of the individual farm business in which he is to become a partner.
8. *Good business judgment in the use of money.* Many young people have "too big ideas" and make investments that plague

---

[1] Elton B. Hill, *Father and Son Farm Partnerships*, Mich. Agr. Exp. Sta. Spec. Bul. 330, 1944, p. 10.

them for years. Excessive risks should be avoided. Young people should seek the counsel of their elders in financial affairs.

9. *Partnership in the entire farm business.* To avoid trouble, participants in the business must be interested in the conduct of the entire farm.
10. *Good partnership agreement.* A sound agreement which fits the farm and the partners is essential. A written agreement helps prevent misunderstanding.

Legal Aspects of Partnerships

In forming partnerships, the partners should know and understand what is involved and give proper attention to legal aspects. Each person entering into a partnership assumes considerable responsibility for actions of the partner. A partner may sell property of the partnership, make contracts for the business, and create partnership debts without consent of other partners. Moreover, each partner has unlimited liability for suits against the partnership.

Usually these things are relatively unimportant in father-and-son partnerships, but provision should be made for handling eventualities—perhaps as one way of insuring that difficulties will not arise. Since laws governing partnerships vary from state to state, a qualified attorney should be employed to help prepare the partnership agreement, incorporating proper safeguards. Adequate insurance should be carried to cover insurable liability claims against the partnership.

Death of either partner automatically terminates a legal partnership. This possibility should be recognized and the method of dissolving the partnership in such event should be included in the agreement.

INCORPORATION

Forming a corporation provides another method of acquiring capital to farm. A corporation is a legal entity authorized by state law and is capable of doing business, making contracts, borrowing money, and the like, the same as an individual proprietor. The procedure for forming a corporation is outlined in the law and should be followed exactly. For this and other reasons services of a competent lawyer are essential for incorporating a business.

Individuals who form a corporation are its owners and are

issued certificates representing shares to show the interest each holds in the corporate assets. The shareholders elect directors to represent them in business policy and management decisions. The directors in turn employ officers who operate the business according to policy established by the directors.

Generally speaking, incorporation is a possiblity in any business of reasonable size. Many family farms are large enough to at least consider incorporating. In general, however, only larger farms have found incorporation advantageous. One reason was the relatively high federal income corporate tax rates, and double taxation of dividends. Revision of federal tax laws in 1958 largely removed this impediment, however, opening the door for greater use of corporations by commercial family farms.

When a corporation is formed to operate a farm business, it takes the place of the farmer as owner and operator. An individual may manage and operate the farm similar to any farmer, but he does so as an employee of the corporation, not as an individual entrepreneur.

Advantages of Incorporation

A corporation provides a means by which a group of individuals may pool their funds and operate a business. Members of a family may organize a corporation to operate the home farm and to facilitate its transfer to a son or a son-in-law without disrupting the business. Other individuals may also form a corporation to carry on a farming operation. For example, two or more families with inadequate capital to farm efficiently on an individual basis may use the assets they do have to advantage by pooling them in a farm corporation.

In addition to serving as a means of obtaining capital, incorporation of the farm business may serve to hold the unit together and permit continuity of operation from one generation to the next. This feature assumes added importance as the size of business increases. Should one shareholder of an incorporated business die or decide to sell out, there is no need to break up the business, as in a partnership. The stock may merely be transferred to a new owner. This ability to transfer ownership of undivided interests provides an easy means for children and others to buy into a farm business. It also facilitates estate planning by permitting parents to divide and transfer estates without reorganizing the business.

Some fringe benefits may be obtained through incorporation, with advantages in terms of benefits and taxes. Since social security benefits are based upon earnings of individuals it may be advantageous for a farm operator to receive a constant salary even though the corporation may show a loss. The availability of profit-sharing and pension plans may favor the corporate form of business in some instances. For example, with a qualified pension plan, some corporate profits can be used to provide retirement income for employees even though they are stockholders. The corporation pays no tax on earnings applied to the pension plan, and the employee is taxed only when he receives the retirement benefits. Somewhat similar benefits accrue from medical payment plans, employee death benefits, and group life insurance.

Disadvantages of Incorporation

There are some problems or disadvantages associated with incorporating a farm business which should be carefully and thoroughly considered. For example, unless proper safeguards are included in the legal framework the business might not be managed in the best interests of minority stockholders. Some expenses are involved in incorporating, and a corporation may pay certain annual fees and taxes which are not required of other types of business organizations. Furthermore, some time and expense are involved in maintaining records of the corporation and in filing the corporate tax returns. Annual meetings must be held, directors and officers elected, and an annual report of the business filed with the Secretary of State.

RENTING

Renting—or leasing—is a common way of obtaining additional capital for farming. Of the 3.7 million farms reported in the 1959 U.S. Census, 19.8 per cent were operated by tenants.

Tenancy usually is thought of as the second rung on the ladder of farm ownership. A young farmer can work, learn, and save until he has enough know-how and capital to obtain and manage a line of machinery and livestock. With this he is in position to rent a farm and begin operating on his own. And, of course, renting does not always stop when farm ownership is attained. Many leading farmers and ranchers who own considerable land, rent additional acreage to utilize more efficiently their managerial ability, and the land, machinery, and equipment they own. The 1959 Census reported that 834 thousand, or 22.5 per cent of the farms in the United States, were part-owner farms.

Types of Leases

Leases are usually classified according to the kind of rent paid. Most of them fall into three general groups: the crop-share lease, the livestock-share lease, and the cash lease. With share leases, a share of the crop or livestock production is paid to the landlord as rent. With a cash lease, rent agreed upon is paid in cash. The various types of leases may be combined or otherwise modified in renting a farm. A common method is to give a share of the grain crops as rent, and pay cash for hay and pasture.

The *crop-share lease* is the most common type of rental arrangement in the United States, and farms operated on this basis are found in all parts of the country. With the crop-share lease, the landlord usually provides the land and improvements and pays related taxes and other expenses, while the tenant pays most of the operating expenses and furnishes power, machinery, labor, and livestock. Some expenses such as seed and fertilizer may be shared with the landlord. Crops produced are shared as agreed upon in the lease.

Farms rented with a *livestock-share lease* are found almost exclusively in the Corn Belt and some adjacent states. The tenant and landlord customarily share both crop and livestock production, as well as some of the expenses. The landlord usually furnishes the land, buildings, and other improvements; the tenant furnishes the machinery, power, and his own labor. The tenant and landlord commonly own the livestock jointly and share the annual expenses of crop and livestock production. The livestock is most often owned on a 50-50 basis, and expenses and income are shared in the same proportions.

Farms rented by *cash lease* tend to be concentrated in the Corn Belt, the South, Eastern Plains, New England States, and in states along the Pacific Coast. Cash leases are used most frequently in areas where yields are relatively stable and where production involves a relatively small amount of risk and uncertainty. They also are frequently used for part-time or residential farms. With cash leasing arrangements, the landlord is paid a specified cash payment and usually furnishes the land, buildings, and other improvements. The tenant furnishes all other items required for production, including labor, machinery, livestock, and operating expenses. The entire production of crops and livestock belongs to the tenant.

The concepts of cash and share rent are sometimes combined in what is called *standing rent*. A fixed rent is agreed upon but in place of cash, payment is made in a fixed measure of products, such as one-third bale of cotton, 25 bushels of corn, or 10 bushels of wheat. The dollar amount of rent the landlord receives varies with price of the product, as it would with share rent, but the amount of product he will receive is known in advance. Thus, the landlord has greater security in years of low yield, while the tenant makes more profit in years of high yield.

Advantages and Disadvantages of Obtaining Capital by Renting

There are a number of advantages and disadvantages to renting, as there are with all methods of obtaining capital. The advantages for the tenant include the possibility of obtaining control of a large amount of capital with relatively little risk, the possible benefit from landlord managerial assistance, and the possibility of having a more nearly adequate farm unit which will facilitate efficient production. On the other hand, when one leases a farm, uncertainty of tenure is involved, living accommodations and farm improvements frequently are inadequate, rental arrangements may not contribute to efficient maximum production, and the cash or share rent must be paid. This rent must compensate the landlord for taxes and any other assessments on the property, maintenance and depreciation of improvements, a competitive or opportunity return on investment, and the risk and uncertainty associated with his investment. Thus, while the tenant avoids these costs and responsibilities by renting, he pays someone else to assume them.

PURCHASE CONTRACTS

A *purchase contract* provides another method of supplementing one's capital. The contract may be known by various names such as *contract for sale, conditional sales contract,* or *land contract,* depending upon local terminology and the type of property involved in the transaction. Such an instrument is used in transactions where the down payment is too small for the buyer to obtain title by financing part of the purchase price with a mortgage. For example, roughly 50 per cent of the purchase price of real estate usually is required as a down payment to obtain financing with a mortgage. In contrast, the usual down payment with a purchase contract is about 20 per cent, and in some cases it runs as low as 5 to 10 per cent.

Terms of a Purchase Contract[2]

A purchase contract is a written agreement whereby one party agrees to convey land and sometimes chattel farm property to another party for an agreed price. Possession of the property passes to the buyer while deed to the property remains with the seller, to be delivered at some future date or upon payment of a specified amount. The contract usually provides for the buyer to keep up or make improvements on the farm. Where livestock are involved, provision usually is made for all livestock raised or purchased and kept on the farm to be considered as replacements for the original livestock, with a specified minimum number to be maintained at all times. If equipment is included, that purchased by the buyer after the contract is in effect usually is considered as replacement equipment, legally belonging to the seller until terms of the contract have been fulfilled. As a general rule, the buyer pays all expenses, including all taxes and property insurance, after a specified date. The kind and amount of insurance usually is specified, with the loss-payable clause being in the name of the seller.

This discussion probably gives the impression that terms of a purchase contract are rather harsh from the buyer's point of view. This is true and should be expected since the seller is, in effect, making a substantially larger loan and taking a greater risk than can any commercial lender, especially when chattel property is involved in the contract. The buyer also assumes relatively great risk and, therefore, should make sure before entering into the agreement that he understands the terms of the contract and has a reasonable prospect of being able to meet them.

---

[2] Legal aspects of purchase contracts are discussed in more detail in Chapter 14.

Advantages and Disadvantages of Purchase Contracts

Properly used purchase contracts have a number of advantages. They offer considerable opportunity for flexibility. For example, while purchase contracts customarily state a total dollar price for the farm and provide for specified cash payments, some agreements may provide for payments based on a share of farm income. As an example, the buyer may be required to maintain a dairy herd of a given size and to assign a portion, say 25 per cent, of the milk check to the seller. In this case the sale price is a fixed number of dollars, but payments vary with production and price of milk. Other purchase contracts base both the sale price of the farm and annual payments on physical quantities. For example, the sale price may be 15,000 hundredweight of milk, with interest at 5 per cent (5 pounds per hundredweight) on the unpaid balance. Annual payments may be based upon production or specified as a given quantity of milk.

From the buyer's viewpoint, as mentioned above, purchase contracts provide a means of low-equity financing. By buying on contract, a family can acquire a farm at an earlier age than by waiting to accumulate capital necessary to purchase with the aid of borrowed funds and a mortgage. Having more nearly optimum farm resources during younger years of greatest physical productivity enables the family to make faster financial progress. Payments usually exceed rent under a lease arrangement which encourages or "forces" the family to save during their younger productive years. Equity accumulated by young families has a longer period of years to "work" for them and develops increased satisfaction for the family. Moreover, a purchase contract may enable a family to acquire a farm at a lower price in a period of rising farm prices than if they waited to accumulate capital to buy outright.

From the viewpoint of the seller, the contract may facilitate selling the farm at a higher price than otherwise would be possible. The seller retains an investment in a business with which he is familiar, over which he has some control, and from which he can receive regular periodic payments. A major part of the farms sold on contract are owned by farmers ready to retire. The contract provides an opportunity to make a major sale without any large return in any given year, thereby possibly providing important tax advantages. Where the down payment is less than 30 per cent, the seller may spread any capital gains from the sale over several years. Thus, if the retiring farmer's income is low, he may pay less than the stipulated 25 per cent capital gains tax. With sufficiently low income and high exemptions, he may be able to claim the entire capital gain as tax-exempt income.

Purchase contracts also have a number of disadvantages. Since legal title remains with the seller, the buyer feels an insecurity of ownership. The payment schedule may fully equal a fair rental. After repairs, improvements, taxes, and insurance costs are added, total payments usually are relatively heavy. *If the buyer is unable to meet an installment, in many states he can be put off the farm, in which case his payments—including the down payment—are forfeited as rent.* However, while the law generally permits fairly rapid and harsh action in case of default in making payments on a contract, experience indicates a fairly lenient attitude on the part of those who sell farms on this basis. For example, a study of 350 farmers in Minnesota[3] showed that of 33 sellers who could have served notice of intention to terminate the contract, only one actually served notice, even though some buyers were in default for as long as three and four years.

Another disadvantage of the purchase contract is the tendency for assets of buyer and seller to become "frozen" during the first few years the contract is in operation. During this period it is difficult for the buyer, in the event he wishes to do so, to sell accumulated equity. The seller's investment also is "frozen," at least in part, since he extends more credit to the buyer than any commercial credit agency could lend. Thus, he has a high-risk investment for the early years of the contract and cannot fully liquidate his investment if he wishes to do so.

The purchase contract also has the disadvantage of possibly tying up limited operator capital in land or chattel property which might be more profitably employed for operating purposes. Moreover, the relatively heavy payment schedule may further deplete operating capital—or at least prevent the accumulating of funds as rapidly as otherwise would be possible. As a result the buyer may be unable to follow good farm management practices.

Some disadvantages of the purchase contract can be reduced by observing certain safeguards before entering into such an agreement. While an advantage of the purchase contract is that it permits low-equity financing, this should not be carried to extremes. Farm-

---

[3] *Minnesota Farm Business Notes,* Univ. of Minn., March 31, 1958, p. 3.

ers starting with a small amount of capital are severely handicapped and run a much greater risk of being completely "wiped out" if adversity is encountered. The Minnesota study, referred to above, asked buyers under contract for deed, What would best safeguard a purchase contract? Most frequently mentioned were a larger down payment of one-third or more, small payments over a long period of time up to 30 or 35 years, and prepayment privileges that permit the buyer in good years to make payments in advance of his repayment schedule. All purchase contracts should contain a provision permitting the buyer to convert the contract to a mortgage after an agreed amount has been paid.

VERTICAL INTEGRATION AND CONTRACT FARMING

Another method of obtaining capital, somewhat related both to purchase contracts and to borrowing, is vertical integration. *Vertical integration* means bringing together under central management two or more of the links in the chain of production and marketing. A farmer whose operations are vertically integrated shares with one or more related businesses—such as his supplier, processor, or distributor—some of his managerial decisions in production and marketing. In return, the supplier, processor, or distributor involved (the *integrator*) provides financing and assumes the associated risks. This linking together of two or more stages of the production-marketing process often is accomplished through contractual arrangements. Thus, it is sometimes called *contract farming*. Since other types of contracts are frequently encountered in agriculture, we use the term vertical integration to avoid confusion.

Farmer-businessman arrangements can vary from connections only slightly closer than conventional open-market relationships to full ownership and management of the farm by the associated business. However, the degree of vertical integration thus far in agriculture generally falls between these extremes, but usually involves varying degrees of financing the enterprise or operation. Therefore, vertical integration is another way for a farmer to obtain capital with which to work.

Vertical integration is not new in agriculture. Contracts of various types have been used for a long time with cannery crops, sugar beets, and the like. However, arrangements where the supplier, processor, or distributor takes over the farm production operation and "stacks" it on top of his normal function is relatively new.

The relative importance of vertical integration or contracting with nonfarm businesses varies considerably among commodities. For some commodities only a small proportion of farm output is produced under vertical integration, for others the proportion is nearly 100 per cent. For example, roughly 95 per cent of the broilers are produced on this integrated basis. Integration and contracting trends in livestock are much less far advanced but are still evolving. Integration, either by contract or by internal coordination of stages of production, develops when regular farm production fails (a) to provide the needed market outlet for a supplier of inputs, or (b) to provide farm products of the proper specifications at reasonable prices for marketing firms.

Advantages and Disadvantages of Obtaining Capital Through Integration Contracts

As in the case with any method of acquiring capital, vertical integration has a number of advantages and disadvantages. Some of the advantages are:

1. The integrator (businessman) assists with, or carries full responsibility for, management of the enterprise covered in the contract. Specialized management, with full information on latest scientific developments in feeding and other practices, probably facilitates more efficient production.
2. Risks are shared with, or completely transferred to, the integrator. While shifting risks does not remove them, it makes them more manageable by consolidation in the hands of the integrator.
3. With more capital, the size of the enterprise can be increased, contributing to greater efficiency in use of labor and equipment.
4. Specialized management and the larger amount of capital facilitates "continuous" production—as with broilers where four batches may be produced each year—thereby making more efficient use of buildings, equipment, capital, labor, and management employed in the enterprise.
5. Transfer of some, or all, management responsibility for an enterprise to the integrator leaves the farmer more time for his other enterprises. From the specialized management of the enterprise under contract, he may also gain useful ideas or knowledge on management of his other enterprises.

6. Enlarging an enterprise by contracting may require additional labor. Where the operator and family are not already fully employed, they now may be able to earn a higher income.
7. For families with limited resources who enjoy rural life, contract farming offers an opportunity to live and work in a rural setting without having to provide all the capital and carry all the risks involved.
8. With a larger enterprise, better breeding stock and seed varieties may be used. These, coupled with specialized management familiar with market demands, result in orderly marketing of a higher quality product that suits the needs of the public.
9. With a large volume of business, the integrator is in a position to use highly specialized equipment in production or processing which would not be possible for the individual farmer.
10. Having partial or complete management control of production phases, the supplier or the processor can better coordinate various phases of the production-marketing process, thereby contributing to efficiency in use of resources and management.
11. Greater efficiency in use of supplier-producer-processor resources and management, coupled with advantages such as higher quality products, contributes to an overall net gain either in terms of higher income for parties involved in the production-marketing chain, or to a higher quality product at a lower cost for the public.
12. Judging from developments in industry, integration in agriculture might facilitate more orderly production and marketing of agricultural products. Real possibilities of gearing production to demand may be inherent in contracts between processors and farmers, or groups of farmers.
13. Vertical integration probably has enlarged the number of farmers who can obtain financing. Some farmers unable to secure financing from other sources probably can obtain capital with which to work by means of a contract.

Seldom if ever are advantages gained without a price—one cannot "have his cake and eat it too." Thus, a number of disadvantages are also involved in integration; their importance, of course, depending upon the degree of integration provided by the contractual arrangements. Some of the disadvantages are:

1. With integration contracts which give full control to the integrator, the farmer gives up all his freedom in making management decisions pertaining to the integrated enterprise. In such cases, he

does not gain control of capital thus acquired, but merely has it to work with. With broiler-type contracts, for example, where the integrator retains title to the birds and provides operating capital, he also makes the management decisions.

2. The price a farmer pays for shifting some or all price and production risks and management to the integrator may be reflected in lower returns.
3. When management decisions are transferred to an integrator, the producer may be little more than a hired hand.
4. Competition among suppliers has been a major stimulus to the rapid growth of vertical integration. Feed dealers, for example, use contracts as a method of increasing sales. Credit used as a sales tool may be overextended.
5. The farmer entering into a contract probably gives up his right to "gamble" on the market. He probably will not have much opportunity to "get rich quick."
6. Country banks may suffer somewhat from vertical integration by losing direct contact with farmers financed through contracts. When integrators are financed by city banks and other lenders which do not provide opportunities for participation by country banks, outlets for loan funds in the local banks are reduced to this extent. If income from agricultural loans is curtailed, country banks may find it necessary to increase other charges.
7. Vertical integration may complicate farm business planning and related finances.
8. If contractual arrangements require the farmer to give highest priority to the vertically integrated enterprise, other enterprises may suffer and result in less net income than otherwise might be the case. In such event, credit to finance the nonintegrated enterprises may be more difficult to secure.

BORROWING

Borrowing constitutes the remaining method farmers use to acquire capital; this has been left until last to facilitate linking this discussion with the treatment of credit in subsequent chapters. Moreover, since most of the rest of the book is devoted to various phases of use and acquisition of credit, this section is limited to a brief discussion of the meaning of borrowing and of credit as a source of capital. It also includes reasons sometimes put forth against borrowing, and advantages which can be realized by using credit.

The word "borrow" means to receive something with the understanding that it or its equivalent will be returned as agreed upon. Stated another way, borrowing means the ability to command capital or services currently for a promise to repay at some future time. In terms of money, borrowing involves obtaining a certain amount of funds to be repaid as specified in the note.

The word "credit" comes from the Latin word "credo" meaning "I believe." Hence, credit is based upon confidence. When one borrows money, the loan is based upon confidence in the future solvency of the person and in his repaying the loan as per agreement. In this sense, credit means ability to command the capital of another in return for a promise to pay at some specified time in the future.

While credit has a somewhat technical meaning of its own, it is used in financial circles and writings as meaning about the same as borrowing. This synonymous usage probably has come about for convenience sake. The word "credit" is short and easy to use. Holding strictly to technical meanings often involves using two words rather than one. For example, a phrase might read "use of borrowed funds." It is somewhat more convenient to say "use of credit."

Borrowing probably ranks next to saving or using one's own capital as a means of obtaining capital to farm. Few commercial farmers operate without using credit. Some have adequate finances of their own but use credit at times throughout the year rather than disrupt investment programs or other use of owned capital.

Using credit as a means of obtaining control of resources is similar in some respects to renting. When funds are obtained by borrowing, interest is paid for use of the capital; while, with a lease, rent is paid for use of the capital. Both borrowing and renting involve employment of capital for a period of time. However, the use of credit permits greater flexibility than renting. Credit can be used to acquire any type of resource or service needed by the farmer, while renting usually is employed to acquire use of fewer types of resources, the most common being farm real estate. Credit permits acquiring varying amounts of a resource according to needs of the farmer, while renting tends to involve fixed amounts or "blocks" of resources, such as a piece of land or a whole farm.

Borrowing involves more risk of losing owned capital than does renting. With renting, the maximum payment which can be demanded is the share or cash rent; this is somewhat comparable with the interest payment on borrowed funds. With share rental arrangements, the payment is automatically cut in case of low production or prices. With borrowing, however, the payment generally includes in addition to a fixed interest charge, part or all of the principal borrowed. If the principal is lost, the borrower may have to liquidate some of his own capital to repay the loan.

Except for special cases, some property or assets must be owned before a loan can be obtained. Since most lenders do not loan their own money, laws or regulations under which they operate require them to obtain the borrower's pledge of security for a loan. Usually the security is some specific property which can be sold to liquidate the loan if it is not repaid as per agreement. Where the loan is not large and where the individual has a good credit rating, only the signature may be required; in such cases the borrower, in effect, pledges all his assets as security. The general intent of the law and regulations is that security pledged be adequate to repay the loan even if it must be sold under unfavorable circumstances. Since most loans which break down do so under unfavorable circumstances, this provision seems reasonable.

Disadvantages of Borrowing

Fear of debt has been a factor in management decisions of farmers for a long time. In some cases farmers expressed this fear by feeling it was bad to be in debt. They felt debt was something to be avoided at almost any cost. This view was expressed long ago by Shakespeare where he had Polonius say:

> Neither a borrower nor a lender be,
> For loan oft loses both itself and friend,
> And borrowing dulls the edge of husbandry.

This attitude continues to be held by some farmers today; these borrow only after they run out of money and have to borrow.

The primary disadvantage of borrowing is the risk of loss associated with use of credit. One never borrows money with the expectation that a loss will be sustained. A reputable lender never makes a loan which he thinks will result in a loss. However, farming is a risky business, and the risk of loss is ever present. Due to crop failure, low prices, insects, disease, and the like, income may fall to a fraction of that anticipated. The results may be disastrous unless the borrower has the risk-bearing ability needed to withstand such adversity.

Closely related to the risk disadvantage is the problem of meeting payments as they come due. Loan proceeds are used in the business and are not always available to meet loan payments. In fact, loan proceeds used to buy land never are available to repay the loan; payments must be made from net income.

A third problem involved in using credit is determining whether or not it will pay to borrow. Borrowing involves repaying not only the principal but also the interest charged for use of the funds. The borrower will be at a disadvantage unless, by using the credit, net income is increased at least enough to cover the interest on the loan. Each of these three points—risk, repayment of loans, and income related to use of credit—is considered in some detail in the following chapters.

Borrowing can be avoided. The way to avoid borrowing is to use the methods of acquiring capital discussed above or hire the items that would otherwise be purchased with the use of credit. A farmer may hire his land plowed, his grain and soybeans combined, and his corn picked, or he may arrange to rent the equipment and do the work himself. Finally, he may contract with the owner of range livestock to feed them out on shares. To escape the risk of borrowing, he may contract with the owners of land, livestock, and equipment to give them a share of the proceeds or a fixed cash rental for the use of the desired items for a limited time. The difference between owning and renting is largely a matter of time and credit. The owner with the use of credit purchases the right to use land indefinitely; the renter purchases the right to use land for a short period, usually one year. This policy of renting and hiring for short periods to avoid the use of credit has much to commend it, because agriculture has such a large element of crop and price risk that is beyond the control of the individual farmer.

Advantages of Borrowing

The use of credit, on the other hand, has definite advantages. If farmers were denied credit altogether and forced to rely on their savings, two undesirable results would occur immediately. Tenant farmers who have been using borrowed capital would be forced to give up farming and hire out as laborers or go into some other line or work. Owner-operators on mortgaged farms would have to give up the ownership of their homes and farmland; they would be tenants again with all the insecurity that goes with this arrangement. Furthermore, those contemplating the step from hired hand to tenant, or from tenant to owner, would have to postpone this action either indefinitely or until they had accumulated through savings the amount they otherwise would have borrowed. In fact, the amount of capital required in farming is in many instances so large that hired hands and tenants would be forced under these circumstances to give up any hope of ever achieving a higher place on the agricultural ladder.

Credit is desirable also because the people who own land and have funds to lend are often not operating farmers. The capital-owning group is made up of older people, retired farmers, widows, endowment funds, estates, banks, and insurance companies, as well as more wealthy individuals with money to lend. These various agencies and individuals are in no sense operating farmers. Operating farmers—fitted by training, experience, and age to carry on crop and livestock production—do not, as a rule, have the necessary capital required to operate a farm. The competent young farmer between the ages of 20 and 35 with a family to support has everything needed for farming except capital. The individuals who have capital, on the other hand, oftentimes do not have the physical ability, training, and experience which the young farmer has. Thus, the two are interdependent. Indeed, the cooperation of these two groups, management and capital, makes for successful farming; either alone would fail.

At this point it might be argued that the capital group could rent capital to young farmers in the form of land, equipment, and livestock. This practice, as pointed out above, is followed to a large extent with land. The policy might be extended to more generally include equipment and livestock and thereby avoid major uses of farm credit. But land, the item best adapted to the rental principle, sometimes suffers when operated under tenancy. Too often the absentee landlord is unable to give his farm the proper attention, and a discouraged tenant, rundown buildings, erosion, weeds, and other objectionable developments result.

Livestock, equipment, and operating expenses are capital items not as easily adapted to the rental process as land and buildings. Owners of livestock and equipment find it exceedingly difficult and costly to provide the supervision necessary for the rental of these items. It is still more difficult for the farmer to make arrangements for the payment of operating expenses such as seed, taxes, labor, and fertilizer unless he has savings or uses credit. The landlord frequently is willing to take a share of the crop in payment for the use of his land, but the laborer must be paid in cash weekly. Thus, it is evident that renting or hiring materials does not provide a satisfactory substitute for the use of credit.

Credit makes it possible for hired men to become tenants, and for tenants to become owners. Moreover, credit makes it possible for farmers to take advantage of new machines, good seed, fertilizer, livestock, and labor, all of which enable the farmer to organize and operate his farm on a more profitable basis.

The trouble is not with credit but with the way it has been used in areas of high risk and in times of high prices, and with its abuse in individual cases. Properly used, credit can be of great assistance, and farmers should think twice before trying to get along without it. Where farmers try to be financially independent they hamper their progress. By attempting to do everything on their own they must restrict their operation. If they never give their banker a chance to help, they lose the advantage of his advice and counsel, as well as the benefit from credit he might extend to them. A carpenter without tools would make little progress. The farmer needs the credit tool in his kit to make maximum progress.

QUESTIONS AND PROBLEMS

1. Why should consideration be given to acquiring capital?
2. Name seven ways by which farmers can acquire capital to farm; discuss each.
3. Why are savings important in the farm business?
4. Observe selected farmers in your community or study your own farm to determine the amount of capital being used, and what it is being used for. Where could the capital be obtained?
5. Are there any family partnerships in your community? If practical, study a partnership arrangement from the viewpoint of obtaining capital.
6. Outline and discuss the essentials of successful family partnership arrangements.
7. Discuss incorporation of a farm business as a means of acquiring capital.
8. Discuss the various types of leases commonly used. Appraise these from the viewpoint of acquiring capital.
9. Explain the difference between a purchase contract and a mortgage. Appraise purchase contracts as a means of obtaining capital.
10. Explain what is meant by vertical integration. Would you recommend that farmers obtain capital from an integrator? Explain.

11. Discuss the advantages and disadvantages of using credit as a source of capital.
12. Compare and appraise the seven methods which farmers use to acquire capital.

REFERENCES

Boyne, David H., *Changes in the Real Wealth Position of Farm Operators, 1940–1960,* Mich. Agr. Exp. Sta. Tech. Bul. 294, 1964.

Clark, Chapin D., and Berry, Russell L., *Buying Farm Land on Installment Contracts,* S. Dak. Agr. Exp. Sta. Circ. 164, 1964.

Frazier, T. L., Padgett, J. H., and Thompson, J. C., *An Economic Appraisal of Hog Marketing Contracts in Georgia,* Ga. Agr. Exp. Sta. Mimeo. Series NS 141, 1962.

Hansing, Frank D., *Contract Egg Production and Use of Credit,* Miss. Agr. Exp. Sta. Bul. 644, 1962.

Harris, Marshall, and Hines, N. William, *Installment Land Contracts in Iowa,* Agr. Law Center, Col. of Law, Univ. of Iowa, Monograph No. 5, 1965.

Henning, G. F., and Burkes, Marshall, *Changes in the Financial Structure of Agricultural Business Organizations,* Ohio Agr. Exp. Sta. Res. Bul. 952, 1963.

Johnson, Jerome E., *Suggestions on Father and Son Farming Agreements,* N. Dak. Agr. Exp. Sta. Bul. 457, 1965.

Mighell, Ronald L., and Jones, Lawrence A., *Vertical Coordination in Agriculture,* USDA, ERS, Agr. Econ. Rept. 19, 1963.

Pine, Wilfred H., and Badger, Ronald K., *Buying and Selling Farms on Contract in Kansas,* Kans. Agr. Exp. Sta. Circ. 390, 1963.

Schaffner, L. W., Loftsgard, L. D., and Owens, W. W., *Economics of Leasing Farm Machinery and Buildings,* N. Dak. Agr. Exp. Sta. Bul. 450, 1964.

Chapter 5

RETURNS AS A GUIDE IN USE OF CREDIT: BASIC CONCEPTS AND APPLICATION

CONSIDERATIONS involved in credit analysis logically fall into three groups pertaining to returns, repayment capacity, and risk-bearing ability—which may be referred to as the *Three R's of Credit.* The concepts involved in these three R's are first briefly outlined in this chapter. The *Three C's of Credit,* another classification of certain factors important in use of credit, are then briefly discussed to show how they relate to the Three R's of Credit. With this background, the remainder of this chapter and Chapters 6 and 7 are devoted to an analysis of use of credit from the viewpoint of the first R—*Returns* which borrowed funds will produce. The other two R's are considered in subsequent chapters.

THE THREE R's OF CREDIT

The three R's of "School Days" fame—Readin', 'Ritin', and 'Rithmetic—long have been considered basic in the educational system. Where necessary, they were "taught to the tune of the hickory stick!" Three considerations in the use of credit which might be referred to as the three R's—*Returns, Repayment Capacity,* and *Risk-bearing Ability*—are no less basic in the use of borrowed capital, and if a farmer and lender do not otherwise learn their lesson, they are "taught to the tune" of loan breakdown and foreclosure.

The first R, Returns, refers to the most profitable amount of credit which can be used in the business, while the other two R's indicate restrictions or limitations which may be necessary in some cases for the loan to be sound. Every loan should pass the three tests:

1. Will it produce sufficient *Returns* to cover the costs? In other words, will it pay to borrow the money?
2. Will the borrower have sufficient *Repayment Capacity* to repay the loan as provided in the note and mortgage? A loan may be profitable, but the farmer still may not be able to meet the payments as they come due.
3. Does the farmer have the *Risk-bearing Ability* to carry the risk and uncertainty involved in using the credit?[1]

These three questions should be considered by the farmer as he makes plans for using credit, and by the lender and borrower together as the loan application is studied. The loan should not be made unless both the borrower and lender can answer all three questions in the affirmative. A negative answer to question No. 1 indicates the loan will be unprofitable, in which case there is no point in using the credit. A negative answer to either question No. 2 or No. 3 indicates the loan may break down, and a loan should never be made with this probability in the picture.

THE THREE C'S OF CREDIT AND THEIR RELATION TO THE THREE R'S OF CREDIT

In terms of the Three C's of Credit, the principal factors to be taken into consideration in analyzing use or extension of credit are *Character, Capacity,* and *Capital.* A fourth, *Conditions,* is sometimes added. The meaning of these terms in connection with credit may be somewhat different from their general usage.

---

[1] Risk-bearing ability has also been referred to as "Financial strength." See: Aaron G. Nelson, *Credit as a Tool for the Agricultural Producer,* N. Cent. Reg. Ext. Publ. No. 4; and Great Plains Agr. Council Publ. No. 15, 1957, p. 9. The term "risk-bearing ability" is used here, however, since it may be somewhat more descriptive of the meaning the term is intended to convey. "Financial strength" seems to connote monetary strength primarily, whereas there are other things which also contribute to ability to stand the risk involved in a loan.

Character

Character consists of those mental and moral qualities which identify an individual. A high sense of what is morally right, honesty, integrity, fairness, responsibility, trustworthiness, industry, and the like, are qualities of a fine character. When these qualities combine to make an individual conscientious concerning his debts, he has credit character. Thus, credit character is set apart somewhat from character in its usual meaning. Conceivably, an individual may have character in the usual sense but rank low on credit character, or vice versa.

Character is one of the basic cornerstones in risk-bearing ability, the third of the Three R's of Credit. Its role in this respect will become evident in chapters dealing with risk-bearing ability. Character, undoubtedly, also has a bearing on returns and repayment capacity, in that men of high character often are outstanding in business affairs. However, as will become evident as they are analyzed, returns and repayment capacity are the results primarily of economic relationships. This is true in part of risk-bearing ability. However, a significant part of risk-bearing ability is comprised of intangibles, of which character is the primary component.

Capacity

Capacity, as one of the Three C's of Credit, signifies the ability to pay when a debt is due. Capacity is a function of income, since payments usually depend upon income rather than upon savings. However, income alone does not indicate capacity. Income may already be so committed to existing obligations that it adds little to capacity.

Capacity is synonymous with repayment capacity of the Three R's of Credit.

Capital

Capital, for purposes of the Three C's of Credit, refers to the equity or net worth of an individual or business. It represents the assurance that funds are available to pay the loan if character and capacity should prove inadequate. Capital is represented by assets which a lender might seize as payment of the debt.

Capital comprises one of the basic cornerstones of risk-bearing ability in the context of the Three R's of Credit. However, it is only one of the aspects of risk-bearing ability, as will become evident in subsequent analysis of the topic.

The concepts involved in the Three C's of Credit are all included in the Three R's of Credit. The Three C's, however, are less comprehensive than the Three R's. The Three R's of Credit embody a number of concepts or factors not included in the Three C's, which should be considered in the use and extension of credit. This is true particularly as far as returns and risk-bearing ability are concerned.

ANALYSIS OF RETURNS PRODUCED

The objective in analyzing *returns produced*, from the standpoint of credit utilization, is to determine the amount of *credit it will pay to use* in the farm business. Obviously, it will pay to use credit as long as returns are at least equal to costs. However, the problem is not that simple. A number of enterprises are involved on most farms, each of which has its own costs and returns. To maximize net income for the business as a whole, each enterprise must make its maximum contribution. To accomplish this objective the farmer must strike a balance among the various enterprises and production practices in determining the amount of capital to use for each. This, in turn, involves determining how much credit to use along with owned capital, or that acquired from other sources. Thus, the problem of determining the amount of credit it will pay to use is a part of the farm management problem of determining how much total capital to use. This determination involves three considerations:

1. Selecting the crop and livestock enterprises which will give the greatest return.
2. Determining the production practices which will be most economical.
3. Determining how large each of the enterprises should be.

Time naturally is involved in these considerations. The farmer is concerned with a period of time in the future, the length of the period depending upon the nature of the decision involved. If the decision pertains to current production, the time period probably is short. If the decision concerns buying a tractor, an intermediate-term period is involved. Decisions related to fixed improvements or purchase of a farm involve a long-term planning period.

Average costs, production, and prices expected to prevail during the period under consideration are used in the analysis of returns related to use of credit. It is recognized that these will fluctuate, perhaps drastically, during the period involved. However, lacking better knowledge, *averages* expected to prevail are used, the "shocks" resulting from fluctuations in costs, production, and prices being "absorbed" by risk-bearing ability, discussed later.

Selecting Enterprises

Selection of enterprises depends upon the locality, type of farm, markets, ability of the farmer, and similar factors. It also depends upon the amount of capital available. This is where credit enters the picture. Farmers often change their operations either in size, which will be discussed under the third consideration, or by adding or dropping enterprises. Credit usually is important in this process since different enterprises require different amounts of capital. For example, with a small amount of capital the farmer may be limited to cash-crop farming, whereas by using credit some livestock enterprises may be added. If, by adding the additional enterprises, net income can be increased, it will pay to use credit for that purpose. Other things being equal, the farmer with limited capital naturally will want to select those enterprises which produce the greatest return. Net income for the business as a whole will be highest when income derived from the last dollar used in each enterprise is equal. As was indicated in Chapter 2, with a given amount of capital, maximum income is achieved by allocating the capital between enterprises Y_1 and Y_2 so that

$$\frac{\Delta Y_1}{\Delta Y_2} = \frac{Py_2}{Py_1} \tag{5.1}$$

or

$$Py_1 \, \Delta Y_1 = Py_2 \, \Delta Y_2 \tag{5.2}$$

where Py_1 and Py_2 represent prices of the two products, Y_1 and Y_2. Equation 5.2 is in the form which can be readily extended to cover any number, n, of enterprises or products as follows:

$$Py_1 \, \Delta Y_1 = Py_2 \, \Delta Y_2 = \cdots = Py_n \, \Delta Y_n \tag{5.3}$$

The marginal value of each product produced can be related to the capital used to produce the product by dividing each part of Equation 5.3 by $(1 + i) \Delta C$ as follows:

$$\frac{Py_1 \, \Delta Y_1}{(1 + i) \, \Delta C} = \frac{Py_2 \, \Delta Y_2}{(1 + i) \, \Delta C} = \cdots = \frac{Py_n \, \Delta Y_n}{(1 + i) \, \Delta C} \qquad (5.4)$$

where ΔC represents the marginal input of capital used to produce the product shown in the numerator, and i represents the interest rate or the opportunity rate of return on equity capital. If the period for which the capital is used is less than or more than one year, the interest rate should be adjusted accordingly.

Expressed in words, Equation 5.4 says that with the optimum allocation of *limited* capital among enterprises, the ratio of the value of the marginal product to the marginal capital employed in producing that product, increased by its cost, is equal for all enterprises. Or, in words used above, when capital is limited, net income for the business will be maximized when the increase in income derived from the last dollar used in each enterprise is equal.

Since only variable costs are pertinent in allocation of capital among enterprises, established farm enterprises with excess capacity —buildings, machinery, and the like—have an advantage in competition for capital in the short run compared with new farm enterprises which require an investment in fixed and working assets. This point was analyzed in some detail in Chapter 3 where allocation of capital to farm and nonfarm enterprises was considered. An example, similar to the one presented there, is given in Table 5.1 to show the pertinent relationships among farm enterprises. It is assumed a total of 9 units of capital are available for use in enterprises Y_1 and Y_2, or in enterprises Y_1 and Y_3. Enterprises Y_2 and Y_3 are assumed to be identical except that Y_3 is a new enterprise under consideration which has not yet been established; i.e. no fixed costs have been incurred in enterprise Y_3, all costs are variable.

The analysis is focused first on allocation of the 9 units of capital between enterprises Y_1 and Y_2. The production possibilities are shown in columns 5 and 6, Table 5.1, and the marginal rate of substitution of Y_2 for Y_1 is shown in column 7. With Y_1 products priced at \$3 and Y_2 products priced at \$2, income is maximized when 4 units of capital are allocated to enterprise Y_1 and 5 units of capital are allocated to enterprise Y_2.

Turning now to enterprises Y_1 and Y_3, the production possibilities with 9 units of capital are shown in columns 9 and 10 of Table 5.1. The marginal rates of substitution of Y_3 for Y_1, shown in column

TABLE 5.1

PRODUCTION FUNCTIONS, PRODUCTION POSSIBILITIES, AND INCOME WITH INCREASING RATES OF SUBSTITUTION, GIVEN 9 UNITS OF CAPITAL
(Hypothetical data)

Inputs of Capital	Output			Production Possibilities With 9 Units of Capital		Marginal Rate of Substitution of r_2 for r_1 $(\Delta r_1/\Delta r_2)$	Income With $P_{y_1} = \$3.00$ and $P_{y_2} = \$2.00$	Production Possibilities With 9 Units of Capital		Marginal Rate of Substitution of r_3 for r_1 $(\Delta r_1/\Delta r_3)$	Income With $P_{y_1} = \$3.00$ and $P_{y_3} = \$2.00$
	r_1	r_2	r_3	r_1	r_2			r_1	r_3		
(1)	(2)	(3)	(4)	(5)	(6)	(7)	(8)	(9)	(10)	(11)	(12)
0	0	0	0	45	0		$135.00	45	0		$135.00
1	9	18	12.0	44	18	.06	168.00	44	12.0	.08	156.00
2	17	34	22.7	42	34	.12	194.00	42	22.7	.19	171.40
3	24	48	32.0	39	48	.21	213.00	39	32.0	.32	181.00
4	30	60	40.0	35	60	.33	225.00	35	40.0	.50	185.00
5	35	70	46.7	30	70	.50	230.00	30	46.7	.75	183.40
6	39	78	52.0	24	78	.75	228.00	24	52.0	1.13	176.00
7	42	84	56.0	17	84	1.17	219.00	17	56.0	1.75	163.00
8	44	88	58.7	9	88	2.00	203.00	9	58.7	2.96	144.40
9	45	90	60.0	0	90	4.50	180.00	0	60.0	6.92	120.00

11, are larger than the marginal rates of substitution of Y_2 for Y_1, shown in column 7, since the level of variable costs is higher for enterprise Y_3 than for enterprise Y_2. As a result it pays to use more of the limited supply of capital in enterprise Y_1. Income is maximized when 5 units of capital are used in enterprise Y_1 and 4 units are used in enterprise Y_3.

It should be noted that the established enterprise has an advantage in competition for capital only so long as the new enterprise is in the planning stage. Once the new enterprise becomes a reality, once the investment in fixed and working assets necessary to its operation have been made, the new enterprise is on the same basis in competition for capital as other established enterprises.

It should also be noted that it is fixed costs involved which give the established enterprise an advantage over a new enterprise being considered. This point is important for two reasons: First, if a new enterprise can be carried on within the existing cost structure of the business, it will not be at a disadvantage in competition for capital. For example, a new grain crop might be produced with machinery and equipment used for producing other crops. Under such circumstances the new crop would be on the same basis as other crops in competition for capital. Second, since it is the existence of fixed costs which give the established enterprise an advantage in competition for capital, the advantage disappears as the planning period is lengthened. The advantage associated with fixed costs involved in working assets (depreciation, and the like) disappears when plans (budgets) are made for an intermediate term of years. Similarly, the advantage associated with fixed costs involved in fixed assets disappears in long-run plans for the business.

Selecting Production Practices

The second consideration—determining production practices which will be most economical—may influence credit decisions since the practice or practices used might determine whether or not it pays to borrow. For example, an Iowa study showed each $1.00 of annual expense on crops (such as fertilizer, seed and seed treatment) added $1.08 to total value of production; that is, a $1.00 input in crop capital services returned itself plus an additional $0.08. Capital invested in machine services (annual expense of repairs, depreciation, fuel and oil) produced a marginal return of

$0.93 for each $1.00 of annual input or expense.[2] In this example, it would pay to use credit for annual crop expense providing funds could be borrowed for less than 8 per cent interest. However, it would not pay to use credit to increase machine services since each dollar of expense would produce only $0.93 of income. Each dollar should be used where it will produce the greatest return, if maximum income is to be produced.

As was outlined in Chapter 2, costs of producing a given product are at a minimum when the ratio of substitution of the two factors is equal to the inverse of their price ratio. Expressed as an equation

$$\frac{\Delta X_1}{\Delta X_2} = \frac{Px_2}{Px_1} \qquad (5.5)$$

where ΔX_1 and ΔX_2 represent the amounts of the two factors X_1 and X_2 which may be used in varying relative amounts (may be substituted for each other) in production of one unit of product, ΔY, and Px_1 and Px_2 represent the prices of the two factors. With Py representing the price of product Y, the optimum combination of factors of production is expressed by the equation

$$\frac{Py\frac{\Delta Y}{\Delta X_1}}{Px_1} = \frac{Py\frac{\Delta Y}{\Delta X_2}}{Px_2} = \cdots = \frac{Py\frac{\Delta Y}{\Delta X_n}}{Px_n}. \qquad (5.6)$$

Expressed in words, this equation indicates that the most efficient combination of factors is achieved when the ratio of the marginal value product of a factor to its price is the same for all factors, Xn, employed in producing product Y.

The Optimum Size of Enterprises

The third consideration—determining how large each enterprise should be—is basic in analyzing the amount it will pay to borrow since credit frequently provides the marginal (additional) units of capital employed as the enterprise expands. For example, a rancher has a unit of 12,800 acres and 300 cows and appurtenant young stock. Of the 20 sections, he owns 14 and rents 6. His equity amounts to about $50,000. The unpaid balance on his real estate mortgage is $20,000, and he owes $10,000 on livestock and equip-

---

[2] Earl O. Heady, *Resource Productivity and Returns on 160-acre Farms in North-Central Iowa,* Iowa Agr. Exp. Sta. Res. Bul. 412, 1954, p. 1073.

ment. In addition, he borrows up to around $20,000 during the year for operating expenses. Thus, this rancher uses credits to supplement his own capital and that which he rents. The size of the ranch, the number of cattle, and the amount spent on operations depend upon the amount of credit employed. In other words, the amount of credit it pays to use is a major factor in determining the size of the range cattle enterprise. It will pay to use credit to expand the enterprise to the point where marginal returns and marginal costs are equal. The *marginal return equals marginal cost* principle serves as a guide in determining both the size of enterprise which is most profitable and the amount of funds it is profitable to borrow.

In applying the principle of marginal cost equals marginal return, the returns side of the equation is fairly simple since, assuming perfect competition, marginal returns consist of a unit of product multiplied by its price. However, the cost side is more complicated since marginal costs represent a composite of costs, each of which is comprised of a quantity multiplied by its price. Written in the form of an equation

$$\Delta X_1 Px_1 + \Delta X_2 Px_2 + \cdots + \Delta X_n Px_n = \Delta Y Py \tag{5.7}$$

where ΔX_1, ΔX_2, and ΔX_n represent marginal inputs of factors used in producing product Y, the symbols Px_1, Px_2, and Px_n represent the prices of the various factors, and Py represents the price of the product, Y.

The left-hand side of Equation 5.7 represents a given amount of capital. In other words, marginal costs are the equivalent of marginal capital. Equation 5.7 may then be written

$$\Delta C(1 + i) = \Delta Y P_y \tag{5.8}$$

where ΔC represents the marginal capital (exclusive of the cost of capital) and i represents the interest rate, or the opportunity rate of return on equity capital. When the period for which capital is used in producing the product is less or more than one year, the interest or opportunity rate should be adjusted accordingly. Thus, with other things being equal, the optimum size of enterprise depends upon the interest rate or the opportunity rate of return on equity capital.

The equality portrayed in Equation 5.8 for one enterprise naturally applies to all enterprises. Thus, the optimum amount of capital will be employed in the farm business when

$$\frac{\Delta Y_1 Py_1}{\Delta C(1 + i)} = \frac{\Delta Y_2 Py_2}{\Delta C(1 + i)} = \cdots = \frac{\Delta Y_n Py_n}{\Delta C(1 + i)} = 1. \tag{5.9}$$

Stated in words, this equation indicates the optimum amount of capital is used in the business when the value of the marginal product in each enterprise is equal to the marginal capital employed in producing the product, increased by its cost.

Equation 5.9 is very similar to Equation 5.4 used in analysis of enterprise combinations. The only difference is that Equation 5.9 is set equal to 1, indicating that marginal returns must equal marginal costs in each enterprise, a necessary condition with maximum capital utilization. When capital is limited to less than the optimum, equality of marginal returns and marginal costs will not be realized. However, to maximize income with the limited capital available, the ratio of marginal returns to marginal costs must be equal for all enterprises, as is indicated in Equation 5.4.

Application of Equations 5.4 and 5.9 may be illustrated by reference to Table 5.2 which gives the value of the marginal product (marginal returns) per $100, with various levels of capital application, for six enterprises which may be included in a farm business.

TABLE 5.2

RETURNS FROM UTILIZATION OF UNITS OF $100 IN
DIFFERENT ENTERPRISES OF THE FARM BUSINESS
(Hypothetical data)

Use of		Annual Returns if Used in					
		Grain Enter- prise	Hay Enter- prise	Machinery Enter- prise	Hog Enter- prise	Beef cow Enter- prise	Dairy Enter- prise
First	$100	$140	$135	$120	$150	$110	$125
Second	$100	140	130	120	150	110	125
Third	$100	135	130	120	140	110	125
Fourth	$100	135	130	115	140	105	125
Fifth	$100	130	125	110	140	105	120
Sixth	$100	130	125	110	130	100	120
Seventh	$100	125	120	105	125	95	120
Eighth	$100	120	115	105	120	90	115
Ninth	$100	115	110	100	110	85	110
Tenth	$100	105	100	95	100	80	100
Eleventh	$100	100	90	90	90	70	95
Twelfth	$100	90	80	80	75	60	90

Assume the farmer obtains a general-purpose loan for $1,000—where should he use the capital? According to Equation 5.4 he should use the capital in those enterprises where the value of the marginal product is highest relative to capital employed. The initial marginal returns are highest in the hog enterprise; it would claim $500. The grain enterprise takes the next $400, and the hay enterprise the last $100. With these applications of capital, the ratio of marginal returns to marginal capital employed is approximately equal for the three enterprises. The grain enterprise ratio is 135 to 100, the hay enterprise ratio is 135 to 100, and the hog enterprise ratio is 140 to 100. Since marginal returns are lower in the other three enterprises, returns for the farm business would be increased by taking some of the capital used in them and applying it in the higher return enterprises.

The maximum amount of capital it would pay to use in the enterprises included in Table 5.2 depends, as indicated above, on the interest or opportunity cost of capital. If the interest rate is 6 per cent, the marginal cost of each $100 unit of capital is $106. Under these conditions it will pay to add additional units of capital in each enterprise so long as marginal returns exceed $106. The total amount it will pay to use is $4500. With this amount of capital, marginal returns and marginal costs for each of the enterprises will be approximately equal (as near equal as is possible with the units of capital given).

Farmers often do not use as much credit as is profitable. The farmer who, for some reason, is overly conservative might increase his returns substantially by borrowing more than he asks for in his application. Good seed or breeding stock are cases in point; a loan of $200 to buy a bull may not be as good an investment as a $500 loan to buy a much better bull. Or when a smaller loan provides only enough livestock to employ half of his time, a larger loan may make it possible for the farmer to buy enough livestock to employ all of his available time. Of course, the farmer may recognize this situation but prefer the smaller loan because of the smaller risk and the desire to have more free time.

Too much credit may be extended. It is easy to go past the point where marginal returns equal marginal costs. It is evident in Table 5.2 that the tenth unit of $100 invested in hogs is not profitable; that is, it does not yield any return, merely returns the principal without interest. When viewed without analysis, a total of $1,200 invested in the hog enterprise which could return an estimated $1,470 might be attractive and satisfactory; but when the transaction is subjected to marginal analysis, it is clear that $900 is all that should be invested, assuming the interest rate is not over 10 per cent. The $900 will yield a marginal return of $1,205, or an increase of $305. An additional investment of $100 will return only the principal, while still further investments of $100 fail to return the principal.

The amount of credit it will pay to use is influenced also by the "balance" which is maintained within an enterprise as it is increased in size. This point is illustrated by an Iowa study of 160-acre farms.[3] Data in Table 5.3 show the marginal returns per dollar of capital used in livestock production with varying amounts of labor.

As additional capital was added in the livestock enterprises, marginal returns declined when labor was relatively fixed. However, when more labor also was added, marginal returns increased as is indicated by going from "Low capital-Low labor" to "High capital-High labor" in Table 5.3. The "balance" facilitated by simulta-

TABLE 5.3

PREDICTED MARGINAL RETURNS PER DOLLAR OF ADDED CAPITAL USED
IN LIVESTOCK PRODUCTION *

Capital Input Group	Labor Input Group		
	Low labor	Medium labor	High labor
Low Capital....................	$1.04	$1.08	$1.18
Medium Capital................	1.00	1.02	1.12
High Capital..................	.90	.96	1.10

* Source: Earl O. Heady, *Resource Productivity and Returns on 160-acre Farms in North-Central Iowa*, Iowa Agr. Exp. Sta. Res. Bul. 412, 1954, Table 17, p. 1090.

neous addition of factors makes it possible to expand an enterprise much further than otherwise would be possible before marginal returns equal marginal costs.

A COMPARATIVE ANALYSIS OF TWO FARMS

Further insight into analysis of returns, repayment capacity, and risk-bearing ability as guides in use of credit can be gained by a comparative analysis of two actual farms. These farms were selected because they represent two entirely different situations. One is a fairly stable type of operation, a dairy-hog type farm of moderate

[3] *Ibid.*, p. 1090.

size located in a fairly stable part of the Corn Belt. The operator of this farm had a substantial net worth and was using credit to expand his livestock program while teen-age boys were at home to increase the labor supply.[4] The other is a fairly high-risk operation, a relatively small wheat-dairy type farm located in one of the high-risk areas of the Great Plains. The operator of this farm had a relatively small net worth and made application for a loan to help buy a quarter section of land.

Factors relating to use of credit on these two farms are analyzed here from the viewpoint of the first R of credit—returns. In later chapters these same two farms are analyzed with respect to the other two R's—repayment capacity and risk-bearing ability.

The Dairy-Hog Farm

Analysis of the dairy-hog farm is based upon data for two years, the "current year" and one "four years ago," when the livestock expansion program began (see Table 5.4). Changes in dollars

TABLE 5.4

ACRES, LIVESTOCK NUMBERS, AND FINANCIAL DATA FOR AN OWNER-OPERATED
DAIRY-HOG FARM IN THE CORN BELT *

Item	Four Years Ago	Current Year
Acres in Farm	160	247
Cropland, acres	140	185
Total Cattle, number	43	50
Total Hogs, number	31	181
ASSETS		
Livestock	$ 7,155	$13,710
Other current assets	7,730	8,183
Land and buildings	11,000	17,500
	$25,885	$39,393
LIABILITIES		
Chattel mortgage loan	$ 1,992	$ 7,333
Real estate mortgage loan		
First mortgage	4,800	7,500
Second mortgage	3,000	4,000
	$ 9,792	$18,833
NET WORTH	$16,093	$20,560

* Source: Aaron G. Nelson, *Credit as a Tool for the Agricultural Producer*, N. Cent. Reg. Ext. Publ. No. 4; and Great Plains Agr. Council Publ. No. 15, 1957, Table 4, p. 31.

---

[4] Nelson, p. 30.

reflect actual changes in numbers and amounts, since livestock, feed, and other resources were valued on about the same basis in both years; and the increase in the value of land reflects an increase in the number of acres and improvements added to existing facilities.

Major changes in this farm during the four-year period included addition of 87 acres, improvements in the land and buildings, and expansion of the livestock enterprises. A major improvement in the farm was modernization and enlargement of the milk house and related equipment. The dairy herd was increased some, but the major expansion was in the hog enterprise. Sows for spring farrowing were increased from 26 to 40, and the addition of fall farrowings further expanded the hog enterprise.

Credit was an essential tool in expansion of this farm business. Use of borrowed funds made possible purchase of the additional 87 acres. Expansion of the short-term loan provided the means for increasing the size of the livestock enterprises and made possible purchase of additional feed throughout the year. The amount of short-term credit used during the year increased about 50 per cent in the four years.

Did it pay this family to use borrowed funds? The farmer's annual net income, before family living expenses and income taxes were deducted, increased from $4,044 to $4,619, or $575 in the four-year period. From this we deduct a return on the farmer's increased assets used in the business. His equity in livestock and other current assets increased $1,667. A 6 per cent return on this amounts to $100. The farmer's net equity in real estate increased $2,800, and a 4 per cent return on that amounts to $112. The $100 and $112 total $212. In other words, this farmer's net income should have increased $212 during the four-year period to pay a return on the larger equity of the farmer. Summary computations are given in Table 5.5.

The $212 deducted from the $575 leaves $363 additional annual net income for operator labor and management made possible by the increased use of borrowed funds. Moreover, the farmer was able to provide profitable employment for his boys. The point also may be made that during the four-year period the farm price-cost squeeze resulted in a drop in the parity ratio in the United States of about 10 per cent. If the parity ratio had remained the same during the four-year period, the increase in net income likely would have been substantially larger.

Each major use of credit should be examined individually to see if it will pay. Because of space limitations, it is not practicable

TABLE 5.5

SUMMARY OF CALCULATIONS IN ESTIMATING THE INCREASE IN NET INCOME FROM USE OF CREDIT ON AN OWNER-OPERATED DAIRY-HOG FARM IN THE CORN BELT*

Increase in net income per year........................		$575
Deduct return on increased net equity of operator:		
$1,667 increase of equity in livestock and other current assets at 6 per cent...............................	$100	
$2,800 increase of equity in the farm at 4 per cent......	112	$212
Estimated annual increase in net income for operator labor and management made possible by increased use of borrowed funds as shown in Table 5.4................		$363

* Source: Aaron G. Nelson, *Credit as a Tool for the Agricultural Producer*, N. Cent. Reg. Ext. Publ. No. 4; and Great Plains Agr. Council Publ. No. 15, 1957, Table 5, p. 32.

to include those analyses here. In this case, use of borrowed funds to buy additional land and to expand the livestock enterprise both were profitable.

The Wheat-Dairy Farm

The wheat-dairy farm used in this example was operated on a crop-share rental basis by a young couple with two small children. It included 320 acres, all of which were in cultivation. The quarter section where the improvements were located was for sale for $16,000 and the young couple wanted to buy it so as to have a home and farmstead to improve and fix up the way they wanted without the threat of having to move. Moreover, they milked about fifteen cows and were concerned whether or not it would be possible to rent another farm with suitable improvements.

The family had made fairly good financial progress and had successfully used some credit. At this time they were free of debt, and their property conservatively valued, including $1,000 in a savings account, totaled a little over $14,000. A copy of their balance sheet is given in Table 5.6.

A preliminary review of the situation with their lender indicated it might be possible to borrow $8,000 on the land if it were purchased and $7,000 on their chattel property. With the $1,000 from the savings account, this would provide funds to purchase the quarter section. The next step was to determine whether it would be sound business to borrow the $15,000. This can be done by applying the 3-R test.

The first question to be answered in applying the 3-R test is

TABLE 5.6

BALANCE SHEET OF A WHEAT-DAIRY FARMER IN THE NORTHERN
GREAT PLAINS, JANUARY 1 *

ASSETS		LIABILITIES-NET WORTH	
Current		*Current*	
Cash............$ 315		(none)	
Savings account... 1,000		*Intermediate*	
Feed, grain, etc.... 2,550		(none)	
Hay and roughage. 750			
4 calves to be sold.. 200			
	$ 4,815		
Intermediate			
18 milk cows......$2,700			
8 replacement stock 800			
Machinery....... 6,000			
	$ 9,500	Net worth..............$14,315	
Total.........	$14,315	Total..............$14,315	

* Source: Personal files of the authors.

whether the returns produced will justify buying the 160 acres.
Would it pay to borrow the $15,000 and withdraw $1,000 from the
savings account? Some figuring is necessary to answer this question.
One approach is to estimate the landlord's income as a basis for
judging how much the real estate might be expected to earn. Since
income fluctuates from year to year, an average based upon a period
of years in the future is appropriate for this purpose. A summary of
these calculations is as follows:

Landlord's gross income per year.....................$1,200
Landlord's expenses: depreciation, taxes, insurance, share
  of seed... 500
Landlord's net income per year.......................$ 700

The tenant estimates that if he owned the farm he could
increase production by building up soil fertility. There probably
also would be some savings derived from things such as not having
to move and being able to plan feed purchases to take advantage of
lower prices. These things he estimates will total $100 per year,
making a total of $800 income per year which could be attributed to
ownership of the 160 acres. This amounts to 5 per cent return on
the purchase price.

By way of comparison, the real estate loan would cost 5 per
cent and the chattel loan 6 per cent, and the opportunity cost of the
$1,000 withdrawn from savings would be 3.5 per cent. The total
dollar cost, therefore, amounts to $855, or $55 more per year than
the dollar income. The family concluded that this small deficit

would be more than offset by the increased satisfaction of having their own home. In other words, in terms of satisfactions it would pay to buy the 160 acres. Thus, the first question posed by the 3-R test—do returns justify using the credit?—was answered in the affirmative.

BUDGET PROCEDURE TO ESTIMATE RETURNS

Some paper work usually will help to provide a basis for judgment as to whether it will pay to borrow; this process is referred to as budgeting.[5] The objective in working out a budget is to project the business into the future and observe what will happen. Where needed for comparison, two budgets are developed, one based upon the business before and the other upon the business after adjustments are made. Comparison of the two budgets indicates the effect of changes in organization, in method of operation, and in the amount of capital used in the business upon net income.

The following outline indicates the procedure to follow in building a budget:

1. Estimate annual total production. Use average yields or production rates expected for each crop and each class of livestock during the period the credit will be used in the business. Unusually low yields or production which are expected to occur should be recognized in estimating average production.
2. Estimate the prices which will be received over the period. It is a good practice to be on the conservative side as a means of insuring against overestimating income.
3. Compute the estimated annual gross income by multiplying price times production.
4. Estimate average farm operating costs per year. The costs estimated might well be on the high side to insure against error and the possibility of rising costs. Unusual costs which are expected to occur should be recognized in arriving at the annual average.
5. Compute net *cash* farm income by deducting cash expenses from gross income.
6. Compute net farm income by adjusting net cash farm income for changes in inventory during the period. Change in inventory should include depreciation on buildings and machinery if repairs have not been adequate to maintain their value.

---

[5] Since budgeting is discussed in detail in a number of bulletins and in some farm management texts, only a summary outline is given here.

It should be recognized that net income figures arrived at by the budget method are the result of production, prices, and costs used. If these have been unrealistic, income estimates will provide an unrealistic basis for judgment. Budgets should be built upon the most reliable data which are available.

A complete budget for the entire farm or for an enterprise should be developed when all finances used in the business or enterprise are considered. However, when only a small part of the business or of an enterprise is being analyzed, partial budgets can be used. Partial budgets save a lot of work and still facilitate analysis of changes in the amount of capital used. Application of fertilizer illustrates the type of situation where partial budgeting might well be used. Net income from adding 20 pounds per acre of nitrogen on the farm's corn acreage can first be examined. Then the additional net income from a second 20-pound unit can be studied. In this manner, successive 20-pound additions can be considered to determine how much fertilizer it will pay to use. With partial budgeting, relatively small additions of capital can be examined to determine whether income produced will be greater than costs involved. Partial budgeting may also be used to estimate the change in net income which would result from reducing the investment in one enterprise and expanding another.

Borrower and lender alike should be thoroughly familiar with budgeting procedures. Both complete and partial budgets provide helpful patterns of analysis which will materially aid in determining whether the returns produced are adequate to warrant making the loan. Lenders may find it desirable to extend the budgeting process by use of linear programming.

QUESTIONS AND PROBLEMS

1. Explain what is meant by the Three R's of Credit.
2. Explain what is meant by the Three C's of Credit and indicate how they relate to the Three R's of Credit. Discuss the advantages and disadvantages of the two classifications.
3. What is marginal analysis?
4. Why is marginal analysis needed in analyzing the use of credit?
5. Why should returns produced be analyzed in connection with use of credit?
6. Outline the economic model which may be used in allocating capital among enterprises within the farm business to maximize income.
7. Outline the economic model which may be used in selecting

production practices or combinations of inputs which are most economical.

8. Explain how one can determine, theoretically, whether all the credit which is profitable is being used in the business.

9. Discuss the desirability of expanding expenditures on farms in your community for livestock, tractors, machinery, labor, seed, fertilizer, fence, buildings, soil erosion control, and drainage. Which expenditure would probably bring the largest return, which the smallest return?

10. According to Table 5.2, how would you invest $1,000, $2,000, and $3,000 with interest at 5 per cent? How much capital would it pay to use in the six enterprises with interest at 5 per cent? With interest at 10 per cent?

11. Outline the budget procedure used in determining whether it will pay to use credit in the farm business.

12. For both the dairy-hog farmer and the wheat-dairy farmer used in the examples, did it pay to borrow? Discuss.

13. Analyze your own farm or one with which you are familiar to determine whether it would pay to use more credit.

Chapter 6

RETURNS AS A GUIDE IN USE OF CREDIT: INCOME STATEMENT ANALYSIS

APPLICATION of economic principles for determining the optimum utilization and allocation of capital, as outlined in the preceding chapter, is contingent upon information being available regarding costs and returns for the business. The value of analysis is directly related to accuracy and adequacy of information available. Some astute farmers glean considerable information from observation coupled with income and expense transactions involved in operating the business. However, as the size of farm increases, the technological revolution progresses, and cash expenses consume an increasingly large part of gross income, management needs more adequate records, properly summarized and analyzed, to provide a reliable basis for judgment in managerial decisions.

One source of information, widely used in credit extension and analysis, is the income statement. Thus, we are concerned with an understanding of this statement and related analyses to determine the information it will provide on costs and returns associated with use of varying amounts of capital in the farm business. How can this statement be organized and summarized to give the needed information? What information will it provide for determining how much credit it will pay to use? These are the types of questions considered in this chapter.

Preparation and analysis of an income statement for a typical farm business is a straightforward, simple, single-entry accounting process involving the listing of receipts and expenditures in general categories. However, it may appear to be a complex and involved undertaking due to the wide range of activities included in the farm business. Most of the problems encountered in determining the income of a large corporate business are found on a smaller scale in computing income of a farm business. Consequently, one needs to have a clear understanding of what an income statement is, the information needed to prepare an income statement, and the way in which it is summarized. The discussion which follows is illustrated by an income statement for a 240-acre hog-beef fattening farm in the Corn Belt. The land, Webster silt loam, is all tillable. Mr. A, operator of the farm, is rated as an average hog-cattle manager and somewhat above average in operating efficiency.

THE INCOME STATEMENT

An *income statement,* also called a *profit and loss statement,* is a summary of receipts and gains during a specified period, usually a year, less expenses and losses during the same period, with a net income or a net loss as a result. It is a measure of output and input in terms of values.

Receipts

Receipts are derived from sales of crops, livestock, and livestock products during the year, and also from government payments and miscellaneous sources. On Mr. A's farm, income from these sources totaled $41,711 in 1965 (see Table 6.1). Any farm products used in the home should be valued and also included in receipts.

The objective in the receipts section of the income statement is to show as accurately as feasible the gross production of the farm, in dollars, during the year. This facilitates comparison of a given farm with other similar farms in the area from a management point of view. It also facilitates analyzing the trend of income on the given farm over a period of years. Therefore, recognition is given to changes in the inventory value of livestock, crops, and other liquid assets during the year. Increases are added to and decreases are subtracted from gross cash receipts to obtain *gross income.* The value of Mr. A's current inventory was $22,158 greater December 31,

TABLE 6.1

FARM BUSINESS A

Income Statement for Year 1965

Receipts		
Livestock sales		
Cattle, fat	$18,183	
Hogs	17,257	
Total		$35,440
Crop sales		460
Government payments		4,893
Miscellaneous income		918
Gross cash receipts		$41,711
Increase (decrease) in current inventory		22,158
Gross income		$63,869
Less: Livestock purchased	$16,808	
Feed purchased	5,072	$21,880
Gross profit		$41,989
Operating Expenses		
Machinery and power	$2,477	
Labor hired	136	
Livestock expense	441	
Seed, fertilizer, etc.	1,957	
Interest on operating loans	701	
Miscellaneous expenses	717	
Total operating expenses		$6,429
Net Operating Income		$35,560
Fixed Expenses		
Taxes, property	$1,750	
Interest on long-term loans	2,764	
Repairs and insurance on improvements	485	
Depreciation on intermediate assets	1,556	
Depreciation on fixed assets	2,218	
Total fixed expenses		$8,773
Net Farm Income		$26,787

1965, than a year earlier. Thus, this amount was added to his gross cash receipts, making a gross income of $63,869 for the year.

Gross income of farms with large purchases of livestock and feed naturally overstates the income produced on the farm. It is customary, therefore, to correct this overstatement by deducting purchases of livestock and feed from gross income (as is "cost of goods sold" in conventional double-entry accounting) to obtain *gross profit*. Mr. A's purchases of livestock totaled $16,808 and feed bought amounted to $5,072. These amounts deducted from gross income left a gross profit of $41,989 for the year.

Money received from the sale of capital assets used in the business (such as real estate, machinery and equipment, and dairy and breeding stock) generally is not included with receipts in the income statement since such income usually is not produced or earned during the period.

Expenses

All expenses or costs involved in operation of the business during the period covered by the income statement should be included in the income statement. Thus, all operating and fixed expenses are included. However, capital expenditures to purchase fixed and working assets such as real estate, machinery, milk cows, and breeding stock are excluded since such items usually are used in the business for several years. The depreciation on these items which occurs during the period covered by the income statement is an expense, however, and should be included.

Operating (variable) and fixed costs customarily are shown separately in the income statement. During 1965, operating expenses for Farm Business A were $6,429 and fixed expenses were $8,773 (see Table 6.1). This procedure facilitates analysis of the farm business and reflects various aspects of net income.

Net Income

Three net income (or loss) figures are useful in analysis of the business: net cash income, net operating income, and net farm income. *Net cash income* equals cash receipts less cash expenses during the period covered by the statement. The primary usefulness of the net cash income figure is in connection with analysis of cash flow. It also is useful in preparing income tax returns when the return is made on the cash basis. Further consideration is given to net cash income in the following section.

Net operating income is computed by subtracting operating expenses from gross profit. Mr. A's net operating income was $35,560 in 1965 (see Table 6.1). This measure of income facilitates comparison of farms with different fixed cost structures; i.e. amounts of mortgage debt, different depreciation schedules, and the like. It also facilitates comparing income from operations on the same farm over a period of years even though fixed costs change, due to changes in mortgage indebtedness and the like.

Net farm income is computed by deducting fixed costs from net operating income. Mr. A's net farm income amounted to $26,787 in 1965 (an unusually high figure, as will be shown later). Net farm income represents the income accruing to operator and family labor, management, and equity capital. Of the three measures of income, it is perhaps the most useful. It represents more nearly than the other two measures of income the "true" net income of the business during the period covered by the income statement. Provided the data used in its preparation are accurate and realistic, net farm income represents the amount available for family living, income taxes, and savings.

The discussion and illustration presented portray the basic structure of the income statement. When the statement provides the detailed information needed for analysis, it may be somewhat complicated. However, keeping the basic objective and structure of the income statement in mind materially facilitates understanding how it should be set up and interpreted. The primary objective is to show the income produced by and the expenses involved in operation of the business during the period covered by the statement, together with the net income (or loss) which is realized. Thus, the income statement is basically comprised of three parts: receipts, expenses, and net income. Within this framework details are added to provide needed information. For example, analysis presented in the latter part of the chapter makes specific use of gross income, gross profit, total operating expenses, total fixed expenses, and the like. Therefore, these details have been included in the income statement for Farm Business A. The final form and content of the income statement depend to a large degree upon the information which is needed.

TREND OF RECEIPTS, EXPENSES, AND NET INCOME

A record of receipts, expenses, and net income over a period of years is invaluable in analyzing a farm business. An income statement for only one year may be misleading, especially where income is highly variable. This point may be illustrated by the record for Farm Business A given in Table 6.2. As was indicated above, income for the year 1965 was unusually high. Net farm income in that year was $26,787 compared with an average of $6,838 for the five years 1960–64. In other words, net farm income in 1965 was nearly four times the average of the preceding five years. On the other hand, the record for 1964, considered alone, would also have been misleading.

TABLE 6.2

RECEIPTS, EXPENSES, AND INCOME SUMMARY OF FARM A, 1960–1965

	1960	1961	1962	1963	1964	1965
			(dollars)			
Cash Receipts						
Cattle, fat	16,632	5,911	. . .	12,481	23,855	18,183
Hogs	8,210	10,602	15,073	12,401	12,919	17,257
Poultry	806	805	864	676	239	. . .
Crops	983	1,701	1,558	7,219	1,602	460
Government payments	. . .	. . .	3,008	2,307	4,200	4,893
Miscellaneous	305	192	134	415	604	918
Total	26,936	19,211	20,637	35,499	43,419	41,711
Cash Expenses						
Machinery and power expense	2,472	2,241	2,202	1,825	3,107	2,477
Labor hired	479	65	55	63	64	136
Livestock expense	124	321	622	373	838	441
Seed, fertilizer, etc.	799	825	1,093	1,123	1,864	1,957
Feed purchases	4,352	7,066	1,949	3,204	8,337	5,072
Livestock purchased	10,392	400	10,742	16,023	9,447	16,808
Miscellaneous operating	483	481	959	362	1,159	717
Taxes, property	150	155	206	1,656	1,678	1,750
Rent	280	280	. . .	. . .	. . .	. . .
Interest	707	724	730	3,687	4,342	3,465
Repairs and insurance on improvements	. . .	. . .	. . .	518	311	485
Total	20,238	12,558	18,558	28,834	31,147	33,308
Net Cash Income	6,698	6,653	2,079	6,665	12,272	8,403
Increase (Decrease) in Current Inventory	(1,003)	1,847	10,190	4,408	(6,630)	22,158
Depreciation						
Intermediate assets	1,190	1,072	1,194	1,350	1,283	1,556
Improvements	. . .	. . .	936	981	981	2,218
Net Farm Income	4,505	7,428	10,139	8,742	3,378	26,787

Net farm income in that year was only about one-half the 1960–64 average.

The trend of receipts, expenses, and net income over time is significant in credit analysis. An upward trend in net income has value in and of itself. Mr. A was a young tenant farmer just getting a good start in 1960. During the years 1960, 1961, and 1962 he rented the farm he was operating from an uncle. In 1962 he and his wife inherited $14,000 and purchased the farm on contract, taking possession January 1, 1963. This change in ownership is reflected both in receipts and in expenses. The trend of net farm income, while erratic, was upward during the six-year period.

Compare net cash income and net farm income. Over a period

of years the two measures of income will average out to about the same figure. In fact, for the five-year period, 1960–64, net farm income for Farm Business A averaged $6,838 and net cash income averaged $6,873. Wide differences occur in individual years, however. In 1962, for example, net farm income was $10,139 while net cash income was only $2,079. The reverse relationship may also occur. In 1964 net cash income was $12,272 while net farm income was only $3,378. Such differences are of considerable significance in repayment capacity and risk-bearing ability, as will be shown in subsequent chapters.

INVENTORY ADJUSTMENTS

Reference was made above to the inventory adjustments which are made in arriving at gross profit. A similar adjustment, as well as an adjustment for depreciation, is made in deriving net farm income from net cash income. In other words, net cash income plus (minus) the increase (decrease) in the current inventory, less depreciation on intermediate and fixed assets, gives net farm income.[1]

Obviously, inventory adjustments are of paramount importance if a reliable net farm income figure is to be obtained. However, constant danger of misrepresentation exists. Increases or decreases in inventory values from the beginning to the end of the year are caused by changes in quantities and prices. Changes in quantities usually do not cause major problems, except possibly where quality or weight per unit or per head changes. But changes in prices may cause distortions in the income picture, giving an incorrect impression of the farmer's ability to produce income. As a result the farmer may be granted too much credit in years of rising prices and too little credit when prices are falling. These points can be

---

[1] Provided depreciation of intermediate assets and fixed improvements is included as an expense (a desirable accounting procedure), adjustments are not needed in the inventory value of these items in computing net farm income. If an increase (decrease) is made in the inventory value of land due to an increase (decrease) in the price level of land, the resulting increase (decrease) in owner equity is appropriately considered the same as a cash addition to (withdrawal from) the business. Such a change is not reflected in net farm income. On the other hand, if an increase is made in the inventory value of land due to an improvement in its productivity as a result of farming methods and conservation practices which are not depreciated, the increased value is appropriately reflected in net farm income, assuming the costs involved have been included in farm expenses. The same would be true if a reduction was made in the inventory value of land due to deterioration of productivity as a result of farming practices.

clarified by reference to the 1965 beginning and ending inventory of current assets of Farm Business A which follows.

January 1, 1965		December 31, 1965	
Corn, 6,800 bu.	$ 7,140	Corn, 9,147 bu.	$ 9,604
Soybeans	....	Soybeans, 756 bu.	1,890
Alfalfa hay, 66 tons	1,188	Alfalfa hay, 70 tons	1,260
Hogs, market, 196 head	3,122	Hogs, market, 262 head	11,829
Sows, 27 head	2,025	Sows, 38 head	2,850
Feeding cattle, 73 head	7,000	Feeding cattle, 110 head	15,200
Total	$20,475	Total	$42,633

The same unit prices were used for corn ($1.05 per bu.), alfalfa hay ($18.00 per ton), and sows ($75.00 per head) in the inventory for January 1 and December 31, 1965. However, the per head price for market hogs was increased from $15.93 January 1, 1965, to $45.15 December 31, 1965, and the per head price for feeding cattle was increased from $95.89 to $138.18. While data are not available to substantiate these increases, they probably were justified by changes in animal weight, quality, or prices from the beginning to the end of the year. Assume, however, for purposes of illustration that the per head price December 31, 1965, was $10 too high for market hogs and $20 too high for feeding cattle. With 262 head of market hogs and 110 head of fattening cattle on hand, the increase in the current inventory would have been overstated by $4,600. Net farm income would have been overstated by the same amount.

FINANCIAL TESTS—RATIOS

Analysis of pertinent financial relationships in the income statement provides information concerning performance of the farm business in addition to that obtained directly by income statement analysis. Without a basis for comparison, such as a summary of like relationships for similar farms in the area or similar information for the subject farm over a period of years, such ratios have little value. However, when a basis for comparison is available, pertinent comparisons provide valuable information. Progressive lenders generally use financial tests of various kinds in loan analysis. Working with a large number of farmers, they are in a position to develop ratio "standards," formally or otherwise, to provide the basis for comparison needed to effectively utilize this type of information.

Four basic ratios which give pertinent information on per-

formance of the business are the capital turnover ratio, the gross
ratio, the operating ratio, and the rate of return on capital. These
ratios are considered in this section.

Capital Turnover Ratio

The objective in analyzing the amount of revenue in relation
to capital used is to ascertain whether the volume of sales is what it
should be for the amount of capital used in the business. The
capital turnover ratio indicates how much gross revenue has been
received for each dollar of capital used in the business. A large gross
revenue per dollar of capital usually is desirable since, assuming the
business is operating profitably, a net return is realized each time
capital is converted into cash.

The capital turnover ratio is computed by dividing gross revenue by capital

$$\frac{\text{Gross revenue}}{\text{Capital}} = \text{Capital turnover ratio} \qquad (6.1)$$

The term "gross revenue" is used purposely in the equation and in
the preceding discussion to convey the concept involved, since it
does not appear in the income statement shown in Table 6.1. As is
often the case, data reflecting real world situations do not precisely
"fit" in models portraying principles. When such is the case, more
than one ratio may be computed. The two most pertinent for Farm
A are the ratio of gross income to capital and the ratio of gross
profit to capital. The 1965 ratio of gross income, $63,869, to total
capital employed, $111,501 (total assets January 1, given in the
balance sheet, Chapter 13), equals .57. A gross income of 57 cents
was realized during 1965 for each dollar of capital employed in the
business January 1. During 1964 the gross income per dollar of
capital employed was 31 cents, substantially lower than the 1965
ratio. It may be noted that net farm income also was substantially
lower in 1964 than in 1965. During 1963 gross income per dollar
employed was 35 cents, somewhat above 1964, and net farm income
also was up. An advantage of the ratio of gross income to total
capital is that changes in the value of the current inventory during
the year are taken into account.

The 1965 ratio of gross profit, $41,989, to total capital em-
ployed equals .38. Thus, with livestock and feed purchases during
the year deducted from gross income, a gross profit of 38 cents was

realized on each dollar of capital employed in the business. Comparable figures for 1964 and 1963 were 16 cents and 18 cents, respectively. As was indicated above, gross profit is calculated to remove the effect of large purchases of livestock and feed, thereby providing a gross revenue figure which is somewhat comparable from one farm to another, and from one year to another for the same farm. Thus, the ratio of gross profit to capital has the same advantage of comparability from farm to farm, and from year to year. Such comparability is invaluable to management.

Gross Ratio

The gross ratio is an overall measure of the income-producing ability of the farm business. It is computed by dividing total expenses by gross revenue.

$$\frac{\text{Total expense}}{\text{Gross revenue}} = \text{Gross ratio} \qquad (6.2)$$

Here, again, we are confronted with a problem in selecting the appropriate data to use in the comparison. One useful comparison is the ratio of total expense to the gross income during the year. Since gross income includes sales of purchased livestock and feed, these items must be included in total expense. Thus, the ratio for 1965 is $37,082 divided by $63,869, which equals .58. Expenses during 1965 amounted to 58 cents for each dollar of gross income. Comparable figures for 1964 and 1963 are 91 cents and 78 cents, respectively.

Another pertinent comparison is the ratio of operating and fixed expenses to gross profit. For the year 1965 the ratio is $15,202 divided by $41,989, which equals .36. Operating and fixed expenses took 36 cents of each dollar of gross profit. Comparable figures for 1964 and 1963 are 82 cents and 58 cents, respectively. This ratio has the advantage of comparability from one farm to another, and from year to year for the same farm.

Operating Ratio

The operating ratio, as the term implies, pertains to the current period of operation. Only operating costs during the year are considered. These are related to gross revenue.

$$\frac{\text{Total operating expenses}}{\text{Gross revenue}} = \text{Operating ratio} \qquad (6.3)$$

With livestock and feed purchases included, total operating expenses during 1965 for Farm Business A were $28,309. Relating this amount to the gross income, $63,869, gives a ratio of .44. Total operating expenses amounted to 44 cents per dollar of gross income. Comparable figures for 1964 and 1963 are 71 cents and 59 cents, respectively.

With livestock and feed purchases excluded, operating expenses for 1965 total $6,429. Dividing this amount by gross profit, $41,989, gives 15 per cent, or 15 cents of operating expenses per dollar of gross profit. Comparable figures for 1964 and 1963 are 45 cents and 22 cents, respectively. As was indicated above, the latter comparison has the advantage of comparability from farm to farm, and from year to year for the same farm, since purchases of livestock and feed have been excluded.

Fixed Ratio

The fixed ratio relates fixed expenses to gross profit.

$$\frac{\text{Fixed expenses}}{\text{Gross profit}} = \text{Fixed ratio} \qquad (6.4)$$

Fixed expenses for Farm Business A were $8,773 during 1965 and gross profit was $41,989. Thus, the fixed ratio was equal to .21, or fixed expenses amounted to 21 cents per dollar of gross profit. Comparable figures for 1964 and 1963 are 37 cents and 36 cents, respectively.

The operating ratio and the fixed ratio combined comprise the gross ratio. Operating expenses for Farm Business A took 15 cents of each dollar of gross profit in 1965. Adding this amount to the 21 cents required to meet fixed expenses gives 36 cents, the amount indicated by the gross ratio. The gross ratio, including both operating and fixed costs, pertains to the long-run situation, whereas the operating ratio pertains to the short-run situation. The fixed ratio is a measure of the importance of overhead costs.

Rate of Return on Capital

The rate of return on capital is obtained by dividing net income by the amount of capital.

$$\frac{\text{Net income}}{\text{Capital}} = \text{Rate of return} \qquad (6.5)$$

While Equation 6.5 provides the general model for deriving the rate of return, the problem is not as simple as indicated. Again, we are faced with the problem of appropriate data to use.

It is desirable to compute two rates of return, one on total capital used in the business and another on owner equity. Net income to be related to total capital used in the business may be derived from net farm income by adding interest paid during the year and subtracting an allowance for operator and family labor, and for management. The calculations for Farm Business A for the year 1965 are as follows:

Net farm income	$26,787
Plus: Interest paid during year	3,465
	$30,252
Less: Operator and family labor	$4,400
Management return	
@ 8% of gross income	5,110
Return to total capital	$20,742

Relating the return to capital to total capital invested in the business January 1, 1965, gives a return of 18.6 per cent.

Net income to be related to owner equity may be obtained by subtracting a wage for operator and family labor, and a return for management from net farm income. Using the figures given above for 1965, the return to Mr. A's equity capital was $17,277. Owner equity January 1, 1965, was $27,778. Thus, the rate of return on equity capital was 62 per cent.

Two cautions should be observed in interpreting the rate of return on capital. First, since deductions from net farm income for operator and family labor and for management return are imputed from farm wage rates and professional farm management fees in the area, they may be either higher or lower than if they were established in the market. Second, the rate of return indicated by one year's operation may be misleading. As was pointed out above, an income statement for only one year may be misleading. Since the rate of return on capital is based directly on the income statement, the rate of return for only one year may not portray a reliable picture. This is the case for the year 1965 as indicated by the following tabulation.

	1960	1961	1962	1963	1964	1965
		—Per cent—				
Rate of return on total capital[2]	− 6	12	22	4	0.3	19
Rate of return on equity capital	−27	19	33	4	−12	62

Obviously, the rate of return in 1965 is not representative of the rate of return which Mr. A might expect on capital. An average of several years is much more reliable.

Another point is worth noting. It will be recalled that Mr. A rented the farm during 1960, 1961, and 1962. Even though he was less experienced and had a smaller business in those years, the rate of return on capital tended to be higher than after he purchased the farm. This normally would be the case. Note, also, the wider fluctuations in the rate of return on equity than on total capital. This is a typical relationship resulting from leverage associated with use of credit, as is indicated by the principle of increasing risk, discussed later in the analysis of risk-bearing ability.

MANAGEMENT FACTORS

Various measures of efficiency other than those related directly to the income statement may be used to indicate the income-producing ability of a farm business. Several of the most commonly used measures are shown in Table 6.3. Data are given for Farm Business A together with the average for a group of similar farms in the area.

Management Return

Management return is derived from net farm income by deducting a wage for operator and family labor and a return on equity capital used in the business. Using 1965 data for Farm Business A we have:

Net farm income		$26,787
Less: Operator and family labor	$4,400	
Interest on equity capital ($27,778 Jan. 1, 1965, @ 6%)	1,667	
		$ 6,067
Management return		$20,720

[2] Excludes landlord capital and landlord income during the years 1960, 1961, and 1962 when the farm was rented. Data were not available.

TABLE 6.3
Efficiency Factor Data for Farm A and Area Average, 1960–1965

	1960 Farm A	1960 Area Average	1961 Farm A	1961 Area Average	1962 Farm A	1962 Area Average	1963 Farm A	1963 Area Average	1964 Farm A	1964 Area Average	1965 Farm A	1965 Area Average
Management Return (dol.)	1,466	2,630	3,442	3,610	4,967	2,312	3,705	(63)*	(803)*	4,099	20,720	6,084
Corn Yield (bu.)	65	73	85	86	96	86	91	98	95	92	100	90
Gross Value of Crops Per Rotated Acre (dol.)	66	57	66	66	68	66	79	82	85	86	86	77
Livestock Income Per $100 Feed Fed (dol.)	121	151	127	150	133	144	122	138	97	133	219	110
Gross Profits Per Man-Year (dol.)	13,012	13,971	15,447	16,425	16,235	18,936	18,217	15,900	18,694	19,629	40,438	16,419
Gross Profits Per $1.00 Expense (dol.)	1.60	2.10	2.14	2.06	1.75	1.87	1.59	1.61	1.22	1.94	2.76	2.08
Machine and Power Cost Per Crop Acre (dol.)	16.07	18.23	16.21	21.13	15.58	21.47	14.50	25.50	19.95	23.10	18.33	25.54

* Figures in parentheses are negative.

It will be observed that management return is derived from net farm income by following a procedure similar to that used in computing the return on capital. Similar cautions to those noted there also should be observed. First, the amount deducted for operator and family labor is estimated on the basis of wage rates for farm labor in the area. The objective is to deduct an amount that would have to be paid hired labor to do the *work*, exclusive of management and supervision, performed by the operator and his family. Similarly, the objective in arriving at interest on equity capital is to estimate the opportunity return the operator could realize by investing his capital elsewhere: i.e. the amount he could earn, say, by putting his money in nonfarm investments. Since both of these amounts are estimates, they may be higher or lower than if they were established in the market place. Second, management return for one year alone may be misleading. It is evident from data in Table 6.3 that Mr. A's management return for 1965 was unusually high. It is nearly double the total of the four preceding years. Similarly, management return for 1964 is misleading, since it is unusually low. Management return for several years should be considered in appraising the capability of the operator.

Comparison of Mr. A's management return with the management return for other farmers operating similar farms in the area provides a basis for comparison in rating Mr. A's relative performance as a manager. On the basis of the six years, 1960–65, Mr. A's management return averaged $5,583 compared with the area average of $3,112. If 1965 is dropped as being atypical, the respective averages are $2,555 and $2,518. If 1964 also is dropped as atypical, Mr. A's average is $3,395, compared with the group average of $2,122. Comparison of individual years shows that Mr. A's management return was above the average three years and below the average three years. Thus, it appears Mr. A's managerial ability, as reflected by management returns, is approximately average for the area, with his trend relative to the area average probably being upward.

Crop Yields and Value

Crop yields provide an indication of a farmer's management ability. Corn yields obtained by Mr. A are relatively high for the area in which he operates, and compare favorably with the average of other farmers for which records were available in the area. There is an indication that his corn yields are improving over time relative to the area average.

Gross value of crops per rotated acre provides a composite picture of crop production. Mr. A also compares favorably in this respect with the average of other farmers for which records were available in the area.

Livestock Income

Livestock income per $100 of feed fed is a measure of management efficiency in livestock production. It is preferable to analyze livestock enterprises individually. However, it is not always possible or economically feasible to keep the necessary records. In such cases, a composite picture of livestock income related to the cost of feed fed is used to portray the overall picture.

Mr. A's record indicates he is not too strong in livestock production. In five of the six years his livestock returns per $100 of feed fed were below the average of other farmers with records in the area. In 1964 his livestock returns were less than the value of the feed.

Livestock returns are a function of the combination of livestock enterprises on the farm, of feeding efficiency, and of the price paid for livestock bought and the price received for livestock sold. Thus, a farmer may be an effective manager in terms of physical efficiency, but ineffective in terms of economic efficiency. The latter often is most critical. Information is not available for Farmer A, but it is likely that low economic efficiency (probably low prices received for livestock) in 1964 caused the loss on feed fed.

Gross Profit

Gross profit per man-year is a measure of efficiency in use of labor. With the cost of labor continually increasing, this measure of efficiency is becoming increasingly important. The level of gross profit per man-year will vary with type of farm and type of enterprise. The ratio naturally will be much lower for labor-intensive enterprises than for labor-extensive enterprises. The ratio is also influenced by the amount of machinery and equipment, and other resources available. Other things being equal, gross profit per man is higher when resources are ample than when they are restricted or inadequate. However, providing machinery, equipment, and other resources for use with labor costs money. The objective is, as was outlined in the preceding chapter, to obtain a "balance" among the various factors of production. Net income is maximized when the last dollar spent on each factor yields the same marginal value product.

Mr. A appears to measure up fairly well to the area average in gross profit produced per man in the latter part of the 1960–65 period, but he was a little low during the first part. The upward trend is encouraging.

Gross profit per dollar of expense (another expression of the gross ratio discussed above) is an overall measure of efficiency in use of resources. Other things being equal, a high ratio indicates a high net income. However, it should be kept in mind that efficiency measures reflect only output relative to input and give no recognition to volume. A moderate level of efficiency, coupled with a large volume of business, may produce more net income than a high level of efficiency and low volume. Both efficiency and volume should be considered in management decisions.

In all but two years of the 1960–65 period, Mr. A's gross profit per dollar of expense was below the average of other similar farmers with records in the area. However, it appears that his ratio improved somewhat, relative to the average during the period.

Machinery and Power Cost

Machinery and power cost per crop acre is included since machinery and power comprise an important cost item which needs to be watched. Machinery and power costs tend to be high on many farms because the farmer has more machinery than is needed.

Mr. A's machinery and power costs per crop acre are low compared with the average of other similar farms with records in the area. He was below the average in all six years, and substantially below in some. This may explain in part why his gross profit per man was not higher than it was, relative to the area average.

APPRAISAL OF INCOME STATEMENT DATA

The income statement gives a good picture of a business. When statements are available for several years, they indicate trends which are very valuable in financial analysis. If statements for other similar farms in the area are available, one can obtain a good picture of how the subject farm ranks on various financial and management factors.

Income statements provide data which are useful in making some long-run decisions, such as the amount to pay for a farm. By adding interest paid on real estate debt to net farm income and deducting a return for management, operator and family labor, and equity capital in intermediate and current assets, the residual return to land and improvements can be obtained. This figure, averaged for several years, may be capitalized to provide one indication of the value of the farm.

Data provided by the income statement have a number of limitations in terms of current financial and management decisions. First, it provides information on the farm as a whole, whereas decisions must be made for enterprises. Thus, enterprise records are needed to supplement the income statement. Second, the income statement provides receipts and expenses, appropriately classified, for the year or period covered by the statement. These figures may be used in various ratios and efficiency measures. However, they do not provide the type of data needed for marginal analysis. For example, the rate of return on capital used in the business is an average rate of return. It is useful in judging whether the farm business is yielding as high a rate of return as might be obtained elsewhere. However, it does not indicate whether too much or too little capital is employed in the business. Neither does it indicate the marginal value of capital in the various enterprises, or of capital in various uses within enterprises such as for feed, fertilizer, labor, and machine services.

It is important to recognize the limitations of the income statement as a source of data, but it is also important to recognize the value of the data it provides as a basis for decisions. The income statement is one of the best tools available for use in analyzing the business. Moreover, it provides valuable data for use in budget analysis to determine whether additional capital can be profitably employed in the business. With present record-keeping methods, the average farmer probably cannot afford to keep the detailed records needed to provide data for marginal analysis. In most cases he must make decisions on the basis of experimental data, coupled with farm or enterprise records.

QUESTIONS AND PROBLEMS

1. What is an income statement?
2. What are the three basic parts of an income statement?
3. What is the value of analyzing trends in receipts, expenses, and net income?
4. How are the following items handled in the income statement: inventory increases and decreases, depreciation, food and fuel used in the home, money withdrawn or added to the business?
5. Outline and explain five financial tests or ratios which may be applied in analyzing a farm business.
6. What indications have you of operator's ability to make money?
7. What information does the income statement give that is useful in determining the amount of capital it will pay to use in the business?
8. What added information would be desirable (in answering No. 7) that the income statement does not provide?

Chapter 7

RETURNS AS A GUIDE IN USE OF CREDIT: INTEREST RATES AND LOAN COSTS

THE ALLOCATION of capital among enterprises of the farm business and the role of the cost of capital were discussed in Chapter 5. The point was made that the optimum allocation of capital is realized when the ratio of the value of the marginal product (ΔYPy) to the marginal cost of capital used in producing the product $[\Delta C (1 + i)]$ is equal for all enterprises. The point also was made that when the value of the marginal product and the marginal cost of capital are equal $[\Delta YPy/\Delta C (1 + i)] = 1$ for each enterprise the optimum amount of capital is being used in the business; i.e. it would not pay to use more credit. It is evident, therefore, that the cost of capital plays an important role both in allocation of capital within the business and in determining the amount of credit which can be profitably employed. Thus, an understanding is needed of the factors which influence interest rates, methods used in figuring interest costs, and other costs in addition to interest which may be encountered in obtaining credit.

FACTORS INVOLVED IN THE INTEREST RATE

Interest is the price paid for use of money or capital; the interest rate is the ratio of the interest to the capital involved. Interest usually is considered to include payment for three things:

1. Pure interest, such as the rate paid on government bonds where there is a minimum of risk or other costs involved. Authorities differ somewhat in their views regarding pure interest. Classical economists viewed pure interest as representing the productivity of real capital. However, from the monetary approach, pure interest is the cost of forbearance or delaying the use of money. A similar view was held by Keynes who considered interest to be "the reward for parting with liquidity for a specified period."[1] With this dual meaning of pure interest, some economists have chosen to consider nonliquidity as a separate factor from pure interest in explaining the interest rate. According to this view, the longer the term of the loan, the greater the nonliquidity. Thus, the nonliquidity part of the interest rate would be higher on long- than on short-term loans.

2. Risk of losing the money loaned. If the risk is high, the interest rate is also high. Lenders, as a rule, compete actively for large loans in low-risk territory. High-risk areas, such as the wheat sections of the Great Plains, are avoided by lending agencies who are looking for relatively safe loans. These agencies are willing to lend on farm mortgages at 5 per cent in the Corn Belt rather than loan at 7 per cent in the drouth sections of the Great Plains.

3. Management and associated costs in making and servicing a loan. This aspect of interest involves both size and term of loan. Overhead costs often run about as high on a small loan as on a large loan. Or, put another way, management and servicing costs per dollar loaned typically run much higher on small than on large loans. As a result, the interest rate on small loans typically is higher than on large loans. Two real estate loans of unequal size, one of $10,000 and the other of $1,000, will illustrate this point. The two farm owners may be operating in the same territory, one with a large, highly productive farm and the other with an unproductive farm having a high percentage of pasture. The applications for the loans, which will be filled out by the lender or his agent, will require the same amount of time for both borrowers. The appraisal, determination of the amount to lend, the making out of loan papers, and closing or completion of the loan will require the same amount of time and expense. Finally, the collection of interest, and any correspondence or

---

[1] John M. Keynes, *The General Theory of Employment, Interest and Money,* Harcourt, New York, 1936, p. 167.

trips to the farm in regard to collections will be about the same for both farms. It is possible, of course, to charge each farmer a flat amount for application, appraisal, collection, and general supervision expense, in addition to the interest charge. But in any event the cost of making the $10,000 loan is not much greater than that for making the $1,000 loan. If the fixed overhead, exclusive of risk, averages $20 annually for each loan, and the cost of funds to the lender is 4 per cent, the lender will need 4.2 per cent to break even on the $10,000 loan and 6 per cent to break even on the $1,000 loan.

The situation is similar for long- versus short-term loans. Initial overhead costs of making the loan are about as high for short- as for long-term loans. Moreover, short-term loans with frequent payments (such as monthly installment loans) involve much more service expense (accounting, and the like), and sometimes more management, than longer-term loans with only one or two payments per year. This is a primary reason that interest rates on short-term loans usually are higher than on long-term loans.

Demand for and the supply of money in the economy have an important influence on interest rates. When product demand and associated income are expected to be high, demand for capital to expand production strengthens. With limited capital available in the economy, interest rates tend to rise under such circumstances, with the result that people tend to save more. The increased supply of capital which is generated is loaned to business firms, which facilitates expanding production. When production has increased sufficiently to supply the demand for products, the demand for capital subsides and interest rates tend to level off or decline. Thus, as this simplified example illustrates, the forces of demand and supply operate in the money market to determine an equilibrium interest rate in much the same way that demand and supply operate in any competitive market to establish an equilibrium price.

While interest rates are subject to economic laws, they are also influenced to a great degree by man-made laws and policy. Monetary phenomena play a very significant role in the economy today, much more than formerly. The interest rate is, to a degree, a monetary phenomenon as evidenced by policy and operations of the Federal Reserve System and the central banks in other countries. Thus, monetary measures are used to cause changes in the money supply and in interest rates needed to bring about desired changes in the economy. The way in which this is accomplished is outlined in a later chapter dealing with commercial banks and the Federal Reserve System.

Interest rates are also influenced by custom and precedent. When rates have been at a given level for a period of time, borrowers and lenders may not expect them to change even though some of the factors influencing interest rates may change. A local credit monopoly may contribute to this situation. If there is only one credit agency making short-term loans in a community, this agency may set rates and maintain them indefinitely unless competing factors or legislation force a change. Several credit agencies may create a local monopoly by agreeing informally on rates and by resisting efforts to bring about a change. There is an upper limit, however, to rates charged, this limit being set by state laws prescribing maximum interest rates. Federally sponsored agencies such as the Federal Land Banks and Production Credit Associations have helped eliminate local credit monopolies. Government-lending institutions such as the Farmers Home Administration have also had a significant effect on interest rates.

INTEREST RATE TRENDS AND VARIATIONS

A major change which has occurred in interest rates over the years has been a narrowing of the spread among regions of the United States. This change is reflected in part by Figure 7.1 which shows average interest rates on *outstanding* farm mortgage debt in the 48 contiguous states, by regions, from 1920 to 1966. The spread among regions was two to three times as wide in the 1920's as in the middle 1930's and subsequently. The Great Depression of the 1930's and the accompanying expansion in governmental activity in the credit field, together with changes and developments in monetary policy, did much to eliminate regional differentials which had existed in interest rates. The various regions of the United States in many respects form a single unified capital market today. The variations in farm interest rates which exist are due in large measure to differences in size of loans, risk, and other costs. A further consideration is the number of loans available in an area. If, as in the western part of the country, available loans are few and far between, the cost of making the loans will be high, causing interest rates also to be relatively high. Moreover, there generally is little competition for loans in such areas since a lender cannot afford to set up a branch office or employ an agent if business in the territory will not provide adequate support.

Interest rates on the farm mortgage debt since 1920 are shown in Figure 7.1 to give perspective. The trend of interest rates has been upward for a number of years, which may give the impression that rates currently are relatively high. However, it is evident that this is not necessarily the case when the current situation is viewed from the long-run point of view.

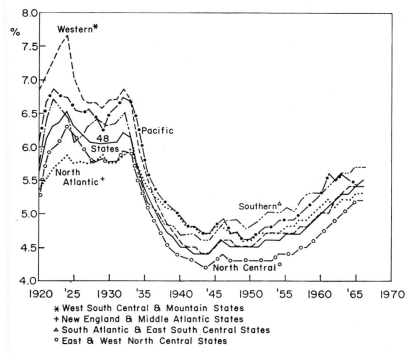

Fig. 7.1—Average interest rates on farm mortgages held by all lenders, 48 contiguous states and by regions, 1920–66. (Data provided by the Economic Research Service, USDA.)

In 1930 the average rate on the outstanding farm mortgage debt in the United States was a little above 6.0 per cent, a level which had prevailed for two decades. By 1940 the rate had dropped to 4.5 per cent, and it remained at this relatively low level until the early 1950's. The sharp decline in the level of interest rates on outstanding farm mortgages from 1930 to 1940 was primarily the result of the Great Depression coupled with monetary policy of the Federal Government. The Government loaned large amounts to farmers during this period at low rates, and also provided an interest rate subsidy on Federal Land Bank loans.

The abundance of loan funds continued during and following World War II. Continuing from the end of the war to the latter part of 1951, the price of government bonds was "pegged," which had a direct effect on the level of interest rates. The method used was purchase of bonds by the Federal Reserve System, which caused a large expansion in the supply of funds available in the economy. Thus, even though the economy was expanding at a fairly rapid rate, the supply of funds was more than adequate to meet demands. Keen competition prevailed among lenders for farm loans, and the prevailing relatively low level of interest rates continued.

When support of government bonds was discontinued in 1951, growth of the supply of funds available for loans did not match the growth in the demand for funds, with the result that interest rates began to increase. In the long period of economic expansion which followed, interest rates moved higher in a series of up and down steps. Rates on 9- to 12-month issues of the Federal Government, for example, rose from less than 2.0 per cent in 1955 to over 5.0 per cent in 1966 (see Figure 7.2). Rates on long-term government bonds increased from less than 3.0 per cent in 1955 to over 4.5 per cent in 1966. Interest rates on farm loans also increased during this period but not as much, proportionately, as the rates on government bonds and other securities more sensitive to the money market.

Interest rates on farm loans are an integral part of the financial structure of the economy. As is evident from Figure 7.2, interest rates on farm mortgage loans follow a trend similar to interest rates on urban mortgage loans and rates on corporate and government bonds. Interest rates on short-term farm loans also follow a trend similar to rates on short-term urban business loans. The interest rate structure of the economy is closely interlinked, with the result that any change which affects the general level of rates also affects farm loan interest rates.

Uniform Interest Rates

As indicated above, interest rates are much more uniform throughout the country now than they were formerly. Operation of the Federal Land Bank system is a primary factor contributing to

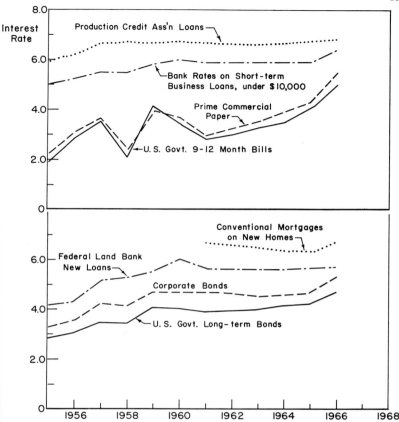

Fig. 7.2—Interest rates on various types of short- and long-term loans. (Data provided by the Federal Reserve Bulletin, Statistical Abstract of the United States, and Agricultural Statistics.)

this uniformity. Each Federal Land Bank charges uniform interest rates on loans it makes throughout the district it serves.

A policy of charging all borrowers the same rate may seem on first thought to be fair and equitable to all concerned. However, is such a policy economically justified? Is it desirable to have the same interest rate for every farm loan, regardless of the size, distance from the agency office, and risk involved?

The uniform rate runs counter to the idea of charging according to cost. Obviously, the small loan of $300 is much more costly to make per hundred dollars than the large loan of $30,000. In business dealings it is customary for buyers who purchase in large volume to obtain a discount or lower price. Small variations in farm mortgage loans would be almost impossible to separate, but differences as large as those indicated between regions in Figure 7.1 might easily be classified into groups. It is difficult to support any definite dividing line, but if loans under $5,000 are taken as one group, those between $5,000 and $10,000 as a second group, and those above $10,000 as the third and last group, the resulting divisions with a sliding scale of charges would be more reasonable than the uniform charge regardless of size.

Uniform rates do not allow for variations in risk. With uniform rates, the farmer in the highly variable yield territory obtains his mortgage loan at the same cost per hundred dollars as the farmer in stable yield territory. Yet experience indicates that losses in the high-risk territory are likely to be heavier than in the low-risk regions. It has been suggested that the credit agency could correct this situation by lending a smaller percentage of the value in the hazardous region. But to make even a small loan in hazardous territory may be more of a risk than to lend 100 per cent of value in safe territory.

Uniform interest rates, in effect, are a subsidy to the farmers who get small loans and to the farmers in the hazardous territory. Any lending agency which sets out to lend at a uniform rate is subsidizing the high-risk areas. Over the years it may be possible to keep the losses fairly low in these areas, but even then the chances are that the losses experienced will be heavier.

Uniform interest rates may tend to discourage the flow of credit extended by private commercial lenders to high-risk areas and to areas comprised predominantly of small farms. A uniform interest rate policy may hold rates at a sufficiently low level that private commercial lenders could not afford to operate in these areas, with the result that the flow of credit would be reduced. Moreover, the lack of competition in credit extension would have a dilatory effect on credit service provided farmers in these areas.

Methods of Charging Interest

There are a number of different ways in which interest may be computed, depending upon the terms of the loan and the policy of the lender. The method used makes a difference in the actual rate paid. Thus, a borrower needs to understand the various methods of charging interest in order to make an intelligent decision on whether it will pay to use credit and, if so, on where and how much to borrow.

Terminology from the mathematics of finance field will be used in the discussion of methods of charging interest. This terminology is well defined and consistently used in literature on mathematics of finance, which contributes to understanding the concepts involved. On the other hand, the student of finance should be aware of what appears to be another set of terminology used in the consumer finance field. This can be confusing since a number of the same terms are used in the two sets of terminology but with different meanings. Terminology long in use and in publications in the mathematics of finance field appears to have been misapplied as consumer credit developed. This hypothesis is supported by the fact that terms are used in consumer credit literature without being clearly defined or explained. As a result, the terminology is not consistently used from one publication to another. Thus, it appears desirable to use terminology as defined in mathematics of finance.[2]

Simple Interest

Simple interest is the product of the principal, the time in years, and the annual rate of interest. For example, the interest on $1,200 for one year with the rate of interest at 6 per cent per annum equals $72.

With simple interest, the amount of interest is computed on the principal for the entire period of the loan. Only one payment of interest is made when the loan matures. Thus, simple interest is suitable for only short periods of time, usually one year or less.[3]

When simple interest is computed for part of a year, the "time in years" is a fraction, the numerator being the term of the loan in days and the denominator the days in a year. When 365 days (366 days in a leap year) are used in the denominator of the fraction, the amount is called "exact" simple interest. For example, with a 60-day loan, using a fraction of 60 ÷ 365 (366 in a leap year) gives the "exact" amount of interest on the loan. When 360 days are used in the denominator of the fraction, the amount is called "ordinary" simple interest. Thus, with a 60-day loan, using a fraction of 60 ÷ 360 gives the "ordinary" simple interest due on the loan.

---

[2] John R. Brake, *Interest Rate Terminology and Calculation,* Mich. State Univ., Agr. Econ. Rept. No. 13, Mar., 1966, pp. 3–4.

[3] It should be noted that simple interest does not correctly describe the nominal rate, as usage often implies. The nominal rate will be defined later.

The 360 days is usually used in computing simple interest by commercial lenders due to the ease of computation. The number 360 has 22 factors (2, 3, 4, 5, 6, 8, 9, 10, 12, 15, 18, 20, 24, 30, 36, 40, 45, 60, 72, 90, 120, and 180) whereas 365 has only two (5 and 73) and 366 only three (2, 3, and 61). Thus, computations can be performed more easily by using 360 than by using 365 or 366.

Since 360 is smaller than 365 (366), ordinary simple interest is always slightly greater than exact simple interest. Lenders also prefer ordinary simple interest for this reason.

Compound Interest

Compound interest is involved in saving or in use of credit whenever interest is paid more than once during the period involved. For example, compound interest is involved when interest is paid two, four, twelve, or n times per year on a savings account, or on a loan. With this type of situation, interest paid for one period, either in cash or by adding it to one's account, is said to be *converted* to principal, or *compounded*. The interval between successive conversions is called the *conversion period*. The total amount due at the end of a conversion period is called the *compound amount*. *Compound interest* is the difference between the compound amount and the beginning principal. The *compound interest rate* is the rate per conversion period which is charged on the outstanding balance for that period; i.e. the compound interest divided by the outstanding balance.

Compound interest is usually thought of in relation to growth of an investment. This subject was discussed in some detail in Chapter 2. However, compound interest has similar significance in use of credit. Borrowing is, of course, the converse of saving and, therefore, both are affected by the same principles.

The similarity of the effect of compound interest on borrowing and saving can be demonstrated, as suggested by Brake,[4] by use of an example such as is presented in Table 7.1. An installment loan of $100 with interest at 1 per cent per month is assumed. It is assumed that no installment payments are made during the year so the results can be readily checked against Appendix Table 1, which shows the amount of 1 at compound interest.

At the end of the first period (month) the interest due is $1.00

---

[4] Brake, p. 23.

TABLE 7.1

ILLUSTRATION OF COMPOUND INTEREST ON A $100 INSTALLMENT LOAN WITH
INTEREST AT 1 PER CENT PER MONTH

Period	Beginning Balance	Interest	Periodic Installment			Ending Balance
			Total	Interest	Principal	
1	$100.0000	$1.0000	$0	$0	$0	$101.0000
2	101.0000	1.0100	0	0	0	102.0100
3	102.0100	1.0201	0	0	0	103.0301
4	103.0301	1.0303	0	0	0	104.0604
5	104.0603	1.0406	0	0	0	105.1010
6	105.1006	1.0510	0	0	0	106.1520
7	106.1516	1.0615	0	0	0	107.2135
8	107.2131	1.0721	0	0	0	108.2856
9	108.2851	1.0829	0	0	0	109.3685
10	109.3679	1.0937	0	0	0	110.4622
11	110.4616	1.1046	0	0	0	111.5668
12	111.5662	1.1157	0	0	0	112.6825

(see Table 7.1). Since no payment is made, the interest is converted to principal, making the ending balance $101.00. Interest for the second period is increased, therefore, to $1.01, which in turn is converted to principal, making the ending balance $102.01. This process continues each month and at the end of the year the compound amount is $112.68. Thus, the compound interest for the year is $12.68, 68 cents more than with 12 per cent simple interest.

Now compare Table 7.1 with Appendix Table 1. The balance at the end of the first period given in Table 7.1 is $101.00. The comparable figure in Appendix Table 1 is found by moving down the column headed n to 1 and across to the column headed 1%. Since the appendix table is set up on the basis of $1.00, the figures in the body of the table must be multiplied by 100 to make them comparable with those in Table 7.1. Multiplying $1.01 by 100 gives $101.00, the same as the ending balance for period 1 in Table 7.1. Similarly, the balance at the end of period 12 given in Table 7.1 is $112.68. Moving down column n in Appendix Table 1 to 12 and across to 1% we find 1.12682503, which when multiplied by 100, and rounded, gives $112.68, the same as the ending balance for period 12 in Table 7.1. Since the compound amount of a $100 loan is the same as the amount of $100 saved at compound interest, it is evident that compounding interest has the same effect when money is borrowed as when it is saved.

The effect of compound interest involved in installment loans is the same regardless of whether the interest is converted to princi-

pal periodically, as in the above example, or whether it is paid at
the end of each period. This point may be illustrated by comparing
two $1200 loans, each with a quoted annual rate of 6 per cent.
Interest is payable annually on loan No. 1 and semiannually on
loan No. 2. Thus, interest payments each year on the two loans are
as follows:

	Loan No. 1	Loan No. 2
Interest paid end of 6 months	0	$36
Interest paid end of year	$72	36
Total	$72	$72

Obviously, the dollar amount of interest paid on the two loans
is the same—$72. However, half of the interest on loan No. 2 was
paid at midyear. Therefore, borrower No. 2 did not have use of the
$36 in his business the last six months of the year as did borrower
No. 1. Since he was borrowing money at 6 per cent interest, paying
the $36 at midyear cost borrower No. 2, in effect, $1.08 more than
borrower No. 1. In other words, compounding the interest semiannually on loan No. 2 increased the interest cost by $1.08.

In the above example, borrower No. 2 paid $36 interest sem-
iannually on his $1,200 loan with a quoted annual rate of 6 per
cent. The $36 may be obtained by *converting* the quoted annual
rate of 6 per cent to 3 per cent semiannually. In other words, the 6
per cent annual rate may be *compounded* semiannually and used to
find the amount of semiannual interest. Such a periodic rate (rate
per period) is referred to as the *compound rate,* the *true rate,* and
the *actuarial rate.* The three terms are synonymous. Thus, the *true*
interest rate is the interest rate applied to the principal each payment period. Therefore, an annual rate can be correctly referred to
as a true rate only when payments are made on an annual basis.
This point should be given special attention since the term "true
rate" is often incorrectly used in writings pertaining to interest.

Nominal and Effective Rates of Interest

When interest is paid two or more times per year, the quoted
annual rate is called the *nominal annual rate,* which is usually
shortened to the nominal rate. Thus, if a loan is payable semiannually and the quoted annual rate is 6 per cent, the true rate is 3 per
cent, and the nominal rate is 6 per cent. When rates are quoted on a
periodic basis, the nominal rate represents the periodic rates con-

verted to an annual basis. For example, if the true interest rate is $\frac{1}{2}$ per cent per month, the nominal rate is 6 per cent.

As indicated in the discussion of compound interest, when interest is converted more than once per year, the compound interest is greater than when it is compounded annually. For example, with $100 invested for one year at 6 per cent, compounded annually, the actual interest earned is $6.00. However, if the quoted rate is compounded semiannually the actual interest earned is $6.09. Thus, because of the effect of compounding, the actual rate earned is 6.09 per cent while the nominal rate is 6.0 per cent. The rate of interest actually earned in a year is called the *effective annual rate* of interest. The effective rate is obtained by compounding the true rate for a period of one year.

When the true rate is compounded more than once a year the result is an effective annual rate which is larger than the nominal rate. The two rates are equivalent, however, since they produce the same amount of interest. Thus, a nominal rate of 6 per cent compounded semiannually is equivalent to an effective rate of 6.09 per cent.

The degree to which the effective rate exceeds the nominal rate depends upon the level of the interest rate and the frequency of conversion. The difference between the two rates is relatively small at low levels (assuming the same number of conversions of interest to principal per year), but increases as the rate increases. With a nominal rate of 6 per cent, the difference is .09 percentage points (the effective rate is 6.09 per cent) when the conversion is semiannual, approximately 0.136 percentage points when conversion is quarterly, approximately 0.168 percentage points when conversion is monthly, and approximately 0.183 percentage points when conversion is daily.[5] Thus, while the nominal rate provides a fairly good basis for comparing loans, the effective rate provides a more precise basis.

Discounted Loans

A lender sometimes will make what is called a discounted loan in which the interest is deducted from the principal at the time the loan is made. For example, a lender may make a $1,200 loan for one year discounted at 6 per cent. The borrower would receive $1,128

[5] H. E. Stelson, *Mathematics of Finance,* D. Van Nostrand Co., Inc., Princeton, N.J., 1963, p. 34.

($1,200 minus 6 per cent) and would pay the lender $1,200 at the end of the year. The 6 per cent rate in this case is called the *discount interest rate*. Thus, in computing the actual amount of interest to be paid, the discount interest rate is applied to the maturity value of the loan; i.e. the value of the note. In contrast, simple interest is figured on the principal—$1,128 in the example. As a result, the simple interest rate on a given discounted loan is always higher than the discount interest rate.

Add-on Interest

With the usual short-term installment plan loan, interest is calculated on the beginning balance and then added to the principal to obtain the amount to be repaid in equal periodic installments. For example, a lender may make a $1,200 installment plan loan to be repaid in 12 equal monthly payments. If he uses a 6 per cent rate, he would add $72 to the $1,200, and the payments would be $106 per month. In this example the 6 per cent rate used by the lender is correctly referred to as a 6 per cent *add-on interest rate*.

It should be noted that an add-on interest rate is not a nominal rate. As indicated above, a nominal rate is figured on the principal balance outstanding, with recognition being given to periodic principal payments. In contrast, the add-on rate is applied to the initial principal, disregarding principal payments which are made periodically throughout the term of the loan.

DETERMINING THE NOMINAL INTEREST RATE

As indicated by the preceding discussion, interest is charged in many different ways, and the method used has a significant influence on the amount of interest paid and on the interest rate on a loan. Interest paid on a discounted loan is greater, other things being equal, than with compound interest. Large differences prevail among various types of installment plan loans. On one type the interest charged is computed on an annual basis on the outstanding balance. On a second type an annual rate is used, but it is applied on the original principal, with no reduction being made for payments on the principal during the year. The amount of interest on the second type of installment plan loan is about twice the amount paid on the first type. Hence, with different types of loans and methods of charging interest, it is difficult to make comparisons. The objective of this section is to present material which will aid in finding the nominal rate which is being charged.

Equal Payment, Regularly Timed Loans

There are a number of methods for determining the approximate nominal interest rate on installment plan loans when payments are equal and regularly timed. Three of these are considered here. Some are more accurate than others and, in general, the methods which give the greatest accuracy tend to be the most complex. Thus, the degree of accuracy desired should be considered in selecting the method to use.

THE CONSTANT RATIO EQUATION

The constant ratio equation can be used to approximate the nominal interest rate when the other terms are known. It is as follows:

$$\frac{2In}{Bt(n+1)} = \text{Approximate nominal interest rate} \qquad (7.1)$$

where I is the interest or finance charge, n is the number of periodic payments required to liquidate the loan, B is the beginning principal (face amount) of the loan, and t is the term of the loan in years. Use of this equation may be illustrated by the example in the discussion of add-on interest. The principal was $1,200, the finance charges were $72, the number of payments was 12, and the term of the loan was 1 year. We, therefore, have

$$\frac{(2)(72)(12)}{(1,200)(1)(12+1)} = 11.0769 \text{ per cent.}$$

The constant ratio equation is based on the assumption that the ratio of principal to interest in each periodic payment is the same as the ratio of the initial principal to the total interest or finance charge.[6] The assumption is not in accord with the facts, however, since with an even-payment installment plan loan the interest portion of each periodic payment gradually decreases and the principal portion gradually increases. Moreover, the longer the term of a loan, the greater the error in the assumption upon which

---

[6] *Ibid.*, p. 201.

the constant ratio equation is based. Therefore, Equation 7.1 gives only an approximation of the nominal interest rate, and a relatively poor one at that, particularly for long-term loans. The rate obtained is usually a little larger than the actual nominal rate.

THE STELSON EQUATION

A more accurate equation than the one just discussed has been presented by Stelson:

$$\frac{2Im}{n(B+a)} = \frac{2I}{t(B+a)} = \text{Approximate nominal interest rate} \qquad (7.2)^7$$

where m is the number of payment periods per year, a is the amount of each periodic payment, I is the interest or finance charge, n is the number of periodic payments required to liquidate the loan, B is the beginning principal, and t is the term of the loan in years. Using our add-on interest example, B is \$1,200, I is \$72, m is 12, n is 12, t is 1, and a is \$106. Therefore,

$$\frac{(2)(72)(12)}{(12)(1,200+106)} = \frac{(2)(72)}{(1)(1,200+106)} = 11.0260 \text{ per cent.}$$

According to Stelson, Equation 7.2 will always give a closer approximation to the nominal interest rate than the constant ratio equation.[8] The rate will be on the high side except when n is very small.

THE DIRECT RATIO EQUATION

While somewhat more complex, the direct ratio equation gives a very close approximation to the nominal interest rate.[9] The equation is as follows:

$$\frac{6Im}{3B(n+1)+(n-1)I} = \text{Approximate nominal interest rate} \qquad (7.3)^{10}$$

where I is the interest or finance charge, m is the number of periodic payments per year, B is the beginning principal, and n is the number of periodic payments required to liquidate the loan.

Applying this equation to our add-on interest example, we have

---

[7] *Ibid.*, p. 76. The m was added by John R. Brake to put the interest rate on a nominal basis. See: Brake, p. 16.

[8] Stelson, p. 76.

[9] *Ibid.*, p. 78.

[10] Brake, p. 17. A similar equation is given by Stelson, p. 79.

$$\frac{(6)(72)(12)}{(3)(1200)(12 + 1) + (12 - 1)(72)} = 10.8926 \text{ per cent.}$$

The direct ratio equation assumes that the amount of interest in each installment is distributed according to the sum of digits. For example, in a 12-month installment loan the first installment is assumed to include $12\frac{2}{78}$ of the total interest, the second installment $11\frac{1}{78}$ of the total interest, and so on until the last installment includes only $\frac{1}{78}$ of the total interest charged on the loan. The approximate nominal interest obtained by using the direct ratio equation is always very slightly too small.

A modification of the direct ratio equation

$$\frac{2I}{B(n + 1)} \left[\frac{3B(n + 1) + (n + 2)I}{3B(n + 1) + (2n + 1)I} \right] m = \text{Approximate nominal} \quad (7.4)^{11}$$
$$\text{interest rate}$$

gives a very accurate approximation of the nominal interest rate. The nominal rate derived by use of this equation is, however, very slightly large. Applying Equation 7.4 to our add-on interest example gives an approximate nominal rate of 10.9046 per cent.

Comparing the approximate nominal interest rates for our add-on installment plan loan derived by use of the methods outlined above provides an indication of the relative accuracy of the equations. The rates were:

The constant ratio equation	11.0769 per cent
The Stelson equation	11.0260 per cent
The direct ratio equation	10.8926 per cent
The direct ratio equation, modified	10.9046 per cent

The nominal rate is actually 10.90 per cent.

Equal Payment, Irregularly Timed Loans

With some installment plan loans, payments are equal and regularly timed except for the last. The last payment is regularly timed, but the amount may be more or less than the preceding payments. In such cases the Stelson equation can be used to calculate the approximate nominal interest rate by letting a represent the amount of the last payment.[12]

---

[11] Stelson, p. 79. I have added m to the equation to put the rate on a nominal basis.

[12] *Ibid.*, p. 77.

A more accurate equation, corresponding to Equation 7.3, which also may be used, is:

$$\frac{6Im}{3n(B + a) + I(n - 4)} = \text{Approximate nominal interest rate} \quad (7.5)^{13}$$

where I refers to the interest or finance charge, m is the number of periodic payments per year, n is the number of periodic payments required to liquidate the loan, B is the beginning principal, and a is used to represent the last payment.

Some installment plan loans are set up so that payments do not commence immediately. For example, on a monthly installment loan, payments may not start until the third month. In such cases the following equation may be used to obtain the approximate nominal interest rate:

$$\frac{2I}{(t + F)(B + a)} = \text{Approximate nominal interest rate.} \quad (7.6)^{14}$$

I is the total interest or finance charge, t is the term of the loan in years, F is the proportion of the year which elapses before payments start, B is the beginning principal of the loan, and a is the amount of the periodic payment.

When payments on an installment loan follow a specified but irregular schedule the following equation will give an approximation of the nominal interest rate:

$$\frac{12In}{BS} = \text{Approximate nominal interest rate.} \quad (7.7)^{15}$$

I, n, and B are used as defined above and S represents the sum of the numbers of those months in the future when payments are to be made.

CARRYING CHARGES AND FEES

Instead of interest as such, some time payment plans involve carrying charges which are added to the balance due. Carrying charges are often called by other names, such as "time differential" payments and credit or finance charges. In some cases, inspection fees and sales commissions include some carrying charges. The car-

---

[13] *Ibid.*, p. 79.
[14] Brake, p. 19.
[15] *Ibid.*, p. 20.

rying charge may take the form of a smaller discount, or an addition to the purchase price. If a percentage rate is used, it will be applied to the face amount of the loan rather than to the unpaid balance. Where carrying charges are involved, the cost of credit is almost always greater than where a loan is secured from a commercial bank, the Production Credit Association, or other conventional lender.

A carrying charge might well be considered a red flag calling for careful consideration and study of costs involved. An example will illustrate the cost of such credit. Assume you are going to trade your old tractor on a new one costing $2,250. The allowance on the old tractor is $1,000, leaving $1,250. A carrying charge of $125 is added, making a balance due of $1,375. Principal payments of $687.50 are due at the end of six months and of twelve months.

Substituting these figures in Equation 7.2, given above, gives

$$\frac{(2)(125)(2)}{(2)(1250 + 687.50)} = \frac{500}{3875} = 12.9 \text{ per cent}$$

as the approximate nominal rate of interest.

Occasionally, interest is charged in addition to the carrying charge. In such cases, interest usually is charged on the face amount of the loan plus the carrying charge, with the result that the actual interest charge is very high.

To figure the cost of credit, it is necessary to include in addition to the interest all fees and charges. The actual cost of a 5 per cent loan may be higher than that of a 7 per cent loan because of the heavy fees and charges on the first loan. Application fees, inspection fees, and other loan charges may easily amount to as much as the interest on a small loan for a short period. For example, loan fees and charges of $7.50 on a 5 per cent loan of $300 for four months are more than the interest. In consequence, comparisons of loans on a cost basis should always be made after all charges have been figured.

Minimum deposit requirements are still another factor accounting for differences in interest charges. If a bank specifies that $200 out of a $1,000 loan must be maintained on deposit, only $800 is used, and the interest should be figured as a percentage of $800, not of $1,000. In effect, however, such requirements are closely allied to service charges which are imposed by banks to compensate the bank for handling checks.

COMMISSIONS

Commissions may be either a flat fee or a fixed percentage of the principal. The fixed percentage commission by itself is economically unsound, yet it is the traditional and common method. Federally sponsored agencies have been eliminating the fixed percentage plan, but it is still commoner than it should be. The chief argument in favor of this method is that it is the easiest and simplest method of paying the individual or firm for negotiating a loan. But a flat charge of so much a loan would be more equitable because most of the expenses in handling a loan have little relation to the size of the loan.

If a flat charge of $50 a loan were made, the negotiator of a loan would get as much for making the $1,000 loan as for making the $10,000 loan. As far as the mechanics involved in making the loan are concerned, this equal compensation would be justified. At least it would be a more reasonable method than paying 1 per cent commission which would amount to only $10 on the one loan and $100 on the other loan. On the percentage basis there is an incentive not only to spend all the effort on the high value farms, but to encourage farmers in all instances to increase their askings because the larger the loan the larger the commission.

A combination of a flat charge and a percentage commission has some advantages over either method by itself. A small charge provides compensation for the loan expenses which do not vary with the amount involved, while a small percentage commission provides compensation for any added expenses, risk, and responsibility which increase with the size of the loan. A flat charge of $25 and a commission of one-fourth of 1 per cent would allow a commission of $27.50 on a $1,000 loan and $50 on a $10,000 loan.

QUESTIONS AND PROBLEMS

1. Why should a farmer be concerned with interest rates and loan costs in connection with use of credit?
2. Define interest and interest rate. What does interest include?
3. Discuss the reasons for variations in interest rates among various regions of the country.
4. What has happened to interest rates on farm mortgages since 1930? Why?

5. How do interest rates on farm loans compare with nonfarm interest rates? Discuss reasons for the differences and similarities.
6. Discuss the uniform interest rate question from the standpoint first of economic soundness and second of public policy.
7. Define and compare simple interest and compound interest.
8. Explain and compare compound interest rate, true interest rate, actuarial interest rate, nominal interest rate, effective interest rate, discount interest rate, and add-on interest rate.
9. Explain what is meant by the following terms as related to interest: convert, compound, conversion period, and compound amount.
10. Is interest compounded on an installment plan loan where periodic payments include both principal and interest? Explain.
11. An installment loan of $1,800 for 9 months is available at 6 per cent ($108). The loan requires principal payments of $200 at the end of each month for 9 months. What is the nominal interest rate? Show computations.
12. Set up an example of an equal payment, regularly timed installment plan loan and compute the approximate nominal interest rate using the constant ratio equation, the Stelson equation, and the two direct ratio equations. Show your computations.

REFERENCES

Botts, Ralph R., *Farmers' Handbook of Financial Calculations and Physical Measurements,* Farm Econ. Div., ERS, USDA, Handbook 230, 1962.

Brake, John R., *Interest Rate Terminology and Calculation,* Mich. State Univ. Agr. Econ. Dept. Rept. 13, 1966.

Cissell, Robert, and Cissell, Helen, *Mathematics of Finance,* Houghton Mifflin Co., Boston, 1956.

Dewey, John, "The Geometry of Capital and Interest: A Suggested Simplification," *The Amer. Econ. Rev.,* March, 1963, pp. 134–39.

Gilson, J. C., *The Cost of Credit,* Univ. of Manitoba Agr. Econ. Bul. 3, 1961.

Neifeld, M. R., *Neifeld's Guide to Installment Computations,* Mack Publ. Co., Easton, Pa., 1951.

Stelson, Hugh E., *Mathematics of Finance,* D. Van Nostrand Co., Inc., Princeton, N.J., 1957.

Trefftz, K. L., and Hills, E. J., *Mathematics of Business, Accounting, and Finance,* Harper and Brothers, New York, 1956.

NOTE: Attention is called to passage of Public Law 90–321, 90th Congress, S. 5, May 29, 1968, titled the *Consumer Credit Protection Act.* Title I of this act, referred to as the *Truth in Lending Act,* provides for disclosure of the cost of consumer credit, defined to include credit primarily for agricultural purposes. The method of determining the rate charged shall be in accordance with the regulations of the Board of Governors of the Federal Reserve System.

Chapter 8

REPAYMENT CAPACITY AS A GUIDE
IN USE OF CREDIT

CONSIDERATION of repayment aspects of using credit deserves more attention than it usually receives. The all-too-common feeling of unwarranted optimism which prevails when a loan is being made influences both the borrower and the lender. As a result production, prices, and income may be overestimated, and the difficulty that may be experienced by the borrower in meeting the loan payments on due dates may be underestimated.

Repayment capacity, the second *R* of credit, comprises the second test which should be applied in determining the amount of credit to be utilized. The question is, Can the loan be repaid in accordance with the terms of the note? Thus, two considerations are of paramount importance in repayment capacity: funds to repay the loan and terms under which repayment is to be made. Repayment capacity from the viewpoint of funds for repayment of loans is considered first, following which repayment terms are outlined. In the following chapter, ways of increasing repayment capacity are considered.

REPAYMENT CAPACITY RELATED TO USE OF CREDIT

Like *returns, repayment capacity* is considered in terms of *average* conditions expected to prevail during the period of the loan. It is recognized that conditions may vary considerably during the period, and that unforeseen conditions may develop. However, repayment capacity is analyzed before a loan is made. At that time the best one can do is estimate average costs, yields, prices, and income expected to prevail during the period of the loan and make the analysis on that basis. This leaves to risk-bearing ability, discussed subsequently, the role of "filling in" when repayment capacity is inadequate due to deviations from the average.

At first thought it may appear that if a loan is profitable, it could be repaid without difficulty. However, if credit is used to the point where net income is at a maximum—where marginal income is just sufficient to cover marginal costs—the marginal net income will be nil. How, then, is the principal amount of the loan to be repaid? The answer depends partly upon the use made of the capital loaned. In other words, the type of assets purchased with borrowed funds influences the amount of indebtedness that can be carried. Assets which are paid for from *gross* income in effect "pay for themselves." Loans for such purposes may be termed *self-liquidating loans*. Other assets must be paid for from *net* income, and loans made to acquire such assets are *not* self-liquidating. Repayment capacity as related to each of these types of assets is discussed in the following sections.

Repayment of Self-liquidating Loans

A self-liquidating loan is one made to an individual, corporation, or other business entity operating a profitable business for acquiring goods or services which are expended or used up in the production process. The goods may be expended or used up completely in one production period or they may be used for a number of years. Seed for annual crops is an example of the former, machinery and improvements are examples of the latter.

Assuming normal production and profitable farm operation, funds used to acquire goods and services which are expended in the production process are recouped as part of gross cash income when farm products are sold. For example, consider Farm Business M, assumed to be earning a 6 per cent return on capital over and above all other variable and fixed costs, including management. Assume, further, that Farmer M borrows $1,000 at 6 per cent annual interest to buy feed for hogs, and that the hogs are sold four months later. The $1,000 plus $20 interest will be received as a part of the gross income from the sale of the hogs. Hence, $1,020 of gross income will be available to repay the $1,000 feed loan plus $20 interest. Therefore, as this example illustrates, loans for operating expenses are self-liquidating, providing the business is paying its way. Similarly, the original capital investment in intermediate assets, such as machinery and breeding stock, and in improvements, such as buildings, is returned to the operator over a period of years as part of gross income. If loan repayment is scheduled to coincide with return of the original capital investment, loans for such purposes also are self-liquidating. However, repayment of loans for intermediate-term purposes usually is scheduled at a somewhat faster rate than the rate of depreciation and, therefore, such loans are only partially self-liquidating.

As indicated by these examples, loans that are self-liquidating are those for purchase of goods and services which depreciate, or are *used up*, in the production process. The original investment or purchase price, or wage paid in the case of labor, becomes a part of gross income as the products they have been used to produce are sold. Therefore, it is evident that such loans are paid from gross income and *as long as the business is profitable* funds will be available to repay the loans. The fact that the business must be profitable is emphasized since if such is not the case, the self-liquidating loan turns into one which is not self-liquidating. When this occurs, repayment becomes even more difficult than with the usual farm loan which is not self-liquidating since the resources acquired with the credit have been lost, thereby reducing the earning capacity of the operator.

Repayment of Loans Which Are Not Self-liquidating

A loan which is *not* self-liquidating is one made to acquire goods which are not expended or used up in the production process. A loan to purchase good land (which does not erode or otherwise deteriorate as it is used in production) is an example of a loan which is not self-liquidating. The concept involved can be illustrated by further reference to Farm Business M referred to in the preceding section. Assume that Farmer M borrows $1,000 at 6 per cent annual interest to buy good land. Since capital in Farm Business M was assumed to earn a 6 per cent return, the $1,000 invested in land will produce $60 of gross income annually, just enough to pay the interest. Hence, there is no gross income to use for repayment of the $1,000 loan, as was the case when a $1,000 loan was used to buy hog feed. Thus, a loan for purchasing land is *not* self-liquidating. It may contribute indirectly to repayment capacity by enabling the farmer to produce more *net* income than would be possible without use of the resources. But the land is not gradually used up in the production process. It does not depreciate and thereby become a part of the gross cash flow available to meet principal payments on the loan. Instead, good land continues as a "perpetual" resource to be used again and again in the production process. Since it is not used up—does not become a part of the commodities which are sold—it only produces an "annual rent" or interest on investment. As equity increases, the amount of "annual rent" required for interest payments gradually declines and net income gradually increases, thereby somewhat increasing repayment capacity.

How then are loans which are not self-liquidating to be repaid? They must be paid from *net* cash income of the family. The fifth step of the budget process outlined in Chapter 5 gives the anticipated net cash income—the amount available for living expenses, income and social security taxes, principal payments on loans which are not self-liquidating, and the like. By deducting estimated living expenses and taxes, an indication is obtained as to the amount of net cash income which will be available for debt payments. Note that loan payments are subservient to minimum living expenses and taxes. The lender can expect nothing by way of repayment until these two prior claims have been satisfied.

Repayment Capacity May Limit Profitable Use of Credit

Repayment capacity may limit the use of credit to less than can be profitably used in the business. The limitation stems from loans which are not self-liquidating. They must be paid from *net* income, so the amount of such loans is governed by the net income available for debt repayment.

These concepts can be illustrated by the *dairy-hog farmer* and the *wheat-dairy farmer* examples discussed in Chapter 5. It will be recalled that the dairy-hog farmer operated in the central Corn Belt and had successfully used credit to expand his business. The wheat-dairy farmer was located in the Great Plains area and was considering use of credit to buy the improved quarter section which he was renting. Pertinent summary figures for the two farms are given in Table 8.1.

The net income of the dairy-hog farmer available for loan payments was estimated to average about $1,000 over the next few years. Principal payments on his real estate loans totaled $319. The entire amount of the chattel loans was used for livestock, feed, and operating expenses—items which, with normal production and income, produce funds to meet repayments, and which are repaid from gross rather than net income. A comfortable balance was left above living expenses, taxes, and debt payments, indicating this family had adequate repayment capacity to carry the obligations they had incurred.

TABLE 8.1

ESTIMATED ANNUAL INCOME, LIVING EXPENSES, AND BALANCE FOR DEBT
PAYMENTS OF TWO FARMERS

Item	Dairy-Hog Farmer *	Wheat-Dairy Farmer
Estimated Average Annual Net Cash Income.........	$3,500	$2,700
Living Expenses, and Income and Social Security Taxes.....................................	2,500	1,500
Balance Available for Loan Payments................	$1,000	$1,200
Loan Payments (principal):		
Chattel loans...................................	....	$1,000 †
Real estate loans..............................	319	89
Balance...................................	$ 681	$ 111

* Source: Aaron G. Nelson, *Credit As a Tool for the Agricultural Producer*, N. Cent. Reg. Ext. Publ. No. 4; and Great Plains Agr. Council Publ. No. 15, 1957, pp. 32–33.

† The reader might wonder why this chattel loan payment is shown, since, as pointed out in the discussion, chattel loans are repaid from gross rather than net income. It will be recalled that, in the example, to purchase the 160 acres would necessitate placing a $7,000 mortgage on the chattel property as a means of raising funds. Since, if the quarter section were purchased, the funds would be used to acquire real estate, the loan would have to be repaid from net rather than from gross income.

Turning to the wheat-dairy farm example, whether their repayment capacity would support purchase of the quarter section depended upon how frugally the family was willing to live. The loan plans extended repayment over as long a period as practicable considering the security and other factors involved—7 years for the chattel loan and 35 years for the real estate loan. Therefore, any further easing of repayment requirements from this source was **not** practical. If the family was willing to live on about $1,500 per year, the budget plans indicated they would have sufficient repayment capacity to meet the loan payments. The standard of living provided by $1,500 is considerably below average for the Great Plains area, however, and unless the family was willing to make the sacrifice to own their home and farmstead, they would not have the required repayment capacity to support the loans. This example illustrates how repayment capacity may limit use of credit even where it is profitable to use the borrowed funds.

As was indicated above, repayment capacity is dependent not only on funds for meeting loan payments, but also on repayment terms of the loan. The 7-year term for the chattel loan and the 35-year term for the real estate loan were important in the repayment capacity of the wheat-dairy farmer. We turn now to a consideration of repayment terms used in extension of credit.

Repayment Terms

Repayment terms are set forth in the note signed by the borrower at the time the loan is obtained. When a note is not involved, the terms of the loan may be evidenced by the customary credit policy of the lender—such as the policy of a business in handling charge accounts. From the standpoint of repayment capacity, the time when the loan is to be repaid, or the schedule of payments, is of paramount importance.

Short- and Intermediate-term Loan Payments

Short-term credit payments may take a number of different forms. Open account credit provided by merchants and dealers is used widely in agriculture. Generally the borrower is billed every 30 days, at which time the loan is due. Usually there is not a specific charge for this type of credit unless it runs for more than 30 days. Some oil dealers customarily grant credit to farmers for 90 days. Some feed, seed, fertilizer, and other supply dealers also offer extended open account credit, with payment to be made after harvest or when livestock are sold. Interest may or may not be charged in such cases.

Installment loans are used to a considerable extent in agriculture, particularly to buy intermediate assets such as machinery and breeding livestock. Some of these loans are formalized with written contracts in the form of conditional sales contracts, open notes, or other types of written promises to pay. Repayment of such loans is sometimes set up on an irregular basis. Some farm machinery companies, for example, schedule payments at nonregular intervals. However, payments are usually scheduled on an equal, regularly timed basis. Loans to dairymen for purchase of dairy cows and operating expenses, for example, generally are repaid on a monthly basis over a period that may run from one to three years. Such loans are adjusted to the dairyman's monthly or semimonthly cream or milk checks. Agreements in some instances are made by the lender with the dairyman and the creamery or milk-buying agency, calling for the direct payment to the lender of a certain portion of the borrower's cream or milk check. Although this arrangement involves extra bookkeeping it does make the loan and the retirement plan unusually attractive to the lender.

Loans to stockmen for operating expenses and the purchase of range cattle and sheep are usually made on an annual or semiannual basis. Actually the loans mature and are renewed each summer or fall when the annual sales occur. When the loans are substantial in amount, they are almost continuous except that they are reduced at marketing time and increased during the year to cover operating expenses. Loans for 3-month intervals, although possible, would be practically the same as 12-month loans because there would be little possibility of payment except at the annual marketing period, unless the lender wanted to sell out the borrower. Certain bank examiners, failing to recognize this fact, would not allow loans of over six months in the range territory. The 6-month loans to the cattlemen in this area were supposed to come due in March and again in September at the time of marketing. In March, however, the banks holding the loans found that renewal was a mere formality because many of the cattlemen were still snowbound, some of them not even receiving their mail at this time of year because roads and trails were impassable. In summer, too, with increased operating expenses to handle the calf crop and to make hay, there was little opportunity for payment. But when the annual sales were made in the fall, the banks were able to settle up and arrange a new year of financing if they so desired. Thus it is not the stated term of the loan which counts, but the natural sales period of the borrower; 12-month loans may be for all intents and purposes as liquid as 6-month loans.

Use of *budgeted loans* is increasing in agriculture. The borrower and lender sit down together prior to the time funds are needed for crop or livestock production and prepare a budget indicating the amount of credit required and when it will be needed. They also estimate the amount and timing of income which can be applied on the loan. The steps involved are outlined in some detail in the next chapter.

Long-term Loan Payments

Three methods commonly used in repaying long-term loans are the *straight end payment, partial payment,* and *amortization plan of payment.* A fourth method, the *variable* or *flexible plan,* has been used in a few instances in the past.

STRAIGHT END PAYMENT LOANS

The straight end, or lump-sum, payment loan calls for payment of the entire loan on the expiration of the term. Historically, the traditional farm mortgage loan was a 5-year end payment loan. The borrower paid the interest each year, and every five years he extended, renewed, refinanced, or paid the loan; usually the loan was renewed or refinanced for a larger or smaller amount according to the losses or profits of the borrower during the preceding five years. Every five years the borrower not only had to find a new lender, if the previous one wanted his money, but even with extensions and renewals, he usually had another commission to pay.

With improvements made in credit service to agriculture, the 5-year end payment loan gradually gave way to longer and modified end payment plans. A partial payment loan has become common, particularly among life insurance companies.

PARTIAL PAYMENT LOANS

The partial payment loan is an end payment loan with small fixed principal payments or installments each year during the 10- to 20-year period of the loan. Principal payments made each year are not large enough to completely repay the loan, with the result that a fairly large amount, referred to as a "balloon" payment, is due at the end of the loan term.

A typical loan of this kind on a well-improved productive farm would be a $20,000 loan for a 20-year term, with interest at 6 per cent annually on the outstanding balance, and with principal payments of $500 per year. The first year the borrower would pay $1,200 interest and $500 principal, or $1,700; the second year, $1,170 interest and $500 of principal, or $1,670; and the twentieth year, $630 of interest and $500 of principal, or $1,130. With this payment schedule, one-half the principal will have been repaid in installments, so when the loan comes due in 20 years, the "balloon" payment would be $10,000. Although there are many varieties of the partial payment plan, the main provisions found in most of them are similar to those outlined.

The partial payment loan meets the need of lenders who have a feeling of uncertainty about the future, a desire to have their farm mortgage loans gradually reduced, and a need for the liquidity provided by a 10- to 20-year loan.

AMORTIZATION LOANS

The amortization plan is a more extensive application of the partial payment plan. Amortization, strictly speaking, means killing by degrees, which may be interpreted as paying a mortgage by a series of installments. It is customary to set up installments on an annual or semiannual basis, though quarterly or monthly plans are sometimes used. Any period can be used which is agreeable to both the lender and borrower. Each installment is made up of principal and interest. The interest portion is just adequate to cover the interest due on the outstanding balance of the loan. The excess of each payment over the interest for the period is the amount by which the principal is reduced. The amount of this principal payment is the amortization.

Two amortization plans, the even payment and the decreasing payment, are used by lenders. The *decreasing plan of amortization,* illustrated in Table 8.2, provides for fixed, principal payments and declining interest payments on the outstanding balance. It is a simple partial payment loan with the payments continued until the loan is completely repaid. The distinctive difference between this type and the even payment plan is that the total payments decrease each time. Where the borrower is able to pay the higher initial installments and the lender has some doubt about future income and values, this decreasing payment type is especially well suited. It has the further advantage of being easier to compute and to understand at any point of time during the existence of the loan. The borrower can visualize quickly the effect which his annual payment has on the outstanding balance. In addition, there is a psychological

TABLE 8.2

EXAMPLE OF LOAN AMORTIZATION TABLE—DECREASING PAYMENT PLAN. PRINCIPAL, $1,000; INTEREST RATE, 5%, 35 YEARS; ANNUAL PAYMENTS

Annual Installment Number	Total Installment	Interest	Principal Payment	Unpaid Balance
1...................	$79.00	$50.00	$29.00	$971.00
2...................	77.55	48.55	29.00	942.00
3...................	76.10	47.10	29.00	913.00
10.................	65.95	36.95	29.00	710.00
30.................	36.95	7.95	29.00	130.00
34.................	31.15	2.15	29.00	14.00
35.................	14.70	.70	14.00	0.00

advantage in the reduction of the total annual payments; it gives the borrower a definite sense of progress to have each payment lower than the previous one.

The *even payment plan of amortization,* illustrated in Table 8.3, calls for equal payments each year, with a larger proportion of each succeeding payment representing principal and a smaller amount representing interest. On a $1,000 loan with interest at 5 per cent annually, written for a 35-year term on an even payment amortization basis, the annual installment is $61.07. The loan is completely paid at the end of 35 years if the annual payments are made regularly for this period. The first payment of $61.07 is divided between interest of $50 and principal of $11.07, which means that the interest payment is 5 per cent and the principal payment is 1.107 per cent. On the next payment, however, the

TABLE 8.3

EXAMPLE OF LOAN AMORTIZATION TABLE—EVEN PAYMENT PLAN. PRINCIPAL, $1,000; INTEREST RATE, 5%, 35 YEARS; ANNUAL INSTALLMENTS

Annual Installment Number	Total Installment	Interest	Principal Payment	Unpaid Balance
1...................	$61.07	$50.00	$11.07	$988.93
2...................	61.07	49.45	11.62	977.31
3...................	61.07	48.87	12.20	965.11
10.................	61.07	43.90	17.17	860.79
30.................	61.07	15.51	45.56	264.60
34.................	61.07	5.69	55.38	58.41
35.................	61.07	2.92	58.41	0.00

amount of interest due is less, $49.45, because the outstanding balance is less. The interest of $49.45 is 5 per cent of $988.93 for a 1-year period. Since the interest payment is less, the principal payment is more because the total payment is always the same under the even payment plan.

With the amount of the total installment given, the other figures shown in Table 8.3 can be readily calculated. But where does one obtain the amount of the total installment—the $61.07 given in Table 8.3? Mathematical equations and tabular material enable one to calculate the total installment without much difficulty.

The equation for calculating the annual payment on an even payment plan loan is

$$P = B \frac{1}{a_{\overline{n}|i}} \qquad (8.1)[1]$$

where P represents the amount of the annual payment (installment), B the face amount of the loan, n the number of years for which the loan is written, and i the annual interest rate. The symbol $\frac{1}{a_{\overline{n}|i}}$, which is read 1 divided by a sub n at rate i, represents the annuity which 1 will purchase for n years with an annual interest rate i. In terms of loan amortization the symbol represents the annual total payment (installment), per dollar borrowed, for n years with annual interest at rate i. Values for the symbol $\frac{1}{a_{\overline{n}|i}}$ are given in Appendix Table 3. To use the table find the number of years for which the loan was written in the column headed n and move across the table to the column headed by the interest rate for the loan.

We are now ready to use Equation 8.1 to compute the annual installment for the loan referred to in Table 8.3. Substituting the appropriate figures in the equation, we have

$$P = 1{,}000 \times 0.06107171$$
$$P = 61.07171$$

The 0.06107171 is found in Appendix Table 3 by moving down the column headed n to 35 and across to the column headed 5%.

Equation 8.1 is not flexible enough to cover situations where payments are made more than once each year. When a loan is amortized by means of more frequent payments the following equation may be used:

---

[1] Justin H. Moore, *Handbook of Financial Mathematics*, Prentice-Hall, Inc., Englewood Cliffs, N.J., p. 169.

$$\frac{P}{m} = B\frac{1}{a_{\overline{nm}|\frac{j}{m}}}. \qquad (8.2)[2]$$

In this equation the terms have the same representations as in Equation 8.1 and, in addition, m represents the number of payments of principal and interest per year (and also the number of times the interest is compounded per year, which is assumed to be the same as the number of payments) and j represents the nominal interest rate.

If the loan referred to in Table 8.3 were amortized on a semiannual basis rather than on an annual basis, the appropriate figures substituted in Equation 8.2 would give

$$\frac{P}{2} = 1,000\frac{1}{a_{\overline{35\times2}|\frac{.05}{2}}}$$

$$\frac{P}{2} = 1,000\frac{1}{a_{\overline{70}|.025}}$$

$$\frac{P}{2} = 1,000 \times 0.03039712$$

$$\frac{P}{2} = 30.40$$

$$P = 60.80.$$

The semiannual installment would be $30.40 compared with the annual installment of $61.07, the smaller total payment per year with the semiannual payment being due to the more frequent payment of interest.

Statements by lenders often show the total installment on loans amortized on an even-payment basis without showing a breakdown of the principal and interest. The amount of principal in any one amortization payment (regardless of the number of payments made during the year) can be found by using the equation

$$\text{Principal payment} = \frac{P}{m}v^m\left(n - h + \frac{1}{m}\right)\left(\text{at rate }\frac{j}{m}\right) \qquad (8.3)[3]$$

where P/m represents the periodic payment of principal and interest made m times per year, n represents the term of the loan in years,

[2] *Ibid.*, p. 344.
[3] *Ibid.*, p. 360.

and h represents the number of years payments, including the payment under consideration, have been made. The use of this equation, including the role of the symbol v, may be clarified by an example in which it is used to compute the amount of the principal payment in installment number 2 of Table 8.3. Substituting appropriate figures in Equation 8.3 we have

$$\text{Principal payment} = \frac{61.07}{1} v^1 \left(35 - 2 + \frac{1}{1}\right)\left(\text{at rate } \frac{.05}{1}\right)$$
$$= 61.07v^{34} \text{ (at rate .05)}$$
$$= 61.07 \times 0.19035480$$
$$= 11.62, \text{ the same as given in Table 8.3.}$$

The value of v^{34} (at rate .05) is obtained by reference to Appendix Table 2, which gives the present value of 1 at compound interest. Move down the column headed n to 34 and across to the column headed 5%.

The amount of interest in any installment can be obtained, of course, by subtracting the principal payment from the total payment.

VARIABLE OR FLEXIBLE PAYMENT LOANS

Loans which call for payments of interest, or of principal, or of both which are scheduled to fluctuate with crop yields or income are designated as variable or flexible payment loans. Loans which provide for optional payments by the borrower, although they are variable payments in one sense, are not included in this group. The development of the variable payment loan was stimulated by the difficulties which lending agencies experienced with fixed payment mortgages of all types in areas such as the Great Plains where annual income fluctuations have been exceedingly wide.

The chief obstacle in the development of the variable payment mortgage has been in finding a satisfactory factor to which the variable payments may be adjusted. The suggestions thus far have centered on four factors:

1. Prices of farm products
2. Crop yields
3. Rental shares
4. Farm income

The *prices of products* plan provides for payments on principal or interest or both varying with a certain price index. The mortgage carries a definite term of years, interest rate, and schedule of principal payments, as for example, a 10-year term at 5 per cent with principal payments of 1 per cent each year. But annual payments as specified in the plan are required only if the index of prices received by farmers for their products is around a certain normal level, for example, 100. If the price index is 120 the interest payment remains the same, but the principal payment increases. If the index drops to 70, not only is the principal payment omitted, but a certain part of the interest due is postponed or added to the principal of the mortgage. This plan fails to work satisfactorily in areas where yields fluctuate. In such areas the plan may be worse than a fixed payment type because a drouth which sends the price index up will call for a higher payment than if the yield is up to normal.

The *crop yields* plan of adapting the payments to crop yields, although not entirely satisfactory, has more in its favor. Payments are scheduled as in the previous plan, with variations in the regular plan if there are large fluctuations in crop yields. If wheat yields of 15 bushels per acre are normal, the payment is regular. If the wheat yield increases to 20 bushels, the principal payment is increased a definite prearranged amount. If, on the other hand, the wheat yield is only 5 bushels, the principal payment is waived and the interest payment reduced according to a schedule, and the unpaid interest extended or added to the principal. However, if yields only are used as a base, the plan does not work well for borrowers when yields are high and prices extremely low, or for lenders when yields are low and prices extremely high. To meet this objection the rental share plan is suggested.

The *rental share* plan is based on crop yields. In essence, the borrower turns over to the lender the share of the crop that he would give to a landlord as rent for the farm. The lender sells this crop share and applies the proceeds first on the interest and the remainder, if any, on the principal. The borrower pays more than a tenant because he agrees to pay the taxes, keep up the buildings, and pay the fire and extended coverage insurance premiums. The borrower is given the privilege of making additional payments on the principal on interest-paying dates. The main advantage of this plan is that the borrower sets aside a portion of the crop at harvest to be applied directly to his mortgage obligation. If he wants to feed this crop to his livestock, he must buy it from the lender. This plan results in a clear-cut division of the crop, with the lender obtaining all that the farmer can well afford to offer because the farmer is giving the lender as much as a tenant would give a landlord and, in addition, is paying the taxes and keeping up the improvements. Another favorable feature is the ease with which this plan is explained and administered. Most farmers are familiar with rental terms and readily recognize that a lender is entitled to the landlord's share. A final advantage is that this plan adjusts for both yield and price variations; if the yield or price is out of line, the lender makes the adjustment through the sale of the share which the borrower turns over.

The rental share plan, however, is not adapted to farms which specialize in livestock or have such a wide variety of crops that the computation of a crop return index or rental share is especially difficult. For such diversified farms the income plan has been suggested.

The *farm income* plan provides for payments adjusted to the farmer's net income. In theory this plan is ideal in that the payments are in line with what the farmer can pay. If crop yields or livestock returns are low the income is low and the payments reduced accordingly, but if the reverse situation occurs income is high and the payments are increased. But this ideal adjustment can be stated only in general terms. When a specific farm is considered, a multitude of questions arise. Should family living expenses be allowed as farm expenses and, if so, what limit, if any, should be placed on these expenses? What allowance, if any, should be made for poor management; if a farmer does not take good care of his crops or livestock, will his payment be reduced because he has done a poor job? What assistance will be given the farmer in keeping and summarizing the detailed records necessary to make this plan work, and who will pay the extra cost of the record-keeping supervision? These questions make the actual working out of this plan a formidable undertaking. The Farmers Home Administration offered a variable payment plan of this type with their farm ownership loans for a period of years. The plan worked fairly well in this instance since farm ownership loans are made only to a select and carefully supervised group of farmers. However, in recent years the Farmers Home Administration has abandoned this plan in favor of optional and reserve payments.

OPTIONAL PAYMENT PLANS

The optional payment provision, an opportunity to make payments on the principal in addition to the regular payments at any time or at any interest-paying date, is a great convenience to the borrower. If the borrower is permitted to refinance at a lower rate when interest rates decline, he saves a substantial amount on his annual interest bill. It is a great advantage, too, if he can apply extra income from a good year on the principal of his loan instead of allowing his funds to lie idle or investing at a low rate.

The optional payment privilege, however, has some disadvantages to the lender. It makes a loan less satisfactory because it may be paid at any time unless certain limitations are specified. A common limitation is to specify that optional payments may not be made until two, three, or five years have expired, which protects the lender against having the loan paid soon after it is made, in which event the lender may lose if he has borne the expense of negotiating the loan. This difficulty may be avoided if a small charge is agreed upon as compensation to the lender if the loan is repaid within the 2-, 3-, or 5-year period after the loan is made. Another limitation is to specify that payments made be in amounts of $100 or multiples of this amount, and also that optional payments may be made only on interest-paying dates. These last limitations simplify the handling of optional payments. An unusual limitation which enables a lender to hold a loan for the entire period is to grant the borrower the option of paying one-half or less, but never more than one-half of the unpaid balance at any interest-paying date. According to this plan, the borrower can never pay the loan entirely until it comes due. Another type of optional payment is to allow principal payments at any interest-paying date up to some fraction, such as one-fifth or one-fourth, of the original principal, provided the funds are derived from farm income. Restriction of the payment to farm income prevents lending agencies from taking loans away from each other.

RESERVE PAYMENTS

Reserve or future payments allow the borrower to make advance payments which are held in reserve to apply at a future date when hardships of one kind or another may make it difficult or impossible for the borrower to pay his interest and principal installment. The lender generally agrees to pay the same interest on the advance payment as is charged on the loan so the farmer does not lose any interest on the transaction.

Such a plan has a special advantage for maximum loans in areas where income is highly variable. If a farmer in such an area had a highly successful year and reduced his mortgage by an extra

$1,000, he still might have trouble the following year meeting his loan payment should he have a crop failure or some other calamity which reduced his income. On the other hand, if he placed this extra $1,000 in the reserve fund it would be earning interest at the mortgage rate and be available for use in a year when he could not otherwise make his interest and principal payment.

One difficulty lenders have experienced with reserve or future payment funds is that they are not built by the borrowers who need them. Farmers who build such reserves tend to be the ones who can meet payments from other sources even in difficult times. The borrower who has limited risk-bearing ability in other ways tends also to forego building a reserve fund to help carry his loan payments in low income years.

OTHER PAYMENT PLANS

Various other repayment plans, primarily combinations of provisions already outlined, have been developed by lenders to meet needs of borrowers. One plan provides for initial deferment of principal payments for up to 5 years. This provision permits the borrower to concentrate on repayment of short-term debts and on accumulation of working capital. While the mortgage lender does not gain added security by principal payments during this period, he does benefit by the stronger current and intermediate capital position developed by the borrower.

Another plan used by some lenders provides for discontinuance of principal payments when the loan has been reduced to a certain level. After the loan has been paid down to a certain level it is carried as a straight end payment loan. This plan recognizes that a conservative perpetual debt might well be carried on good farm real estate. It also leaves the farmer free to choose whether or not be should continue to save to accumulate equity in real estate.

QUESTIONS AND PROBLEMS

1. Explain what is meant by repayment capacity.
2. Why is repayment capacity important in use of credit?
3. Distinguish between loans which are self-liquidating and those which are not. How do each of these types of loans influence repayment capacity?
4. From what source are self-liquidating loans paid? Loans which are not self-liquidating?

5. Explain how repayment capacity may limit profitable use of credit.
6. Describe and explain the payment provision on short-term loans which you as a lender would offer borrowers in your territory.
7. Would these provisions meet the requirements of the borrowers?
8. Do you believe that a loan carry-over is ever justified on a crop loan which the borrower would have difficulty in paying in a low price or low yield year?
9. From the borrower's point of view, what is the best payment plan on a long-term loan? From the lender's point of view, what plan is best?
10. What is the difference between the even and decreasing payment plan of amortization? Compute the intervening payments on interest and principal between the third and tenth payments in Tables 8.2 and 8.3.
11. The face amount of a loan is $1,000, the annual interest rate is 2 per cent, and the loan is to be amortized, using the even payment plan, over a 2-year period. Set up two tables similar to Table 8.3, one on the annual installment basis, and the other on the semiannual installment basis. Complete the tables for all installments.
12. Using Equation 8.3, compute the amount of principal in the third semiannual payment (installment) derived in Question 11.
13. Why are variable payment plans suggested? What is the chief obstacle encountered in developing a satisfactory variable plan?
14. Explain the difference between optional payments and reserve payments.

REFERENCES

Botts, Ralph R., *Farmers' Handbook of Financial Calculations and Physical Measurements,* Farm Econ. Div., ERS, USDA, Handbook 230, 1962.
Morelle, Wilellyn; Hesser, Leon; and Melichor, Emanuel, *Merchant and Dealer Credit in Agriculture,* Board of Governors, Fed. Res. System, 1966.

Chapter 9

STRENGTHENING REPAYMENT CAPACITY

MANY FARMERS are able to profitably use more credit than their repayment capacity will support and they have the ability to successfully manage and operate a larger unit than they are able to finance. The challenge is to develop repayment capacity so as to be able to use as much credit as is profitable, and thereby increase net income.

The ways by which repayment capacity is strengthened can be summarized in four general groups:

1. Building more owner equity or net worth in the business.
2. Adjusting the business so self-liquidating loans will be used as far as possible.
3. Organizing and operating the business so as to increase net income.
4. Planning the repayment schedule to conform with income.

These four methods are, of course, somewhat related and overlapping, but such a grouping facilitates studying how repayment capacity can be improved.

BUILDING NET WORTH BUILDS REPAYMENT CAPACITY

Farm families build repayment capacity by saving or accumulating net worth. As the farm business expands through accumulation of more resources, both gross and net income generally increase, thereby contributing to increased repayment capacity. Moreover, a demonstrated ability to save often contributes to more favorable loan terms and thereby indirectly adds repayment capacity.

Even a small growth in net worth may add substantially to debt-carrying capacity. On many farms most loans which are not self-liquidating are on real estate and such loans usually are or can be written for a fairly long term of years. In such cases principal payments are small compared with the face amount of the loan. A relatively small annual or semiannual payment will support a substantial loan. For example, the annual principal installment is $285.71 on a 35-year, $10,000 loan written on a decreasing-payment plan basis. In other words, with this type and term of loan, annual income of $290 will provide the repayment capacity necessary to meet the principal payments on a $10,000 debt.[1] It should be kept in mind that this example portrays the debt-payment relationship when the loan is made and that as the loan gradually is repaid the size (unpaid balance) of loan supported by the payment gradually decreases. Moreover, this example portrays one of the higher debt-payment ratios. With some other payment plans and with shorter term plans the size of payments increases, of course, relative to the face amount of the loan.

Using Self-liquidating Loans Increases Repayment Capacity

Keeping loans which are not self-liquidating to a minimum provides a means of increasing or "stretching" repayment capacity. This method is widely recognized and used by farmers who rent part or all the land they operate, employ custom operators, and the like, to avoid such loans.

Increasing Income Strengthens Repayment Capacity

A well-organized and operated farm will produce more gross and net income than one which is poorly organized and operated. Other things being equal, more income will be available

---

[1] Interest payments would have to be made in addition to principal payments. However, interest is paid from gross income and if it was profitable to borrow the funds, as discussed in preceding chapters, gross income would be increased enough to cover the added interest expense.

for debt payment on a well-organized and operated farm than on one which is poorly organized and operated.

Considered from the viewpoint of income, good repayment capacity ordinarily can be attributed to one or more of the following factors:

1. A farm business of sufficient size to produce an adequate gross income. Size of business does not refer necessarily to acres in the farm, but rather to total production. One problem which confronted the wheat-dairy farmer used in the example in Chapter 8 was size of business: His farm was too small; it did not provide an adequate base for producing a very large income.
2. A combination of high profit enterprises which "fit" together as a well-coordinated team facilitating use of each dollar where it will contribute most to net income.
3. Emphasis upon enterprises which give a fast "turnover" of capital.
4. Low cost operation facilitated by combinations of factors which permit maximum efficiency.
5. Low overhead costs and general farm expenses.
6. High yield or production per unit.
7. Effective marketing of products resulting in a good price per unit.
8. An ambitious and well-informed manager with an interested, cooperative spouse and family.

Poor repayment capacity usually can be traced to one or more of the following:

1. A small farm business yielding a small gross income.
2. A poorly organized farm resulting in "bunching" of machine and labor requirements and other inefficiencies.
3. Low production per unit due to poor land, untimely and inefficient operation, unfavorable growing conditions, and poor management of crops and livestock.
4. High production costs due to poor judgment in purchases, and in use of fertilizer, seed, feed, and other resources.
5. High overhead costs due to a heavy debt load, high taxes, high maintenance costs, and unprofitable use of labor caused by a farm business too small to provide full-time employment for operator and family labor.
6. Low price for products sold due to poor quality and poor marketing.

7. A slothful and uninformed manager with a disinterested spouse and family.

It should be obvious that to build greater repayment capacity from an income point of view, the farmer must strive to develop characteristics and acquire resources such as those associated with strong repayment capacity summarized in the eight points listed above. Similarly, he must eliminate, as far as possible, things contributing to low repayment capacity summarized in the seven points immediately above. Maximum repayment capacity stems from having a maximum of the favorable and a minimum of the unfavorable factors.

PLANNING REPAYMENT OF LOANS INCREASES REPAYMENT CAPACITY

Planning payments on loans so they will come due when income will be available to meet them will strengthen repayment capacity by coordinating obligations with income. This may seem elementary, but failure to make repayment plans causes borrowers a lot of trouble. In addition to lowering the credit rating of the borrower, it may cause financial loss if the farmer is forced to sell livestock, for example, before they are ready for market. When times are difficult, due dates can be hard taskmasters in the hands of unsympathetic lenders, or lenders who have prior obligations they must meet. The late Albert A. Goss, former Master of the National Grange, related this personal experience: "When I was a kid I got chased by a turkey and was nearly scared to death; and I have been chased by a bull. But if you ever want to get a real case of being chased by something that's tough, it's being chased by a due date."[2]

Budgeting Use of Credit During the Year

Borrowers should plan their borrowing or use of credit just as they plan their crop and livestock programs. It is easy to see the advantages of a good crop plan and of anticipating the requirements of labor, materials, and equipment for the different crops. It is likewise clear that it pays to plan the livestock program in advance, anticipating the labor, feed, and shelter which will be

[2] Aaron G. Nelson, *Credit as a Tool for the Agricultural Producer*, N. Cent. Reg. Ext. Publ. No. 4; and Great Plains Agr. Council Publ. No. 15, 1957, p. 16.

required. But it is just as important to go a step further, anticipating as accurately as possible the credit that will be needed to finance the crop and livestock programs.

One method which helps assure that funds will be available to meet loan payments when they come due is to budget *use* and *repayment* of credit. The objective is not to determine the amount of credit it will pay to use, as was the case in the discussion of budgeting in Chapter 5. Rather, after the amount of credit which can be profitably employed has been determined by that process, budgeting use and repayment on credit involves recording in a systematic manner when credit will be needed during the year and when funds will be available to repay the loans.

A cash budget for Farm Business A for the year 1965, by months, is shown in Table 9.1. The budget was developed "after the fact" on the basis of records available for the year to serve two purposes. The first was to illustrate the gross flow of and requirements for cash throughout the year. The second purpose was to provide an example of how a cash budget might be set up for *planning* the amount and timing of credit needs throughout the year and of cash available for repayment. The budget shows cash income and expenses of the farm business by months, together with a total for each item for the year. Family living, including income taxes, also is shown by months and for the year. On the basis of these data a cash surplus or deficit is derived for each month and for the year.

The effect of the monthly cash surplus or deficit on the cash and credit position of the business is shown in the latter part of Table 9.1. On January 1, 1965, the bank balance was $506 and short-term bank loans, primarily for purchase of feeder cattle and feed, totaled $8,003. The cash deficit of $1,231 in January was covered by borrowing $1,200, with the checking account absorbing the remaining $31. Therefore, on February 1, the bank balance was $475 and current loans totaled $9,203. The deficit of $4,536 in February was financed by a loan of $4,500 and reduction of the bank balance by $36, with the result that on March 1 there were $439 in the checking account, and the current loan balance stood at $13,703.

A substantial cash surplus was generated in March by sale of hogs and by government payments. Mr. A applied the major part of the surplus on his bank loans, reducing the balance outstanding to $7,200. During the spring and summer, income was nil, yet cash was required for farm operations and for family living and income taxes. As a result the current loan balance again increased, reaching

TABLE 9.1

Cash Budget for Farm A by Months, 1965

(dollars)

Item	Jan.	Feb.	March	April	May	June	July	Aug.	Sept.	Oct.	Nov.	Dec.	Year 1965
1. Farm Cash Sales													
2. Cattle, fat								8,290	9,893				18,183
3. Hogs			7,805					9,452					17,257
4. Crops										460			460
5. Government payments			1,957						2,936				4,893
6. Miscellaneous				350						432	136		918
7. Total			9,762	350				17,742	12,829	892	136		41,711
8. Operating and Fixed Cash Expenses													
9. Machinery and power expenses	50	185	396	362	176	100	146	98	224	306	295	139	2,477
10. Labor hired				36			42			58			136
11. Livestock expenses			45	210					140		46		441
12. Seed, fertilizer, etc.		1,418	182	295	62								1,957
13. Feed purchases	264	301	269	235	306	292	292	301	195	2,107	250	260	5,072
14. Livestock purchases										16,808			16,808
15. Miscellaneous operating	60	60	60	60	60	59	59	59	60	60	60	60	717
16. Taxes, property				1,750									1,750
17. Repairs and insurance on impr.	51		182		50							202	485
18. Interest paid			137					197	263	104	2,764		3,465
19. Total	425	1,964	1,271	2,948	654	451	539	655	882	19,443	3,415	661	33,308
20. Net Cash Operating Income (deficit) (Item 7 – Item 19)	(425)*	(1,964)	8,491	(2,598)	(654)	(451)	(539)	17,087	11,947	(18,551)	(3,279)	(661)	8,403
21. Capital Expenditures													
22. Machinery and equipment		2,082											2,082
23. Improvements											2,218		2,218
24. Total		2,082									2,218		4,300
25. Loan Payments, Intermediate and Long-Term			1,400								2,400		3,800
26. Family Living and Income Taxes	806	490	490	510	490	540	480	470	520	500	490	524	6,310
27. Cash surplus (deficit) (Item 20 – Items 24, 25, and 26)	(1,231)	(4,536)	6,601	(3,108)	(1,144)	(991)	(1,019)	16,617	11,427	(19,051)	(8,387)	(1,185)	(6,007)
28. Effect on Cash and Current Loans													
29. Beginning cash balance	506	475	439	537	429	385	494	475	3,692	15,119	468	581	506
30. Cash surplus (deficit) (line 27)	(1,231)	(4,536)	6,601	(3,108)	(1,144)	(991)	(1,019)	16,617	11,427	(19,051)	(8,387)	(1,185)	(6,007)
31. Beginning current loan balance	8,003	9,203	13,703	7,200	10,200	11,300	12,400	13,400	0	0	4,400	12,900	8,003
32. Loan obtained, current	1,200	4,500	0	3,000	1,100	1,100	1,000	0	0	4,400	8,500	1,007	25,807
33. Loan payment, current	0	0	6,503	0	0	0	0	13,400	0	0	12,900	0	19,903
34. Ending current loan balance	9,203	13,703	7,200	10,200	11,300	12,400	13,400	0	0	4,400	0	13,907	13,907
35. Ending cash balance	475	439	537	429	385	494	475	3,692	15,119	468	581	403	403

* Figures in parentheses are negative.

a high of $13,400 on August 1. This balance was completely liqui-dated by the large cash surplus generated in August. Another cash surplus occurred in September, raising the bank balance to $15,119 October 1.

During the fall months Mr. A purchased his replacement cattle and some feed to supplement that produced on the farm. The loan payment on the farm mortgage came due in November. Mr. A's bank balance covered part of these expenses, but a substantial amount of bank credit was needed also. At the end of the year the current loan balance stood at $13,907.

The cash budget for Farm Business A illustrates the "ebb and flow" of cash throughout the year. Large sums are involved, much larger than is indicated by year-end figures. The total amount of new short-term credit used by Farm Business A during 1965 was $25,807, more than three times the amount outstanding at the beginning of the year.

The primary usefulness of a cash budget is for planning pur-poses and, therefore, it should be prepared *before* the cropping season commences and before funds are needed for livestock enter-prises. It is desirable to prepare a cash budget summary for the business at the end of the year to provide data for preparing the projected budget for the coming year. A summary of annual cash budgets for a number of years provides an excellent basis for pro-jecting receipts and expenses. Such a summary, coupled with a monthly summary for a year or two, facilitates preparing a reliable projected budget for the coming year and also simplifies the under-taking.

Preparing a cash budget before financing is needed facilitates obtaining a budgeted loan. An example of the transactions involved in a budgeted short-term loan is provided in Table 9.2. A budgeted loan has three primary advantages.

1. It provides an opportunity for the lender and the borrower to review and analyze the entire business operation together. In this analysis the lender has an opportunity to study the business and the farmer, and to determine how the financing institution might be of greatest assistance. The farmer has an opportunity to dis-cuss various aspects of the business and of financing with the lender. Together they can analyze the amount of capital which can be profitably and safely used, and where it should be used within the business.

2. A budgeted loan provides assurance that funds will be available to carry out business operations. With a budgeted loan the lender gives an overall commitment of funds which the financing institution will provide during a given period. Without such an assurance the farmer may be unable to obtain credit to carry out plans underway.

TABLE 9.2

EXAMPLE OF A BUDGET LOAN

Date	Purpose of Advance or Source of Repayment	Amount Advanced	Principal Repayment	Balance Outstanding	Days Outstanding	Interest Accrued at 6½ Per Cent
Jan. 10..	Purchase 3 cows........	$600				
	Labor........	50				
	Fertilizer......	150				
	Interest on real estate mortgage.......	175				
		$ 975	...	$ 975	85	$14.76
Apr. 5..	Seed........	125				
	Fuel........	125				
		250	...	1,225	71	15.49
June 15..	Feed........	150				
	Fencing......	175				
	Interest on real estate mortgage.......	175				
		500	...	1,725	5	1.56
June 20..	Sale of 14 hogs.	...	$ 700	1,025	56	10.22
Aug. 15..	Taxes........	125	...	1,150	21	4.30
Sept. 5..	Labor........	150	...	1,300	96	22.23
Dec. 10..	Sale of corn....	...	750	550	10	.98
Dec. 20..	Sale of 11 hogs.	...	550 *	...	..	...
	Total.....	$2,000	$2,000 *	...	..	$69.54

* Also paid $69.54 interest. If the member borrowed the whole $2,000 for an entire year his interest would have been $130 instead of the $69.54 actually paid on the budgeted loan.

3. A budgeted loan usually is more economical than a series of individual loans or one straight end payment loan for the entire amount. Interest is paid only for the period the funds are used, and repayment of a portion of the loan can be made at any time surplus cash is available. In the example of a budgeted loan given in Table 9.2, interest savings were $60.46 compared with an annual straight end payment loan.

Coordinating the Repayment Plan and Term
of Loan With Income

Another phase of planning loan payments to increase repayment capacity involves selecting the repayment plan and term of loan which is most suitable with the amount and timing of income available. Loan payments and income are automatically coordinated with budgeted loans. However, with other types of short-term loans, and with intermediate- and long-term credit, attention to this point may materially strengthen repayment capacity.

How do each of the repayment plans outlined in the preceding chapter influence repayment capacity? The variable payment plan has some characteristics which contribute to repayment capacity and some which may lead to major weakness. The fact that the loan is reviewed each year with the lender facilitates mutual understanding and adjustment of the loan payments as is mutually desirable. If the loan is on the "weak" side the lender likely will put on a little pressure for increased payments, particularly in good years, which may contribute considerably to the welfare of the loan. However, the fact that payments can be "put off" under certain circumstances may contribute to less management, work, and thrift than if a rigid schedule of payments were specified in the loan contract.

For years *quasi-variable* payment plans have been used as a means of financing intermediate assets such as machinery and breeding stock. The loan is written on an annual basis, with the unpaid balance being "carried over" from year to year. Some real estate lenders also permit what amounts to a quasi-variable payment plan through various types of prepayment privileges when income is high, and deferments when income is low, providing the loan justifies such action.

The quasi-variable payment plans strengthen, and deter, repayment capacity in much the same way as regular variable payment plans. In addition, the fact that the lender is the final judge as to loan payments comprises a major weakness. The lender and not the borrower determines whether the loan is to be renewed, and, if so, for how much. The borrower has nothing in writing upon which to base plans. Whether or not his repayment capacity is adequate depends entirely upon the lender. It should be added, however, that with a reputable lender this hazard is not as great as it sounds. A reputable lender works for the welfare of the borrower and does not call for an unusually large principal payment on a loan unless, in his judgment, it is in the best interest of the borrower, or unless he is forced to do so by prior commitments or legal provisions. Full repayment of a loan is called for in the best interest of the borrower only when the loan has developed major weakness and shows little promise of "getting well," and a lender generally is not forced to call loans by prior commitments or legal provisions unless conditions in general are "pretty bad." In these circumstances it is doubtful if the borrower would be able to improve his position with another type of repayment plan.

The even and decreasing amortization payment plans generally add to repayment capacity by providing for periodic payments of principal and interest. For most people it is easier to repay a loan in installments than in a lump sum. Assuming a loan must be repaid, periodic payments usually have an advantage over lump-sum payments. An exception may be a farmer who is trying to build up his business and wants to use all available income for a period of time to achieve this objective; and making periodic payments on a loan may substantially retard his progress. In such cases a lump-sum payment plan may contribute more to repayment capacity than periodic payments.

Another point to consider in analyzing the merits of regular periodic payments is the notable irregularity of income in agriculture. In such circumstances amortized loans might easily become delinquent. Over a period of years average income might be fully adequate to cover the payments, but in a low income period, income may fall to the point where loan payments might go delinquent. It might be argued that for this reason lump-sum payments may be preferable to periodic payments. Since periods of low income can also affect accumulation of lump-sum payments, the practice followed by lenders of combining variable payment features with periodic payments alleviates to a considerable degree this objection to periodic payments.

Whether the even or decreasing payment plan will contribute more to repayment capacity depends upon the earning ability of the farmer involved. Often the even payment plan works out best since it puts a smaller strain on the borrower in the early years. For example, with a 35-year 5 per cent loan, the initial payment per $1,000 principal is $61.07 with the even payment plan, compared with $79.00 with the decreasing payment plan. However, a farmer's earning capacity may be greater in his younger years, in which case, if the loan is written for a long term, the decreasing payment plan may work out best. With this plan, payments gradually decline until at the end of the period they are only about half as much as those paid with an even payment plan.

From the above discussion it probably is evident that by lengthening the term of loan, the size of payments can be reduced. For example, with a $1,000 even payment plan loan at 5 per cent, an annual payment of $230.97 (principal and interest) is required to liquidate the loan in 5 years, whereas by lengthening the term to 10 years, annual payments of $129.50 will do the job. Annual payments of $80.24 are required to repay the loan in 20 years, and by extending the term to 35 years, the payments are reduced to $61.07 annually.

Adjusting the term of loan is one of the most powerful means available for increasing repayment capacity. By increasing the term, a larger loan can be serviced with a given payment, or the same size loan can be serviced with a smaller payment. Consider, for example, how this principle might affect the wheat-dairy farmer referred to in Chapter 8. In estimating whether he would be able to repay the loans necessary to buy the 160 acres, the term of the $7,000, 6 per cent loan secured by chattel property was placed at 7 years, and the real estate loan was set up on a 35-year basis. With these terms, payments on principal totaled $1,089 the first year. However, if the terms had been set at 5 and 20 years, respectively, total principal payments would have been $1,642—$553 more than with the longer terms. Interest costs the first year would have been the same in both cases. Therefore, increasing the terms of the loans as described reduced principal payments by about $550 without changing the amount of credit. Or stated conversely, lengthening the terms of the loans added about $550 to repayment capacity of the farmer the first year.

Generally speaking, for maximum repayment capacity, the length of loan should correspond with two things: the length of time it takes to recover the investment when the borrowed funds are used for self-liquidating purposes, and the net income-producing capacity of the borrower when borrowed funds are used for other purposes. Some margin of safety should be included in the plans to cover fluctuations in income and unforeseen risks. Considerations relating to this phase of credit analysis are discussed in the following chapters.

QUESTIONS AND PROBLEMS

1. List and discuss the methods for strengthening repayment capacity.
2. What is meant by budgeting credit? Explain the procedure to follow.
3. What is the purpose of budgeting credit?
4. What is meant by a cash budget? Outline the types of information it provides.
5. What use can be made of a cash budget?
6. When should a cash budget be prepared? Why?
7. Analyze the various repayment plans discussed in Chapter 8 in terms of their effect on repayment capacity.
8. Compare the repayment capacity of the dairy-hog and wheat-dairy farmers discussed in Chapter 8.
9. Analyze the repayment capacity of the farm you used in problem 13 of Chapter 5.

REFERENCES

Mueller, Allan G., "Flow-of-Funds Analysis in Farm Financial Management," *Jour. Farm Econ.*, Aug., 1966, pp. 661–67.

Wehrly, J. S., and Atkinson, J. H., *Debt Loan Capacity of Farms*, Purdue Univ. Agr. Exp. Sta. Res. Bul. 780, 1964.

Wirth, M. E., and Brake, John, R., *The Michigan Farm Credit Panel— Cash Flows and Use of Credit—1961*, Mich. Agr. Exp. Sta. Res. Rept. 8, 1961.

Chapter 10

RISK-BEARING ABILITY AS A GUIDE IN USE OF CREDIT

RISK-BEARING ABILITY, the third R of Credit, is a major factor in determining the amount of credit which can be safely used on most farms. In fact, it is probably the primary factor limiting use of credit. As was indicated above, many commercial farmers probably could profitably use more credit. Under such circumstances, operating and intermediate capital loans are largely self-liquidating—assuming repayment of the intermediate loans is scheduled to approximately coincide with the rate of depreciation. Thus, repayment capacity, the second R of credit, imposes only limited restraint on credit use for these purposes. Risk-bearing ability serves as the primary restraining factor.

Analysis of the amount of credit which can profitably be used and of the amount which can be repaid is made, as indicated above, on the basis of average production, costs, and prices expected to prevail during the period of time the credit is to be used. In contrast, analysis of risk-bearing ability is made in terms of the amount of *variation* in income and expenses, including nonfarm (family) expenses, which *might* occur during the period of credit utilization. The point of focus is on the extent to which expenses may be higher and income lower than the average, and the frequency of such deviations.

The meaning of risk-bearing ability, its influence on use of credit, and conditions which make risk-bearing ability necessary are discussed in this chapter. Ways and means of strengthening risk-bearing ability are considered in Chapters 11 and 12. In Chapter 13, risk-bearing ability indicated by balance sheet analysis is analyzed.

MEANING OF RISK-BEARING ABILITY

Risk-bearing ability means ability to stand unexpected low income and unpredictable losses and expenses, and continue in farming. It is made up mainly of five things:

1. *Ability to make and save money.* An operator who can make money can soon recover from a bad year or an unexpected loss. If, with average conditions, his income is at a level where he is able to save and reinvest part of his income in the business, he will be able to withstand a moderate drop in income without having to draw funds from the business to cover living expenses. Savings ability is important because a good income does little to strengthen risk-bearing ability if it is all spent on family living.

2. *Stability and reliability of income.* If income were the same every year and could be counted on to continue, there would be no need for risk-bearing ability except to meet unusual family expenses, such as sickness. Since farm income fluctuates, risk-bearing ability, in addition to that required to cover unusual family expenses, is needed to enable the farm business to withstand unexpected expenses or a drop in income. The amount of risk-bearing ability needed will vary with the size of fluctuations in income and characteristics of the family. Farmers located in high-risk areas or in high-risk types of farming should have greater risk-bearing ability than those in stable areas with a stable type of operation.[1]

3. *Ability to borrow in both good and poor times.* This is determined by the credit rating of the operator and the ability and willingness of the lender to "stay with" the borrower.

4. *Ability to reduce operating and living expenses in poor periods.* This point is closely related to stability and reliability of income. Income available for loan payments will be much more stable if operating and living expenses can be reduced in low income periods.

---

[1] No distinction is made in this book between risk and uncertainty except as is evident from the discussion.

5. *Owner equity—the backbone of risk-bearing ability.* Since risk-bearing ability means ability to meet unusual expenses or loss of income and keep operating, owner equity for that purpose, or as a basis for credit, is the primary factor in risk-bearing ability.[2]

Risk-bearing ability also involves personal characteristics of the operator. Some operators are "gamblers" willing to take long chances on a "shoe string." Others are extremely conservative—afraid to take more than a little chance. From a risk-bearing point of view neither extreme is desirable. Chances taken by the "gambler" are likely to be so great that his risk-bearing ability will be too thinly spread. It would be "only a drop in the bucket" compared with his need. At the other extreme, the individual afraid to take a chance may progress too slowly and thereby fail to develop risk-bearing ability. Some may argue that such an individual needs little risk-bearing ability, but that generally is not true considering the technological revolution going on in modern agriculture. Many farmers are incurring substantial risk today by just not "keeping up."

Moral characteristics of an individual play a very important role in risk-bearing ability. The characteristics here referred to are all those that go to build a good credit rating: honesty, integrity, assumption of responsibility, and dependability. The individual with determination and a will to work and sacrifice, if necessary, to fulfill an obligation or a contract will overcome much greater difficulties than the individual who quits when the going gets rough.

IMPORTANCE OF RISK-BEARING ABILITY

Since the future is not known with certainty, there is a need for risk-bearing ability to offset fluctuations which might occur in expenses and income and to compensate for errors in judgment regarding returns and repayment capacity in use of credit. Considering how much one should borrow (from a risk-bearing viewpoint) has been likened to loading a truck.

> One would be foolish to load a truck to the point where an axle would break if a wheel hit a chuckhole in the road. A farm family would be equally unwise to take on a credit load to the point where they would go "broke" if adversity hit.

---

[2] Based upon: Aaron G. Nelson, *Credit as a Tool for the Agricultural Producer*, N. Cent. Reg. Ext. Publ. No. 4; and Great Plains Agr. Council Publ. No. 15, 1957, pp. 10–11.

Just as some highways have more holes than others, some areas and types of farming involve greater hazards and risk than others. Farmers in high-risk areas or with high-risk enterprises should take on a lighter debt load in relation to their equity than those in stable areas or in a type of farming where fluctuations in income are relatively small.[3]

Risk-bearing ability provides the "last line of defense" in use of credit. If a promising venture proves to be unprofitable, risk-bearing ability must shoulder the load. If a farmer borrows funds for operating expenses and because of risk and uncertainty—such as natural hazards and low prices—income is inadequate to cover them, his repayment capacity from current income also becomes inadequate and the load is shifted to risk-bearing ability. In other words, risk-bearing ability plays the role of "Goal Tender" on the Three-R Credit "hockey" team. When the other two R's fail, it is up to the third R, Risk-bearing Ability, to "block" failure of the loan. This does not mean that the first two R's do not have important roles to play. The first, Returns, indicates the maximum amount it will pay to borrow—something which risk-bearing ability cannot do. Similarly, the second R, Repayment Capacity, indicates how much credit can be repaid—again something risk-bearing ability cannot do. Each R has its own role to play in analysis of use and extension of credit.

EXAMPLES OF HOW RISK-BEARING ABILITY INFLUENCES USE OF CREDIT

The important role which risk-bearing ability plays in extension and use of credit may be illustrated by the two farm examples used in Chapters 5 and 8 to illustrate how returns produced by use of credit and repayment capacity influence the amount of credit employed in the business. The loan made to a dairy-hog farmer in the Corn Belt was compared with an application for a loan from a wheat-dairy farmer in the Great Plains.

The Dairy-Hog Farm Example

The dairy-hog farmer used as an example had a fairly high earning and savings capacity. His net income in the "current year"

---

[3] *Ibid.*, p. 10.

was $4,619, and after living expenses, taxes, and an allowance for labor of the children were deducted, $2,019 remained to build owner equity in the business. Moreover, it was estimated that about $1,000 could be added to owner equity annually with *average* production, prices, and other conditions. Such a level of income and savings contributes materially to risk-bearing ability.

Stability and reliability of income also ranked relatively high for this farmer. Both dairying and hog production are fairly stable enterprises, and the farm is located in a relatively stable part of the country. It was recognized, however, that there would be some variation in income due to fluctuations in production and price. Moreover, unusual losses might occur if disease should strike either the dairy herd or the hogs. Family sickness could also cause unusual and unexpected losses. It was estimated that loss of income plus unusual expense from such causes might total as much as $3,000 in one year. Since savings (increase in net worth) were estimated to average about $1,000 annually, a deficit of $2,000 might occur in any one year. Would the business stand this amount of loss?

To answer this question we should take a look at the assets and liabilities of the dairy-hog farmer given in Table 5.4 of Chapter 5. In the "current year," value of livestock and other current assets totaled $21,893 compared with a chattel mortgage of $7,333, indicating there was more than adequate collateral to cover normal requirements for operating funds throughout the year. The mortgage of $11,500 on $17,500 of real estate was relatively high compared to customary commercial lending practice. But considering total assets and liabilities it appeared the financial structure of the business was adequate to support the current debt load and an additional $2,000 of credit, should that become necessary.

Thus, it appeared that from the overall point of view this farmer had fully adequate risk-bearing ability to carry the amount of credit he was using in his business.

The Wheat-Dairy Farm Example

Turning to the wheat-dairy farmer in the Great Plains, we estimated that if he bought the 160 acres his annual net income over a period of years would average about $2,700 (see Table 8.1, Chapter 8). If the family cut living expenses to about $1,500 they would be able to meet loan payments totaling about $1,100 annually. In other words, by holding living expenses to about $1,500 the wheat-dairy farm family would be able to add about the same amount to owner equity each year as the dairy-hog farmer in the Corn Belt. The net effect on risk-bearing ability probably would be less, however, because of the difference in amount allowed for family living. The smaller amount budgeted for the wheat-dairy farmer would permit less curtailment in case of a drop in income, which in turn would add less to risk-bearing ability.

Being located in a high-risk area of the Great Plains, relatively wide fluctuations in income were anticipated for the wheat-dairy farmer. It is not uncommon for two successive years of drouth to occur in the area, and such periods deal a devastating blow to farm income as is shown by the estimates given in Table 10.1. It was estimated that liquidation of assets during the first drouth year would provide funds to cover all expenses except interest on the real estate loan. It was assumed the principal payments could be deferred. During the second drouth year, assumed further liquidation of assets would help cover expenses, but continued high costs of providing feed for the milk cows would result in a larger deficit the second year. The year following the drouth, large deficits would be incurred during the first half year to provide finances for the business and for living. On a cumulative basis, the wheat-dairy farmer would need nearly $5,000 in addition to current cash income during the 2-year drouth period and the year following to cover expenses which could not be deferred.

Budget estimates indicate the financial structure of the wheat-dairy farmer would deteriorate drastically as a result of the 2-year drouth. The figures are shown in Table 10.2. While total assets do not show a very drastic decline due to land and cow values having been held constant (a possibly unrealistic assumption), net worth declined drastically. The nonreal-estate loan nearly equals the value of nonreal-estate assets by the end of the second drouth year, and before a crop would be assured in the year following the drouth, it would be nearly 50 per cent above the value of those assets. This is more of a risk than commercial lenders will assume.

All considered, the wheat-dairy farmer did not have the risk-bearing ability to assume the financial obligations necessary to buy the 160 acres. While purchasing the quarter section looked good from a returns viewpoint, and possibly permissible from a repayment capacity viewpoint, analysis of risk-bearing ability indicated the undertaking would be unwise.

TABLE 10.1

Estimated Income, Expenses and Loan Payments for Two Drouth Years, and the Year Following the Drouth for a Wheat-Dairy Farm in the Northern Great Plains

	Drouth Years		Year Following Drouth				
	First	Second	Jan.–Mar.	Apr.–June	July–Sept.	Oct.–Dec.	Calendar Year
Cash Income............	$6,000	$5,000	$ 450	$ 450	$5,500	$1,200	$7,600
Cash Expenses (including living expenses & taxes).........	6,000	6,000	2,550	1,500	1,200	1,100	6,350
Cash Surplus (+) or Deficit (−).........	0	−1,000	−2,100	−1,050	+4,300	+100	+1,250
Real Estate Loan Payments (interest and principal).....	400*	400*				489	489
Chattel Loan Payments (principal)...........	0	0				761	761
Balance...........	−$ 400	−$1,400	−$2,100	−$1,050	+$4,300	−$1,150	0

* Interest only.

TABLE 10.2

Estimated Assets, Liabilities, and Net Worth of the Wheat-Dairy Farm in the Northern Great Plains, Assuming Two Drouth Years in Succession

	Year Preceding Drouth December 31	Drouth Years		Year Following Drouth			
		First Dec. 31	Second Dec. 31	Mar. 31	June 30	Sept. 30	Dec. 31
ASSETS							
Real estate..........	$16,000	$16,000	$16,000	$16,000	$16,000	$16,000	$16,000
Nonreal estate......	13,315	11,400	9,900	9,400	8,400	10,000	10,600
Total............	29,315	27,400	25,900	25,400	24,400	26,000	26,600
LIABILITIES							
Real estate loan.....	$ 8,000	$ 8,000	$ 8,000	$ 8,000	$ 8,000	$ 8,000	$ 7,911
Nonreal-estate loan..	7,000	7,400	8,800	10,900	11,950	7,650	8,039
Total............	15,000	15,400	16,800	18,900	19,950	15,650	15,950
NET WORTH........	$14,315	$12,000	$ 9,100	$ 6,500	$ 4,450	$10,350	$10,650

The Principle of Increasing Risk

The principle of increasing risk accentuates the need for risk-bearing ability. The tendency for risk to increase at an increasing rate as the relative amount of owner equity in a business decreases is referred to as the principle of increasing risk. Thus, as a farmer uses relatively more credit in his business, financial leverage facilitating increased returns is gained, but the chances of losing his own capital increase. The way in which the principle works is illustrated by data in Table 10.3. It is assumed that the operator has

TABLE 10.3

ILLUSTRATION OF PRINCIPLE OF INCREASING RISK (Hypothetical data)

Line	Item	Per Cent Equity			
		100	75	50	25
	(1)	(2)	(3)	(4)	(5)
1.	Owned capital used in business.....	$15,000	$15,000	$15,000	$15,000
2.	Borrowed capital used in business..	0	5,000	15,000	45,000
3.	Total capital used in business......	$15,000	$20,000	$30,000	$60,000
	Income when rate earned on investment is plus 10%:				
4.	Gross returns on capital............	$ 1,500	$ 2,000	$ 3,000	$ 6,000
5.	Cost of borrowed capital @ 5%....	0	250	750	2,250
6.	Net return on capital used.........	$ 1,500	$ 1,750	$ 2,250	$ 3,750
7.	Rate earned on owned capital......	10%	12%	15%	25%
	Income when rate earned on investment is minus 10%:				
8.	Gross loss on capital..............	$ 1,500	$ 2,000	$ 3,000	$ 6,000
9.	Cost of borrowed capital @ 5%....	0	250	750	2,250
10.	Total loss on capital used..........	$ 1,500	$ 2,250	$ 3,750	$ 8,250
11.	Rate of loss on owned capital.......	10%	15%	25%	55%

$15,000 of his own capital and can borrow additional funds at 5 per cent interest. He can use his $15,000 alone and have full equity in a relatively small business, or he can borrow additional capital and operate a larger business. Columns 2, 3, 4, and 5 of the table illustrate the situation with equity ratios (per cent of total assets owned by the operator) ranging from 100 per cent down to 25 per cent.

Consider first the situation portrayed in column 2 where the operator has full equity in his business. When a 10 per cent return is earned on capital used in the business, the gross return is $1,500 and since there is no interest to pay, a 10 per cent return also is earned on the owner equity. Similarly, when a 10 per cent loss is realized on capital used in the business, a 10 per cent loss is realized on the owner's capital.

The situation changes, however, when credit is used. As shown by the figures in column 3, with a 75 per cent equity, a 10 per cent return on capital used in the business produces a 12 per cent return on owner equity. However, if a 10 per cent loss occurs, the owner loses 15 per cent on his equity. As the ratio drops to 50 per cent, a 10 per cent return on capital yields a 15 per cent return on owner equity, but an equal loss on total capital causes a 25 per cent loss of owner equity. With an equity of 25 per cent, the operator could realize a 25 per cent return on his own capital if the return on total capital was 10 per cent, but he would stand to lose 55 per cent of his equity if a loss of 10 per cent occurred on total capital used in the business.

The trends shown by figures on lines 7 and 11 of Table 10.3 comprise the center core of the principle of increasing risk. Two things are evident from these figures: (1) as the relative amount of credit used increases, there is a tendency for the spread between possible gains and losses to increase, and (2) with an equal percentage gain and loss on total capital used in the business, the magnitude of loss is greater than the magnitude of gain on owner equity. Those who borrow money to increase the size of their business should realize that while credit provides a valuable tool to increase income, it may also serve to multiply losses. Like many other tools, the credit tool can cut two ways. Properly used, it can contribute to a larger income, but unwisely used, it is a threat to the financial future of the user. Tools which are dangerous, such as circular power saws, have a guard to help protect the user. Risk-bearing ability is a guard to help protect the one who uses the credit tool. The principle of increasing risk should be used as one guide in determining the amount of risk-bearing ability which is needed.

CONDITIONS WHICH MAKE RISK-BEARING ABILITY NECESSARY

As indicated by the above discussion, conditions which make it necessary for a farmer to have risk-bearing ability as one basis for use of credit stem from fluctuations in income and expenses, and from risk and uncertainty in operation of the farm business and household. Fluctuations in expenses and income and imperfect knowledge of the future, which make risk-bearing ability necessary, stem from five different kinds of change or uncertainty.

Production Uncertainty

Production uncertainty is a very important factor contributing to the need for risk-bearing ability in use of credit. Production uncertainty is caused by variations in weather, and by things such as disease, insects, and other biological pests. Production uncertainty is concentrated particularly in those areas where weather is unstable. For example, precipitation varies widely from year to year and *period* to *period* in parts of the Great Plains.[4] These areas have come to be known as high-risk areas because of their great variability of production. Wide swings in yields around the relatively low average create great uncertainty in production. With relatively low average yields—12 to 14 bushels for wheat in some areas—net income is low after costs of operation have been met. Under such conditions, below average yields do not merely mean lower net income, as may be the case in higher income areas. When yields are low, income is inadequate to cover costs and, as a result, cash deficits accumulate.

The risk would not be so great if a poor year were followed by one which was average or above average. However, two or more years of drouth often occur together. Drouth periods sometimes extend for 5 to 10 years. Such conditions create extreme risk and explain why the area has become known as a high-risk area.

Other areas than the Great Plains and other crops than wheat suffer from natural hazards. Fruit orchards, for instance, have a highly variable production record. Disease and adverse weather conditions, including freezes, windstorms, and hail, often have a marked effect on production. A farmer in the Middle West may lose a crop because of chinch bugs, hail, drouth, or excessive moisture. Farmers along rivers may be flooded. Boll weevils, floods, and excessive moisture may destroy the cotton farmer's crop.

Major problems of production uncertainty are also found in arid and semiarid grazing areas as is portrayed by Figures 10.1 and 10.2. These pictures were taken at the same site in a pasture on the

---

[4] States usually included in the Great Plains are North Dakota, South Dakota, Nebraska, Kansas, Oklahoma, Texas, Montana, Wyoming, Colorado, and New Mexico.

Fig. 10.1—View of the Texas Range Station near Barnhart prior to an extreme 3-year drouth. (Courtesy of the Texas Agricultural Experiment Station.)

Fig. 10.2—The same site as Figure 10.1, but viewed from a different direction, following the extreme 3-year drouth. (Courtesy of the Texas Agricultural Experiment Station.)

Texas Range Station near Barnhart where range management practices were being studied intensively.[5]

The picture in Figure 10.1 was taken prior to a severe 3-year
drouth and shows good ground cover on the range area despite
heavy grazing. The enclosed area had not been grazed for a decade
and shows excellent ground cover. Three years of severe drouth took
a heavy toll, however, as indicated by the picture in Figure 10.2.
Note the tire tracks in the foreground, indicating the dearth of
ground cover on the range. Continued heavy grazing contributed to
this situation, but most of the short vegetation in the enclosure died
despite the fact that it had not been grazed, indicating the devastating effect of the drouth itself on range forage production.

Not only was the quantity of forage production reduced, but
the quality also deteriorated due to the drouth. The more desirable
plants of the "climax species" made up 25 to 50 per cent of the
range plants before, and only 0 to 25 per cent after the drouth. At
the same time, "invader" plants such as mesquite trees and prickly
pear increased, thereby laying a basis for added expense in rebuilding the range at a later date.

Through its effect on range forage production, drouth also
affects livestock production. Numbers of livestock in the area where
pictures in Figures 10.1 and 10.2 were taken dropped 24 per cent
during the 3-year drouth period and liquidation continued on into
the succeeding year. Moreover, the range deterioration and accompanying drop in livestock numbers tell only part of the story.
Large amounts of feed were purchased to maintain the livestock
which were held. Whereas the normal feed expenditure is
approximately $3.00 per animal unit, an average of $25.00 per
animal unit was spent for feed during the drouth period.

Other hazards besides drouth affect livestock production.
Death losses from disease and adverse weather conditions are common. Hog losses from cholera, contagious abortion, or tuberculosis
in a dairy herd may strike an individual farmer unusually hard.
Losses from bad weather conditions at farrowing, calving, or lamb-
ing time also affect production.

Crops, livestock, and improvements are subject to damage

---

[5] These pictures were obtained from Harley Bebout, Agricultural and
Mechanical College of Texas, College Station. The picture shown in Figure 10.2
and one similar to that shown in Figure 10.1 (the same picture was not available)
are included in the publication, *Some Economic Effects of Drouth on Ranch
Resources*, by C. A. Bonnen and J. M. Ward, Tex. Agr. Exp. Sta. Bul. 801,
1955, p. 6. The discussion relating to these two pictures is based upon material
given in this publication.

from windstorms, fire, and lightning. A tornado sweeping through a farm area may destroy almost everything in its path. Such losses may severely retard or reduce production, and add materially to expenses as well.

In brief, natural hazards in all types of production are great and make extension and use of credit a risky business. These factors need to be given full recognition in consideration of risk-bearing ability.

Price Uncertainty

Closely associated with weather and other natural hazards which influence risk-bearing ability is the risk of price decline which the borrower and lender must face. The connection between natural hazards and price risk is evident if the analysis includes gross farm income, the resultant of yield multiplied by price. It is desirable, however, to treat these two causal factors separately in order to recognize their individual importance.

Price uncertainty always has been a major consideration in farming. Many forces cause prices to fluctuate: the level of national prosperity, production of other farmers, and changes in consumer tastes. Prices change from week to week, from month to month, from year to year, and from period to period, and since credit is used for varying lengths of time on most farms, all these fluctuations contribute to uncertainty in use of credit.

Considerable attention has been devoted to the problem of fluctuations in crop, livestock, and livestock product prices. As a result, government price support programs have been introduced for a number of crops and products. These have helped reduce price uncertainty, but plenty remains to be concerned about. And, of course, a number of crops, livestock, and livestock products are not included in the price support programs. Moreover, fluctuations in farm product prices have added significance today due to the relatively narrow margin of net return involved in farming. With the advance of the technological revolution more of the inputs involved in production are purchased. Some aspects of production formerly performed on the farm have been transferred to the processor. Competition and volume production have reduced the farmers share of the consumer's dollar in most cases. The combined effect of such forces is that today a high proportion of gross income is required to cover purchased inputs. As a result, the farmer is particularly vulnerable to fluctuations in farm product prices.

The effect of product price fluctuation on farmers may be severe. It is not uncommon for wheat prices to fluctuate 25 cents per bushel from one year to the next. If a farmer had 500 acres, with an average yield of 20 bushels per acre, a 25 cent drop in price would mean a reduction in income of $2,500. If financing had been arranged on the basis of the higher price, such a drop in income might put the loan in jeopardy. Similarly, hog prices sometimes drop as much as $5.00 per hundredweight from one year to the next. On 200 market hogs weighing 225 pounds each, such a drop in price would mean a reduction in income of $2,250. Here, again, such a cut in income might well cause problems if a loan had been obtained on the basis of the higher price.

The more risky the enterprise the greater the risk is of loss due to price uncertainty. Cattle fattening is a relatively risky venture and large losses are not uncommon. Many farmers lost $50 to $75 per head in the 1963–64 feeding season. Cattle-feeding losses were a major factor in the drop in net farm income for Farm Business A from $8,742 in 1963 to $3,378 in 1964.

Short-term price fluctuations comprise an important aspect of risk-bearing ability for short-term use of credit. Long-term fluctuations should also be considered in use of long-term credit. A long-term downward trend in the price of a farm product should be recognized in analysis of returns and repayment capacity. The longer the term, however, the greater is the chance for error in judgment. Thus, allowance should be made for risk-bearing ability to cover errors of judgment in returns and repayment capacity as well as the short-term deviations of commodity prices from the average.

Technological Uncertainty

Another type of uncertainty arises from new techniques or methods of production. New crop varieties, fertilizer mixtures, feed combinations, models of machines, and the like, are continually being developed by research workers and business concerns. While these new developments usually are based on approved experimental procedures, the results realized may be different from expected on a given farm. For example, a new crop variety may have been tested, experimentally, for a three-year period and promise a five-bushel yield increase. However, for various reasons, a given farmer may realize no increase in yield. This type of technological uncertainty may force the farmer to use his risk-bearing ability if the new practice does not work out as anticipated.

Another type of technological uncertainty relates to the rapidity of technological change. A new method may be adopted, but a still better method may follow close behind, making the investment in the new method somewhat obsolete. The first mechanical corn pickers were soon made obsolete by improved models; the same was true of cotton pickers, combines, and balers. In such cases, a substantial portion of the investment in the machine disappears as soon as the new model comes on the market, and risk-bearing ability is needed to stand the loss.

A third type of uncertainty associated with technological change stems from the possibility of being "left behind" by not adopting new technological developments and adjusting the business to make full use of them. Many farmers who, a decade or so ago, had sufficient earning capacity and risk-bearing ability to use credit successfully now have become "questionable" credit risks. They have been slow to adopt new and improved practices and are operating the same size of unit as formerly. This has reduced their earning capacity in three ways: (1) by failing to adopt improved practices they have been unable to reduce costs; (2) by continuing to operate the same size of unit they have been unable to "spread" their increased fixed costs related to machinery and equipment; and (3) by continuing to operate the same size unit they have precluded the possibility of a larger income which many of their competitors have realized through expanding the size of business. Farmers incur risk of loss by not using credit or by not using enough credit as well as by using too much credit.

Uncertainty Caused by Actions of Other Businesses and People

The course of action which will be followed by firms and people the farmer does business with causes a fourth type of uncertainty. If the farmer acquires part of his capital by renting, for example, the future action of his landlord creates uncertainty. The landlord may decide to increase the rent, rent to his brother-in-law, or sell the farm. If such things should occur, they might reduce the tenant's earning capacity, and thereby curtail his risk-bearing ability. Similarly, if the farmer obtains part of his capital by borrowing, uncertainty may be caused by not knowing just what the lender will do. Customary financial arrangements allow some leeway for future negotiations or adjustments and the attitude of the lender at some point of time in the future may have an important bearing upon success of a farm venture. Government farm programs and various types of public action, such as taking of land for highways, all create a question as to what the future holds. Actions of businesses and people such as these create uncertainty in varying degrees which must be considered in analyzing risk-bearing ability.

Uncertainty Caused by Sickness, Injury, and Death

No one knows what the future health of family members will be, when a serious illness may occur, or when death will take some of the family members who are important in the business operation of the farm. Medical and hospital expense caused by a major illness may be substantial. When the farm operator is incapacitated, income suffers from loss of his labor and management in the business, and if he should die, a prime asset of the business is lost. Uncertainty arising from family health is of major importance in the farm business and should be fully recognized in considering risk-bearing ability.

QUESTIONS AND PROBLEMS

1. What is meant by risk-bearing ability? Why is it important in use of credit?
2. Outline the conditions which make risk-bearing ability necessary.
3. Using the dairy-hog and wheat-dairy farm examples, show how risk-bearing ability may limit the amount of credit which can be safely used.
4. What is the principle of increasing risk?
5. Set up a hypothetical table, such as Table 10.3, to illustrate the principle of increasing risk. Assume that total capital in the business remains constant and that equity declines. Does your illustration and the one in Table 10.3 support the same conclusions?
6. How does owner equity influence risk-bearing ability?
7. Explain how natural hazards cause a need for risk-bearing ability in use of credit.
8. What is the relationship of production uncertainty to risk-bearing ability in use of credit?

9. Explain how price fluctuations and price uncertainty cause a need for risk-bearing ability in use of credit.
10. What is meant by technological uncertainty? Why is it a factor in risk-bearing ability?
11. How do actions of other people influence the need for risk-bearing ability?
12. Why is risk-bearing ability needed to cover sickness, injury, and death?

REFERENCES

Aanderud, Wallace G., Plaxico, James S., and Lagrone, William F., *Income Variabiliy of Alternatie Plans, Selected Farm and Ranch Situations, Rolling Plains of Northwest Oklahoma,* Okla. Agr. Exp. Sta. and Farm Econ. Div., ERS, USDA, cooperating, Bul. B-646, 1966.
Bostwick, Don, *Studies in Yield Variability,* Mont. Agr. Exp. Sta. and Farm Econ. Div., ERS, USDA, cooperating, Bul. 574, 1963.
Boykin, Calvin C., *Cattle Ranch Adjustments to Drought in the Southern Plains,* Dept. Agr. Econ. and Soc., Tex. Agr. Exp. Sta., and Farm Econ. Div., ERS, USDA, cooperating, Rept. 2, 1964.
——, Gray, J. R., and Caton, D. D., *Ranch Production Adjustments to Drought in Eastern New Mexico,* N. Mex. Agr. Exp. Sta. and Farm Econ-Div., ERS, USDA, cooperating, Bul. 470, 1962.
Finley, Robert M., *The Influence of Acreage and Yield Changes on Crop Production in Nebraska,* Nebr. Agr. Exp. Sta. Res. Bul. 212, 1963.

Chapter 11

STRENGTHENING RISK-BEARING ABILITY

UNCERTAINTY caused by natural hazards, price fluctuation, and other risks is so great it may appear surprising that lenders are willing to advance credit to farmers, and that farmers are willing to assume the added risks involved in using credit. Fortunately, there are ways and means of strengthening risk-bearing ability to meet these challenges.

The means of strengthening risk-bearing ability are indicated by the five factors which make up risk-bearing ability as outlined at the beginning of the preceding chapter. The following measures will strengthen or improve these factors and, in turn, increase risk-bearing ability.

INCREASING INCOME AND SAVINGS

Ways of increasing income were discussed in the chapters on Returns as a Guide in Use of Credit. As was pointed out, using credit and capital obtained by other methods can help increase income *if marginal returns are greater than marginal costs.* Thus, ability to make money can be increased by increasing use of capital to the point where marginal costs and returns are equal.

The ability to save money depends in part on goals of the

individual and on the organization of the business. By developing clear-cut family goals, the amount of capital needed becomes evident and the goals serve as an incentive to save. Savings can also be increased by organizing the business to "force" an accumulation of equity. Generally, savings are greater where capital stays in the business and "grows" without being turned into cash periodically. When cash is available, it is easier to spend than when something must be sold to obtain cash. Indebtedness incurred for production items also tends to "force" savings, since a specified schedule of payments must be met.

PRICE ANALYSIS AND FORECASTING

Price analysis, the essential tool in forecasting market prices, is an aid in increasing income, and may also contribute to some of the measures for increasing risk-bearing ability. Prices go up and down as a result of certain combinations of forces which are at work in the economy. An analysis of the various supply, demand, and institutional forces which are operating at any one time is a complicated task because of the large number of factors involved. Nevertheless, some progress is being made in penetrating the mystery which surrounds the future. Reliable forecasts of future prices contribute much to risk-bearing ability by enabling the manager to plan his operations to attain maximum income.

Another advantage of price studies is the loan experience and perspective which they provide lenders and borrowers. Memory is short; it exaggerates the present and the immediate past. Reliable price studies serve as a "stabilizer," showing price fluctuations in the past, and what they are likely to be in the future.

Real estate loans as well as crop and livestock loans are subject to an unavoidable risk from price declines. Land value fluctuations, the bugbear of the mortgage lender, stem, in large part, from fluctuations in crop and livestock prices. Land values reflect the judgment of men regarding income from land for not one year but for many years into the future, each additional year having less weight. The present and immediate past have such a strong influence on man's judgment of the future that a period of low crop or livestock prices normally will pull down the value of crop or range land. Similarly, a period of high prices normally causes land values to rise. A longer perspective provided by price studies improves the basis for judgment and thereby strengthens risk-bearing ability.

Caution should be observed in using price forecasts. Carefully prepared forecasts are useful, but those who use them correctly do not expect them to be 100 per cent accurate.

PRODUCING A STABLE AND DEPENDABLE INCOME

Stability and reliability of income, the third factor contributing to risk-bearing ability, can be strengthened by measures which alleviate the types of risk and uncertainty discussed above. If all risk and uncertainty could be eliminated, the business could be planned and operated to yield a stable income year after year. It is not practical to strive for this goal in agriculture, however, because of the costs involved. In most cases, increasing stability of income reduces profits since a maximum product is not obtained from a given amount of resources, or conversely, the farm organization or type of operation does not permit a minimum cost for a given output. But survival of the business firm is essential to continued production, so failure of the business must be prevented if profits over a period of years are to be maximized. Therefore, it will pay to adopt measures essential to survival even though there may be a certain cost involved. Stability of income should be "purchased" by adoption of "stabilizing" practices until marginal costs involved (in terms of reduced profits) are equal to the marginal returns over the long run (which would automatically include the value of survival).

One method used to reduce the effect of yield variations is storage in good years to be utilized or sold in poor years. Farmers and ranchers have used this method for years to assure minimum hay supplies for livestock, particularly the breeding herd. Liquidation of the basic breeding herd affects production for several years, as was illustrated by analysis of risk-bearing ability of the wheat-dairy farm given in the preceding chapter. Quality as well as quantity of production may be affected when breeding herds developed over a period of years must be liquidated. Equally high quality replacement stock often are not available at reasonable cost. Any disruption of production which occurs naturally causes a disruption in the flow of income. But the disruption in income often is accentuated by differences in the price received when liquidating a herd versus the price for replacements. A section of the country and a large number of animals often are involved, which serves to depress the price received and to raise the price which must be paid. Moreover, animals sold as a result of drouth usually are thin, which further depresses the price received. Thus, storage of sufficient feed to carry basic breeding herds through normal drouth periods contributes materially to stabilizing income.

Other forms of storage also contribute to stabilizing production and income in drouth areas. Summer fallow coupled with proper tillage improves the chances for a satisfactory yield the following year. Range improvement practices, proper stocking, and the like, help develop good grass stands which contribute to greater carrying capacity in poor as well as in good years. Grass cured on the stump also constitutes another form of storage.

Expenditures in good years to improve the productivity of the farm unit help to insure the flow of income over time. Soil conserving practices do much to improve production as well as to preserve resources. Repair and renovation of buildings, and improvements in good times help forestall physical deterioration which occurs with use, functional obsolescence which results from progress of the technological revolution, and economic obsolescence which arises out of economic and social change, and thereby contributes to continued efficient production during poor periods. Expenditures on farm machinery and equipment have a similar effect. In each case, productive capacity can be stored in the business by making such expenditures in high income periods, thereby easing the requirements of the business for funds during poor periods and helping to sustain production and income.

As is evident from the above discussion, much can be said for storage as a means of smoothing the flow of income over time. However, not all the arguments are on the positive side. Expense is involved in storage, so it may not always be economically justified. Moreover, high yields and income must be obtained before reserves can be built. Even if this fortunate sequence occurs, high production on many farms is inadequate to build sufficiently large reserves to be of much assistance. Thus, there are pertinent arguments against as well as for the plan. However, it will contribute to stability on some farms and, therefore, merits consideration.

Storage may have some advantages from an income tax point of view, and thereby contribute to increasing risk-bearing ability. By helping to smooth the flow of income over time, the aggregate tax may be reduced, leaving more income available for other purposes. However, this point has less significance now than before 1964, due to a change in the law which permits farmers to use the *income averaging method* in computing their taxes. To be eligible to use the method, fluctuations in income must be substantial. Thus, it may be of little or no use to many farmers. In any event, it does not rule out the advantages of storage in helping to stabilize income over a period of years.

DIVERSIFICATION, ENTERPRISE SELECTION, AND PRODUCTION PRACTICES

One of the most common methods long employed to alleviate risk and uncertainty is diversification. By "distributing the eggs among several baskets," the chance of a large loss from a single misfortune or at any one time is reduced. Similarly, by having more than one enterprise in the farm business, the chance of a large loss from a given hazard is reduced. Losses may occur in each enterprise, but chances are against major losses occurring simultaneously in all enterprises, which reduces variability of net income for the whole business. Moreover, since each diversified enterprise is but one part of the total business, a major loss in one enterprise is smaller, relative to the size of the business.

When diversification is given as a means of reducing risk and uncertainty, it is assumed that the diversified business is organized so as to reduce rather than increase risk and uncertainty. It is possible to actually increase risk and uncertainty through diversification by adding "risky" enterprises to a fairly stable business, or by expanding the business materially in the diversification process.[1] For diversification to be most effective, enterprises included in the business should not be subject to the same hazards—or at least not to the same degree. If all crops included are equally affected by drouth at a given time of the year, little will be gained by diversifying. Similarly, if the enterprises added to the business are affected by the same price fluctuations as the enterprises already in the business, little stability of income will be attained by adding the new enterprises. Diversification is effective in combating risk and uncertainty to the extent the enterprises added are affected by different forces, or are basically more "stable" than those already in the business.

FLEXIBILITY

Flexibility has some advantages over diversification as a method contributing to stability and dependability of income. As

---

[1] For further elaboration of these points see: Earl O. Heady, *Economics of Agricultural Production and Resource Use,* Prentice-Hall, Inc., Englewood Cliffs, N.J., 1952, pp. 510–16.

time passes and added information is obtained, a flexible business can be adjusted to meet new circumstances, whereas an inflexible business allows little room for change. With an inflexible business, a farmer may anticipate a drop in income, but be unable to do anything about it. Moreover, enterprises which involve great risk and uncertainty usually also hold the possibility of great gain. Reducing risk and uncertainty by diversification simultaneously reduces the possibility of obtaining a large gain. Flexibility, on the other hand, facilitates adjustments to avoid risk and uncertainty, while still allowing the business to take advantage of larger gains which may be forthcoming.

Flexibility in organization of the farm business can be of three types: time, cost, and product. *Time flexibility* refers to the time involved in producing a product. Beef requires more time to produce than broilers. An orchard represents an inflexible production plan, while considerable flexibility exists with annual crops. A permanent building likewise may be less suited to flexibility than buildings with a shorter life.

Cost flexibility is attained by keeping fixed costs low in relation to total costs. Fixed costs, such as taxes, depreciation, and interest payments, do not vary with volume of production or income. Principal payments on intermediate- and long-term debts also are fixed outlays which have about the same effect as fixed costs. These fixed costs and outlays can be held down by various methods—custom operators can be used instead of buying expensive machines; land and livestock can be rented on a share basis and thereby the fixed obligations incurred by cash rental arrangements or by purchase can be avoided. In such ways, fixed costs and other obligations can be kept relatively low, enabling the farmer to more readily adjust costs of the business as current conditions justify.

Product flexibility refers to the possibility of adjusting the product produced to meet changing conditions. Grain-livestock producers have the choice of marketing grain or livestock. Ranchers operating on a cow-yearling basis can market either yearlings or calves, depending upon current feed and price conditions. A general-purpose building is constructed to permit a wider range of uses than one designed for a specific product. Some farmers raise dual-purpose cattle to facilitate emphasis on beef or milk production as current conditions justify. Products which are storable also add some flexibility in the business since they can be sold or stored, depending upon conditions at time of harvest.

It is evident that introducing flexibility considerations into the business increases the alternative opportunities open to the farmer, and thereby increases risk-bearing ability. Two cautions should be noted, however: (1) The increase in alternative opportunities means the farmer will have more choices to make—and, therefore, more opportunities for mistakes; and (2) other things being equal, a flexible farm business generally is less efficient than one which is inflexible. Therefore, striving for too much flexibility may actually reduce net income. And, since the level of net income is one factor influencing risk-bearing ability, it becomes clear that there is a limit as to how much flexibility a farmer should strive to achieve. Increasing flexibility will increase risk-bearing ability only as long as the marginal risk-bearing ability produced by flexibility is greater than that produced by the income sacrificed in achieving flexibility.

CONTRACTS

Contracts provide another method which can be used to help assure a dependable income and thereby strengthen risk-bearing ability. It may be argued that contracts are the exact opposite of flexibility—that by their very nature they create inflexible situations—and that both, therefore, cannot contribute to stability and dependability of income and risk-bearing ability. It is true that contracts create inflexible situations; that is their purpose. But, since they extend into the future or pertain to a future time period, they permit the farmer to compute his costs and income ahead of time and determine whether he should consider borrowing money. In this way, they contribute to a dependable income, although in doing so they eliminate the possibility of large "windfall" profits as well as large unexpected losses.

There are many different types of contracts. One major type involves "hedging" on the futures market. Hedging is the buying and selling of futures contracts in such a way as to reduce the risk of loss through a change in price. For example, the cattle feeder may hedge against a drop in price by selling a futures beef contract at the time he buys feeders. When the cattle are ready for market he purchases an offsetting contract and sells the cattle in the open market. If the price declines during the feeding period, the price paid for the offsetting contract is less than the price received for the futures contract sold initially. Thus, a profit is realized on the futures contract to offset the loss from the decline in price of the live animals.

Hedging may also be used by grain farmers as a protection against price declines during the growing season. For example, at planting time a wheat farmer may sell a futures contract for the amount of wheat he expects to produce. At harvest time he can purchase an offsetting contract and sell his wheat on the open market. The procedure and associated protection against a price decline is similar to that outlined for beef futures. However, grain futures may afford less protection than beef futures, and may actually increase the risk involved, due to differences in production uncertainty. Gains during the fattening period may be inefficient, and some death loss may occur. However, production generally turns out to be about as planned. Thus, approximately the same amount of beef is available for sale on the open market as is involved in the futures contracts. As a result, profits and losses will about offset each other, as was outlined above. However, grain production often does not turn out as planned, particularly in high-risk areas. If production is less than the hedged contract and the price of grain increases, hedging will increase a farmer's losses. A simplified example will illustrate what is involved. Assume a wheat farmer sells a 10,000-bushel futures contract at $1.50 and the price per bushel increases 50 cents during the growing season. If the farmer produces 10,000 bushels of wheat, all will be well—the offsetting contract will cost $20,000, the same as received for the 10,000 bushels in the open market. Thus, $15,000 is received for the crop, the amount obtained initially from sale of the futures contract. However, if production turns out to be only 5,000 bushels, the cost of the offsetting contract will be $10,000 more than the wheat will bring on the open market. As a result, the farmer will realize only $5,000 for his crop, or $5,000 less than if he had not hedged.

INSURANCE

Various types of insurance contribute to stability and dependability of income. This subject is considered in some detail in the following chapter.

DEVELOPING ABILITY TO BORROW

Ability to borrow in both good and poor times is developed over a period of years. It depends upon two things: (1) the ability of the borrower to qualify for a loan, and (2) the ability of the lender to understand and meet the credit requirements of the borrower. Requirements to qualify for a loan have comprised the subject of the last six chapters. The way in which a lender looks at a borrower is summarized in Chapter 15. Suffice it here to point out for emphasis that a basic ingredient is a sound credit rating. Such a credit rating must be built over a period of time on a foundation of honesty, integrity, willingness to assume responsibility, dependability, and a determination and will to work and sacrifice, if necessary, to fulfill an obligation or a contract.

The second consideration in developing ability to borrow—selection of a lender who understands agriculture and can meet credit requirements of the borrower—involves more than may "meet the eye." The right lender can contribute much to success of the farm business. Lenders build a "service rating" over a period of time the same as a farmer builds a "credit rating." The ingredients of the two have many similarities. Both are forged from changing economic and technological conditions. Only performance under different types of conditions indicates the true rating. By teaming up with a lender who has a high "service rating," the borrower will contribute materially to his ability to borrow.

People are inclined to think it is important to have the right lender only in financially difficult periods. The point of emphasis is on having a lender who will stay with the borrower during such periods. It is important to have a helpful, understanding, and sympathetic lender in difficult times. The difference between foreclosure and continued farm operation might well depend upon the lender. However, *it may be even more important to have the right lender in average and good times.* During such times, a lender with a high "service rating" can help a farmer build sufficient risk-bearing ability to safeguard the business against financial jeopardy in difficult periods.

An important ingredient of a high "service rating" is knowledge of the type of farming being carried on by the farmer and of related new technological developments, coupled with business management ability to visualize money-making possibilities. This type of knowledge enables the lender to visualize opportunities open to the farmer and to work with him in analyzing how much credit it will pay to use.

Ability of a lender to visualize how credit can help a farmer depends upon the administrators and personnel of the institution who are responsible for loan policy, loan analysis, and loan service.

Personnel who work directly with agricultural loans should have a broad and fairly detailed knowledge of the agriculture they serve. Technical knowledge of the physical sciences is necessary to provide an understanding of physical input-output relationships. These form the basis for business management decisions regarding how much capital can be profitably employed. Knowledge of economic principles is essential to provide the tools for sound business management decisions. Lenders without a knowledge of the economic concept of marginal analysis, for example, may arrive at incorrect management decisions. The type of situation which might be involved was illustrated in Table 5.2 of Chapter 5. A loan analyst may conclude it would be profitable to invest $1,200 in the hog enterprise, since the total return of $1,470 would give a nice profit. Marginal analysis, however, indicates it would not pay to put more than $900 in the hog enterprise.

In addition to being staffed by well-trained men, the lender selected must be permanent if the farmer is to be able to borrow in both good and poor times. By permanent is meant a lender who will continue to provide loan service over a period of years. Personnel of such lenders are also fairly permanent, which adds another important plus factor favoring continued reliable service.

A lender, such as a commercial bank, that is in a position to provide loan service in poor times must have made preparations in good times. Two types of preparation are needed. First, adequate reserves for losses must be developed. Financial institutions have problems in developing reserves the same as individual farmers. Earnings usually are not such as will permit rapid building of reserves. Moreover, usually only a small annual accrual to reserves for losses may be deducted as an expense item in arriving at income tax liability. Thus, prudent management provides for accumulating reserves for losses, both primary and secondary, over a period of years. Second, the board of directors and officers of the lending institution must develop a "liberal," as opposed to a "conservative," loan policy, together with the associated required knowledge. A conservative loan policy would limit maximum loans to that amount which the individual farmer could carry through the worst period likely to occur as indicated by past experience. Such a policy would mean no loans at all or only small loans to well-situated farmers.

A more liberal lending policy would be based on the knowledge that long periods of drouth and other severe losses do not occur frequently enough to warrant their use in limiting the amount loaned. The lender would stay with the farmer in case of one crop failure by financing him the next year, and still another year if necessary.

A liberal policy, such as the one outlined, requires several supplementary conditions. A local bank could put only a small amount of its funds into this type of investment. The reserve to meet possible losses from successive low crop years would have to be invested in securities which did not suffer from the same risk as the crop loans. Furthermore, the interest charged on these crop loans would have to be high enough to compensate for the losses that experience indicates are likely to occur. Finally, if the lending agency is a local bank, it may seriously question how far to go in making local crop loans because of its obligation to local depositors. A bank, as will be pointed out later, has a primary obligation to its depositors. The farmers who put their reserves on deposit in the bank would undoubtedly want to use those reserves during a series of bad crop years, at just the time when the bank would be least able to hand out the funds because these same farmers would be unable to pay either interest or principal on their crop loans.

Government credit may be necessary to supplement local bank credit in hazardous territory. A local bank is justified in following a conservative loan policy in hazardous crop territory, but a lending agency directly or indirectly connected with the Government is in a position to follow a liberal policy because the support of the Government makes it possible to balance the losses of successive low years against the better years.

The "normal" concept, developed during the Great Depression of the 1930's, is helpful in extension and use of credit in areas subject to wide fluctuations in income. Use of the "normal" concept is, in simple terms, an attempt at forecasting. "Normal" represents an estimate of what well-informed people think will happen in the future. As such it is not infallible. However, the concept extends the focus of attention from the present to the future and connotes a systematic effort to recognize conditions expected to prevail over a period of time in current decisions. Thus, the concept tends to give encouragement in poor periods, and to dampen enthusiasm in good times, thereby contributing to risk-bearing ability.

ABILITY TO REDUCE OPERATING AND LIVING EXPENSES

Ability to reduce operating and living expenses in poor periods contributes to risk-bearing ability by, in effect, reducing the need for it. If operating and living expenses were perfectly flexible there would be no need for risk-bearing ability. If income were poor these expenses could be curtailed as necessary to "make ends meet." An extreme degree of flexibility obviously is impractical, but to the extent expenses can be kept flexible, risk-bearing ability is strengthened. Success or failure of a loan might well depend upon ability and willingness of the family to "tighten the belt" in poor times. Just a willingness to "tighten the belt" is not enough; more important is good judgment in knowing which expenses to cut. A farmer with financial problems who buys a new expensive car and a new tractor, as one Great Plains farmer did, does not demonstrate an ability to curtail expenses which contribute to risk-bearing ability. In contrast, the farmer who put down an irrigation well and bought fertilizer showed an ability to choose among expenses so as to increase risk-bearing ability.

BUILDING OWNER EQUITY—THE BACKBONE OF RISK-BEARING ABILITY

Owner equity, or net worth, forms the backbone of risk-bearing ability by (a) helping to increase income, (b) reducing cash-fixed expenses, (c) providing funds to meet losses and unusual expenses, and (d) contributing to a basis for credit.

Capital which is owned by the farm family increases income by saving the interest which would have to be paid if the money were borrowed. Moreover, when capital is owned, fixed interest expenses are avoided, and avoiding fixed costs is one method of maintaining flexibility which contributes to risk-bearing ability. Probably more important than these is the role owner equity plays in providing capital for the farmer to work with. Owned capital can be used directly in the business and it also provides a basis for borrowing additional funds. The amount of capital a farmer employs in his business is an important determinant of his income-producing capacity, and in turn of his risk-bearing ability. In addition, owner equity contributes to risk-bearing ability by providing funds directly and through credit to meet losses and unusual expenses. This assumes, of course, that owner equity is not spread too thinly or "tied up" in fixed assets. Owner equity has risk-bearing value from the viewpoint of providing funds for emergencies, only to the extent that funds are in reasonably liquid form or that they contribute to a base for "reserve" borrowing capacity. For maximum risk-bearing ability, reasonable current, intermediate, and fixed liability-asset ratios should be maintained to facilitate obtaining funds necessary to meet obligations. This point is considered in some detail in Chapter 13.

QUESTIONS AND PROBLEMS

1. Give the ways by which risk-bearing ability can be strengthened.
2. Explain what is meant by price analysis and forecasting. How can these strengthen risk-bearing ability?
3. How can producing a stable and dependable income strengthen risk-bearing ability?
4. Name four methods which can be used to stabilize farm income.
5. In what ways does ability to borrow increase risk-bearing ability?
6. What is the "normal" concept? How does it contribute to risk-bearing ability?
7. Is there a normal value of cattle, sheep, corn, wheat, cotton, or farm land? If "normal" is an average, what years should go into the average and what method should be used to determine these years? What advantages, if any, does the "normal" concept have in farm financing?
8. Explain how reducing operating and living expenses strengthens risk-bearing ability.
9. How does owner equity influence risk-bearing ability?
10. Using the farm you used in question No. 13, Chapter 5, analyze the business to determine how risk-bearing ability could be increased.

REFERENCES

Economic Problems in Great Plains Ranching, Proceedings of GP-2 Symposium, Bozeman, May 23–24, 1962, Great Plains Council Publ. 22, published by Mont. Agr. Exp. Sta., 1964.

Grossman, P. A., and Headley, J. C., *Yield and Income Variability for Major Crops in Illinois: A Basis for Farm Decisions,* Dept. of Agr. Econ., Agr. Exp. Sta., AERR 73, 1965.

Management Strategies in Great Plains Farming, Proceedings of a Workshop held by Great Plains Research Technical Committee GP-2, May 5–7, 1959, Great Plains Council Publ. 19, published by Nebr. Agr. Exp. Sta., 1961.

Skold, M. D., Epp, A. W., and Hughes, H. G., *Profit Maximizing Plans for Farms in Southeastern Nebraska: By Type and Size of Farm,* Nebr. Agr. Exp. Sta. and Farm Econ. Div., ERS, USDA, cooperating, Bul. 219, 1965.

Skrabanek, R. L., Banks, V. J., and Bowles, G. K., *Farmer Adjustments to Drouth in a Texas County,* Tex. Agr. Exp. Sta. Bul. B-1005, 1964.

Chapter 12

RISK-BEARING ABILITY,
INSURANCE, AND INVESTMENT

RISK, a big factor in farming, varies by regions, by crops, and by individuals. The youthful tenant of a wheat farm in western Kansas has one combination of risks, while the middle-aged owner of a New York dairy farm has an entirely different combination. But both can use insurance and, we hope, investments to strengthen their risk-bearing ability. Insurance and investment considerations, especially important where credit is being used, are:

1. Recognition of risks
2. Use of reserves
3. Kinds and amounts of insurance to purchase in a given situation
4. Investments

In the setting up of reserves, as well as in the use of surplus funds, questions of investment arise which will be discussed following the consideration of risk and insurance.

RISKS

Farmers face two major kinds of risk—natural hazards and price fluctuations. Although most of the discussion in this chapter is devoted to insuring against natural hazards, this is only because insurance lends itself to this area. The risk from price fluctuations, one of the major hazards of farming, was treated in Chapters 10 and 11.

Natural hazards in farming are of two types. The first type centers around abnormal actions of the elements. Too little or too much rain, too little or too much heat, hail, unexpected frosts, lightning, tornadoes, and floods are the kinds most generally experienced. Damage to crops and property which any one farmer experiences may be small, viewed from the standpoint of society as a whole, but, and this is important, the damage to this individual farmer may be extremely large.

The second type of hazard centers around the individual. Accidents of all kinds and death are the principal kinds which are involved. A tractor may overturn, a hired man may break his leg from a fall in the barn, an auto collision may occur on the road to town, or disease may strike the operator or one of the family. These hazards may be small and inconsequential in terms of society, but, on the other hand, they may be a tragic occurrence on the individual farm.

RESERVES

To take care of very small risks and those not insurable the farmer can use reserves. Such small risks as having windows broken in the barn and a motor burn out are the type which the farmer can handle himself. In one sense, he can set up his own insurance agency to handle them. He has enough of these small risks, and they are sufficiently unconnected, so that he can predict with assurance that they will not all happen in the same year. A small sum set aside each year can be used for two purposes: first, to take care of what losses there are; and second, to build up a reserve to handle any abnormal losses that might occur. Wherever the risks are small, it is obvious that the farmer saves by carrying his own insurance because in this manner he does not have to pay the expense of running an insurance agency. However, it must be emphasized that this applies only to those small risks which the farmer can handle himself.

Reserves are especially useful for those large farm risks which are uninsurable. First and foremost is the risk of falling prices. In this case the bigger the reserve the better. Unfortunately, there is no accurate method to use in calculating the reserve needed, because we do not know how far prices may fall.

In building reserves, it is safe to allow for more than appears necessary in good times and for less in poor times. At least, that tends to compensate for the natural failing—to be incautious in prosperous times and overcautious at the tail end of a depression. Here again, we do not have an infallible guide, because what appears to be a period of depressed conditions may actually turn out to be a period of relatively good times. What is necessary at all times is recognition of the individual's inability to forecast price conditions with accuracy.

Reserves should be available at all times. We will give this matter more consideration in the discussion on investments. At this point, it is sufficient to insist that in order to serve as reserves any sums set aside must be in a "liquid" form, that is, be convertible into currency or bank deposits on short notice.

INSURANCE

Some risks are insurable and others are not. The difference will be found in the predictability of the occurrence and the extent of its coverage.

Natural hazards based on the elements vary in their insurability. Those such as fire, lightning, windstorms, and hail have been successfully incorporated into an insurance system because they are not only predicted with reasonable accuracy but they do not cover wide areas. Where the occurrence is isolated, as the usual farm fire, a local insurance company covering a county can handle most of the risks. But where the occurrence is a windstorm or hail which might cut a wide path, then a state or nationwide unit is better able to handle the risk than is a county unit.

Crop failures due to drouth which may cover wide areas are difficult to predict, such as a sequence of low crop yields which sometimes occurs in the Great Plains. As a consequence, neither local nor state units are big enough to do the insuring. Only a nationwide agency is big enough to cope with this type of risk.

Personal hazards lend themselves to insurance because they occur with predictable frequency when large numbers are included. It is unlikely that in any one area all individuals will be affected. It is, however, desirable that the agency doing the insuring have a

large volume of cases so it can be assured of experiencing about the
average frequency of loss.

Price fluctuations do not lend themselves to insurance as well
as do natural hazards because they are not as predictable and
because they are likely to affect wide areas, or even the whole nation
at the same time. Price fluctuations, which do not oscillate about a
fixed normal, are the product of man's actions—wars, unbalanced
budgets, monetary and fiscal policies, tariff regulations, and the like.
It is true that "normal" prices are estimated but there are no forces
which make prices average out over time equal to this "normal."
Hence any agency which attempts to insure against low prices has
little actuarial basis on which to operate. For this reason the Federal
Government is the only agency that dares attempt any sizable program of insurance in the price field. So far the Government's attempts have included price supports and insurance of certain mortgage loans made through the Farmers Home Administration, both
of which have congressional support.

Insurance and Pooling of Risks

Insurance is the combining or pooling of enough small unpredictable risks so that the annual losses for the combined group are a
predictable percentage of the total. What is a burdensome risk for
the individual farmer becomes in the pool an easily carried, relatively constant, annual loss expense for the insurance agency.

By paying his proportionate share or expense of the losses for
the group as a whole, plus his share of the expenses of running the
company, the individual is able to avoid the burden of a loss which,
if it struck him alone, might put him out of business or set him back
for years. The premium paid by the individual can be charged as an
expense to take care of the particular risk involved.

Fire insurance illustrates this pooling of risks especially well.
The farmer never knows for sure when he sets out for town with his
family whether a fire may destroy his barn or his home before he
returns. For years, or all his life, he may not have any fire, and then
again it may strike when he least expects it and result in an extremely heavy loss. In contrast to this extreme fluctuation in annual
loss and unpredictability, there is the relatively stable annual loss
figure per $1000 of insurance for the farm fire mutuals in the United
States. Data published by the U.S. Department of Agriculture show
that in the long period from 1914 through 1964 (the latest year for

which data are available) the average loss for mutual fire companies in the United States varied from a low of $1.38 per $1000 in 1952 to $2.49 in 1932. More than chance was no doubt responsible for the $2.49 figure at the bottom of the depression because there is so much pressure to get cash in such a period. But even with this factor included there is relatively little change from year to year in the losses experienced.

Insurance, in order to pay, has to cover not only the losses but also the expenses of running the agency. For the fire mutuals these expenses between 1914 and 1964 varied between a low of 58 cents a thousand in 1922 to $1.04 a thousand in 1964. In recent years both losses and expenses have been going up. An average figure in recent years would be $1.90 a thousand in losses and 90 cents a thousand in expenses or a total of $2.80 a thousand of insurance. From this it is evident that the expense of the agency itself may be one-third of the premium cost, with the actual losses around two-thirds of the premium.

All phases of insurance, fire, crop, liability, and life, rest on the same principle of pooling unpredictable individual risks into a group risk total for which the annual loss can be predicted within narrow limits. Crop insurance, as we shall see, presents some special problems because the actuarial base is so indefinite. But fire, liability, life, and associated types of insurance lend themselves readily to the pooling principle. This is not to say that the predictable life or liability rates for large groups never change, because they do, as indicated by rates for automobile insurance. But the changes that do occur can be measured, and appropriate changes made in premiums so that insurance cost is kept in line with loss experience and cost of running the insurance company.

Kinds of Insurance

The different kinds of insurance and the factors which determine the amount which should be purchased can be discussed advantageously in four different categories—fire and windstorm, crop, liability, and life.

FIRE AND WINDSTORM INSURANCE

Although farm fires frequently result in a total building loss because of the absence of fire-fighting equipment, farmers may easily and inexpensively insure against fire. An invariable rule of nearly all mortgage lenders is to require fire and windstorm insurance on the farm buildings located on mortgaged real estate. The average cost of fire insurance through county mutuals, according to the U.S. Department of Agriculture, has varied between $2.16 and $3.38 a thousand during the period 1914–64. During recent years the cost has averaged about $2.80 per thousand of insurance. These average costs are for the United States as a whole. Consequently, they do not reveal the variations between states which, it happens, are extremely wide, varying from practically nothing to over $10.00. A large number of states, however, are in a narrow range, with annual costs in the neighborhood of $3 per thousand dollars of mutual fire insurance. For a set of buildings valued at $15,000, fire insurance covering 80 per cent of the value, or $12,000, would cost about $36 a year, a small amount considering the risk and the financial embarrassment to an indebted farm owner if he has a bad fire and no insurance. Farm mortgage lenders usually have the fire insurance policy assigned to them so that they are protected in the event of any fire losses. If a fire should destroy the barn on a mortgaged farm, the lender has the right to insist on using the funds to replace the barn or to reduce the principal of the mortgage.

Windstorm insurance, like fire insurance, is cheap compared to the heavy loss which may be suffered by an individual farmer. In fact, some fire insurance policies cover windstorm damage as well. Windstorm damage, including losses from tornadoes, cyclones, and hurricanes, is much more common in some areas than in others. The Pacific Coast and New England rarely have windstorms, but if such storms do occur, they may be so disastrous as to wipe out the life savings of a farm family.

Windstorm insurance is less costly than fire insurance. An average cost figure which is based on fifty years of experience is $1.355 per $1,000. For the set of buildings valued at $15,000, coverage of 80 per cent would cost only $16.26 a year. Lenders follow the same policy with windstorm insurance as with fire, requiring an assignment so that proceeds from losses may be used in rebuilding or in reducing the mortgage.

CROP INSURANCE

Private insurance companies have offered general crop insurance at different times. Attempts were made in 1899, 1917, 1919,

1931, and 1937.[1] Every attempt failed, with five principal reasons being listed by Buckler as responsible. First of all, price risk was assumed as well as yield risk. Second, the premiums were not high enough, due to lack of good actuarial data. Third, adverse selectivity prevailed, with many instances of applications being accepted from farmers whose crop prospects were already poor. Fourth, there was poor administration. Fifth, there was not enough capital in the insuring agency to withstand several years of poor crops.

The demand for general crop insurance persisted, with Congressional hearings and inquiries. In the meantime, the Federal Government was finding it necessary to extend large quantities of relief credit in areas of crop failures. It seemed reasonable that a procedure could be devised that would enable farmers to purchase insurance to cover the great risk of a crop failure—a risk which could reduce them from solvent business units one year to bankrupt units the next. As a result of the agitation for a crop insurance system, Congress established the Federal Crop Insurance Corporation in 1938.

Many problems and heavy losses were experienced during the early years of the program. As a result Congress decided in 1947 to put the program on an experimental county basis. Emphasis was placed on establishing a good actuarial base, efficient administration, and an attractive insurance policy that would gain the support of a large number of substantial farmers. In order to improve the quality of risks to develop a sound program, some very high-risk land in many counties and fourteen whole counties in the "Dust Bowl" area of the Great Plains were excluded. This improved the financial results and indicated that a satisfactory actuarial base could be established. For the 1948–65 period, as shown in Table 12.1, premiums exceeded indemnities.

Counties in which the program operated during the period 1948–65 and the related loss experience are shown in Figure 12.1.

In 1961, emphasis shifted from experimenting to develop a sound basis for insurance to expansion of service to farmers. The Corporation's progress in this direction is shown by the following comparisons:[2]

---

[1] James L. Buckler, "All Risk Crop Insurance." Thesis submitted to George Washington Univ., 1950, pp. 3–7. (Mimeo.)

[2] Figures from the 1965 Annual Report of the Federal Crop Insurance Corporation.

	1961	1966	Per Cent Increase
Number of insurance counties	890	1,304	46
Number of county programs	1,597	3,025	89
Premium income	$ 18,150,000	$ 37,014,000	104
Protection provided	$271,709,000	$639,953,000	135

Crop insurance becomes increasingly important as cash costs of producing crops increase, and profit margins narrow. The Federal Crop Insurance Corporation is expanding its service to meet the needs of farmers as rapidly as possible within the limitations imposed by legislation and the availability of funds and experienced personnel. The list of crops insured by the Corporation is shown in Table 12.1.

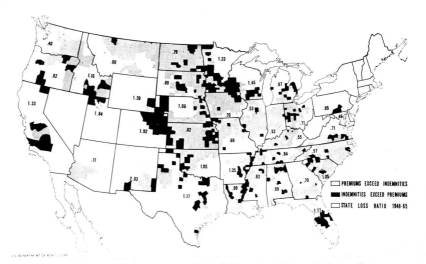

Fig. 12.1—Location of counties in which the Federal Crop Insurance Corporation operated during the 1948–65 period and its loss experience. (Courtesy of the Federal Crop Insurance Corporation.)

Intensive study and effort have been made by the Federal Crop Insurance Corporation to modernize the insurance plans, including contract provisions, coverages, and rates. Major improvement has been made in most insurance plans not only by reworking the actuarial structure, taking into consideration higher farm yields made possible by advanced technology, but also through simplification of the contract provisions.

Insurance for most crops is in the form of a guarantee of a

TABLE 12.1

FEDERAL CROP INSURANCE EXPERIENCE FOR THE PERIOD 1948–1965, BY CROPS*

Crop	Net Premiums	Indemnities	Excess of Premiums Over Indemnities	Loss Ratio
	(thousands)	(thousands)	(thousands)	
Apple............	$ 391	$ 181	$ 210	.46
Barley...........	6,136	4,744	1,393	.77
Bean............	2,992	3,797	−805	1.27
Cherry...........	112	227	−116	2.03
Citrus...........	4,387	8,533	−4,146	1.94
Combined Crop....	30,168	35,979	−5,811	1.19
Corn............	47,379	59,446	−12,067	1.25
Cotton..........	34,172	30,479	3,694	.89
Flax............	11,722	9,540	2,181	.81
Grain Sorghum....	2,037	1,510	527	.74
Oat.............	2,168	1,198	969	.55
Orange..........	1,806	2,012	−205	1.11
Pea, dry.........	198	119	79	.60
Pea, green........	930	1,625	−695	1.75
Peach...........	2,143	3,193	−1,050	1.49
Peanut..........	2,139	1,574	565	.74
Potato..........	791	1,854	−1,063	2.34
Raisin...........	1,567	1,344	223	.86
Rice............	193	102	90	.53
Safflower........	2	8	−6	4.03
Soybean.........	12,914	11,030	1,884	.85
Sugarbeet........	89	26	63	.29
Tobacco.........	38,131	21,912	16,219	.57
Tomato.........	84	25	59	.30
Tung Nut........	25	2	23	.08
Wheat..........	182,061	164,739	17,322	.90
Total........	$384,738	$365,200	$19,538	.95

* SOURCE: *Summary of Experience, Federal Crop Insurance Corporation, 1948–65,* Fed. Crop Ins. Crop., USDA.

specified number of bushels or pounds per acre. On some fruit and specialty crops, all-risk insurance is not practical, and only losses from certain named specific risks are insured against. However, more than 90 per cent of the insurance offered by FCIC is all-risk insurance, which means that if the farmer does not produce the amount of the insured crop guaranteed by his insurance contract due to loss from insurable causes, he receives an indemnity payment. Indemnities are paid in cash at a price per bushel or pound selected by the insured, from among several options, before the insurance becomes effective. For instance, a wheat grower with a coverage of

20 bushels per acre and a yield of only 10 bushels would be paid $20 per acre if he had selected $2 per bushel for computing indemnities, and $15 per acre if he had selected $1.50.

The statutory maximum quantity which may be guaranteed is 75 per cent of the average yield for the farming unit. If 75 per cent of the average yield represents generally more protection than the investment in the crop for the area, the percentage guaranteed must be reduced accordingly. Because yields and risks may vary greatly, most counties are divided into two or more areas for the purpose of setting coverages and rates. Premium rates in many instances are set on the basis of dollars per $100 of coverage.

Premiums are also adjusted to reflect individual experience. If a farmer has had no losses for which he was paid an indemnity for three years, he gets a 5 per cent premium discount; if he has had no losses for four years, the discount is 10 per cent; for five years, 15 per cent; and for six years, 20 per cent; and if he has had no loss for seven years, he gets a 25 per cent discount. Beginning with the 1967 crop year, a discount of 5 per cent after the first and second years with no indemnified loss, and a 10 per cent discount after the third year is allowed on a number of crops. No change was made in the discount provisions for other years.

Another premium discount plan applies on wheat. It provides that if the crop is continuously insured and the premiums paid by a farmer exceeds indemnities paid to him by an amount as large as the full coverage on the current crop, he gets a reduction of 50 per cent in his premium. In the case of wheat and cotton, a discount is granted, ranging from 4 per cent to 20 per cent for large acreages.

Crop insurance covers loss in quality as well as loss in quantity of production. Quality and quantity are not separate but blended together so that large production in quantity may offset loss in quality. The method used for the different crops varies with the marketing practices, but the most usual method is to adjust the quantity of production downward by a formula if the quality is poor.[3]

From a credit standpoint, crop insurance has an outstanding advantage: It can be assigned to the lender as collateral for the payment of a loan. A lending agency which cannot lend to a farmer because he has little if any security, may find that with the guaranty of crop insurance, it can finance the farmer's crop expenses. The Federal Crop Insurance Corporation recognizes the importance of

[3] William H. Rowe, *Federal Crop Insurance in Brief*, FCIC. Revised, Mar., 1966.

this feature by providing regular forms on which a collateral assignment can be made to a lender by the farmer and approved by the Corporation. During the 1965 crop year, crop loans totaling around $40 million were made, using Federal Crop Insurance policies as collateral.

HAIL INSURANCE ON CROPS

Hail insurance is being used without Federal crop insurance, but also it is being used as a supplement to Federal crop insurance where the farmer wants more protection. Mutuals, stock companies, and some state departments have written hail insurance for years. In recent years nearly $3 billion of hail insurance has been written annually, at a cost of approximately $110 million in premiums and with losses paid amounting to $65 to $75 million.

A young farmer with a heavy debt load is the one who needs hail insurance the most. And he is the one who usually finds the premium hard to pay. Farmers usually buy hail insurance when they have an excellent crop prospect and pass it over when the crop prospect is poor. Rates vary according to the risks involved. Average losses paid per $100 of hail insurance coverage, by states, during the period 1952–63 are shown by the map in Figure 12.2. The high risk

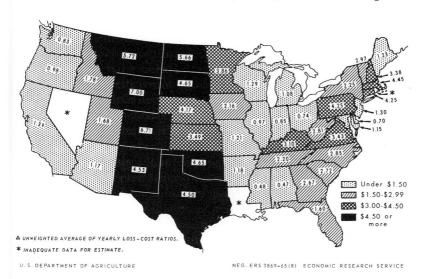

△ *UNWEIGHTED AVERAGE OF YEARLY LOSS-COST RATIOS.*

∗ *INADEQUATE DATA FOR ESTIMATE.*

U. S. DEPARTMENT OF AGRICULTURE   NEG. ERS 3869–65(8) ECONOMIC RESEARCH SERVICE

Fig. 12.2—Losses paid per $100 of hail insurance coverage, average 1952–63. (Courtesy of the Economic Research Service, USDA.)

of hail in the Great Plains, where drouth is a serious factor, is evident.

From the credit standpoint, hail insurance offers additional risk-bearing ability. Where the borrower is short on equity, is dependent for his income largely on grain, and is located in a high-risk hail area, hail insurance provides a ready-made answer to the search for more security. And it is much better for the young farmer to take out hail or crop insurance at once and stop if he wishes after he has been hailed out and reimbursed, than to wait until hail has caught him without insurance and then, as so many do, take it out the next year.

LIABILITY INSURANCE

Liability insurance takes many forms. The farmer's dog may injure a visitor, a hired man may suffer an accident, or the driver of the farmer's truck may be involved in an accident on the highway.

Auto liability insurance would cover this last type. And the company which has insured the farmer would defend him in court. This insurance gives peace of mind and security to the farmer at a relatively small cost. In addition to liability for bodily injury or death, liability is also included for damage to the property of others caused by automobile or truck.

Other forms of liability are covered in what is termed a comprehensive personal liability policy and an employer's or workmen's compensation policy. The first covers such acts as the dog biting a visitor, the second takes care of the accident to the employee. The workmen's compensation policy has the advantage that it provides medical payments to the injured employee. Farmers with hired help will do well to go into the details of these policies to be certain that they have protected themselves and their employees against these kinds of risk.

LIFE INSURANCE

Farmers have to face the risk of death. Fortunately, a highly developed system of insurance is available to serve the farmer in this area. A good example of the types of policies offered is provided by a sample list of rates at different ages, the rates being based on the American Experience Mortality Table at a 3 per cent interest rate. These are shown in Table 12.2.

TABLE 12.2

Net Premiums Per $1,000 of Life Insurance for Different Types of Policies and Different Ages*

Type of Policy	Age in Years When Policy Is Issued			
	20	30	40	50
10-Year Term	$ 7.80	$ 8.64	$10.73	$17.50
Ordinary Life	14.41	18.28	24.75	36.36
20-Pay Life	23.13	27.19	33.14	42.95
20-Year Endowment	40.77	41.37	43.01	48.24

* Source: Based on American Experience Mortality Table. Taken from *Life Insurance for Farmers*, USDA Misc. Pub. 621, 1947, p. 5. The premiums shown do not allow for expenses, so that rates actually charged may be higher but, on the other hand, no allowance is made for dividends because of more favorable experience than is used in this table.

Term Life Insurance

Strictly speaking, term life is pure life insurance. No savings are involved. It is like fire, auto, liability, or other forms of insurance in that if the event does not happen during the period, there is no payment. If you take out a 10- or 20-year term policy and do not die in this period there is no payment at any time during the period or at the end. And similarly, if you had your house insured against fire for 20 years and did not have any fire, you would not expect any payment during the period or at the end.

Term is the ideal insurance to go with farm credit. A farmer buying a farm with a $10,000 mortgage can take out $10,000 of term insurance to cover this mortgage at a relatively low cost and in this way protect his family against the burden of the mortgage in case he dies. In the same manner, the young farmer can protect his family during the period when his children are growing up and he is accumulating a reserve to take care of his and his wife's old age.

Term insurance, however, does not provide any savings. For savings, an ordinary life, 20-pay life or an endowment policy should be used.

Ordinary Life, 20-pay Life, and Endowment Insurance

These policies provide what their names signify. *Ordinary life* is a policy on which the insured pays his premium each year as long as he lives. Unlike term, though, he is certain that his beneficiary will collect the full amount of the policy when he dies because the policy has no termination other than the death of the insured.

A *20-pay life,* or similar type policy, provides for a limited number of years in which the insured pays premiums. Other variations of this type are those policies which specify "paid up at age 65" or at some other age. In all these policies the insured can figure a specific number of years during which he must pay a fixed premium. At the expiration of this period, he has paid-up life insurance for the rest of his life. On his death the beneficiary gets the face value of the policy. This naturally costs more per year than ordinary life because the payments cover fewer years.

An *endowment policy,* which includes a large element of savings, provides for the accumulation of the entire policy sum in a given number of years. At the end of this period the insured, if he is still living, receives the face amount of the policy.

For a farmer who is short of capital, term insurance is generally the most desirable form to purchase, with ordinary life next, and with short-period endowment the least attractive. Various combinations are available in policies designed to serve given situations; for example, family income policies are available that provide a combination of term and ordinary life. Life insurance has many angles and deserves a lot of study. All that we have done here is to outline some of the main principles, leaving the details to be worked out in specific cases.

Other insurance policies of the personal type include *accident, health,* and *hospital.* These and life insurance are being made available in an increasing number of instances on a group basis. Where farmers can avail themselves of protection through a group policy offered by one of the organizations to which they belong, it is likely that the cost can be reduced through the savings made possible by handling the insurance on a wholesale basis.

Annuities, providing protection for old age, can be purchased in a lump sum or by paying in amounts over a period of time. An annuity can be arranged in several different ways. A straight life annuity is a payment per month or per year for the rest of the person's life or for the rest of both the husband's and wife's lives, if desired. If the people insured live a long time the company loses, but makes up on those who die earlier than expected. This is just the opposite of life insurance. Another type called "refund" annuity calls for the return of the fund accumulated, which means that if the person dies early his beneficiary gets the balance due him.

INVESTMENTS

For many farmers, particularly those in debt, their own farm provides all the opportunity they need or can use for investing any savings that become available. It is true that these farmers may want to have a small reserve available for an emergency, but otherwise their savings would be invested in livestock, fertilizer, principal payments on the mortgage, and the like, on their farm. There are other farmers, fortunately, for whom the question of investment presents interesting and important problems.

Let us take, for example, the tenant who is accumulating a fund to use in buying a farm. He has his livestock, machinery, and all his chattels free of debt and at the end of the year has $3,000 available which he wants to invest temporarily until he has enough saved to make a good down payment on a farm. Another example is the farm owner of middle age who has his farm and all his livestock and equipment paid for and no desire to buy additional land. He wants to invest $3,000 from farm earnings so he can use it later, when he retires.

Whether to invest inside or outside the farm requires an evaluation of the specific situation. There is nothing inherently bad about putting savings into some form of asset outside the farm. In fact, there are many situations where such action is desirable. To have a reserve invested in readily available form outside the farm may add much to risk-bearing ability. On the other hand, in another situation, it may be better to invest the savings at home on the farm in more fertilizer, more livestock, or in extra payments on the farm mortgage.

Reserves outside the farm have been referred to as a desirable form of investment. One reserve of an emergency character is the advance payment on a farm mortgage where this payment is segregated to be used when the farmer has a bad year. Since the mortgage agency, usually a Federal Land Bank or an insurance company, allows the farmer the same rate of interest on this advance payment as on the mortgage loan, the effect is the same as using the payment to reduce the principal of the loan. But the advantage of this reserve payment is that in case of a bad year, the reserve funds can be used to take care of the interest as well as any required payment on the principal.

Diversification is a valid reason for outside investments. Since farming is a business with considerable risk, especially in some areas, it is logical for the farmer to safeguard his future by taking his savings out of farming and placing them in some assets that will not be affected by the same ups and downs as farming, If farming is unprofitable for a period, the farmer may find that his outside investments have stood up well and that he can retire as he planned even though farm income has not been up to expectations. Or if farming becomes very prosperous and his outside investments do poorly, he may still have the necessary funds from farming to retire as he planned.

What may hurt the farmer is a period of adversity which hits both the farm and the outside investments. A severe economic depression, for example, can easily affect adversely both the farm and the outside investments. However, there are ways, such as placing the outside investments in cash or government bonds, which minimize this risk. In short, if farming is in a depression, with low land values and low prices for farm products, the investments in government bonds or the bank deposits will provide a helpful cushion against the shock of this low price situation.

For those farmers who find it desirable to invest outside the farm there exist a large number of possibilities of which the following six general classes represent the principal ones:

1. Cash and bank deposits
2. Savings accounts and government bonds
3. Insurance and annuities
4. Nongovernment bonds
5. Corporation stocks and mutual funds
6. Nonfarm real estate

The setting aside of funds in cash or bank deposits calls for little, if any, explanation. It should be pointed out, though, that a small reserve of this type provides not only security of mind but an extremely useful method of handling unforeseen emergency expenditures. Cash and bank deposits are the first line of defense in an emergency. They constitute the liquid funds that can be used at a moment's notice.

The second line of defense is the fund invested in savings accounts and government bonds. Information on these avenues of investment can be had from banks or from the post office. Some liquidity is sacrificed in these investments but, in return, a small interest return is received. Another feature of these investments is that they are in dollar form so that if prices go down, their purchasing power increases correspondingly. In short, they represent a hedge against deflation. The balance sheet of agriculture, presented in Chapter 1, shows that farmers have built up substantial reserves in both deposits and government bonds.

Insurance and annuities, the third class, are another dollar hedge not only against death and old age but also against deflation. One of the weaknesses of this type of investment is the loss of purchasing power which occurs if the price level rises. Those who put money away for their old age when prices are at, say, an index of 100 and then retire when prices are up to an index of 200 know what this loss of purchasing power means. On the other hand, insurance as a protection in case of death, accidents, and the like, is similar to an expense of running the business.

Bonds of various kinds are another form of dollar investment which are available. Municipal, industrial, and public utility bonds are the principal types. Before an investment is made in bonds, however, a careful study and investigation should be made to determine the financial position of the company or organization issuing the bonds and the likelihood that sufficient income will be available, even in low income years, to meet the bond interest. Inquiry at a bank or other financial agency will usually result in information of the kind desired, plus ratings which are available on different bond issues.

The last two investment types, stocks and real estate, provide a hedge against inflation; that is, they generally go up along with the general price level. Unless a farmer has his farm paid for, he probably will not be interested in investments of this type because his farming enterprise itself is an excellent investment for an inflationary or price-rising period. For one who is considering stocks or real estate, careful investigation, similar to that recommended before buying bonds, is suggested. A few shares of stock in a widely diversified, well-established company provide an opportunity to get acquainted with modern business organization and at the same time earn a substantial return in dividends if times are good. The annual reports and other information issued by the corporation can be studied to obtain an understanding of the profits or losses made; in short, an investment of this kind may lead to an interesting education in business organization and finance. For those not interested or not sufficiently informed in selecting individual stocks, there are various mutual funds available which at a somewhat greater cost provide a diversified investment in common stock.

Real estate presents even more problems because it is not bought and sold in small units or shares like stocks. And though it is not hard to sell real estate on a rising market, it may be difficult to sell at other times. Finally, real estate usually takes special management or the hiring of some qualified personnel or agency to do the managing. This is not to say that real estate investments are not recommended, because they may be at the top of the list in certain situations as, for example, the purchase of a home in town by the farmer who is looking forward to retirement from the farm and has the funds to invest in such a home.

In all of his decisions involving insurance and investments, the farmer will do well to keep in mind his overall program. The insurance program should be gone over carefully to see that all of the risks are considered, with protection purchased where it is deemed advisable. And the investment program also should be scrutinized with care to see that the proper balance between reserves and farm investments is obtained and that the desired balance between inflation-proof and deflation-proof investments exists.

QUESTIONS AND PROBLEMS

1. What is the difference between the risks faced by a farmer and a drug store proprietor in your community?
2. What risks on a farm are difficult or impossible to insure? Why is this true?
3. Explain the principle of insurance. What is needed to set up an insurance company to insure a certain risk?
4. What are the rates for fire, windstorm, and hail insurance in your community? Estimate the proportion of the rate which is used for expenses and the proportion paid out in losses to policyholders.
5. Explain how Federal crop insurance works. (Material from the Federal Crop Insurance Corporation, either from the state or Washington, D.C., offices, may be obtained to be used by the class in answering this question.)
6. Discuss advantages and disadvantages of different types of life insurance for a farmer with a mortgage on his farm.
7. Explain how insurance can be used to strengthen risk-bearing ability.
8. What is meant by inflation-proof and deflation-proof investments? Give examples.
9. Explain how investments can be used to increase risk-bearing ability.

REFERENCES

Barr, Wallace, and Dougan, Riley, in cooperation with Hempy, Edgar, *Crop Insurance,* Ohio Agr. Ext. Serv. Bul. 392, Aug., 1959.

Botts, Ralph R., *Insurance Facts for Farmers,* USDA Farmers' Bul. 2137, 1963.

Collins, G. P., and Hayward, J. W., *Insurance as Related to Farm Financial Risk in Payne County, Oklahoma,* Okla. Agr. Exp. Sta. Bul. B-609, 1963.

Federal Crop Insurance Corporation, *Annual Reports.*

Garland, S. W., *Insurance for Farmers,* Canada Dept. of Agr. Publ. 1188, 1964.

Jones, Lawrence A., and Larson, Donald K., *Economic Impact of Federal Crop Insurance in Selected Areas of Virginia and Montana,* ERS, USDA, Agr. Econ. Rept. 75, May, 1965.

Perkinson, Leon B., *Crop-Hail Insurance in the United States,* ERS, USDA, ERS-249, 1965.

Rowe, William H., *Events Leading Up to the Passage of the Federal Crop Insurance Act in 1933,* Fed. Crop Ins. Corp., 1965. (Mimeo.)

Chapter 13

RISK-BEARING ABILITY INDICATED
BY BALANCE SHEET ANALYSIS

IN the three preceding chapters the meaning and significance of risk-bearing ability have been discussed, together with factors which comprise risk-bearing ability and ways in which these can be strengthened. Owner equity was included as one of these factors; in fact, this is the factor which plays the important role of being the backbone of risk-bearing ability. Thus, risk-bearing ability is reflected directly by the balance sheet, the financial statement which indicates the owner's equity. The balance sheet shows much of the ability of the business to weather storms and pick up speed in prosperous times. It shows the fundamental soundness of a business.

The objective of this chapter is to analyze the balance sheet to determine the information it provides relative to use of credit, particularly risk-bearing ability. Factors which influence the owner's equity are considered, together with the need for physical data to aid in proper interpretation of the financial data. The relationship of assets to liabilities is analyzed from the viewpoint of credit requirements versus prospective income, another factor related directly to risk-bearing ability. As background for this analysis a brief discussion is given of the balance sheet and how it is organized.

The Balance Sheet and Its Organization

The *balance sheet,* also called the net worth statement, is a summary of the assets and liabilities of a business, together with a statement of the owner's equity. The owner's equity is also commonly referred to as the net worth of the business. The balance sheet is a comparatively simple statement and has come into common usage in the business world. The lender or lender's agent usually obtains a statement as a part of every loan application, whether it be for a short-, intermediate-, or long-term loan. Local banks often make it a practice to keep on file an up-to-date statement of the financial condition of each borrower. Financial statements also are used by farmers in record keeping and in making out income tax reports, and may be used by landlords in interviewing prospective tenants.

The balance sheet has two characteristics that should be kept clearly in mind: (1) It *always refers to a specific date or point in time,* and (2) it *always is divided into three parts:*

1. The assets or value of things owned
2. The liabilities or amounts owed
3. The difference between these two, which is the *owner's equity* or *deficit.*

It is this last item, the owner's equity or deficit, which makes the statement balance.

The record of Farm Business A, introduced in Chapter 6, will be used as an aid in studying the balance sheet and in developing the analysis related to risk-bearing ability. The record covers the first half of the 1960's, giving an opportunity to observe changes which occurred over time and how these are involved in the analysis. A balance sheet for Farm Business A as of January 1, 1959, in its simplest form, is shown in Table 13.1.

The first point to observe in a balance sheet is the date. A balance sheet represents a snapshot of the business at just one instant of time, in this example at the close of business on December 31, 1958, and the beginning of business on January 1, 1959. Since the ending of one year is the beginning of the next, the instant of time is midnight on December 31. The statement given does not hold for the end of the day on January 2 because Farmer A may have sold a load of grain during the day to a neighbor. Obviously, this

TABLE 13.1

FARM BUSINESS A
Balance Sheet as of January 1, 1959

Assets		Liabilities and Owner's Equity	
Cash	$ 206	Accounts Payable	$ 142
Grain	3,624	Notes	12,982
Hay	982		
Livestock	6,052		
Machinery	8,042	Owner's Equity	5,782
TOTAL	$18,906	TOTAL	$18,906

transaction would affect the balance sheet. It is important, there-fore, that the balance sheet be recognized for what it is, *a statement of the financial position of the farm business as of a certain date.* A snapshot is a good analogy because a balance sheet is a picture of the business at the time, and only at the time, the picture is taken. An income statement, as was shown in Chapter 6, is more like a moving picture which shows what happens through a period of time.

The form shown is the conventional one used in accounting; the assets, or items owned on January 1, 1959, are listed on the left side of the statement. The total of these assets as shown is $18,906. Supposedly, this is the sum for which Farmer A could sell his farm business within a reasonable time. Whether he could actually sell for this amount brings up issues that will be reserved for later discussion. On the right side of the statement are the liabilities, or the debts owed, totaling $13,124. The difference between the assets and liabilities is $5,782, which represents the owner's equity, or net worth, of Farmer A in his business. Thus a farmer may be operating a farm business with assets of $100,000, but if he has debts of $80,000, he as an individual is worth only $20,000. It is the net worth, not the assets, that indicates the solvency of the borrower.

The question is often raised as to why the net worth figure is placed on the liability side of the statement. It is placed there to show that the owner, like other creditors, has a claim against the business equal to the net worth figure. The balance sheet gives the inventory value of property owned, subtracts from this the total debts owed, and calls the remainder the equity or net ownership of the farmer in his business. Thus the assets are the first considera-tion. After they are valued, the people and businesses who have given Farmer A credit are allotted a portion of the assets equal to their total loans, and the remainder of the assets are considered as belonging without qualification to Farmer A. If the assets were sold, the creditors would come first and Farmer A would get what was left, which would be more or less than the net worth, depending on whether the assets actually sold for more or less than they were valued on the balance sheet. So the net worth actually is a liability of the business, for the business owes that amount to the owner, just as it owes stated amounts to the lenders.

When the value of liabilities, or debts, is greater than the value of assets, the difference is called *net deficit,* and the farmer is insolvent to that extent. A net deficit is placed on the "Assets" side of the balance sheet because it represents the *shortage* of assets. Thus, when the tangible assets and the shortage of assets are added, they will equal the total liabilities—and the two sides of the balance sheet really balance.

Assets usually are listed according to the ease with which they may be converted into cash, beginning with cash on hand and ending, as in the examples, with land and buildings which are difficult to sell on short notice. The listing may be in the abbreviated form as in Table 13.1, but it is desirable to divide the assets into current assets, such as cash and livestock; intermediate assets, such as machinery; and fixed assets, such as land.

Liabilities are listed either in the order of their length of term or in the order of the assets to which they apply, as for example, livestock, machinery, and real estate loans, in the order named. The balance sheet of January 1, 1960, shown in Table 13.2, illustrates the grouping of assets and liabilities.

Classifying assets and liabilities as current, intermediate, and fixed (or long-term) contributes to analysis of the liquidity of the business. This point is considered in detail later in the chapter.

Need for Physical Data

Information conveyed by, and analysis of, balance sheets is severely limited if physical data are not given in the statements to aid in interpreting the values. For example, the balance sheet shown in Table 13.1 shows grain valued at $3,624, but no information is given as to the kind or amount of grain on hand. The value exceeds the value of corn in the balance sheet for January 1, 1960, but there is no indication as to whether the quantity increased or decreased

TABLE 13.2

FARM BUSINESS A
Balance Sheet as of January 1, 1960

Assets		Liabilities and Owner's Equity	
Current		Current	
		Account payable, hardware store	$ 167
Cash	$ 262	Account payable, tractor fuel	95
Corn, 3,550 bu.	3,443	Note at bank, feeder cattle	4,100
Soybeans, 561 bu.	1,122	Note at bank, feed	3,291
Hay, alfalfa, 67 tons	1,006		
Hogs, market, 87 head	1,394	Total	$ 7,653
Sows, 12 head	380		
Feeding cattle, 36 head	4,178		
Poultry	140	Intermediate	
Total	$11,925	Loan from Dad, unsecured	$ 5,220
Intermediate		Long-term	
Truck and auto (farm share)	$ 1,150	(None)	
Machinery and equipment	7,023		
Total	$ 8,173	Owner's Equity	$ 7,225
Fixed			
(None)			
TOTAL	$20,098	TOTAL	$20,098

from the beginning to the end of the year. Similarly, no information is given in the balance sheet for January 1, 1959, on the kind or numbers of livestock on hand. The total value is approximately the same as on January 1, 1960. But without physical data in the January 1, 1959, balance sheet one does not know whether the values are similar because the numbers and weights were similar, or whether a change occurred in numbers and weights, and also in unit prices.

A similar problem is involved when real estate comprises part of the assets of a balance sheet. The value of real estate shown in the balance sheet may not change from one year to the next, but without physical data a lender unfamiliar with the situation would not know whether the acreage had changed. He might assume that the same acreage was involved, but he could not be sure. Or perhaps the value of real estate may be $12,000 higher at the end than at the beginning of the year, as was the case in 1965 for Farm Business A. Was more acreage added or was the value per acre increased? Without physical data one does not know.

A detailed balance sheet which makes it possible to separate changes in the financial condition of the borrower according to whether they are caused by value changes or by changes in the physical inventory is essential if a complete and accurate analysis is to be made of the financial condition of the farm business. The balance sheets for January 1, 1960, shown in Table 13.2, and those for January 1, 1965, and January 1, 1966, given later in Tables 13.3 and 13.4, are presented in detailed form to show both the physical numbers and value data needed to make an analysis of the condition of the business. Information on quality and weight also is needed and might well be included in the statement, particularly for market livestock such as hogs and feeding cattle. Information of this type to supplement that given in the balance sheet may be obtained by personal inspection of the property.

VALUATION DIFFICULTIES

The need to show physical as well as value data in the balance sheet is primarily due to difficulties in valuation of the assets. This difficulty increases progressively from the liquid to the fixed assets. Cash, government bonds, grain on hand, and livestock ready to sell are easy to value on a present market basis. Breeding stock and machinery cannot be converted into cash as readily and, consequently, are valued with more difficulty. Land is the most difficult of all to value because it is infrequently sold, is not standardized in quality, and is sold only after considerable effort is expended to obtain a buyer who is interested in the farm. Unfortunately, the land value item on the balance sheet is usually the largest, a fact which makes interpretation of land value figures extremely important in balance sheet analysis. For example, a modest increase of $25 per acre for a 240-acre farm would cause an increase of $6,000 in the value of the land. This might well overshadow any other changes which occurred in the balance sheet.

Accuracy in valuing assets can only be approximated and must be defined with reference to some period for which the values are expected to hold good. It is possible to value corn, hay, cotton, hogs, and wool according to the market price on the day specified in the balance sheet. But land, a fixed asset which is seldom sold and has no standardized market, is much more difficult to value. A good practice to follow with land and other nonliquid assets is to value them on a conservative basis. One way to do this is to enter them at cost less depreciation and less any loss from a drop in selling price. They would not be increased for any gain in selling price because this gain might later be canceled by another drop.

Valuing at cost or market, whichever is lower, is a good rule but it is not entirely satisfactory. It leads to some strange situations, especially when one farm is compared with another. For example, one farmer may have bought his farm in 1950 for $40,000. After allowance for depreciation and improvements it may be valued, using the "cost or market, whichever is lower" method, at $45,000 in 1965. A second farmer may have bought a similar farm in 1965 and paid $75,000. Other things being equal, the second farmer would show a total asset figure $30,000 greater than the first farmer. The owner's equity of the second farmer would also be $30,000 greater than that of the first farmer.

When land values rise over long periods of time, as they have done over the past three decades in the United States, it is desirable to make adjustments periodically in balance sheet values to keep them in line with conservative current values. The values used should be sufficiently below the market value to allow for costs which would be involved if the farm were to be sold. Adjusting values periodically facilitates analysis of the equity and liquidity position of the business, as well as the rate earned on equity capital and on assets managed. Thus, the balance sheet will portray a realistic picture of the business, which would be an advantage in submitting an application for a loan.

Trend Analysis

As was indicated in Chapter 6, an income statement for one year may not portray a reliable picture of the income which might be expected. Similarly, a balance sheet as of a given time may not give a representative picture of the financial situation, due to unusual forces affecting production or prices at the time. Thus, it is desirable to have a series of balance sheets for a business to provide a representative financial picture and also to show trends in the financial structure of the business. These are reasons why lenders make a practice of obtaining a current balance sheet with each loan application.

While balance sheets for Farm Business A were not available for all years, those for January 1 of 1960, 1965, and 1966 provide considerable information on trends which occurred during that period of time. The balance sheet for 1965 is given in Table 13.3 and the one for 1966 in Table 13.4. Farmer A made good financial progress during this period, which is shown by a comparison of the balance sheets. One major change reflected by the balance sheets is the addition of a farm which is reflected in the balance sheet for January 1, 1965. The balance sheets show that this farm was purchased sometime between January 1, 1960, and January 1, 1965, but they do not indicate the time. If annual balance sheets were available the year could be identified, but still the time within the year would be unknown. This point is made to emphasize that the balance sheet does not provide a record of what goes on *during* the year. As indicated above, it only shows the situation at a given time.

TABLE 13.3

FARM BUSINESS A
Balance Sheet as of January 1, 1965

Assets			Liabilities and Owner's Equity		
Current			**Current**		
Cash	$	506	Accounts payable	$	118
Corn, 6,800 bu.		7,140	Note at bank, feeder cattle		5,406
Hay, alfalfa, 66 tons		1,188	Note at bank, feed		2,479
Hogs, market, 196 head		3,122	Total	$	8,003
Sows, 27 head		2,025			
Feeding cattle, 73 head		7,000			
			Intermediate		
Total	$	20,981			
			Note at bank, machinery	$	1,400
			Loan from Dad, unsecured		5,220
Intermediate					
			Total	$	6,620
Truck and auto (farm					
share)	$	1,100			
Machinery		5,420			
			Long-term		
Total	$	6,520			
			Real estate contract		$ 69,100
Fixed			**Owner's Equity**		$ 27,778
Real estate, 240 acres		$ 84,000			
TOTAL		$111,501	TOTAL		$111,501

TABLE 13.4

FARM BUSINESS A
Balance Sheet as of January 1, 1966

Assets			Liabilities and Owner's Equity	
Current			**Current**	
Cash	$	403	Accounts payable	$ 146
Corn, 9,147 bu.		9,604	Note at bank, feeder cattle	9,875
Soy beans, 756 bu.		1,890	Note at bank, open	3,886
Hay, alfalfa, 70 tons		1,260		
			Total	$ 13,907
Hogs, market, 262 head		11,829		
Sows, 38 head		2,850		
Feeding cattle, 110 head		15,200	**Intermediate**	
Total	$	43,036	Loan from Dad, unsecured	$ 5,220
Intermediate			**Long-term**	
Truck and auto (farm share)	$	963	Real estate contract	$ 66,700
Machinery		6,083		
Total	$	7,046	Owner's Equity *	$ 60,255
Fixed				
Real estate, 240 acres	$	96,000		
TOTAL		$146,082	TOTAL	$146,082

* Gain due to change in inventory value of real estate, $12,000.

Owner's equity of Farm Business A increased from $7,225 January 1, 1960, to $27,778 January 1, 1965, and jumped to $60,255 January 1, 1966. The increase in owner's equity of $20,553 from January 1, 1960, to January 1, 1965, may be considered on first thought to represent financial progress from farm income over the 5-year period. However, as indicated in the income statement analysis, Mr. A and his wife inherited $14,000 which they used to help buy their farm. Thus, not more than $6,553 of the increase in owner's equity can be attributed to farm income, and perhaps some of that came from nonfarm sources. While a comparison of two balance sheets in time gives an *indication* of financial progress over the period, information as to sources of the financial progress must be ascertained from the income statement and records showing funds added to or withdrawn from the business.

The $32,477 jump in owner's equity from January 1, 1965, to January 1, 1966, is unusual and deserves further consideration. As indicated by the note in the January 1, 1966, balance sheet, $12,000 of this increase resulted from an increase in the value of the real estate. The farm had been valued at the price for which it was purchased in 1962 and the increase was made to reflect a conservative market value for the farm at the beginning of 1966.

The higher inventory values per head of market hogs and feeding cattle accounted for $12,295 of the increase. Perhaps the animals on hand January 1, 1966, were heavier and of better quality than those on hand a year earlier. We do not have information on this point. The fact that the same unit prices were used in valuing the other current assets in both balance sheets encourages one to believe that the values for hogs and fat cattle were realistic. But in any event, since some physical data are given, comparison of the two balance sheets indicates there was a substantial increase in the physical inventory between the two dates. The quantity of corn, alfalfa, and soybeans all increased, some substantially. The number of livestock also increased considerably. Of the $32,477 increase in owner's equity, over $8,000 *appears* to have been due to an increase in the physical inventory.

Analysis of the balance sheets for Farm Business A demonstrates the need for physical data in interpreting the financial data and in analyzing trends. Yet, obviously, space limitations limit the amount of physical data which can be recorded in the balance sheet. One method for keeping physical data in a clear and systematic manner to supplement the balance sheet is to record it in a form designed specifically for that purpose. In addition to quantities or numbers, weights and grade or quality could be shown. Such a physical trend record would show the amount of assets at different dates on a comparable basis, thereby providing a sound basis for judgment regarding changes occurring in the business.

Good credit analysis is often a matter of perspective—a long overall view of the situation. To obtain perspective, both physical and financial records over a period of time are needed.

RATIO AND COMPARATIVE ANALYSIS

A number of ratios have been found to be important indicators of financial progress and of risk-bearing ability. As was pointed out in the analysis of income statements, usefulness of such ratios depends to a considerable degree on availability of a reliable basis for comparison, to enable one to judge whether the ratio for a particular farm is good, fair, or poor. However, this factor is not as critical with balance sheet ratios as with income statement ratios since balance sheet ratios have more significance in and of themselves. Moreover, budget analysis can be used in connection with the ratios to test pertinent financial relationships.

A classic measure of financial condition used in balance sheet analysis is the current ratio which indicates the current liquidity of the business.

$$\frac{\text{Total current assets}}{\text{Total current liabilities}} = \text{Current ratio} \qquad (13.1)$$

As of January 1, 1966, the current ratio for Farm Business A was 3.09, or the business had $3.09 of current assets for each dollar of current liabilities. Comparable ratios for 1965 and 1960 were 2.62 and 1.55, respectively. Thus, the current liquidity position of Farm Business A improved considerably over the 6-year period.

In portraying the current liquidity of the business, the current ratio indicates the likelihood that current liabilities could be liquidated by use of cash or sale of current assets. Since current assets include those normally turned into cash within one year, the current ratio in effect reflects liquidity within one year's time. In case this period is too long the *quick ratio,* also referred to as "the acid test" ratio, may be used. It is used to reflect the adequacy of cash, accounts receivable, and marketable securities (bonds, stocks, and the like) to cover all current liabilities.

Another measure of current liquidity relates current liabilities to owner's equity. The reasoning back of this ratio is that owner's equity reflects ability to pay either by use of current assets or by borrowing. A business may show a very poor current ratio, but if the operator has a high net worth the financial position of the business may be relatively secure. However, for this ratio to be meaningful, the owner's equity must be in a sufficiently liquid state so it could be used either directly or indirectly to meet the current liabilities.

The intermediate ratio is used to reflect the intermediate liquidity position of the business in much the same way as the current ratio is used in the short-run situation.

$$\frac{\text{Total current and intermediate assets}}{\text{Total current and intermediate liabilities}} = \text{Intermediate ratio} \quad (13.2)$$

Over an intermediate period of time both current and intermediate assets will be converted into cash in the normal operation of the business. This ratio reflects the likelihood that cash derived in this process will be adequate to cover the liabilities coming due during the same period of time. The intermediate ratio for Farm Business A was 2.62 on January 1, 1966, 1.88 on January 1, 1965, and 1.56 on January 1, 1960. The latter two ratios appear adequate for the size and type of business operated by Farmer A; i.e. it is unlikely that the value of the current and intermediate assets would decrease, either due to physical losses or price declines, to the point where they would not cover the current and intermediate liabilities. The increase over a period of time in the ratio is a favorable sign. An upward trend in the ratio adds risk-bearing ability in and of itself in use of intermediate credit.

The long-run liquidity position of a business is indicated by the net capital ratio.

$$\frac{\text{Total assets}}{\text{Total liabilities}} = \text{Net capital ratio} \qquad (13.3)$$

This ratio reflects the likelihood that sale of all assets of the business would produce sufficient cash to cover all liabilities. The ratio for Farm Business A was 1.70 January 1, 1966, 1.33 January 1, 1965, and 1.56 January 1, 1960. Since Mr. A was a tenant farmer in 1960, no real estate was involved in his net capital ratio at that time. Purchase of a farm on contract naturally reduced his ratio. Ordinarily, a somewhat higher net capital ratio is needed when no real estate is involved because chattel assets usually fluctuate in value more than real estate.

The net capital ratio is considered a long-run concept since real estate is involved. However, since good land is not converted into cash through the production process, as are other assets, the period involved is really the time required to sell the farm. Thus, the time-period concept involved in the net capital ratio differs from that involved in the intermediate and current ratios.

Another overall measure of liquidity commonly used is the ratio of total debt to owner's equity.

$$\frac{\text{Total liabilities}}{\text{Owner's equity}} = \text{Debt-to-equity ratio} \qquad (13.4)$$

This ratio for Farm Business A was 1.42 on January 1, 1966, 3.01 on January 1, 1965, and 1.78 on January 1, 1960. In other words, on January 1, 1966, Mr. A's debts were 1.42 times his equity in the farm business. This was a much smaller ratio than on January 1, 1965. Purchase of the farm on contract in 1962 was partly responsible for the relatively high ratio in 1965. Relatively large real estate debt incurred by use of purchase contracts may cause a farmer's debt-to-equity ratio to be high. But this should not be interpreted as meaning that real estate debt will always cause a high debt-to-equity ratio. Conventional mortgage loans on real estate usually do not run much over 50 per cent of the value, and periodic payments may gradually reduce this percentage. It is not uncommon for relatively larger loans to be made on chattel property.

Equity is often related to the value of assets. The ratio is

$$\frac{\text{Owner's equity}}{\text{Value of assets}} = \text{Equity-to-value ratio.} \qquad (13.5)$$

The ratio of equity to value for Farm Business A was .41 on January 1, 1966, .25 on January 1, 1965, and .36 on January 1, 1960. The drop in the ratio from 1960 to 1965 was caused by purchase of the farm on contract. The improvement in the ratio from 1965 to 1966 showed increased strength in the financial structure of the business.

While the equity-to-value ratio may be used to reflect the overall situation, it is more commonly used to depict owner's equity in an individual item. Reference to the amount or per cent paid down in purchase of an asset reflects the ratio of owner's equity to value of the asset.

Equities of less than 25 per cent are usually scrutinized with extreme care by lenders. But this figure is by no means a strict borderline. A high equity of 50 per cent at one time may be no safer than a 25 per cent equity at another time when values were lower but rising. The type of asset involved also has a bearing on the size of the ratio which may be considered safe in terms of risk-bearing ability.

The ratios of current assets to current liabilities, of intermediate assets to intermediate liabilities, and of fixed assets to fixed liabilities are often used as a simple test to determine whether debts are properly distributed among current, intermediate, and long-term obligations. In 1966, the current ratio for Farm Business A was 3.09, the ratio of intermediate assets to intermediate liabilities was 1.35, and the ratio of fixed assets to long-term liabilities was 1.59. The current ratio should be wider than the other two ratios because maturing short-term obligations are likely to be embarrassing if they fall due when cash is not available to pay them, or because they fall due frequently and thus cause extra work in arranging renewals. Moreover, it is often possible to obtain lower interest rates on long-term loans. Of course, if the debts are relatively small, the farmer probably will have them on a short-term basis so he can pay them when money is available.

Questions and Problems

1. Discuss the meaning of owner's equity, or net worth; of net deficit. Explain how each is derived.
2. How may balance sheets be used by borrowers in deciding how much to borrow? By lenders in deciding how much to lend?
3. What does the balance sheet indicate? What does it fail to show?
4. Prepare a typical balance sheet for a young tenant farmer starting now in your community; prepare another statement for the same farmer five, ten, and twenty years later. Assume that prices are low at the five-year point, high at the ten-year point, and average at the twenty-year point.
5. Prepare a beginning balance sheet for a farmer who started five years ago; then show his balance sheet five years later. Make a trend sheet to show physical inventories at beginning of each year. Discuss.
6. What do you think of Farmer A's financial progress as shown by records presented in this chapter?
7. Explain how the current ratio is computed. What does it show relative to risk-bearing ability?
8. How is the intermediate ratio derived? Does it have significance in terms of risk-bearing ability?
9. What is the net capital ratio and how does it relate to risk-bearing ability?
10. Compute pertinent financial ratios for the farm business you used in question No. 4 and discuss their meaning and significance.

Chapter 14

CREDIT INSTRUMENTS AND
LEGAL ASPECTS OF BORROWING

THE large number of credit instruments and papers which are a part of loan procedure awe and discourage the farmer when he obtains his first loan. To read and understand all the fine print contained in notes and mortgages seems a formidable task. Reading and understanding the *Uniform Commercial Code,* adopted by practically all the states, is a much more formidable undertaking. When additional affidavits, acknowledgments, releases, waivers, and abstracts have to be obtained or studied, the borrower is truly bewildered. The difficulty lies not only in the large number of documents, but also in the unfamiliar legal language included in long paragraphs of small type. The best approach is to take each document by itself and to place most of the emphasis on the main provisions. When this is done, the meaning and the reason for each of the credit instruments is made clear.

THE NOTE

The promissory note is the primary document in most credit transactions. It is the written promise of the borrower to repay the loan. When the lender gives the loan funds to the borrower, he receives in exchange a note signed by the borrower promising to pay the lender a certain stated principal amount with interest on a certain date (see Fig. 14.1).

The dominant position of the note in all credit transactions should be clearly understood. There may be a tendency to overlook the note because it is a small form with much less printed matter than mortgages or extension agreements, but such an oversight may prove costly because the borrower's signature at the bottom of a note is a direct obligation holding him liable for the payment of the loan according to the terms stated on the note. If the property mortgaged by the borrower in connection with the loan fails to cover the amount due at a foreclosure sale, the borrower usually is

Fig. 14.1—A promissory note.

still liable and the lender may have other nonexempt property of the borrower sold to satisfy the deficiency. Hence, the borrower should *read carefully and thoughtfully* the provisions of the note before he signs it. He should verify the amount, the rate of interest, the penalty provisions if any, and the time and place at which the payment is to be made. Furthermore, he should make a record of these items on an extra note form so that he will have at hand at all times correct information on the terms of his obligations.

If the lender requires an additional signature to the note—a common condition where the borrower is a young farmer with little capital—the endorser should study the provisions of the note as carefully as if he were the borrower. The importance of the endorsement is evident by the fact that the lender will not make the loan without it. In effect, the endorser himself is borrowing the funds, because he is making himself liable for the payment. Many times, an endorsement, given as a friendly gesture with scarcely a thought, may turn out to be a tragic mistake. A farmer once related that his farm, which had been entirely clear of debt, was mortgaged for all it was worth because an endorsement on a note to a relative caused him to lose almost everything he had.

The Mortgage

The mortgage, which follows the note, is a specific listing of certain property set aside to guarantee the payment of the note. Although mortgages, like notes, may take on a multitude of variations in detail, they are almost identical in their chief provisions (see Fig. 14.2). The provisions not only identify the property to

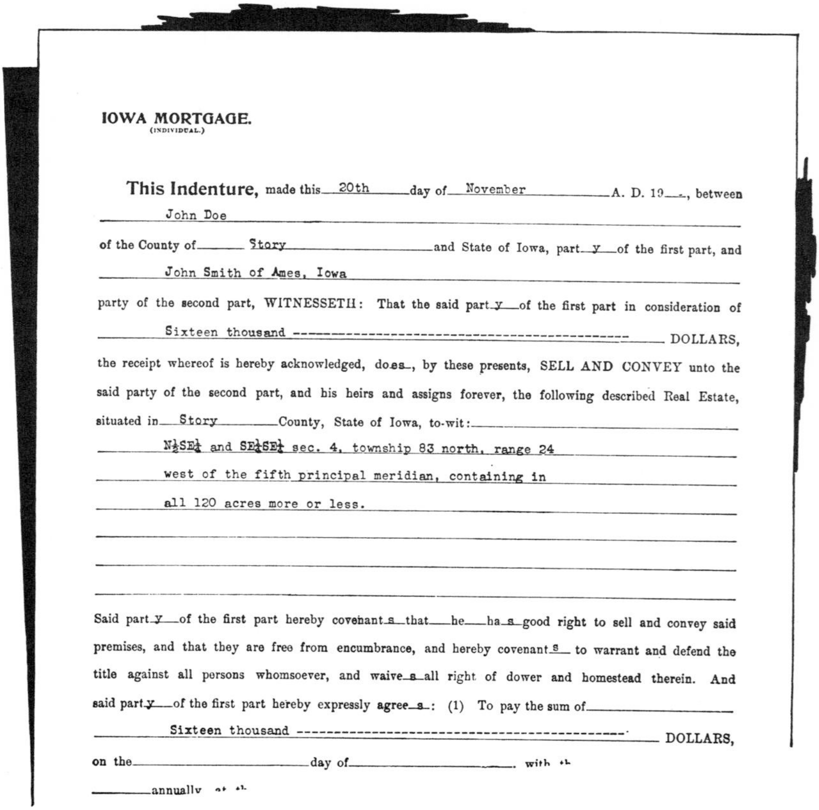

IOWA MORTGAGE.
(INDIVIDUAL.)

This Indenture, made this 20th day of November A. D. 19__, between John Doe

of the County of Story and State of Iowa, party of the first part, and John Smith of Ames, Iowa

party of the second part, WITNESSETH: That the said party of the first part in consideration of Sixteen thousand -- DOLLARS,

the receipt whereof is hereby acknowledged, does, by these presents, SELL AND CONVEY unto the said party of the second part, and his heirs and assigns forever, the following described Real Estate, situated in Story County, State of Iowa, to-wit:

N½SE¼ and SE¼SE¼ sec. 4, township 83 north, range 24 west of the fifth principal meridian, containing in all 120 acres more or less.

Said party of the first part hereby covenants that he has good right to sell and convey said premises, and that they are free from encumbrance, and hereby covenants to warrant and defend the title against all persons whomsoever, and waives all right of dower and homestead therein. And said party of the first part hereby expressly agrees: (1) To pay the sum of Sixteen thousand -- DOLLARS,

on the ______ day of ______ with th

______ annually at th

Fig. 14.2—A farm mortgage.

back up the note but they establish a priority of claim among lenders according to the time of filing or recording of the mortgage at the county courthouse. In some places the evidence of debt which accompanies the mortgage is a bond rather than a note, but the general effect is the same.

A mortgage is recorded or filed at the courthouse to give notice to the world in general and all interested lenders in particular that the borrower has given a mortgage or pledge of certain property to a certain lender. Any subsequent lender, therefore, will have to take a second, or junior, mortgage on this same property; and he cannot say he did not know that the property was already mortgaged, because the records or files at the courthouse are kept open for public inspection. Few people among the general public appreciate the significance of these mortgage records and files. It is a large and continuing task, a task that on the whole is handled efficiently.

Real Estate Mortgages

The distinctive features of the real estate mortgage, and of the *deed of trust* which is sometimes used as a mortgage, are the unchanging character of the security, the length of term covered, and the permanence of the mortgage record. Since land does not change position except through erosion, it is relatively easy to describe and to locate through long periods of time. Legal descriptions, especially by rectangular survey, provide a highly efficient method of designating the exact property concerned, and none other. The importance of land ownership and the relatively high value of land itself has established the practice of making permanent copies of mortgages in the records at county courthouses.

The recording of a mortgage is considered public notice to everyone concerned. Anyone buying a farm may find what mortgages, if any, exist, either by going through the county records or, as is commonly done, by obtaining the information from an abstractor or a title insurance company. Abstracts are used in some parts of the United States and title insurance in others. An *abstract of title* is a brief summary of all recorded transactions or events that have affected the land in question, and of these transactions, mortgages are one of the most important. When an abstract is brought "down to date," it shows the current status of the title, including any outstanding mortgages. Title insurance insures the title to the subject property against defects, except for those shown in the policy. If a recorded mortgage is outstanding against the property, it will be included in the exceptions.

When a mortgaged farm is up for sale, two different methods of purchase may be specified in the deed: The farm may be bought subject to the mortgage; or the purchaser may buy the farm, assuming the mortgage. The difference between "subject to the mortgage" and "assuming the mortgage" is greater than many realize. The term *subject to the mortgage* means that the buyer does not agree to pay the mortgage although if he fails to pay or meet any of the terms of the mortgage, the lender may foreclose, and the property in due course will be sold at foreclosure sale. The term *assuming the mortgage* means that the buyer, in effect, is endorsing the original mortgage note and hence is liable up to the limit of his property, which may be attached for sale to settle any debts not covered by the real estate mortgaged. This distinction, however, applies only to cases where a farm is bought with a mortgage on it and the mortgage is not paid. If a new mortgage is made at the time of purchase, the purchaser, of course, is liable. Two farmers who bought farms at high prices had experiences which illustrate the difference in the two methods of purchase. Both farmers had 160-acre farms clear of mortgage. They both bought additional quarter-section farms at $300 an acre. Both of the farms purchased had existing mortgage indebtedness averaging $200 an acre. Both farmers paid down $100 an acre in cash, but Farmer A assumed a $200-an-acre existing mortgage while Farmer B bought subject to the $200-an-acre mortgage. During the depression that followed, Farmer A not only lost the farm he bought but also lost his unencumbered farm as well because he had to mortgage it to meet the payments for which he was liable on the second farm. Farmer B, on the other hand, since he had no liability on the $200-an-acre mortgage, allowed the lender to foreclose the mortgage and kept his first farm clear of debt. The original borrowers, in both cases, were still liable even after they had sold the farms to A and B. The person who has signed or endorsed a note is liable for its payment until it is paid or is outlawed by the passage of time after the term has expired.

A real estate mortgage does not mean what it says in one important particular, which may seem a contradictory statement, but a careful reading of a mortgage will bear out the contention. Most mortgages provide for the outright transfer of the property to the lender or mortgagee at the time the mortgage is signed. If the borrower pays the note, however, the property is to be returned to him; that is, fulfillment of the conditions in the mortgage prevents

the conveyance from taking effect. In case of default by the borrower, the mortgage specifies that the property is to belong to the
lender. But in actual practice this does not occur because the courts
have ruled otherwise. Property mortgaged is not transferred to the
lender in spite of what the mortgage says, either at the time the
mortgage is signed or upon default by the borrower. A lender must
take his plea before the court and obtain a judgment, and even then
he does not get the actual property mortgaged. The court, in most
states, has the sheriff sell the property at a public sale to the highest
bidder, the proceeds of the sale being remitted to the lender after
costs have been deducted. If the sale brings more than the amount
due, the surplus goes to the borrower. If the amount obtained from
the sale is not sufficient to meet the judgment and costs, the lender
may obtain a *deficiency judgment* against additional property of the
borrower.

Interpretation of mortgages varies by states, some states adher-
ing to what is called the title theory and others following a more
liberal view, called the lien theory. According to the *title* theory, the
borrower actually gives the lender title to the property, but the title
reverts to the borrower if he fulfills his obligations. If the borrower
defaults, the title, in effect, belongs to the lender even though the
lender may have to sell the property or have a sale made by the
court in order to obtain a settlement. If the borrower, after defaulting, makes sufficient payment to place the mortgage in good standing, he must obtain a deed from the lender under the title theory to
regain his former position.

According to the *lien* theory, the lender with a mortgage
obtains only an interest in the property regardless of the wording in
the mortgage. If the borrower defaults, the lender has a claim on
the property for the amount due, but the lender has no right to the
property other than that of obtaining the amount due him. If the
borrower, after defaulting, places his mortgage in good standing
and if there is no foreclosure action, the borrower's title to the
property is the same as before the default.

The contradiction between the wording and meaning of a
mortgage may be traced back to the time when the lender did
receive title to the mortgaged property as a pledge at the time the
loan was made, and the lender became the unquestioned owner of
the property if the borrower defaulted. In eighteenth-century England, the mortgagee or lender could take immediate possession of
the mortgaged farm if the borrower failed to meet any of the terms
in the note or mortgage. Borrowers fought this procedure so vigor-

ously that in time jurisdiction over mortgage defaults was taken over by courts of equity. A lender who sought to collect a defaulted loan could no longer take the mortgaged property directly, he had to appeal to the court which in turn heard the claims of both sides and, if the lender's pleas were considered valid, sold the property and distributed the proceeds according to priority of lien. But as this change in legal action was taking place there was no corresponding change in the wording of the mortgage; hence, the mortgage of today, handed down by tradition from generation to generation, has lost some of its original meaning.

Chattel Mortgages

Laws governing use of mortgages on movable property, called chattel mortgages, have been replaced in practically all of the 50 states by provisions of the Uniform Commercial Code discussed in the next section. Except for pledges,[1] the emphasis is changed under the Code from the form of the agreement to the kind of collateral involved. However, chattel mortgage forms still are usable under the Code and, indeed, are used in Code jurisdictions. Moreover, they still are utilized in states (and in other countries) where the Code has not been adopted. Hence, it is desirable for the student of finance to be familiar with them.

Chattel mortgages have a number of characteristics which distinguish them from real estate mortgages. Chattel mortgages, as a rule, run for a relatively short period of time, are subject to frequent changes as the property or chattels covered by the mortgage are sold or changed, and are not permanently recorded in the county courthouse. Instead, only copies are filed and then withdrawn when the mortgages are released. The valid term of a chattel mortgage varies by states, common terms being from three to five years. At the expiration of the term, it is necessary to renew the chattel mortgage; otherwise, it ceases to be in force.

Movable property or chattels are subject to frequent changes. Machinery wears out; grain is fed; animals reproduce, fatten, and are sold; some animals die, others stray or are stolen. Crops may yield bountifully or fail to yield anything because of drouth or

---

[1] A pledge is a security interest in chattel property created by manual delivery of the chattel to the creditor under an agreement that the creditor is to retain possession until the debtor has paid in full. A good example is pawning an item of personal property at a pawn shop.

other natural hazards, and stored products may depreciate either in quality or in value. In short, chattel mortgages cover property that is undergoing change. The extent of this change varies with the kind of property included.

Chattel mortgages, subdivided according to type of security covered, may be classed as livestock, crop, commodity, equipment, or miscellaneous. Although livestock chattel mortgages can be specific and accurate in describing the security at the time the mortgage is drawn, the situation may change with sales, deaths, and increases. Whenever sales are made it is necessary for the borrower to obtain the consent of the lender, which usually results in an agreement between the lender and borrower on the use to be made of the proceeds from the sale of the mortgaged property. The chattel mortgage does not as a general rule apply to the proceeds from the sale of the mortgaged property. To protect himself, the lender usually specifies that the check representing the proceeds be made out to him, or that the proceeds be sent directly to him, or that the sale be made by the borrower acting as the agent of the lender. The lender may then prepare and file a partial release of the security which has been sold. The question of increase has been a difficult one because there is no easy way to decide how far into the future a present mortgage may cover the increase, and courts of different states have not been uniform in their rulings.

Crop mortgages are naturally indefinite throughout the whole period of their existence. A crop mortgage on 160 acres of wheat which has just been seeded is entirely different from a commodity mortgage on 2,000 bushels of wheat in a bin. Even shortly before harvest there still may be some doubt as to what the crop will yield because of risks from hot winds, hail, or rust. A question arises frequently as to when a crop mortgage becomes effective. One interpretation is that the crop must be seeded; otherwise, the crop does not have any existence and cannot be mortgaged. Another interpretation is that the validity of the crop mortgage depends on the interest of the borrower in the land on which the crops are raised. According to this second view, the crop mortgage may be binding for several years; that is, on crops that will not be seeded for several years, providing the borrower is still in possession of the land. If the borrower dies or sells the farm, the crop mortgage is no longer in force. In line with this interpretation, lenders on real estate mortgages frequently have their mortgages filed as chattel mortgages also, the objective being to make each year's crop serve as security for payment of the interest due on the mortgage, and to prevent other creditors from filing a chattel mortgage which might siphon all available funds so the farmer could not meet his real estate mortgage payments.

Property acquired after a chattel mortgage is negotiated presents an interesting question when the mortgage provides that any property so acquired is included under the mortgage. If a farmer with three dairy cows buys three more dairy cows, giving a chattel mortgage covering all six cows, the question concerns any additional cows that may be bought. If the chattel mortgage specifies as security the six cows, their increase and other cows which may be acquired, the usual interpretation is that such a mortgage is valid and binding, particularly between the mortgagor and mortgagee. The calves from the cows are included as security under the mortgage as well as any other cows purchased or otherwise acquired by the borrower during the term of the chattel mortgage. The mortgage, however, must specifically state that it covers the increase and such livestock or other property as may be acquired after the mortgage is made.

If the chattel mortgage is foreclosed, which generally involves the sale of the property by the sheriff at a public sale, the borrower is allowed certain exemptions—property items which are exempt from foreclosure sale. This list of exemptions depends on the laws in each state. According to the wording in most chattel mortgages, however, the borrower gives up these exemption rights.

Filing of a chattel mortgage is important. If a chattel mortgage is taken by a lender but not filed, the lender may find his mortgage of little value because another lender may get in ahead of him by filing a later mortgage which becomes a first claim against the property if it is the first mortgage filed. Also, the lender may lose if the borrower sells the property to another person who has no knowledge of the unfiled chattel mortgage. In this event, the purchaser is not responsible because he had no notice of any mortgage. Finally, the lender may lose if some creditor has the property attached to collect a claim which is due him.

Failure to search the files for existing mortgages and to identify the property mortgaged may prove costly. A lender in the Corn Belt made a loan to a tenant farmer on the strength of the farmer's statement that he had thirteen head of cattle as well as other property which he was willing to mortgage for this loan. The lender failed to check the property described by the farmer, took a chattel mortgage on it, filed the mortgage at the courthouse, and handed the farmer $700. A short time later a Federal loan agency, learning of this loan, reported to the lender that they had a loan and a prior chattel mortgage on all the chattels of the farmer and that according to their records the farmer had three head of cattle, not thirteen. When the lender appeared at the farm to check his security, the borrower took him across the road and showed him thirteen fine-looking cattle. Later, a close inspection by the Federal loan agency and the lender revealed that the thirteen head belonged to a neighbor and were only being pastured temporarily on the borrower's farm.

The Uniform Commercial Code

As indicated in Chapter 1, great changes have occurred in recent years. Many and significant changes in the business world have generally accompanied the technological revolution in agriculture. Methods of transportation have become more varied, communication has become more reliable and faster, business methods and records have been revolutionized, and the number and size of transactions have multiplied. Such changes called for changes in the laws under which business functions—more rapid change than was generally being made in state laws. Also, even though effort had been made to obtain uniformity in state laws, much variation existed which caused inconvenience for business, particularly where the territory served or involved in a business lay in more than one state. Out of a multitude of such pressures, coupled with the understanding and foresight of wise men, developed the monumental effort and consensus required to draft the Uniform Commercial Code.

The Uniform Commercial Code was prepared under the joint supervision of the National Conference of Commissioners on Uniform State Laws and the American Law Institute. It was first adopted by Pennsylvania, where it became effective in 1954. The Code has now been adopted by all states except Louisiana. The objective is its adoption by all 50 states.

Two objectives of the drafters of the Uniform Commercial Code were to improve laws relating to commercial transactions, and to facilitate uniformity in commercial laws throughout the country. The latter objective was primary and the bulk of the Code remains uniform throughout the states in which it has been adopted. However, in enacting the Code a number of states amended some provisions. Therefore, complete uniformity does not exist. Moreover, the authors of the Code left some alternatives from which each state could make a choice, such as the place for filing the "financial statement" under Article 9. The states have selected different alternatives which also add some nonuniformity. Thus, the need to check individual state statutes should be recognized.

The Uniform Commercial Code is divided into nine articles which extend over the law of sales, negotiable instruments, documents of title, bank collections, investment securities, bulk sales, letters of credit, and secured transactions. Each article is comprehensive and detailed. Some of the more general provisions of Article 9, which relate to secured transactions, are outlined in this section.

A number of terms new in law are used in the Code. Under Article 9, the two parties in a secured transaction are the *debtor* (borrower or buyer) and the *secured party* (lender or secured seller). The secured party obtains a *security interest* (lien) in *collateral* (personal property, given as security) by entering into a *security agreement* (an agreement which creates or provides for a security interest) with the debtor.

The concept involved in the *security interest* represents a major change in law pertaining to secured transactions. It is a simple, unified concept of a *single* lien. In states which have adopted the Code it replaces the chattel mortgage, reservation of title by a conditional seller, the assignment, and the like. This is true regardless of whether state legislation enacting the Uniform Commercial Code repeals applicable earlier statutes, since a later law supercedes an earlier one where they are inconsistent.[2]

Some concepts involved in *collateral* also represent a new approach in secured transactions. The personal property subject to a security interest may be tangible or intangible. *Tangible* personal property, called "goods," includes all property which is movable at the time the security interest attaches. "Goods" are classified into four categories according to the function or "purpose" they serve: (1) *Consumer goods* include tangible property bought or used for personal, family, or household purposes. (2) *Equipment* consists of personal property which is bought for use *primarily* in business, including farming. (3) *Farm products* include crops, livestock, and supplies *used or produced* in farming operations. They also include *products* of crops or livestock in their "unmanufactured" states, such as milk, eggs, wool clip, ginned cotton, maple syrup, and honey, if they are in the possession of a debtor engaged in farming operations. If goods are farm products they are neither "equip-

---

[2] Charles Bunn, *et al., An Introduction to the Uniform Commercial Code,* The Michie Co., 1964, p. 12.

ment" nor "inventory." (4) *Inventory* includes goods held by a person who holds them for sale or leasing, or to be furnished under contract of service. Inventory also includes raw materials, work in progress, or materials used or consumed in a business.

Intangible personal property includes items such as promissory notes, bonds, stock certificates, accounts, and contract rights, which have little or no value in and of themselves but are valuable because of the legal right or rights they represent. It is classified in six groups: (1) *Instruments* include items such as a promissory note, bond, and corporate stock certificates. (2) *Documents of title* are items such as warehouse receipts, dock receipts, and gin tickets. (3) *Chattel paper* means "a writing or writings which evidence both a monetary obligation and a security interest in or a lease of specific goods. . . ." [U.C.C. 9–105 (1) (b)]. For example, a farmer buys a tractor "on time," and gives the tractor as the *collateral* for the obligation. The farmer signed a written *security agreement,* which identified the tractor and acknowledged the debt. Together the *security interest* in the tractor and the *obligation* of the farmer comprise one form of *chattel paper.* (4) An *Account* is any right to payment for goods sold or for services rendered which is not evidenced by an instrument or chattel paper, such as accounts receivable. (5) A *Contract right* is "any right to payment under a contract not yet earned by performance and not evidenced by an 'Instrument' or 'Chattel paper.' " [U.C.C. 9–106.] (6) *General intangibles* are any personal property not included in the above classifications. Rights under insurance policies and pass book accounts are examples.

The classification of goods or collateral involved in a transaction is very important since the classification determines what method is used in the perfection of a security interest against claims of third parties.

A security interest may arise in two ways: in connection with purchase or rental of property, and by obtaining a loan on property already owned. The first, called a *purchase money security interest,* enjoys the greatest protection against the claims of third parties under provisions of the Uniform Commercial Code. Such an interest is created when the seller of collateral retains a security interest to secure all or part of the purchase price. For example, a farmer might buy a tractor "on time," paying $1,000 down and giving the machinery dealer a *purchase money security interest* in the tractor as collateral for the balance of the purchase price. A purchase money security interest is also created when a lender makes a loan to enable the borrower to acquire rights in or use of collateral, providing the loan is in fact made for such purpose. In our tractor example, the farmer might have gone to his banker and told him he wished to borrow the money to buy the tractor. If the bank made the loan and entered into a security agreement with the farmer, the bank would have a *purchase money security interest* in the tractor as collateral for the loan, assuming the loan proceeds were in fact used to purchase the tractor.

In order to have a *security interest* "attach" to collateral already owned by a farmer (1) there must be a security agreement, (2) value must be given, and (3) the farmer must have "rights" in the property. "Attach" means, loosely, "create." Thus, "a security interest attaches to collateral" means "a security interest is created in collateral." "Value is given" when a loan is made by the lender or "secured party." The farmer has "rights" in crops when they are planted or when they otherwise become growing crops; he has "rights" in the young of livestock when they are conceived. If the security is to cover crops, oil, gas, minerals, or timber to be cut, the land related to the collateral must be described in the security agreement. The security agreement should provide a complete description of the collateral. However, collateral may be referred to by general kind or class if it can be so identified.

In order to "perfect" a *security interest* which is valid against (immune to attack by) third parties, other than those having a prior perfected security interest or other superior rights, such as tax liens, it is necessary for the lender (secured party), subject to certain exceptions which are discussed shortly, to take possession of the collateral *or* file the proper notice in a public office. Taking possession of collateral is feasible when it is intangible, as in the case of negotiable instruments and investment securities. When tangible security is involved, filing a "financing statement" usually is necessary. The financing statement is not to be confused with a financial statement such as a balance sheet. The financing statement must show the name and mailing address of both the debtor and secured party, and a description of the collateral together with a description of the associated real property if the collateral is crops or timber. The financing statement must be signed by both the debtor and secured party. No affidavit or witnesses are required.

Policing of collateral by the secured party is not required under the Code to validate a security interest. However, as a practical matter, policing is still essential to make certain that the collateral is not being dissipated. A security interest, even though valid, is not very valuable if the collateral is gone.

Filing of the financing statement is in either the county or the state capital, or in both places. The place of filing depends upon which alternative provision of the Code was adopted by the state involved.

The financing statement may be filed either before or after the security agreement has been executed. Filing should be done promptly to prevent intervening rights attaching to the collateral. Presentation of the financing statement or a copy of the security agreement to the filing officer along with the proper fee, and his acceptance of them, constitute filing under the Code.

In some instances and under certain circumstances it is not necessary for the secured party (lender) to file or take possession of the collateral in order to perfect a valid security interest. This is the case, for example, when there is a "purchase money security interest" in farm equipment having a cash price of less than $2,500. Moreover, in certain cases a security interest is temporarily perfected for a period of 21 days without filing or taking possession by the secured party.

A properly filed financing statement is effective for a period of five years from the date of filing. The period can be extended beyond five years by filing a continuation statement prior to the expiration date.

When a secured obligation is paid in full and no further commitments to extend credit are contemplated, the secured party must, upon written demand of the debtor, give the debtor a statement terminating the security interest. Failure to provide such a termination statement within ten days after proper demand is made would subject the secured party to all actual damages suffered by the debtor, plus a penalty of $100 if the failure was in bad faith.

When a secured party desires to assign or transfer his interest in any collateral on which a financing statement has been filed, a statement covering the assignment also may be filed. If an assignment is made concurrently with filing of the financing statement, the assignment may be endorsed on the financing statement before it is filed.

A security interest in crops, growing or to be grown, which is perfected by filing with the proper government official, becomes unperfected when the crops are harvested and removed from the farm. However, if the financing statement covers proceeds, the security interest remains perfected in any income received from sale or other disposition of the crops.

Article 9 permits a lender and a borrower in one transaction and in one financing statement, properly filed, to create a security interest in all the various classes of collateral, including future advances and after-acquired property. The floating lien was invented in pre-Code days and used in "factoring" under so-called "factor's lien acts" of some eastern states. A major contribution of the Code was to extend the floating lien beyond the old "factoring" cases and make it available for use in all states which adopt the Code. However, availability of the floating lien may deter extension of open-account credit by suppliers.

The Code includes a provision requiring exercise of good faith in all transactions which it covers. Thus, a lender with a comprehensive security agreement with a farmer is required to exercise good faith in financing the business. Should he refuse to make further credit extensions, which he may have the right to do under his agreement, there may arise the question of whether he can also prohibit the farmer's seeking funds elsewhere by giving a second security interest in his assets. Under certain circumstances the lender may be held liable for losses suffered by the borrower which resulted from insufficient credit.

PURCHASES ON CONTRACT

Farm chattels are frequently purchased on contract, or what is often called a *conditional sales contract*. In states which have not yet adopted the Uniform Commercial Code, buying chattels on contract means they are bought without the buyer obtaining title to the property. No mortgage is involved because the borrower is not the owner and hence cannot give a mortgage. The borrower gets possession and the lender retains title. The advantage to the lender is that if the terms of the contract are not fulfilled it is possible for the lender to regain possession without the necessity of foreclosure. The advantage to the borrower is that he can purchase equipment and the like with a smaller down payment by this method.

In states which have adopted the Uniform Commercial Code the situation is much different. Article 2, which deals with the law of sales, is a complete revision and modernization of the Uniform Sales Act which was in force in most of the states. The Code covers a much larger area of sales law than the old statute, and provides all sorts of rules and procedures for dealing with problems which arise. The principal change from a financing point of view is that generally the rights of the buyer and the seller are no longer determined by when title to the goods is passed. A "sale" of goods constitutes passing of "title" from the seller to the buyer for a price. In other words, in transactions covered by Article 2, title passes to the buyer at the time the goods are delivered, or a contract is entered into for their purchase, regardless of whether payment has been received. Generally, under Article 2 there is no way in which the seller can retain title once the goods are sold or contracted for and, thereby, protect his financial interests as was the case before adoption of the Code. However, the seller can obtain the traditional protection of a "conditional sales" contract by entering into a "security agreement" with the buyer, thereby creating a "security interest" in the delivered goods which he can perfect under Article 9 of the Code. Article 2 governs the interests of the buyer and seller, while the interests of the debtor and creditor are governed by Article 9.

Land purchase contracts are often used as a method of buying land (see Fig. 14.3). In fact, many farmers would not be able to purchase otherwise because they do not have the down payment required for purchase with deed. Land contracts may provide for the giving of a deed when the buyer has paid from 30 to 50 per cent of the purchase price, or when the full purchase price has been paid. Some insurance companies who prefer not to sell on contract sell with a down payment of 25 per cent and give deed at the time of sale. Sellers on contract, however, frequently sell with down payments of not more than 10 per cent at the time the buyer takes possession.

Farmers who buy land on contract should read their contracts carefully in order to understand fully their position in case of default. Failure to pay any amount due on the date specified may cause the entire amount to become due and payable and may give the seller the right to repossess the property, with all previous payments of the buyer considered as rent payments and liquidated damages. Although the buyer may have only one more payment to make before being eligible to receive a deed, failure to make a required payment on the date due may forfeit all of the previous payments and place the buyer in the same position as a tenant whose lease has expired. Instead of instituting foreclosure of a mortgage, the seller has only to serve legal notice on the buyer of his

REAL ESTATE CONTRACT

FORM 3329-2   14-1-38   IOWA, MINN., S. DAK.   F 30-31-38

THIS AGREEMENT, Made and entered into this......15th..................day of................December........,

19......., by and between Bankers Life Company, of the County of Polk, and State of Iowa, party of the first part,

and ......John Doe..

....

of......Story..........................County, State of..................Iowa....................., part..y.... of the second part,

WITNESSETH:

That the said party of the first part, in consideration of the covenants and agreements of said part..y..... of the
second part, hereinafter contained, agrees to sell unto the said part..y..... of the second part the following described
real estate situated in..........Story...................County, State of..................Iowa........................., to-wit:

   SW¼ of Sec. 3, township 83 north, range 24 west of the
   fifth principal meridian, containing in all 160 acres more
   or less.

for the sum of...........twenty two thousand four hundred...
Dollars, payable as hereinafter set forth.

   And the said part..y..... of the second part, in consideration of the premises, hereby agree.... to purchase all
of the right, title and interest of the party of the first part in and to the real estate above described, and to pay
therefor to said party of the first part, its successors or assigns, at its office in the City of Des Moines in Polk
County, Iowa, the said sum of......twenty two thousand four hundred...
Dollars at the times and in the manner following, to-wit:

.............two thousand two hundred and forty...Dollars

on the execution of this agreement and the remaining sum of......twenty thousand one hundred................

.............and sixty..Dollars, as follows:

.............five hundred and sixty...Dollars on the

.............1st.....day of......March................., 19....., ...and five hundred and........................

.............sixty dollars on March 1, 19...

Fig. 14.3—A real estate contract.

default on the contract and take possession after the period of time provided by law has elapsed. If the buyer takes the case to court, he will have to contest the provisions in the contract which he voluntarily signed when he purchased the farm.

Since the buyer on contract is often in a poor bargaining position, it is important for him to compare the price he is paying, including not only the quoted price but the financing charges as well, with the price he would have to pay if he were buying the same goods or land for cash, or if he were buying with enough down payment to obtain title and give a mortgage for the difference. On the other hand, the lender or seller will want to make sure that the buyer is not making as small a down payment as possible, with the intention of using the land or goods as long as possible before they are repossessed.

OTHER CREDIT INSTRUMENTS

A large number of written instruments may be encountered in farm credit that have not been discussed up to this point. Of these the most important are abstracts, title insurance, waivers, nondisturbance agreements, extensions, assignments, and releases.

A *chattel mortgage abstract* is a record of any chattel mortgages given by the borrower that are still on file at the county courthouse. A *real estate abstract* contains a brief account of all deeds, mortgages, foreclosures, and other pertinent facts which affect the title to the land. Before a buyer completes a farm purchase he should insist on an up-to-date abstract and should have the abstract examined by a competent attorney to make sure that the seller has good title. In some areas *title insurance* is used in place of the real estate abstract. It is issued by a licensed title insurance company upon payment of a premium, and insures the buyer or mortgagee against defects in the title other than those which may have been specifically excluded.

Efforts have been made at different times to introduce a system of titles based on registration and certificates. This system, called the *Torrens system* after Sir Robert Torrens who started it in Australia, provides for public registration of the property by the owner if he can establish clear and undisputed ownership. Registration entitles the owner to a certificate which carries with it complete evidence of ownership. When the property is sold the new owner has the old certificate canceled and a new one issued in his name.

A *waiver* is a relinquishment of a claim. A landlord may waive his lien on a tenant's crop in favor of a lender who wants to make the tenant a loan. In some areas lenders will not extend short-term credit to tenants without a waiver of the landlord's lien. The landlord's lien is the right which the landlord has to the crops produced on his land in settlement of any amounts which the tenant may owe the landlord. In some states the landlord lien extends to all property owned by the tenant, but the trend in state legislation is definitely toward a limitation of the lien to the crop raised by the tenant.

A *nondisturbance agreement,* as the term implies, is a promise by one lender to a second lender that he will not start any action against the borrower during a stated period of time. A short-term lender may be unwilling to lend to a borrower with a heavy mortgage debt unless the mortgage holder will sign a nondisturbance agreement to cover the period of the short-term loan.

An *extension agreement* is a written statement setting forth the terms on which a lender agrees to postpone a payment due him.

An *assignment* is a transfer of notes, mortgages, and other property from one party to another. A common *assignment* is the transfer of a mortgage from a mortgage company which makes the original loan to an insurance company which buys the note and mortgage. The mortgage company in this instance is the assignor, and the insurance company is the assignee.

A *release* or *satisfaction* is a cancellation of a claim, usually of a real estate or chattel mortgage. A release when recorded gives notice to all concerned that the mortgage to which it refers no longer exists as a claim against the property specified. A *partial release,* commonly used when a highway strip, portion of a farm, or some livestock are sold, cancels the mortgage claim against that part of the property which is sold.

FORECLOSURE OF MORTGAGES

The foreclosure of a farm mortgage may be divided conveniently into four steps: default on the mortgage by the borrower; court proceedings; foreclosure sale of the land by the sheriff; and redemption period.

Default on the mortgage occurs when one of the numerous terms of a mortgage is not met. If a mortgage provides for fixed payments on principal in addition to interest, and if the principal payment is not made when required or within the period of grace allowed, the mortgage is in default, and the lender has the right to start foreclosure proceedings even though the interest is paid and all other terms have been met. These other terms include payment of all taxes and assessments when due, and payment when due of premiums on fire and tornado insurance on buildings. Actually, few lenders start foreclosure proceedings on a minor default in payment, although they have this right if it is specified in the mortgage. Foreclosure is commonly recognized as a last resort after every other means of settlement has been tried. There is good reason to support this policy since lenders are not primarily operators of farm land. Moreover, the present operator as an owner is usually willing and able to pay the lending agency as much or more than he would as tenant. Finally, farms acquired by lending corporations must be rented on a short-term basis, since they are for sale. Since tenants with short-term leases are not interested in maintaining buildings and improvements, lenders find it to their advantage to work out loan extensions or deferments to help the present owner retain title to the farm.

Court proceedings vary by states but usually consist of three parts: (1) the institution of foreclosure by the lender, (2) the hearing of the case, and (3) the rendering of the decision by the court. Since most foreclosure cases are clear-cut defaults about which there is no argument, the judge almost invariably renders a judgment against the borrower for the amount due plus accumulated interest and costs. In the depression period beginning in 1931, however, a successful defense by borrowers against foreclosure was made in the form of a plea for a moratorium.

The *foreclosure sale* is a public auction conducted by the sheriff. In depressed periods most sales are perfunctory affairs, with the only bid being that of the lender who has brought suit. A common practice followed by lenders is to bid an amount slightly less than the amount due and then ask the court that they be appointed as receiver during the redemption period to collect the rents and apply them on the deficiency.

The *redemption period* is an interval following the foreclosure sale in which junior creditors and the previous owner may purchase the farm by paying the amount of the foreclosure sale plus interest and other costs after the sale. The period allowed varies by states from no time at all to more than two years.

In states that have not adopted the Uniform Commercial Code, the foreclosure of a chattel mortgage is similar to that of a real estate mortgage. In order to collect his claim against the borrower, the lender usually has to institute foreclosure proceedings, obtain a judgment, and ask for a sale of the mortgaged property to satisfy the judgment. The sheriff conducts a public sale after proper notice has been given. But state laws sometimes provide for the summary foreclosure of chattel mortgages by notice and sale, without court action. If the sale does not bring an amount sufficient to cover the judgment, the lender may obtain a deficiency judgment for the difference. If the lender desires, he may use the deficiency judgment to force the sale of other property owned by the borrower, provided some other party does not have a prior claim on it.

In states which have adopted the Uniform Commercial Code the procedure for foreclosure is set forth in Part 5 of Article 9. When a debtor is in default under a security agreement, the secured party, with certain exceptions, has the rights and remedies provided in the security agreement. In general, these may include repossession, sale, acceptance of the collateral in satisfaction of the debt, or any other available judicial procedure. Except in the case of certain consumer goods, a secured party who takes possession of collateral after default may, providing proper notices are given as specified in U.C.C. 9–505, keep the collateral in satisfaction of the indebtedness if a written objection is not received within certain time limits. However, if the debtor makes a timely written objection, the secured party must sell, lease, or otherwise dispose of the collateral (U.C.C. 9–504). Disposition of the collateral may be by private or public proceedings, as a unit or in parcels, at any time and place, and on any terms, but "every aspect of the disposition including the method, manner, time, place, and terms must be *commercially reasonable. . . .*" (U.C.C. 9–504). The secured party may purchase the collateral if it is disposed of at a public sale, and also under certain other circumstances. The debtor (or any other secured party) may redeem the collateral any time before its disposition, providing he has not otherwise agreed in writing after default. To redeem, the debtor must make all payments due, including reasonable expenses incurred by the secured party in retaking, holding, and disposing of the collateral (U.C.C. 9–506). The secured party must account to the debtor for any surplus after disposition of collateral (U.C.C. 9–504). Unless otherwise agreed or provided in the security agreement, the debtor is liable for any deficiency. The secured party is obligated to comply with the Code in taking action on a default; otherwise, the debtor or any other person with proper rights may recover damages or loss caused by the failure to comply with the Code provisions.

QUESTIONS AND PROBLEMS

1. Why are so many credit instruments needed in farm credit transactions?
2. What are the main characteristics of a note that should be remembered? Of a mortgage?
3. Has the Uniform Commercial Code been adopted in your state? How does the Code affect the legal aspects involved in use of credit?
4. What is the difference between buying a farm *subject to the mortgage* and *assuming the mortgage;* between buying a farm *on contract* and with a mortgage?
5. Explain how a real estate foreclosure is conducted.

6. What is an abstract? Title insurance? Compare the two.
7. What is a waiver? When would it be used?
8. Why might there be a need for a nondisturbance agreement? For an extension agreement?
9. Explain how an assignment is used.
10. What is meant by a "release" or "satisfaction" of a claim? Can a borrower obtain a release of a "security interest"? If so, explain how this is accomplished.

REFERENCES

"A *Permanent* Frazier-Lemke Law?" *Farm Policy Forum,* Vol. 3, No. 8, Iowa State Univ. Press, Aug., 1950.

American Jurisprudence, 2nd Ed., Vol. 15, Lawyers Cooperative Publ. Co., Rochester, N.Y., 1964, pp. 729–91.

Bunn, Charles; Snead, Harry; Speidel, Richard; and Redden, Kenneth R., *An Introduction to the Uniform Commercial Code,* Michie Co., Charlottesville, Va., 1964.

Cameron, Arnold G., *The Torrens System: Its Simplicity, Serviceability, and Success,* Houghton Mifflin Co., New York, 1915.

Hawkland, William D., *A Transactional Guide to the Uniform Commercial Code,* Vols. 1 and 2, Joint Committee on Continuing Legal Education of the Amer. Law Inst. and the Amer. Bar Assoc., 101 N. 33rd St., Philadelphia, Pa., 19104.

Luce, Kenneth K., *The Uniform Commercial Code,* Wisc. Bar Bul. Apr., 1963, pp. 27–33.

Montague, William L., *Uniform Commercial Code's Article 9—When Filing Is Not Required To Perfect a Security Interest,* Ky. Law Jour., Vol. 52, No. 2, pp. 422–28.

Pine, Wilfred H., and Logan, James K., *Acquiring and Transferring Farm Real Estate in Kansas,* Kans. Agr. Exp. Sta. Circ. 367, 1958.

Schrampfer, William H., *Law in Its Application to Business,* Rev. Ed., New York, Holt, Rinehart, and Winston, 1961.

Spies, Emerson G., *Law of Farm Tenancies in Virginia,* Publ. No. 29 of the Southeast Land Tenure Committee, Va. Agr. Exp. Sta. Bul. 490, 1958.

Spivack, Oscar, *The Uniform Commercial Code,* Tenn. Law Rev. Vol. 31, No. 1, pp. 20–33.

Weeks, Silas B., *Legal Terms and Obligations Common to the Farm Business,* N. H. Ext. Bul. 137, 1959.

Chapter 15

LENDER'S ANALYSIS AND
SERVICING OF A LOAN

THE preceding chapters have outlined principles and practices relating to agricultural credit. While most of the discussion applies to both borrowers and lenders, the point of emphasis has been somewhat more from the viewpoint of the borrower. Moreover, those who have not had firsthand experience in borrowing money tend to view the matter with a certain degree of awe, and possibly skepticism. Abusive policies which some lenders have used, coupled with unhappy experiences of some farmers with credit, cause some people to look upon the lender as synonymous with Shakespeare's Shylock in the *Merchant of Venice* demanding his "pound of flesh" regardless of the consequences. Few lenders deserve such a reputation, of course, and more information about lenders is needed to clarify how they operate. Furthermore, a broader knowledge of loan and service policies of lenders and of their obligations and responsibilities will aid the borrower in formulating plans for use of credit. Such information will enable the borrower to understand better the viewpoint of the lender and why he must do certain things, thereby contributing to a greater degree of mutual understanding essential for most effective teamwork. The objective of this chapter is to help provide this type of information regarding specialized lenders.

A LENDER'S BUSINESS IS "SELLING" LOANS

A lender's business is "selling" credit and loan services in a competitive market, and this fact has an important bearing on his loan and service policies. He must offer a competitive product to stay in business. A lender's major source of income is usually interest on loans. It follows that, other things being equal, the larger the volume of loans a lender has outstanding the larger his income. Therefore, he competes in the market for loans in a similar manner that other businesses compete for business. His methods may assume a little different emphasis. Lacking a tangible product to display—things such as a shiny new car or a new dress design which attract public attention because they are new and different—he tends to emphasize building goodwill through superior service, supporting worthwhile community projects, building business and social relationships with other businesses, and cultivating the friendship and support of various agricultural organizations and leaders by supporting their programs. But he also competes on the basis of price and product, the same as any other business. The lender's price tags are in terms of interest rate, loan-closing fees, and the like. His products are comprised of various types and sizes of loans and loan services. He competes by offering improved service, by developing new types and terms of loans which better meet the needs of agriculture, by increasing the size of loan, and sometimes by cutting interest rates and loan fees.

Competition among lenders encourages them to review continually their loan policies and practices with a view to making improvements which will increase their business. It encourages lenders to "keep on their toes." In general, competition helps insure against credit abuses. Most areas of the United States have enough lenders to provide a fairly competitive loan market, particularly in prosperous times. (Somewhat in contrast with other business, competition among lenders tends to diminish during recessions and depressions.) The government-sponsored cooperative Farm Credit banks and associations, and direct government loans through the Farmers Home Administration and other government agencies add competition and provide credit service in areas and for farmers with limited opportunity for loans from commercial lenders.

Lenders Generally Lend Other People's Money

Most lenders do not own the money they lend. Lenders may loan some of their own capital (part of the capital and surplus of the institution) but the bulk of their loan funds are either owned by other people or represent contractual obligations for insurance coverage and the like. It is not our purpose here to study the source of loan funds—that subject will be covered in the chapters dealing with various lenders in Part II of the book. But it is important here to understand and recognize the basic ownership of loan funds since it has an important influence upon loan and service policy of lenders.

Since lenders lend money belonging to someone else, they, in effect, serve as managers or trustees of the money. In their role as manager they are obligated to obtain the maximum return consistent with good business practices. In their role as trustee, lenders are obligated to take proper safeguards in investing the funds to insure against loss.

To help protect the financial interests of the public, numerous federal and state laws have been enacted to govern the activities of lenders. As will be brought out in subsequent chapters, these laws outline the legal framework within which lending institutions operate. They define the type, size, and quality of individual loans, as well as the aggregate amount of loans which may be made. Real estate loans, for example, are generally limited by law to about 65 per cent of the appraised value of the security. The size of individual loans is further limited either in absolute terms or relative to the capital structure of the lending institution. In addition to limits on size of individual loans, lenders are limited by law in the aggregate amount of loans they may extend. For example, commercial banks must maintain specified reserves and the banks and associations of the Farm Credit System cannot exceed specified ratios of loans to capital. Moreover, the law provides for periodic examinations by federal or state examiners to determine whether operation of the institution is in accordance with the law under which it is operated. One part of this review is examination of the loans of the institution to help assure that they meet standards for sound investments. Loans which do not meet these standards must be "made good." The lender may be able to do this by working with the borrower either to obtain more collateral or a partial payment which will strengthen the security position of the loan. If the loan cannot be "made good" by such a procedure, the lending institution is obligated to "write the loan off." Loans which are charged off are carried as undeclared assets on the books of the institution. They are eliminated from the balance sheet, or from assets pledged as security for loans.

To the extent of their resources, lenders must stand the losses realized on loans they make. Depositors, policyholders, or bondholders realize a loss only when the lending institution becomes insolvent. Using other people's money to make loans possibly totaling several times the capital and surplus of the lending institution subjects the lender to great risk if the loans are not properly made. The risk assumed by the lender multiplies as illustrated by the *Principle of Increasing Risk* discussed in Chapter 10. If unforeseen conditions develop which adversely affect a substantial portion of the outstanding loans, it is easy to see how rapidly the lender's capital and surplus could disappear. A small percentage of loan breakdowns is a natural expectation. Farmers suffer losses from drouths, excessive rainfall, and other natural hazards, and they, or members of their families, suffer from sickness, injury, or death. Family quarrels, poor management, or mistakes in appraisal sometimes make it necessary to foreclose a mortgage. Every farm loan institution should be prepared for a small percentage of loan breakdowns for such reasons. But they must guard against any large-scale breakdown of loans. The "life" of the lending institution depends upon avoiding such a "catastrophe."

Procedure Followed in Making Loans

The procedure lenders follow in making loans varies somewhat in detail, but the general principles are the same. Lenders develop their own detailed forms and approaches and, as would be expected, these vary somewhat. The procedure followed also varies from borrower to borrower. With a new applicant the lender must gather more information and make a more detailed study of the business than with a borrower who has been doing business with the lender for a period of time, and of course the procedures must be adjusted to fit the type of loan being considered. But through all this variation run some common practices, and the purpose of this section is to outline these in general terms. The information needed by the lender is discussed first, and then the general procedures followed in making loans are considered.

In order to give a complete picture of loan procedures it is assumed, unless otherwise indicated, that the application of a new borrower is being considered. Some "short-cuts" are often possible with established borrowers. It is also assumed that the loan being considered involves a fair amount of money. Lenders generally dispose of very small loans rather promptly by either deciding to make them as quickly as possible or, on the basis of a brief review of the facts involved, decline to extend the credit. This statement should not be interpreted to mean lenders generally frown on small loans. The average lender is not inclined to say "No" very readily. But he must consider the economical use of time, as must any businessman, and, therefore, small loans usually are handled with dispatch.

Information Needed—the Credit File

The lender needs certain information relative to the applicant, his family, and the business for use in analyzing a loan application. For this purpose he sets up a credit file or loan folder for each borrower. The credit file generally includes the following basic records:

1. Loan application
2. Comment sheet (often not used for real estate loans)
3. Balance sheet
4. Income statement
5. Inspection report if a chattel loan, or an appraisal report if a real estate loan
6. Miscellaneous records such as resolutions, legal papers, and insurance policies where required

A more complete credit file will also include other information—depending upon the type of loan—such as inventory forms, schedule of advances and repayment agreement, mortgage abstracts or abstracts of liens, aerial photographs, photographs of buildings, and soil maps. Frequently, correspondence pertaining to the loan is also kept in the credit file. The objective in developing the credit file is to have a place to assemble information pertinent to a loan for convenient reference. It should contain all information which may have a bearing on success or failure of the loan.

THE LOAN APPLICATION

The loan application is the initial document involved in a loan transaction. It usually shows the date, name, address, and telephone number of the applicant, as well as the amount of credit requested, the purpose for which the funds are to be used, the proposed plan of repayment, and the security, if any, the applicant offers. For convenience the balance sheet and the income statements sometimes are made a part of the application. A sample application form, complete with financial statement, supporting schedules, and profit and loss statement, is reproduced in Figures 15.1a to 15.1e.

THE COMMENT SHEET

The comment sheet provides a record of miscellaneous information to supplement other forms. Since the farm household and farm business are integrally related, personal information about the borrower and his family often is recorded in the comment sheet. Information on the family's needs, wants, and desires helps the lender understand goals of the family and provides background knowledge useful in analyzing a loan application. The number and ages of children at home not only helps indicate family living costs but also the amount of family labor available, which in turn influences the amount of labor to be hired. Health of the family members, their spending habits, and their interest in the farm all have an important bearing upon success of the business, and the lender seeks to obtain as much of this type of information as possible.

If the applicant is a new borrower, the lender is interested in learning of his experience and ability as a farmer, his credit history, and related information. These things are recorded on the comment sheet if other forms do not provide for the information. Information on the credit rating of the applicant obtained from other businesses may be recorded on the comment sheet. A comment sheet also provides a convenient place to make a record of visits to the farm after the loan is closed.

THE BALANCE SHEET AND INCOME STATEMENT

If the loan applied for appears reasonable and for a sound purpose, the balance sheet and income statement are prepared. The loan officer and the applicant may complete the two financial state-

FINANCIAL RECORD—AGRICULTURE

SECTION I—LOAN APPLICATION

APPLICANT(S) .... Name *Leopold Hhustlmeier*   Date *Jan. 8, 1965*
Address *R # 7 Westford*   Telephone *030 - 9999*

Married: yes ☑   Wife's Name *Patricia*
no ☐

Age *51*

No. of Dependents *2*   Ages: Boys *17* *14*
Farming Experience: Total *30*   yrs.   Girls   Present Farm *10*   yrs.

LOAN REQUEST .... Amount $ *5,200*   Maturity *11/30/65*
Purpose *Annual operating Capital*

Collateral Offered *Livestock and growing Crops*

Repayment Plan *From Sept., Oct., and Nov. sales of hogs, Cattle, and Corn.*

Comments _____

FARM OPERATED .... Location *Green Valley Township*

                                               (Owned)   (Rented)
Total Acres *436*   Tillable *290*
                                  Other *146*

Landlord: Name *None*
Address _____

                                       Annual Cash
Lease Expires _____ 19____   Rent $ _____
Major Product(s) Sold *Hogs*
Contracts for Sale
of Products *None*
                                      (To whom and terms of contract)

FINANCIAL FACTORS ...... Checking Account: Amount $ *600.*   Bank *Green Valley State Bank*
Savings Account: Amount $ *-0-*   Bank _____
Contingent Liabilities $ *None*
Explain _____

Pending Judgments or Lawsuits
Explain *None*

REFERENCES .... Credit *Green Valley State Bank, 101 W. Main St. Westford*
                   (Name)   (Address)
Westford Mortgage Co., 220 W Main St., Westford
Farmers Friend Feed Co., Bruce St., Westford
Business *Green Valley Tractor and Implement Co., Bruce St. Westford*
(trade)   (Name)   (Address)
Central Hardware Co., Long St., Westford

Personal *Mr. Josiah Friendly*   *R # 7 Westford*
              (Name)   (Address)
Mr. A. M. Upp   *10 N. Main St., Westford*

REMARKS .... *Mr. Hhustlmeier wishes to transfer his banking business to us.*

I (we) the undersigned certify that the foregoing statement and representations constitute to the best of my (our) knowledge true and correct statements.

Date signed *Jan. 8, 1965*   Signature *s/ Leopold Hhustlmeier*

Fig. 15.1a—Financial Record—Loan Application. (Courtesy of the American Bankers Association.)

ments together or the applicant may be given the forms and asked to prepare them at his convenience.

It often happens that the financial statements need to be confirmed or supplemental information needs to be obtained. In such instances the lender may advise the applicant that he would like to visit his farm. The lender summarizes the results of his visit

SECTION II—FINANCIAL STATEMENT

Financial Statement of:

Name _Leopold and Patricia Whistlemier_   Major Enterprise(s) _Hogs_

Address _R # 7 Westford_   Statement Date _Jan. 1_   19_65_.

TO: _Westford State Bank_

ASSETS				LIABILITIES			
CURRENT				**CURRENT**			
Cash on Hand		$	_-0-_	Notes Payable to Our Bank	(Sched. I)	$	_-0-_
Cash on Deposit (Bank) _Sun Valley State Bank_			_600_	Notes Payable to Relatives	(Sched. I)		_-0-_
Notes Receivable	(Sched. A)		_-0-_	Notes Payable to Others	(Sched. I)		_1,000_
Accounts Receivable	(Sched. A)		_-0-_	Accounts Payable	(Sched. I)		_800_
Livestock Held for Sale	(Sched. B)		_3,845_				
Crops Held for Sale and Feed	(Sched. C)		_9,980_	Portion of Intermediate-Term Debt			
Cash Investment in Growing Crops	(Sched. C)		_-0-_	Due Within 12 Months	(Sched. J)		_-0-_
Securities (Marketable)	(Sched. D)		_-0-_	Portion of Long-Term Debt Due			
Cash Surrender Value				Within 12 Months	(Sched. K)		_2,400_
of Life Insurance	(Sched. E)		_1,800_	Rent, Taxes, and Interest Due and Unpaid			_-0-_
Other (Specify)_____			_-0-_	Loans Against Cash Surrender Value of Life Insurance			_-0-_
				Other Debt Due Within 12 Months			_-0-_
TOTAL CURRENT		$	_16,225_	TOTAL CURRENT		$	_4,200_
INTERMEDIATE				**INTERMEDIATE-TERM**			
Autos and Trucks (Net)	(Sched. F)	$	_888_	Notes Payable to Our Bank	(Sched. J)	$	_-0-_
Machinery and Equipment (Net)	(Sched. F)		_14,417_	Notes Payable to Others	(Sched. J)		_-0-_
Breeding and Dairy Livestock	(Sched. B)		_12,512_				
Securities (Not readily marketable)	(Sched. D)		_-0-_	Maturities of over 1 but under 10 years for			
Other (Specify)_____			_-0-_	other than seasonal needs—less portion			
				applied to current liabilities.			
TOTAL INTERMEDIATE		$	_27,817_	TOTAL INTERMEDIATE-TERM		$	_-0-_
				LONG-TERM			
FIXED				Mortgages on Farm Real Estate			
Farmland	(Sched. G)	$	_103,500_	(Less portion applied to current liabilities)	(Sched. K)	$	_73,600_
Farm Improvements (Net)	(Sched. G)		_8,000_				
Nonfarm Real Estate	(Sched. H)		_-0-_	Mortgages on Other Real Estate			
Household Furnishings			_-0-_	(Less portion applied to current liabilities)	(Sched. K)		_-0-_
Other (Specify)_____			_-0-_	Other (Specify)_____			_-0-_
TOTAL FIXED		$	_111,500_	TOTAL LONG-TERM		$	_73,600_
				TOTAL LIABILITIES		$	_77,800_
				NET WORTH*		$	_77,742_
TOTAL ASSETS		$	_156,542_	TOTAL LIABILITIES & NET WORTH		$	_156,542_

* Net worth resulting from upward reevaluation of fixed assets ($ _18,500_)

GENERAL INFORMATION

1. Insurance
   a. Real and Personal Property _Complete coverage for mach., livestock, bldgs, and household_
   b. Liability _$ 50,000 Rural Mutual Insurance Co._
   c. Workmen's Compensation _One hired man equivalent_
   d. Other _Hail_

2. Taxes
   a. Personal Property _est. $315._
   b. Real Estate _est. $1,265_
   c. Income _est. $800._
   d. Other_____

For the purpose of procuring and maintaining credit from time to time in any form whatsoever with the above-named bank, the undersigned submit(s) the above Financial Statement as being a true, complete, and accurate statement of my (our) financial condition on the above date, and agree(s) that if any change occurs that materially reduces the means or ability of the undersigned to pay all claims or demands against me (us), the undersigned will immediately notify the bank in writing; and unless the bank is so notified, it may continue to rely upon the statement herein as a true, complete, and accurate statement of the financial condition of the undersigned.

Signed /s/ _Leopold Whistlemier_ Date _Jan. 8 1965_

/s/ _Patricia Whistlemier_

Certified by:_____

Fig. 15.1b—Financial Record—Financial Statement. (Courtesy of The
American Bankers Association.)

to the farm in an inspection report. This report is used especially if
an unsecured loan or a loan secured by a chattel mortgage is made.
If a real estate mortgage is taken to secure a loan, a real estate
appraisal report is obtained. With a chattel loan the lender studies
the business from the viewpoint of its management and operation,
while with real estate loans greater emphasis is placed upon the
appraisal report.

SECTION III—SUPPORTING SCHEDULES

A. RECEIVABLES

	Type	From Whom	Amount Original $	Amount Present $	Date Due	Collateral
Notes		*None*				
. . . .		TOTAL	$	$		
Accounts		*None*				
		TOTAL	$	$		

B. LIVESTOCK

	No.	Description	Value Per Unit	Total Value
Held for Sale	150	Market Hogs @ 90 lbs.	$ 13	$ 1,950
	80	Market Hogs @ 25 lbs.	7	560
	13	Beef Cattle	95	1,235
	5	Baby Calves	20	100
			Total	$ 3,845
. . . .	44	Sows	$	$ 2,052
Held for Breeding (Including Dairy)	2	Boars		85
	36	Beef Cows & Heifers		6,275
	3	Bulls		600
	19	Dairy Cows & Heifers		3,500
			Total	$ 12,512

C. CROPS

	Units	Description	Value Per Unit	Total Value
Held for Sale or Feed	7,000 bu	Corn	$ 1.10	$ 7,700
	300 bu	Oats	.60	180
	140 ton	Hay	15.00	2,100
			Total	$ 9,980
. . . .	Acres			Investment to Date
	94	Hay & Pasture		$ —0—
Growing	31	Seedings to Legumes & Grass		—0—
			Total	$

D. SECURITIES

	Description	Present Total Value	Pledged	Amount Owed
	None	$		$
Marketable				
		Total $		$
. . . .	*None*			
Nonmarketable				
		Total $		$

E. LIFE INSURANCE (OWNED)

Face Value	Company	Insured	Present Cash Surrender Value	Annual Premium	Pledged	Amount Owed
$ 10,000	Utopian Insurance Co.	Leopold	$ 1,800	$ 264	No	$ —0—
$	Total		$	$		$

Fig. 15.1c—Financial Record—Supporting Schedules. (Courtesy of The American Bankers Association.)

Where data are available, many lenders develop comparison statements and a loan history sheet for the borrower. Past records in the credit file of established borrowers provide a good source of such information. The comparison statements show the trend of balance sheet and income statement items over a period of years to facilitate trend analysis as illustrated in Chapters 6 and 13 and in Figure 15.2.

Section III—Supporting Schedules (continued)

F. MACHINERY AND EQUIPMENT (MAJOR ITEMS)

	Article	Year Purchased	Cost	Accumulated Depreciation	Present Value
Auto and Truck	Auto (sedan)	1961	$ 2,216	$ 1,328	$ 888
	Total		$	$	$
All Other	No. 1 Tractor	1964	$ 5,700	$	$ 5,090
	No. 2 Tractor	1961	4,800		2,000
	Corn Picker	1961			1,600
	All other mach. & equipment				5,727
	Total		$	$	$ 14,417

G. FARMLAND AND IMPROVEMENTS

	Date Purchased	Description	Purchase Cost	Present Value	Title
Land	3/15/55	190 A. Tillable plus 146 A. Nontillable	$ 48,000	$ 66,500	Leopold + Patricia
	9/1/63	100 A. Tillable	45,000	45,000	" "
	Total		$93,000	$111,500	

	Date Purchased	Description	Cost of Improvements	Accumulated Depreciation	Present Value
Improvements (Farm Structures)	3/15/55	Residence ($6,000 Value)	$	$	$
		40' x 60' barn ($1,000 Value)			
		and other buildings ($1,000 value)			
		included above			
	Total		$	$	$

H. NONFARM REAL ESTATE

Date Purchased	Description	Purchase Cost	Present Value	Title
None		$	$	
Total		$	$	

I. NOTES AND ACCOUNTS PAYABLE

	Date Originated	Original Amount	Balance Due	Holder	Terms Collateral	Repayment
Notes	9/1/63	$ 9,000	$1,000	Green Valley State Bank	Livestock+Equip	3/15/65
	Total	$	$			

	Amount Due	To Whom	Repayment Arrangements
Accounts	$ 800	Farmers Friend Feed Co.	Sale of hogs in Spring
	$	Total	

J. INTERMEDIATE-TERM LIABILITIES

Date Originated	Original Amount	Balance Due	Holder	Purpose
	$ None	$		
Total	$	$		

K. LONG-TERM LIABILITIES

	Date Originated	Original Amount	Balance Due	Holder	Repayment Arrangements
Farm	3/15/55	$ 39,000	$	Hartford Mortgage Co.	$2400 principal in Oct.
	9/1/63	36,000			plus interest at 5 3/4 %
	Total	$ 75,000	$ 76,000	Mortgages combined in 1964	
Other	Total	$	$		

Fig. 15.1d—Financial Record—Supporting Schedules (continued). (Courtesy of The American Bankers Association.)

The loan history sheet provides a record of credit used and repaid over a period of time.

THE INSPECTION REPORT

The purpose of the inspection report is to provide firsthand information on the farm family and business which will be used in

SECTION IV—PROFIT AND LOSS STATEMENT

Statement of: *Leopold Whistlemeier Farm*   Period Covered:
Address: *R#7 Westford*
Prepared for: *Westford State Bank*   *Jan. 1* 19 64 through *Dec. 31* 19 64

RECEIPTS				OPERATING EXPENSES	
Gross from Sale of Livestock and Livestock Products (describe):	Units			Feeder Livestock Purchased	$ −0−
Cattle	(35)	$ 2,545		Feed Purchased	3,302
Hogs	(443)	13,378		Hired Labor	3,553
Milk	(45,000 lbs.)	1,552		Fertilizer and Lime	1,245
Eggs	(630 doz.)	138		Pesticides	136
	Subtotal Livestock	$ 17,613		Seeds and Plants Purchased	612
				Machine Hire	722
Gross from Sale of Crops (describe):				Machinery Maintenance and Repairs	1,471
Corn	(2,104 bu.)	$ 2,378		Fuel and Oil	1,052
Soybeans	(124 bu.)	319		Livestock Expenses (breeding, veterinary, medicine)	746
Goff. Payment	( )	2,171		Maintenance and Repairs (other than machinery)	781
	Subtotal Crops	$ 4,868		Rent and Leases	−0−
				Utilities (farm share)	177
Other from Farming (describe):				Taxes and Insurance (farm share)	1,577
Misc.		$ 580		Farm Interest	2,005
				Other Cash Expenses (specify):	
				Auto	215
				Hail Insurance	140
	Subtotal Other	$ 580		*Misc*	421
Gross Receipts From Farming		**$ 23,061**		**Total Cash Operating Expenses**	**$ 18,158**
				Net Cash Income From Operation	**$ 4,903**

Adjustments for Change in Inventory:

	Feed	Market Livestock	Supplies
Beginning Inventory	$ 7,140	$ 4,778	$
Ending Inventory	10,130	4,866	
Net Change (±)	$ +2,990	$ + 88	$
	(Plus if increased, minus if decreased)		

— . . . . (±)$ + 3,078

Net Operating Profit . . . . **$ 7,981**

Adjustments for Capital Items:

	Machinery and Equipment	Breeding Livestock	Improvements
Beginning Inventory	$ 8,862	$ 11,427	$ 9,072
Plus: Purchases	4,802	67	363
Less: Ending Inventory	10,933	11,577	8,080
Sales	−0−	2,990	
Net Change (±)	$ −2,731	$ +3,073	$ −1,355

— . . . . (±)$ −1,013

Profit (Loss) From Operation . . . . **$ 6,968**

Information Only

Depreciation taken this year:

Machinery and Equipment	$ 2,731
Breeding Livestock	−0−
Improvements	1,355
Total	**$ 4,086**
Annual Nonfarm Income:	$ −0−

I (we) hereby certify that the above is a complete and accurate statement of my (our) profit and loss record during the period shown to the best of my (our) knowledge and belief.

Signature(s) */s/ Leopold Whistlemeier*

Date *Jan. 8* 19 65

Fig. 15.1e—Financial Record—Profit and Loss Statement. (Courtesy of The American Bankers Association.)

analyzing the loan and preparing the chattel mortgage. Prepared by the loan analyst himself or by his representative, the inspection report generally gives a detailed list of all chattel property owned by the applicant to give a complete picture of what he has to work with. Any property which is not to be included in the chattel

COMPARATIVE ANALYSIS SHEET—AGRICULTURE

Leopold H. Kistlemeier   Address *R # 7 Hereford*

Statement date	1/1/61	1/1/62	1/1/63	1/1/64	1/1/65
ASSETS					
Cash	600	0	20	1,600	600
Receivables					
Inventory held for sale and feed	12,466	16,245	15,354	12,242	13,825
Marketable securities and CSVLI	1,450	1,450	1,450	1,700	1,800
Cash investment in growing crops					
Other					
Total Current Assets	14,515	17,695	16,824	15,542	16,225
Autos and trucks (net)	120	886	666	444	888
Machinery and equipment (net)	8,100	10,614	12,119	12,866	14,411
Breeding and dairy livestock	12,380	10,205	10,775	12,365	12,512
Securities (not readily marketable)					
Other					
Total Intermediate Assets	20,600	21,705	23,560	25,675	27,817
Farm land	66,500	66,500	66,500	111,500	163,500
Farm improvements (net)					8,000
Other					
Total Fixed Assets	66,500	66,500	66,500	111,500	111,500
Total Assets	101,615	105,900	106,884	152,717	156,542
LIABILITIES AND NET WORTH					
Notes payable	2,500	4,000	1,000	9,000	1,000
Accounts payable	100	210	150	2,070	800
Portion of intermediate- and long-term debt due within next 12 months					2,400
Rent, taxes, and interest due				tax 200	
VLI loan					
Other debts due within 12 months					
Total Current Liabilities	2,600	4,210	1,150	11,270	4,200
Total Intermediate-Term Liabilities					
Mortgage on farm real estate	36,000	34,000	33,000	32,000	73,600
Mortgage on nonfarm real estate				86,000	
Total Long-Term Liabilities	36,000	34,000	33,000	68,000	73,600
Total Liabilities	38,600	38,210	34,150	79,270	77,800
Net Worth	63,015	67,690	72,734	73,447	77,742
PROFIT AND LOSS STATEMENT					
Gross receipts from farming	22,806	21,364	25,773	23,061	
Total cash operating expenses	17,949	17,004	17,491	18,158	
Net change in inventory	+1,562	+ 482	- 2,450	+3,078	
Net change in capital items	+1,833	- 442	- 1,875	-1,013	
Net (loss) from operation	8,252	4,405	3,927	6,968	
FINANCIAL TESTS—RATIOS					
Current (line 7÷line 25)	5.58	4.20	14.63	1.38	3.86
Debt to Worth (line 30÷line 31)	.61	.56	.47	1.08	1.00
Gross Receipts to Total Assets (line 32÷line 18)	.22	.20	.24	.15	
Debt to Total Assets (line 36÷line 18)	.081	.042	.037	.046	
Annual Debt Servicing to Gross Receipts				.36	
AMOUNT PER $100 OF GROSS RECEIPTS					
Cash operating expenses	79	80	68	79	
Profit	36	21	15	30	
MANAGEMENT FACTORS					
Yields					
Corn (Unit) bu/a.	93	90	73	85	
Soybeans bu/a.	-	-	43	28	
Oats bu/a.	40	30	67	25	
Livestock Production Rates					
Pigs (Unit) per litter	5.6	4.8	6.7	6.1	
Hogs feed cost per 100# gain	$ 10.17	$ 10.37	$ 10.55	$ 10.20	
Beef Cattle feed cost per 100# gain	$ 12.61	$ 15.06	$ 9.54	$ 14.82	
Value of Crops per Tillable Acre					
Livestock Returns per Dollar Feed Fed Hogs	$ 1.62	$ 1.52	$ 1.17	$ 1.34	
Work Days per Farm					
Work Days per Man					
Power and Machinery Cost per Tillable Acre	$ 25.73	$ 36.21	$ 31.63	$ 22.12	
Value of Farm Production per Tillable Acre	$ 118.25	$ 108.05	$ 102.27	$ 87.90	
Cost of Farm Production per Tillable Acre					
Other					

Fig. 15.2—Comparative Analysis Sheet. (Courtesy of The American Bankers Association.)

mortgage is properly identified on the record form. Each item of property is described in reasonable detail to facilitate identification at a later date if necessary and to provide information for the chattel mortgage. Description of items listed in the mortgage must be reasonably explicit since, when filed, it constitutes a public notice of items covered by the lien. A conservative market value is given for each item of property for use in analyzing the loan. Income and expenses for the coming year also are estimated for use of the loan analyst. The inspector adds remarks at the end of his report to explain any unusual items about the family and business, and to provide additional pertinent information not covered otherwise in the report.

THE APPRAISAL REPORT

Preparation of an appraisal report for a real estate loan generally is a somewhat more specialized job than preparing an inspection report on chattel property. As the terms indicate, the one is an inspection and the other is an appraisal. Farm and ranch appraisal comprises a major field of specialization in and of itself. It constitutes one of the major agricultural professions, and many agricultural colleges and universities have a course of study devoted exclusively to the subject. Therefore, only a very brief summary of the concepts of appraisal for farm real estate loans will be given here for the benefit of the student not acquainted with the subject.[1]

Purpose of Appraisal

The main purpose of appraising a farm for a real estate loan is to obtain a dependable estimate of the value of the land and buildings. An indication of the debt-paying capacity of the farm and its operator also may be gotten from the appraisal. In addition the appraisal will alert the lender to any risks or other special features connected with the farm.

Farm values estimated in appraising farms for real estate loans may or may not differ from values established for other purposes such as taxation, settlement of estates, and litigation cases. In general, one or the other of two concepts of value will be used in the appraisal. Under one concept the farm will have its value estimated as nearly as possible at its true current market value or sales price. Some lenders, however, appraise on the basis of "normal values." A normal value usually is thought of as being an estimate of the future value of the farm over a long period of years. Obviously a normal value may be the same, or higher, or lower than the actual market value at any particular time.

---

[1] For a comprehensive treatment of the subject the reader is referred to the text, *Farm Appraisal and Valuation,* 4th ed., by William G. Murray, Iowa State Univ. Press, Ames, 1961.

Appraisal Methods

Three general methods of estimating the value of a farm are used in appraisals. Some lenders may use one of these methods while others may employ a combination of two or more of them. These methods are:

1. The capitalization method
2. The sales price approach
3. The comparative method

The capitalization method of appraisal is based largely upon the capacity of a farm to produce net income. In using this method it usually is assumed that the values of farms in an area will have a fairly consistent relation to the average annual net incomes they will produce over a period of years. The relation, or ratio, which farm values in an area may have to net incomes is called the *capitalization rate* for the area. Sometimes this rate is the same as the percentage rate charged on farm mortgage loans in the area, but it may be considerably higher or lower than the loan rate.

Stated in simple terms, the process of converting net income to value may be expressed as follows:

$$\text{Value} = \frac{\text{Annual net income}}{\text{Capitalization rate}}, \quad \text{or} \quad V = \frac{a}{r}.$$

As used in this equation, annual net income usually represents the residual income available to farm land and buildings. It equals gross farm income minus farm production expenses; taxes, upkeep, and depreciation on buildings and equipment used in the farm business; and an allowance for operator and family labor and for management. A deduction should also be made for interest on nonreal-estate farm capital such as livestock and machinery. Because the capitalization rate for an area may differ from the mortgage loan rate, it ordinarily must be determined by study and experiment. Comparisons between actual net incomes and values in the area will give one measure of the capitalization rate to use.

The capitalization method may be illustrated by listing a few summary data for a hypothetical farm. First the appraiser sets up a cropping pattern and livestock program likely to be followed by a typical operator on the farm in the future. He then estimates the amount of average annual gross income that will be received from sales of crops and livestock to be $12,000 as shown below. Taxes and depreciation on buildings and equipment are estimated at $1,400 per year. Farm production expenses total $4,600, and operator and family labor and management are valued at $3,600. The appraiser summarizes these estimates as follows:

Gross farm income.........................	$12,000
Deductions	
Taxes and depreciation................$1,400	
Production expenses................... 4,600	
Value of labor and management........ 3,600	
Total deductions................	9,600
Net remaining to land and buildings.....	$ 2,400

Based on his experience and studies he has made, the appraiser knows that when income from a farm of this type, size, and quality is estimated from the viewpoint of the owner-operator as was done in this case, it should be capitalized at about 6 per cent in the area where this farm is located. He accordingly divides the 6 per cent rate into the net income of $2,400 and obtains an estimate of $40,000 as the value of the farm.

In estimating the income, expenses, and value of a farm, some lenders may instruct their appraisers to use standards based on current conditions. This would mean that the appraiser would assume recent practices would be continued as the basis of operation on this farm. Farm products sold would be valued at the level of commodity prices received in the last few years. Farm costs would be assumed to be the same as present costs. Other lenders, using a "normal" concept in estimating incomes, costs, and values, would attempt to anticipate future trends. They would allow for the temporary effects of any wide swings in recent prices, costs, and values. In high-risk areas normal standards can be used to keep appraised values and loans on a sound basis, thereby reducing the possibility of losses.

The capitalization method has the advantage that it relates the value of a farm to its income. Since the amount of a real estate loan is based on the value of a farm, this means that the amount of loan can be geared reasonably well to the capacity of that farm to repay the loan. Certain deficiencies, however, also characterize the capitalization approach to appraisals. Relatively small inaccuracies made in estimating income and expenses for the farm can have a material effect on the value obtained. This results from the high leverage which the capitalization rate has in converting income into value. For example, an error of only $300 in the income and expense estimates in the above illustration could change the resulting value of the farm by $5,000! In a similar manner, an error of only 0.5 per cent in the capitalization rate used could change the value by more than $3,000.

Best results in estimating farm values by the capitalization method probably are obtained in areas where rental practices are well established. Because farm rents in such areas are pretty closely related to farm values, a better basis exists for capitalizing net income into value. Where renting of farms is common, it is possible for the appraiser to estimate a net income to the landlord as well as to owner-operators. Both net incomes can then be capitalized into values. The two values thus obtained can be checked against each other for consistency. Appraisals based on capitalization tend to be less accurate in fairly widespread parts of the country where renting of farms is not common. Estimates of value obtained by capitalization are likely to be least accurate in areas where farm values are affected by nonagricultural influences. Establishment of industries in rural areas that create opportunities for earning off-farm income, and construction of through highways which open farm areas to residential uses, are creating levels of values for farm land no longer wholly related to the farm income from the land alone.

In most cases an appraiser will make certain adjustments in the value obtained from the capitalization method. He may increase the value somewhat if the farm has several desirable attributes. Factors which might add to the value would include proximity to market, an efficient farm layout, good general condition, suitable drainage, and absence of soil erosion. But the appraiser might discount the capitalization value if he should see some risks or weaknesses. Things such as poor soils, rough topography, or a run-down condition of the farm would cause the appraiser to discount the estimated value.

The sales price method of appraisal attempts to estimate the value of a farm as closely as possible to the price that would be paid for it by a typical buyer. To do this the appraiser usually assembles information on what farms in the area have sold for in past years. He then uses these actual sales data to estimate a reasonable market value for the farm being appraised.

Some lenders may modify this method to make it conform to a concept of normal values. For example, if it is expected that the level of farm values in an area during the life of a loan will differ from the values existing in recent years, the value obtained by use of actual sales prices can be adjusted to make it conform to the future normal level.

Appraisals based on sales prices have an advantage in that they can closely approximate true market values. In some areas, however, the sales price method has a distinct disadvantage. Sometimes farms in an area become overpriced in relation to the ability of the farm to earn income and to repay a loan. When the sales price approach results in overlending in such areas, the overlending can be a disservice to borrowers. Borrowers may not be able to repay excessive loans, and as a result may be forced into bankruptcy. Farms in a region can be overpriced from optimism generated by a temporary boom in the demand for a farm product. Sometimes overpricing is a legacy from the past. Competition may force an area to shift out of producing a profitable farm product and into another enterprise where the whole scale of incomes, living standards, and values is lower. When such a change occurs, there may be a lag in farm values and they may not immediately reflect the changed conditions.

The comparative method of appraisal attempts to take the best parts of the other two appraisal methods and combine them into a unified approach. Three general steps must be taken to place this method into operation:

1. Policy determination—The lender first takes a broad look at long-term trends in farm commodity prices, farm costs, farm living expenses, and farm real estate values on a national basis. Past trends are examined and probable future levels are considered. An attempt is made to discount any unusual factors that may have affected recent trends and relationships. On the basis of this study, the lender determines on a policy basis what levels of farm commodity prices, production costs, living expenses, and real estate values reasonably may be assumed for the foreseeable future.
2. Values for bench mark farms—Policy determinations made under (1) are then applied in the appraisal of carefully selected and representative bench mark or key farms in each lending area. Values for these key farms are carefully estimated by comparisons with actual sales of similar farms. It is then determined whether the net income, based on the policy assumptions, represents a reasonable rate of return on that amount of investment. This method of appraisal differs from the capitalization method in that the rate of return is used as a check on appraised value rather than allowing a predetermined rate of return to be a determining factor.
3. Appraising the individual farm—When the appraiser appraises

an individual farm, he uses the same general standards in estimating income as were applied to the bench mark farms in the
area. The farm being appraised is related to the most comparable
bench mark farm with respect to income and value characteristics. No two farms are exactly alike, so it requires considerable
judgment, born of experience in appraising many farms, to make
valid comparisons of this type. The appraiser attempts to set his
final estimate of the value at a level which reflects the capabilities
of the individual farm and is consistent with the values on the
bench mark farms. The resulting value not only indicates the
income-producing and debt-paying capacity of the individual
farm but also is geared to values established for other farms in
the area and across the country.

Many authorities consider the comparative approach as the
most scientific and soundly based method being used in appraising
farm real estate. Because essentially it is a combination of several
approaches, with the final estimate carefully cross checked, it
usually gives the most dependable estimate of the value of a farm. It
is best adapted for use by the larger institutional lenders which have
the facilities for doing the research and making the studies on which
appraisals of bench mark farms are based, and a sufficient concentration or volume of loans to make them worthwhile.

Methods Used by Various Lenders
The comparative method of making appraisals was developed
after the disadvantages of other methods became apparent. At present it is being used mainly by Federal Land Banks and by some of
the larger insurance companies active in making farm loans. Some
commercial banks in the farm loan business as well as a few independent appraisal services are using a modified comparative
method.

Most other lenders and appraisal services use either the capitalization, the sales price approach, or a combination of the two
methods, in making farm appraisals.

Analysis of Loans

The analysis a lender makes of a loan consists primarily of
determining how much credit should be extended, together with the

repayment plan, and the collateral to be required. In discussing these points it is assumed the borrower has applied for a maximum loan. Where less than a maximum loan is involved it may be possible to shorten the analysis. It is also assumed that the lender has the ability and desire to work with the borrower in analyzing use of credit.

HOW MUCH CREDIT?

The information assembled in the credit file, together with the material covered in earlier chapters, indicates the type of analysis followed in extension of credit. Needs, wants, and desires of the family provide one indication of how much credit should be extended. Along with this information the lender considers the current financial position of the applicant and the trend of his financial progress. Other things being equal, a strong and improving financial position generally is considered a favorable factor while a weak and declining financial position is considered a danger signal. Looking to the future, the banker analyzes the farm business as a basis for judging how much it will pay the farmer to borrow: With what amount of credit will Returns *added* by the use of the *added* funds just cover the *added* costs? He also analyzes the amount of credit which should be extended from the viewpoint of Repayment Capacity and Risk-bearing Ability.

REPAYMENT PLAN

Many lenders strive to schedule loan payments to come due when income for loan repayment is available, as was outlined in Chapter 9. With this objective in mind the majority of real estate loans made by commercial lenders are written on a long-term, amortized repayment basis, and some short- and intermediate-term loans are made on the budget basis. However, this is far from a universal rule. Many of the real estate loans made by individuals provide for a lump sum payment at expiration of the term. Some lenders make short-term loans payable upon demand, while some have notes come due several times during the year, primarily to bring the borrower in to see the lender periodically to discuss progress.

The majority of short- and intermediate-term loans are written on a 3-, 6-, 9-, or 12-month basis. When some of these loans are made, it is recognized a balance will still be outstanding at the end

of the term, which will be renewed. This procedure has been successfully used by some lenders for years, with some borrowers being
provided with intermediate-term credit on an annual renewable
basis for 10 to 20 years. In this connection it should be recognized
that annual renewals work well as long as all goes well. In fact, the
lender can logically loan more on an annual renewable basis than
on an intermediate-term loan basis. But the difficulty arises when
"the going gets tough" either for the borrower or the lender. Then
the borrower may find himself confronted with meeting a substantial intermediate-term debt at the end of a 12-month period. To
help alleviate this possibility and, in some cases, to provide a basis
for more credit, lenders have started making some loans on an
intermediate-term basis. Credit for bulk milk tanks, machinery, and
breeding stock are examples of such loans. Usually such loans are
written on an amortized basis for a term of 1 to 7 years, depending
upon the item financed and some related factors.

SECURITY REQUIREMENTS

The next step in analysis of a loan involves consideration of
security requirements. While collateral security is almost universally
required for real estate loans, little unanimity of opinion exists
among lenders concerning collateral security for chattel loans. Some
lenders make a large percentage of their nonreal-estate loans on an
unsecured basis; others make few such loans which are not protected
by specific collateral. There are also wide differences geographically
which seem to be a matter of custom.

Credit Rating of Applicant

The most important consideration in determining whether
collateral security is necessary for a loan is the credit rating of the
applicant. This *Rating* may be referred to as the fourth R of credit.
It is determined by the credit character of an individual. Credit
character comprises those qualities of a borrower which make him
want or intend to pay when a loan is due—qualities of honesty and
integrity, denoting determination to fulfill his obligations irrespective of contingencies that may arise. To live up to the promise above
their signatures, some borrowers are willing to sacrifice much more
than others, making great sacrifices and denying themselves and
their families the prime essentials of life. On the other extreme,

there are those having little regard for moral obligations, who would escape payment through a legal loophole if they could find one.

A borrower's previous record in meeting obligations is much more impressive to a lender than any amount of promises. A farmer cannot live in a community even for a few years without indicating to the businessmen of the community and to other neighboring farmers the amount of respect which he has for his financial obligations. Credit ratings, which have developed to a high degree in cities on the basis of monthly bill payments, exist also in the rural areas, although these rural credit ratings are not worked out by formula and are not published in a rating book.

One farmer with a good financial statement and earning record applied for a loan a few years ago to buy livestock and to pay operating expenses. After the local bank refused to make the loan, the farmer applied to a federally sponsored agency in a town in an adjoining county. The agency's examination and analysis of the financial statement and income record indicated that the applicant was entitled to a loan. But a routine request for references revealed that this farmer had taken bankruptcy twice, and had refused to cooperate with another federally sponsored agency which sought to work out a method of payments that would eventually put the real estate mortgage in good standing. The local bank claimed it had lost over $1,200 on a $1,600 note, and the mortgage agency had been forced to take a loss through foreclosure. The farmer was a money-maker, however, and had staged a quick comeback. When he was confronted with his personal record, he admitted that a lender had good reason to hesitate before making him a loan but he protested that he would never again attempt to cheat his creditors. The record itself was the decisive factor, however, and this farmer did not get the loan.

Physical Security

Lenders generally consider it desirable to require security if one or more of the following situations prevail:

1. The borrower has a "split line" of credit; i.e. where credit is obtained from two or more lenders. Established legal procedures in all states permit seizure of certain kinds of unencumbered property for satisfaction of overdue debts. Under such circumstances the lender usually protects his interests by requiring security which, in turn, may help the borrower repay the loan by

assuring continuity of the farm operation during the life of the loan.

2. The borrower has had no opportunity to build a credit rating in the community. The lender usually requires security when the borrower has not established the fact that he will perform according to his promise.

3. The lender does not have full information about the character and personal ability of the farmer and his farm. The lender usually tries to secure full information, but where this is impracticable he makes the loan if it appears justified and the security is adequate.

4. The borrower's loan is "full," i.e. the borrower has the maximum amount of credit which it is safe for him to use. The lending institution which does a good job by its borrowers endeavors to provide them with all the credit they can profitably and safely use, as indicated by the three R's of credit discussed above. Moreover, the lending institution which attempts to maximize its net income and that of its stockholders, will expand its loan volume to the point where marginal costs, including losses on loans, are equal to marginal returns. Such progressive and successful lenders are apt to have a number of loans requiring collateral security.

The usual form of pledging property as security is for the borrower to give the lender a chattel mortgage, or other type of security agreement, or a real estate mortgage on specific property he owns. Other forms include depositing with the lender collateral consisting of negotiable stocks, bonds, notes, and other similar property rights of value to be forfeited if the loan is not paid.

The chattel mortgage or security agreement usually covers not only the property purchased with the loan proceeds but also additional property. If the borrower obtains a loan to buy six dairy cows, it is natural that the six dairy cows should be given as a pledge for the loan payment. The same may be said for loans to purchase all kinds of livestock, tractors, equipment, and other farm property. But the lender usually wishes to include property other than that bought with the loan funds unless the borrower has invested a substantial sum of his own. In making a loan to buy six dairy cows, for example, the lender may ask for a total of twelve dairy cows as security in a chattel mortgage; in advancing funds to buy a carload of feeder cattle, he may ask for a chattel mortgage covering not only the cattle purchased, but also hay, grain, and other feed equal in value to the value of the cattle purchased; or in making a $300 loan for operating expenses he may ask for a chattel mortgage covering property valued at $600. Sellers of equipment have similar requirements in the form of cash down payments.

Lenders often make the mistake of specifying the amount of security required by using a fixed ratio or percentage. They may require, for example, that the security shall have a value equal to twice the amount of the loan. Any fixed proportion will later be recognized as too liberal during prosperous high price periods and too conservative during depressed low price periods. A more reasonable plan is for lenders to require less equity in low price periods and more in high price periods. Such a policy would aid the borrower by allowing him to expand during periods of depressed prices and curtail his expansion during high prices.

Endorsement

When inadequate physical security is available, the borrower may meet the lender's requirements by securing an endorsement. Endorsement means obtaining an additional signature on the front or back of the note. The person who adds his signature becomes liable for payment of the note if the borrower fails to do so, the same as though he had borrowed the money himself. Too many farmers have taken the obligation of an endorser altogether too lightly in the past. Before endorsing a note, the endorser should study the loan as outlined above and be convinced that the borrower can repay the loan. No borrower should ask a friend or relative to endorse his note unless this friend or relative is fully aware of the obligations he is assuming in endorsing the note.

Closing the Loan

When a lender has decided to make the loan, the actual closing process is relatively simple. The procedure varies in some degree from state to state due to statutory requirements and custom. The procedure also is slightly different for chattel than for real estate loans. But the main steps are as follows:

1. Verify the borrower's title to the property offered as security by a search of the public records. This step is necessary, of course, only when the loan is to be secured by a mortgage or security agreement.

2. Preparation and execution of the note (or bond) and mortgage or security agreement if the loan is secured by such an instrument. In some states a deed of trust is used rather than a mortgage for real estate loans. All loans need to be accompanied by a signed note as evidence of the fact that an obligation exists between the borrower and lender. The usual policy of most banks is to have the husband and wife sign the note and mortgage or security agreement jointly.
3. Recording of the mortgage or security agreement or deed of trust if one was prepared.
4. Examination of insurance policies covering property pledged as collateral for the loan to determine that coverage is reliable and adequate, and that the loss-payable clause is made in favor of the lender.

As soon as the required legal instruments have been signed and other requirements of the closing process completed, the proceeds of the loan are made available to the borrower.

SERVICING LOANS

The progressive lender has two broad objectives in servicing loans: (1) to fulfill his responsibility in safeguarding funds entrusted to the lending institution, and (2) to help the borrower make effective use of the credit—thereby adding to goodwill and business potential of the lender in the community. Safeguarding the funds involves checking the borrower's compliance with the purposes for which the credit was extended. A part of the loan procedure involves an agreement between the lender and borrower concerning the use to be made of loan proceeds, and the general operating program for the farm business and household. The lender is responsible for checking on the borrower's compliance with this agreement and on his general progress. Some modification of mutually agreed upon plans often is advisable as conditions develop, and good business practices require that the lender keep abreast of the borrower's affairs.

The second objective of creating goodwill by assisting the borrower in making effective use of credit is related to the objective of safeguarding loan funds. Services which help the borrower and create goodwill usually also strengthen the loan. Notwithstanding conscientious efforts of both the lender and the borrower to forecast accurately all cash requirements, frequently because of some modification of plans, unusual weather, or other unforeseen conditions, the need arises for additional advances. Handling these in an intelligent and businesslike manner is an important phase of loan servicing which can both strengthen the loan and build goodwill.

The type of loan service needed varies somewhat with type of loan. Real estate loans usually are on the books for a fairly long period of years and involve somewhat different servicing than chattel loans. Installment notices on real estate loans are mailed to the borrower, and under normal circumstances most payments are made as scheduled. Loans which become delinquent or require other servicing, such as partial releases for road right of ways, are investigated either directly by the lender or by his correspondent (representative) to determine the proper procedure. Insurance on improvements and other property must be kept in force and since unpaid taxes create a prior lien, tax records must be checked periodically to be sure taxes are current. Such things are involved in the minimum service for real estate loans. Progressive lenders give additional service, as outlined above, with a view to developing goodwill and additional business.

Service on chattel loans is somewhat broader than on real estate loans. Since chattel loans involve movable property which generally is much more subject to depreciation and can be disposed of more readily, the lender is obligated to keep a closer check on the property. Most borrowers are honest, but some become careless, and others do not fully realize that the security is not being kept up. Still others sometimes inadvertently dispose of chattel security without keeping the lender informed. Attention also must be given to taxes and insurance on chattel property the same as on real estate. When loans are secured by cash crops the lender maintains a careful check on progress and needs of the crop, and at harvest time makes proper arrangements for liquidating the loan.

The type of service rendered by progressive lenders on chattel loans was summarized by Nicholas Jamba, National Bank and Trust Company of Norwich, New York, in a letter to the authors:

> After the loan is approved the modern and progressive banker then usually considers that particular farmer and the loan made to him as his personal obligation and responsibility and he watches this line of credit to see if the agreed upon repayments are being complied with, and visits the farm often enough to keep in touch with the farm operations and the progress being made by the farmer. This type of work is what we consider servicing farm loans. In our bank, for instance, we

try to keep one jump ahead of everything that takes place on the farms of our farm customers. It is our plan to anticipate things that happen to our borrowers. We try to know, for instance, if there is an adequate amount of roughage stored on the farms of each of our customers to feed his animals out properly during our seven-month stabling season. We visit the farms often enough to check on the care and attention given to the livestock. We are continually making observations as between farms to determine the quality of the over-all farm operations. We try to see our customers often enough to establish a certain feeling of confidence between the loaning officers and the borrowers. In this manner our customers will discuss with us their future plans and present problems so that we can give the benefit of our advice and experience.

In the case of an established customer, we would do exactly the same thing, but perhaps visit the farms of those making satisfactory progress less frequently and devote a little more time to those owing us large sums and involved in one kind of a problem or another for various reasons.

A well-trained and experienced lender can contribute a great deal to a borrower's success, particularly if he will take time to visit the farm and discuss problems and opportunities with the farmer. A farmer will do well to select a lender who can and will render this service.

QUESTIONS AND PROBLEMS

1. Discuss what is meant by saying that a lender's business is "selling" credit and loan services. Why is this important from the viewpoint of credit extension?
2. What is the significance of the fact that lenders do not own most of the money they lend?
3. Explain why the risk assumed by a lender multiplies as illustrated by the principle of increasing risk.
4. Outline the general procedure followed by lenders in making loans.
5. What is the credit file? Describe its contents.
6. What is a loan application? What is its purpose?
7. Why does a lender obtain a balance sheet and income statement from the applicant?
8. Describe an inspection report. What is its purpose?
9. Describe or explain the three general methods of appraisal.
10. Outline the procedure generally followed by lenders in analyzing a loan application.
11. Outline the steps involved in closing a loan.
12. Describe what is meant by servicing loans.

REFERENCES

American Institute of Banking, *Agricultural Credit,* Amer. Bankers Assoc.,
New York, N.Y., 1954.
Beckman, Theodore N., and Bartels, Robert, *Credits and Collections in
Theory and Practice,* McGraw-Hill, New York, 1955.
Crouse, Earl F., and Everett, Charles H., *Rural Appraisals,* Prentice-Hall,
Inc., Englewood Cliffs, N.J., 1955.
Farm Credit Analysis Handbook (various regional editions), Agr. Com-
mittee, Amer. Bankers Assoc., New York, N.Y., 1965.
Murray, William G., *Farm Appraisal and Valuation,* 4th Ed., Iowa State
Univ. Press, Ames, 1961.

Part 2

ANALYSIS OF LENDING AGENCIES

"—no matter how adequate is the nation's supply of savings, it is of little benefit to agriculture unless there exist proper channels through which the farmer can tap this fund of savings."

NORMAN J. WALL

Chapter 16

FUNCTION AND RELATIVE IMPORTANCE
OF AGRICULTURAL LENDERS

THE primary role of the first part of this book has been to outline and explain credit principles and practices with a view of providing a guide to effective use of credit. In this part the objective is to give information the borrower needs in deciding which lender to select. Each of the major types of lenders is considered in some detail in subsequent chapters. The purpose of this chapter is to provide related background information on the overall credit picture, the function played by lenders in general, and the relative importance of the various types of lenders in the making of agricultural loans.

AGRICULTURAL CREDIT IN PERSPECTIVE

The amount of credit available is the product of supply and demand the same as with any other commodity. The supply of loanable funds comes from two sources: (1) savings, and (2) commercial bank credit. Savings available for loans stem largely from individuals, insurance companies, trust funds, and the like, who have funds over and above current needs. Other businesses also have savings but generally, in recent years, they have reinvested all their net income. Only funds in excess of current needs of the business are available for loans to others. Commercial bank credit is derived from reserves generated by the banking system as a whole. This source of credit will be explained in greater detail in subsequent chapters dealing with commercial bank loans.

Demand for credit comes from governments and a wide variety of private sources, including agriculture. Data on public and private debt at the beginning of 1966, and comparative figures for three earlier years are given in Table 16.1. Note the strong growth trends

TABLE 16.1

PUBLIC AND PRIVATE NET DEBT OUTSTANDING IN THE UNITED STATES,
JANUARY 1 OF SELECTED YEARS*
(Billions of dollars)

Item	1950	1955	1960	1966
Total Public and Private Debt	448.4	612.0	846.4	1267.5
Total public debt	236.7	263.6	298.8	362.1
Federal Government and agency†	218.6	230.2	243.2	269.8
State and local governments	18.1	33.4	55.6	92.3
Total private debt	211.7	348.2	547.5	905.4
Corporations	118.0	182.8	281.7	445.6
Long-term	56.5	82.9	129.9	207.5
Short-term	61.5	100.0	151.7	238.1
Individuals and unincorporated enterprises	93.7	165.4	265.8	459.8
Farm‡	12.0	17.6	23.7	39.3
Mortgage	5.6	8.3	12.3	21.2
Nonmortgage	6.4	9.3	11.4	18.1
Nonfarm§	81.8	147.8	242.1	420.5
Mortgage	50.6	94.7	160.8	284.8
Nonmortgage‖	31.2	53.1	81.3	135.7
Memo: Total Farm Debt as Per Cent of Total Public and Private	2.7%	2.9%	2.8%	3.1%

* Source: Survey of Current Business, U.S. Dept. of Commerce. Data for state and local governments are for June 30 of the preceding year.
† Includes categories of debt not subject to the statutory debt limit.
‡ Comprises debt of farmers and farm cooperatives to institutional lenders and Federal Government lending agencies, and debt owed to individuals and others.
§ Data are for noncorporate borrowers only.
‖ Comprises debt incurred for commercial (nonfarm), financial, and consumer purposes, including debt owed by farmers for financial and consumer purposes.

in each debt category. Note, also, the three major groups: governments, corporations, and individuals and unincorporated enterprises, and the relative importance of each. Credit used by agriculture is included in the latter group and comprises about 3 per cent of the total debt. It is clear, therefore, that agricultural producers do not have their own individual supply of credit but must compete with all other segments of the economy for borrowed funds, and the competition is very impressive.

Lenders financing agriculture comprise a part of the total credit facilities and structure of the nation. These facilities constitute the mechanism whereby supply and demand forces of credit work themselves out. They mobilize available funds from the multitude of individual sources throughout the country and channel or distribute them to those who want to use the credit. Those with surplus funds naturally look for the highest returns consistent with the risk and uncertainty involved. Those wanting to borrow similarly look for the lowest cost. When the supply of funds is fully adequate to meet demands, as was the case for a period following World War II, lenders compete for loans and interest rates, and related costs drop. On the other hand, when credit is tight (the supply is inadequate to meet all demands) lenders raise their interest rates and loan requirements, which serves as a means of rationing available loan funds. Thus, the financing institutions provide the means whereby changes in supply and in demand for funds are reflected in the ease or tightness of credit and in the general interest rate structure. Availability of and interest rates on agricultural credit are closely affected by this overall situation since the institutions financing agriculture are a part of the overall financial structure.

Flow of Capital From Investor to Borrower

There are four general methods by which funds may flow from the investor to the borrower: The first, which may be called the *direct method,* includes all loans made direct by the investor to the borrower. No intermediary or middleman is involved. The investor, as a matter of fact, acts as his own middleman or credit agency by finding the borrower and negotiating the loan. Loans from father to son, between relatives, and between farmers in closely knit communities are of this type. The conditions which favor this method are the proximity of investor and borrower, and the confidence of the investor in the borrower, such as exists in a father-and-son relationship. With the direct method the borrower competes with others for credit more on the basis of acquaintance and reputation than on business principles, and the competition is firsthand. In other words, the farmer himself enters the local financial market and bids for funds.

The second method is the *agency* or *middleman system*. The person or organization negotiating the loan with the farmer acts as an agent of the investor or sells the farm loan direct to the investor. In either case the investor holds the note and mortgage of the farmer. This method is often followed in making real estate loans which investors are desirous of holding until they mature, and in short-term equipment or tractor loans which are negotiated by a local implement dealer for the company manufacturing the equipment or tractors. Private mortgage companies have used a variation of this method to obtain funds of private investors by selling certificates which represent shares in a given mortgage. These certificates or shares are arranged in denominations to suit the investor. The farm mortgage company under this plan acts as a trustee or middleman.

With the agency or middleman system, both the investor and the borrower enter the financial market individually, but the financial agency serves as the go-between. The amount paid the investor and charged the borrower is mediated by the agency. If the agency is chartered to make only agricultural loans, farmers as borrowers compete only with each other. Otherwise, they must compete directly with other segments of the economy in obtaining credit.

The third method is the *pooling* or *bond system*. The credit agency pools or groups the loans which it makes. On the security of this pool of farm loans, the credit agency issues bonds which it sells to investors in convenient denominations. Although the bonds may or may not cover specific loans described in detail, the investor does not hold the note or mortgage of the farmer. Instead he has an obligation of the credit agency which is secured by the farm loans. The Farm Credit System has used this method extensively. Here again farmers enter the local financial market individually, but the basic competition is transferred to the pooling agency. In effect, all farmers borrowing from the agency pool their competitive efforts and enter the national wholesale financial markets in direct competition with major business concerns and governments. With this method competition is at the wholesale rather than at the retail level.

The fourth method is a completely *indirect method*. The credit agency borrows from investors and lends to farmers with no direct connection between the two operations. The commercial bank follows this method in accepting or creating deposits and making loans to farmers; or farmers may borrow from merchants who in turn borrow from commercial banks. An insurance company receives premiums and invests these premiums in various securities, among them farm mortgage loans. Funds loaned by this indirect method may pass through several hands before finally reaching the farmer. With this method farmers generally enter into individual direct competition with other segments of the economy at the retail credit level. Farmers compete directly with local merchants, builders, auto dealers, and the like, in securing credit.

The four methods whereby funds flow from investors to farmers may be illustrated by alternatives open to a doctor in a county seat town located in a farming community:

1. The doctor, having $1,000 of savings to invest, may hear of a young man, son of a patient, who wants to borrow money to start farming in the spring. If the doctor makes the loan and takes the note, endorsed perhaps by the father and secured by a chattel mortgage on livestock and machinery, he is making a direct loan, a transaction typical of the first method.
2. The doctor, in a conversation with the local banker, may learn of a mortgage loan of $1,000 at 6 per cent which the bank has recently made to a farmer in the community. If the doctor wants to buy the loan, the bank will sell and assign it to him for the payment of a commission. Investing his savings in this manner, he will be following the second method, the agency or middleman system.
3. The doctor may ask the banker what mortgage bonds are available. The banker may offer him a Federal Land Bank bond at the current market price. If the doctor buys this bond with his $1,000, he will be following the third method, the pooling or bond method.
4. If the doctor decides to leave his savings in a savings account in the bank, he will be following the fourth method of indirect lending.

In the first method the doctor negotiates the loan directly with the farmer and holds the farmer's note and mortgage. In the second, he holds the farmer's note and mortgage negotiated by an intermediary agency. In the third, he holds a bond issued by an intermediary agency which in turn holds the note and mortgage of the farmer, the bond being backed by the note and mortgage. In the fourth method, he holds a savings deposit certificate from a bank which makes farm

loans, but there is no specific statement in the certificate of any
note or mortgage securing the certificate.

Loans Made by Various Types of Lenders

Lenders financing agriculture fall naturally into groups, depending upon the type of institution involved. Five different types
of lenders discussed in subsequent chapters are as follows:

1. Commercial banks
2. Insurance companies
3. Merchants and dealers
4. The Farm Credit System
5. The Farmers Home Administration

Data on agricultural loans customarily are divided into two
classes: real estate and nonreal-estate loans. Lenders making real
estate loans are referred to as long-term credit agencies and those
making nonreal-estate loans as short- and intermediate-term credit
agencies. Some lenders, of course, make both types of loans. The
volume of outstanding loans held and those made by the various
types of lenders is one indication of their relative importance in the
agricultural credit picture.

Farm Real Estate Mortgage Loans

During the year 1965, the volume of farm real estate mortgage
loans *made* in the 48 contiguous states of the United States totaled
$5,159 million. Data for Alaska, Hawaii, and Puerto Rico were not
available. The breakdown by type of lender is given in Table 16.2.

The three major institutional lenders—commercial banks, insurance companies, and Federal Land Banks—make the major portion of real estate loans, accounting for 57 per cent of the number
and 63 per cent of the volume of such loans in 1965. The large
number of commercial bank farm real estate loans is due in part to
real estate mortgages taken as additional security for short- and
intermediate-term loans. The large volume of real estate loans made
by commercial banks is partly accounted for by those which they
subsequently transfer or sell to insurance companies. In addition to
loans obtained through commercial banks, insurance companies as a

group make a large volume of loans to farmers both directly and through middlemen.

Individuals also comprise an important source of farm real estate credit. This group represents a wide range—the farmer-owner who sells his farm on contract or who takes a mortgage as part of the sale price of the farm, a relative of the farm buyer who lends a portion of the funds to buy the farm and is given a first or second mortgage as security, the professional man in the small town who lends his savings to the farmer on farm mortgage security, and finally, the private investor in some distant city who buys a farm mortgage as an investment from a bank or loan agency.

TABLE 16.2

FARM MORTGAGE LOANS **MADE** IN THE UNITED STATES BY TYPE OF LENDER
DURING THE YEAR 1965 *

Lender	Number (*thousands*)	Average Size (*thousands*)	Volume	
			Amount (*millions*)	Per cent of total
Commercial Banks and Trust Companies †...................	92.9	$11.2	$1,037	20.1
Insurance Companies †.............	24.0	40.2	964	18.7
Federal Land Banks ‡.............	58.0	21.3	1,238	24.0
Farmers Home Administration §.....	19.5	14.5	264	5.1
Production Credit Associations † ‖....	33.5	13.7	458	8.9
Savings and Loan Associations †.....	15.5	12.8	199	3.9
Individuals †.....................	47.5	17.1	812	15.7
Miscellaneous † ¶.................	13.9	13.5	187	3.6
All Lenders......................	304.8	$16.9	$5,159	100.0

* Source: *Farm Mortgages Recorded*, Farm Credit Admin., July, 1966. Data for 48 contiguous states only. Estimates for Alaska, Hawaii, and Puerto Rico not available.
† Estimates made by Federal Land Banks from farm mortgages recorded in sample counties.
‡ Actual numbers and amounts of loans made, including outstanding balances of borrowers obtaining additional funds.
§ Data provided by the Farmers Home Administration. The average size is based on number and amount of initial advances only.
‖ Mortgages secured by farm real estate primarily as additional security for operating and capital purpose loans.
¶ Includes mortgages of investment companies, state and local government agencies, and any cases where the mortgage cannot be specifically identified.

In many tabulations, loans by individuals and miscellaneous lenders are grouped together. The miscellaneous lender group, which also encompasses widely divergent types of lenders, includes real estate loans made by investment companies, credit unions, endowment funds of schools, fraternal societies, cemeteries, hospitals, and the like. Such institutions are interested in obtaining a good return on a long-term investment without having to bother with frequent reinvestment of their funds. Farm mortgage companies, loan agents, and investment companies occasionally make farm mortgage loans from their own funds, but in the main these agencies act as mortgage middlemen between farm borrowers on the one hand and individual investors, insurance companies, banks, and other farm mortgage holders on the other. The miscellaneous group also includes loans made by state and local government agencies.

Production Credit Associations, included in the miscellaneous group in many tabulations, appear as strangers in a farm mortgage loan tabulation since, as is pointed out in Chapter 25, they are chartered to make short- and intermediate-term loans. Farm mortgages recorded by Production Credit Associations are taken primarily as additional security for operating and intermediate-term capital loans.

Note the relative size of loans made by the various types of lenders shown in Table 16.2. The average size of insurance company loans is twice to three times the average size of loans made by other lender groups. Reasons for this variation in size of loans will become evident as the various types of lending institutions are discussed in subsequent chapters.

The volume of farm real estate mortgage loans *outstanding* (unpaid balance) January 1, 1966, totaled $21,196 million (see Table 16.3).

TABLE 16.3

FARM MORTGAGE LOANS **HELD** IN THE UNITED STATES, BY TYPE
OF LENDER, JANUARY 1, 1966

Lender	Unpaid Balance Outstanding	Per Cent of Total
	(millions)	
All Operating Banks...........................	$ 2,934	13.8
Life Insurance Companies.....................	4,813	22.7
Federal Land Banks...........................	4,234	20.0
Farmers Home Administration.................	627	3.0
Individuals and Others.......................	8,588	40.5
All Lenders..................................	$21,196	100.0

* Source: *Agricultural Finance Review*, Farm Prod. Econ. Div., ERS, USDA, Oct., 1966. Preliminary data for the 48 contiguous states. Complete data for Alaska and Hawaii are not available.

In this tabulation, "Individuals and Others" include the latter four groups given in Table 16.2; i.e. individuals, miscellaneous, Production Credit Associations, and savings and loan associations. These lenders as a group hold the largest proportion of the outstanding real estate loans. As of January 1, 1966, they held 40 per cent of the total. Insurance companies are the second most important source of long-term credit, holding $4,813 million, or 23 per cent of the total January 1, 1966. The Federal Land Banks ranked next with 20 per cent, and commercial banks fourth with 14 per cent. The smaller percentage of loans *held* than *made* by commercial banks results partly from the relatively shorter term of commercial bank real estate loans and partly from transfer of loans to insurance companies, as indicated above. Bank-insurance company relationships were instrumental in bringing to rural areas approximately $1 billion of the farm credit outstanding in 1959.[1] The Farmers Home Administration, which makes government loans, held a relatively small proportion of the real estate loans.

Data on farm mortgage loans given in Tables 16.2 and 16.3 show the relative importance of the various types of farm mortgage lenders as of a recent date, but consideration should also be given to the long-term picture. The relative importance of the various groups has changed in the past and probably will change in the future as economic conditions and alternative investment opportunities change. Thus, the long-run picture becomes even more important than the short-run situation in appraising the relative importance of various types of lenders in providing mortgage credit for agriculture.

The farm mortgage debt held by major lenders as of January 1 from 1910 to 1966 is portrayed in Figure 16.1. Note the predominance of loans made by individuals and others in recent years and during the early 1920's. But note also their shrinking importance starting in the late 1920's and extending into the 1940's—the time when farm foreclosures reached their peak and many farmers were in desperate need of credit. Individuals generally are an unsatisfactory source of long-term credit since just at the time when the farmer most needs the finances, the individual also needs them. Moreover, individuals who hold long-term mortgages may be seriously hurt when low farm income prevents the farmer from meeting his payments of interest and principal. Retired people and others depending on such payments for a livelihood sometimes suffer hardships.

The trends of farm mortgage loans held by insurance compa-

---

[1] Lawrence E. Kreider, American Bankers Assoc.

nies and commercial banks follow somewhat the same pattern as that of individuals. In general, these groups expand their loans during favorable or prosperous years and contract their financial service during depressions. The reason for this pattern of lending is perfectly logical, as will be shown in chapters dealing with these lenders. But the point is brought out here, in connection with the historical review of farm mortgage loans, to show that these lenders are not always as important, relatively, as they are at the present time.

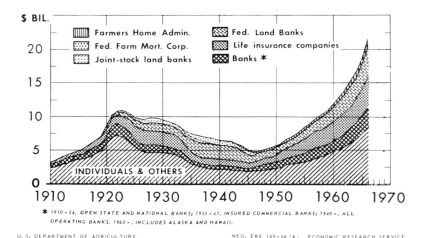

U. S. DEPARTMENT OF AGRICULTURE   NEG. ERS 149-66 (6)   ECONOMIC RESEARCH SERVICE

Fig. 16.1—Farm mortgage debt held by major lenders groups, United States, January 1, 1910–66. (Courtesy of the Economic Research Service, USDA.)

During unfavorable or depression years, loans by the Government or Government-sponsored agencies expand. Note the great expansion of Federal Land Bank loans in the 1930's. (Today some people disagree with calling the Federal Land Banks Government-sponsored institutions since they are entirely farmer owned, but there is little question that they were Government sponsored, and operated by virtue of Government financial support during the 1930's.) The Federal government created the Federal Farm Mortgage Corporation in 1933 as an affiliate of the Federal Land Banks to help provide urgently needed financing for agriculture during the Great Depression of the 1930's. The Corporation was abolished in 1961. Most of its loans had been repaid by that time and the balance were sold to the Federal Land Banks. The Farmers Home Administration, originally called The Resettlement Administration, was also created during the Great Depression to assist in financing agriculture. It was created too late to share, to any great degree, in the mammoth real estate financing undertaking of the Government in the 1930's, but there is little question but that it would shoulder a major part of the Government load, if not practically the entire load, in any future depression. Whereas the Government used Federal Land Banks and the Federal Farm Mortgage Corporation as a means of relieving farm mortgage distress in agriculture during the 1930's, the Farmers Home Administration likely would be used for that purpose in the future.

Nonreal-estate Farm Loans

Nonreal-estate loans of farmers outstanding January 1, 1966, totaled about $20.4 billion as shown in Table 16.4. Of this total,

TABLE 16.4

Nonreal-estate Loans Outstanding in the United States, by Type of Lender, January 1, 1966

Lender	Volume Outstanding	Per Cent of Total	
		Including CCC	Excluding CCC
	(millions)		
All Operating Banks *	$ 7,677	37.6	40.4
Production Credit Associations *	2,579	12.6	13.6
Other Financing Institutions—Loans and Discounts From Federal Intermediate Credit Banks *	139	.7	.7
Farmers Home Administration *	717	3.5	3.8
Nonreporting Creditors †	7,880	38.7	41.5
Total, Excluding Loans Guaranteed by CCC	18,992	93.1	100.0
Commodity Credit Corporation * (Loans Made or Guaranteed)	1,408	6.9	
Total, Including Loans Guaranteed by CCC	20,400	100.0	

* Source: *Agricultural Finance Review*, Farm Prod. Econ. Div., ERS, USDA, Oct., 1966. Some of the loans have real estate as security but all have short and intermediate terms. Data include 50 states.

† Source: *The Balance Sheet of Agriculture 1966*, p. 20, Agr. Info. Bul. No. 314, ERS, USDA. Data are for the 48 contiguous states. Includes loans and credits extended by dealers, merchants, finance companies, individuals, and others.

$1.4 billion was accounted for by price-support loans made or guaranteed by the Commodity Credit Corporation, which will be discussed later in the chapter. Excluding these loans from the total, as often is done in referring to the nonreal-estate farm debt, leaves a balance of $19.0 billion. This figure probably is less accurate than that for the farm mortgage debt because a considerable amount of short-term debt is not recorded or filed at the courthouse. Accurate data, however, are available for the institutional lenders.

A large proportion of the short- and intermediate-term credit used in agriculture is extended by miscellaneous lenders. This group, which held 42 per cent of this type of debt outstanding January 1, 1966, is comprised of two types of lenders: (1) business concerns which provide credit to farmers as a supplementary service either in selling equipment and materials or in buying the farmer's produce, and (2) individuals and miscellaneous lending institutions. Commercial companies or businesses selling goods to farmers are an important source of farm credit. Implement companies and feed stores often extend credit in connection with sales. Dealers who contract to buy the farmer's produce or are interested in handling the produce as a middleman may advance funds during the growing season or production period and deduct the principal and interest when the crop or commodity is delivered. Individuals making nonreal-estate loans to farmers include relatives, landlords, and other individuals in the local community. Nonrelated private investors at a distance from the farm are not able to provide this type of credit satisfactorily because of distance, short duration of this type of loan, and the nature of the security. Rural credit unions, building and loan associations, and similar lenders are important sources of credit in some communities where such facilities have been developed to serve agriculture.

Loans by commercial banks outstanding January 1, 1966, amounted to $7,677 million, or 40 per cent of the total, which indicates their predominant role in nonreal-estate financing of agriculture. Production Credit Associations accounted for 14 per cent and the Farmers Home Administration for 4 per cent of the nonreal-estate loans outstanding January 1, 1966. Loans of these lenders are discussed in some detail in later chapters.

A historical picture of nonreal-estate farm loans held by banks, Production Credit Associations, and the Farmers Home Administration is given in Figure 16.2. Throughout much of recorded history commercial banks have played an important role in financing short- and intermediate-term needs of agriculture. However, during periods of depression, and when farm income has been depressed for other reasons, their importance has declined. Figure 16.2 shows the great contraction in commercial bank loans during and following the Great Depression. The demand for credit generally increases during such periods but commercial lenders often are unable to meet demands due to reduced farm income and lower chattel security values. Lending ability of commercial banks also is influenced by the shrinkage of deposits which occurs during such periods. Thus, they often are unable to supply the credit needs of many farmers, especially tenants and smaller farmers who have little equity in real estate. To fill the gap, Government-sponsored and Government credit agencies were created during the Great Depression. The Production Credit Associations were sponsored by the Government to provide a means, as will be explained in a later chapter, whereby farmers could provide their own credit. The Farmers Home Administration also was created to help alleviate the situation by making direct Government loans to farmers. As is shown by Figure 16.2, these two types of agencies were important

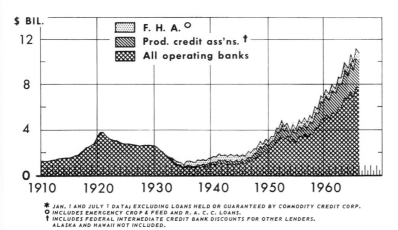

Fig. 16.2—Nonreal-estate loans to farmers held by banks and federally sponsored agencies, United States, 1910–66. (Courtesy of the Economic Research Service, USDA.)

sources of credit during and following the Great Depression. It was not until the late 1940's that commercial banks again took major leadership. Production Credit Associations also expanded their loan volume along with commercial banks, while credit extended by the Farmers Home Administration decreased since, in accordance with the law under which it operates, it makes loans only to farmers who cannot obtain credit upon reasonable terms from other lenders.

Commercial lenders probably will continue to restrict their agricultural loans during periods of low farm income as they have done in the past, leaving the load for the Government to carry. A severe widespread depression such as that which prevailed during the 1930's fortunately has not occurred in recent years. However, small areas have suffered severe financial distress. Experience with drouth in the Southern Great Plains during the first half of the 1950's indicated commercial lenders "were unwilling or unable to supply needed credit to many farmers, especially tenants with smaller units and full or part owners whose equities in real estate were low. Security requirements for bank and PCA loans to farmers have remained essentially unchanged during the current drouth."[2] It is noteworthy that the Production Credit Associations, which the Government sponsored in the 1930's to enable farmers to provide for their own credit needs, contracted their service in the drouth area along with commercial banks. The Farmers Home Administration alone was left to relieve the distress by greatly expanding direct Government loans to agriculture.

COMMODITY CREDIT CORPORATION LOANS

Reference was made above to $1.4 billion of nonreal-estate loans made or guaranteed by the Commodity Credit Corporation (CCC) in connection with its farm commodity price support operations. These are not ordinary loans; they usually are made "without recourse" which means in most cases the borrower need not pay the balance if the commodity upon which CCC loans does not sell for enough to pay the loan. Since these are not ordinary loans, they are not discussed in later chapters, as are the regular types of loans, but a brief discussion is included here to give a general picture of the Corporation and its activities.

The Commodity Credit Corporation, organized in 1933, is an agency of the U.S. Department of Agriculture. It is managed by a board of directors appointed by the President and confirmed by the Senate, subject to the general supervision and direction of the Secretary of Agriculture, who is, ex officio, a director and chairman of the board. In addition, the Corporation has a bipartisan advisory

[2] Marlowe M. Taylor, *Farm Credit in a Southern Great Plains Drouth Area, a Study of Cimarron and Texas Counties, Okla., 1950–1954*, USDA Agr. Res. Serv. Mimeo. Publ., ARS 43–12, June, 1955, p. 68.

board of five members appointed by the President to survey the general policies of the Corporation and advise the Secretary with respect thereto.

The Commodity Credit Corporation, often referred to as the CCC, is a wholly owned Government corporation with an authorized capital stock of $100 million and statutory authority to borrow up to $14.5 billion. Funds are borrowed from the U.S. Treasury and may also be borrowed from private lending agencies.

CCC carries on several activities, including the price-support, commodity stabilization, storage facilities, supply and foreign purchase, commodity export, and surplus sales and distribution programs. In terms of impact on the national economy, the most important of these are the price-support and commodity stabilization programs. CCC also handles certain financing and operating functions in connection with the International Wheat Agreement and export sales for foreign currencies.

Price support was mandatory in 1965 for corn, oats, rye, barley, grain sorghum, wheat, cotton, rice, most types of tobacco, peanuts, milk, butterfat, wool, mohair, tung nuts, and honey. Also supported under permissive provisions of the price law were flaxseed, soybeans, cottonseed, dry edible beans, and crude pine gum.

Support is achieved through loans, purchases, and payments for some commodities, all at announced levels. Under recent legislation, market price support for some commodities is being set at or near levels competitive in world markets with supplementary price-support payments and wheat marketing certificates issued to producers to maintain their incomes.

For most commodities, loans are made directly to producers on the unprocessed commodity through Agricultural Stabilization and Conservation Service county offices. Smaller amounts of many are also purchased from producers. Butterfat and milk are supported through purchases of processed dairy products, and cottonseed prices are supported through purchases of cottonseed oil. Price support on tobacco, peanuts, and naval stores is carried out through loans to producer cooperative associations that in turn make price support available to producers.

Loans are available for periods of six to eight months following harvest. Depending on the commodity, loans generally mature one to three months following the end of loan availability. Purchases from producers are made at the time of loan maturity for the crop. In recent years, farmers also have been able to continue their price-support loans on certain grains in farm storage beyond the first year, earning storage payments during the loan extension ("re-seal") period.

Price-support loans to producers are, as indicated above, "non-recourse." With this type of loan, producers are not obligated to make good any decline in the market price of the commodity they have put up as collateral. If market prices rise above support prices, producers can pay off their loans and market their commodity. If market prices fail to rise above support prices, producers can deliver the commodity to CCC, with appropriate adjustments for quality and quantity, and discharge their obligation in full.

Commercial banks or other eligible financial institutions partic-ipate in financing CCC price-support loans by the conversion of loan drafts drawn on CCC to Certificates of Interest, or by request-ing Certificates of Interest in connection with loan advances made to producer cooperative associations. These Certificates of Interest evidence participation in a pool of price-support loans for a crop year. They are transferable, payable by the Corporation upon de-mand at their face value plus accrued interest, subject to call by the Corporation, and mature on August 1 of the year following the crop year of the pooled loans. Effective January 14, 1966, a rate of 4.90 per cent per annum was specified on such Certificates of Interest. CCC also reserves the right to offer for sale additional Certificates of Interest in pools of price-support loans. Such offers, when made, are by special announcement.

The loan policy of the Commodity Credit Corporation, by itself, would be ruinous for a private lending agency. However, it should be recognized not as a loan policy so much as a price stabilization policy whereby the Corporation absorbs losses while the farmer benefits from any gains associated with price increases during the term of the loan. With such a policy, losses are practi-cally inevitable. Net realized losses on CCC price-support program operations from organization through March 31, 1966, totaled $15.4 billion. Of this amount the feed grains (corn, grain sorghum, bar-ley, oats, and rye) accounted for $5.5 billion, dairy products $3.7 billion, wheat and wheat products $2.5 billion, cotton $1.6 billion, oils and oilseeds $661 million, and all other commodities $1.4 bil-lion.

Loans to Farmer Cooperatives

Some of the credit used by farmer cooperatives is provided by the lenders referred to above, but most of the financing is provided

by the Banks for Cooperatives and the Rural Electrification Administration. The Banks for Cooperatives are a part of the Farm Credit
System, and the Rural Electrification Administration is a Government agency which provides the credit used by the rural electric and
telephone cooperatives. These lenders and the financing of cooperatives in general are discussed in Chapter 26.

QUESTIONS AND PROBLEMS

1. Discuss the function of agricultural lenders.
2. Explain where loan funds come from.
3. Using summary groupings, explain who borrows money.
4. What proportion of the total credit being used is attributable to
   farmers?
5. If your home farm community had to rely on local savings for
   credit, do you estimate it would have sufficient or insufficient
   credit? Would the period of loans be acceptable to both borrowers and lenders? Discuss.
6. Give four methods by which loan funds may move from the
   investor to the farmer.
7. List five different types of lenders who make loans to farmers.
   Discuss the relative importance of each type from the viewpoint
   of the amount of real estate and nonreal-estate loans made to
   farmers. From the *Agricultural Finance Review*, determine the
   proportion of loans made by each type of lender to farmers in
   your state.
8. Why do individuals account for such a large proportion of all
   farm mortgage holdings? Why do they figure less prominently in
   short-term loans?
9. Why do commercial banks have a small proportion of long-term
   loans and a large proportion of short-term loans?
10. What is the function of the Commodity Credit Corporation?
    What type of loan does it make? Could similar loans be made
    successfully by a commercial lender without the Government
    insurance feature?

REFERENCES

Agricultural Finance Review, USDA (issued semiannually) .
Agricultural Statistics, USDA (issued annually) .
Balance Sheet of Agriculture, USDA (issued annually) .
Survey of Current Business, U.S. Dept. of Commerce (issued monthly) .

Chapter 17

COMMERCIAL BANKS AND BANK CREDIT

THE country bank ranks high among farm credit lenders in both number of institutions and volume of credit extended. A large majority of the 13,800 commercial banks in the United States are located in towns with less than 10,000 population. In a limited sense these rural banks are farm credit service stations, leading all agencies in volume of nonreal-estate farm loans and ranking high in real estate loans made. In addition they provide a variety of services, including checking accounts, savings accounts, trust counseling, farm management services, and safe-deposit boxes. From the farmer's point of view, commercial banks have several advantageous features. First, they give prompt credit service with a minimum of red tape; second, they are readily accessible; and third, they alone provide checking account and other banking services in the local community.

THE NATURE OF COMMERCIAL BANKS

Commercial banks are corporations chartered under Federal or state law. Banks which are chartered under Federal law are called national banks and obtain their charter from the Comptroller of the Currency, a bureau of the Treasury Department of the Federal government. State banks are chartered by state chartering authority, usually known as the superintendent of banking, commissioner of banking, bank commissioner, or banking board.

As corporations, commercial banks are legal and economic entities the same as other incorporated businesses. They are capable of doing business, owning property, making contracts and the like, as defined by their charters, similar to individual proprietors. Since corporations are recognized as separate entities from the people who own, manage, and work for them, they can continue indefinitely without interruption.

Commercial banks are owned by stockholders of the corporation. Stock of many smaller banks is held by individual families, or by a few individuals, while that of larger banks usually is bought and sold on over-the-counter markets and is owned by a wide variety of investors. Thus, commercial banks are organized as private profit-making businesses and operate within a framework of competition the same as other commercial enterprises, although they are regulated in somewhat greater detail than most businesses.

Commercial banks are controlled by a board of directors, elected by the stockholders on the basis of one share, one vote. The National Bank Act provides that each national bank shall have not less than five or more than twenty-five directors, each elected for a term of one year. Provisions for election of directors of state banks vary widely among states. A major requisite of a director is that he be a man in whom the public has confidence since, particularly in small communities, the public judges a bank to a considerable degree by its directors. Major lines of business from which the bank draws its customers generally are represented on the board by directors who are well and favorably known in their field. By this means, expert opinion on general prospects and developments in the various fields of business and industry is provided the board. Moreover, such a selection of directors facilitates mutual understanding with various segments of the public.

Federal and state supervisory agencies have been given broad powers over the banking system to insure that banks comply with the extensive body of regulatory law under which they operate. This fact has an important bearing on bank operations and loan and investment policy which is sometimes overlooked by the public. State chartered banks are subject to supervision and examination by banking departments or agencies in the respective states. The Comptroller of the Currency, a bureau of the Treasury Department, has primary responsibility for supervision and examination of national banks. The Board of Governors of the Federal Reserve System and the Federal Reserve banks have broad powers of examination and supervision over member banks. Since the Comptroller is specifically charged with responsibility by law for supervision and examination of national banks, the Board and Reserve banks rely primarily on the Comptroller for examination of national banks and direct their main efforts to examination and supervision of state member banks. The Federal Deposit Insurance Corporation which provides deposit insurance examines insured state banks which are not members of the Federal Reserve System.

From the foregoing discussion it is evident that commercial banks are similar in many ways to other incorporated businesses. They are privately owned and operated on a commercial basis and, like other lending institutions, are examined and supervised by public agencies. However, commercial banks are *distinct from all other lenders in their ability, as a group, to create money* in the form of bank deposits by making loans and investments. The way in which this distinctive function is accomplished will be discussed shortly, but first, we consider the reserves which commercial banks are required to maintain, since these are an essential part of the money-creating process.

REQUIRED RESERVES LIMIT CREATION OF DEPOSITS

The amount of deposits which the banking system can create depends on reserve requirements. All national banks and state banks in most states are required by law to maintain minimum reserves in cash or its equivalent. These required reserves are computed as a percentage of the bank's deposit liabilities. Thus the amount of deposits a commercial bank can create depends upon the amount of "excess" reserves it has available after providing the required reserves. Suppose, for example, the reserve requirement is 20 per cent and that a bank has deposits totaling $100 million; its required reserve would then be $20 million. If its reserves amount to $25 million, the bank would have $5 million of excess reserves and could, assuming there was a demand, create more money in the form of deposit liabilities by making loans and investments. However, as the bank's deposits approached $125 million, its required reserve would rise to $25 million; there would no longer be an excess of reserves, so the bank would have to cease making additional loans to avoid having more deposits than its reserves would legally support. The functioning of bank reserves will be discussed in greater detail in the next chapter, but as this simplified example illustrates, when a bank's reserves are low (close to the required minimum) its ability to make new loans is curtailed. On the other hand, when a bank has excess reserves it may expand loans and investments. Moreover, the amount of deposits a given dollar amount of reserves will support depends upon the reserve requirement percentage. Thus, in the above example, if the reserve requirement were 10 per cent rather than 20 per cent, maximum deposits could be $250 million instead of $125 million.

Note that the primary function of reserves is to govern the amount of funds banks can create rather than to protect depositors, as was the case historically. In earlier times reserve requirements were imposed by law to assure that banks maintained a cash fund adequate to meet withdrawals of depositors. Such reserves, however, did not effectively protect depositors during periods of stress. Banks could not use their required reserves to meet demands for cash without drawing them below the established minimum and threatening ability of the bank to continue in business. Establishment of the Federal Reserve System helped alleviate this situation by providing a source from which commercial banks could obtain additional reserves in time of temporary need. Moreover, other means, such as the Federal Deposit Insurance Corporation, have been developed to protect depositors. Thus, required reserves are no longer regarded primarily as a means of protecting depositors but rather as a medium of credit and monetary control. This aspect of reserves will be discussed in the next chapter.

COMMERCIAL BANKING SYSTEM CREATES LOAN FUNDS

In contrast to all other lenders, who can lend only their own capital or money entrusted to them by others, commercial banks create most of the funds which they lend. In making loans, commercial banks create deposits, each loan normally giving rise to a deposit placed to the credit of the borrower. When checks are drawn against the deposit and placed or deposited in other banks, the newly created funds are dispersed throughout the banking system. Thus each loan which is made adds an equivalent amount to the deposit total of the banking system. When a loan is repaid the reverse situation occurs, with the deposit total of the banking system being reduced by the amount of the loan payment.

An individual bank cannot make an unlimited expansion in its loans and investments, of course. The limit is roughly determined by the bank's excess reserves. A borrower obtains a loan for the purpose of using the funds, and therefore the bank which makes the loan must be prepared to supply cash or settle through the clearing house for checks deposited in other banks. A bank which expands its loans and investments beyond the amount of its excess reserves runs the risk of a reserve deficiency.

An illustration of how the multiple expansion of deposits works will help clarify the process by which funds are created. Assume reserves required equal 20 per cent of deposits and that there is a demand for all the funds which can be created with such a required reserve ratio. Also assume that Bank A has no excess reserves and that it receives a deposit of $1,000 in currency which had previously been withdrawn from circulation and kept in a safe-deposit box. Receipt of this deposit of "new money" gives Bank A $1,000 of reserves, of which 20 per cent, or $200, are required as reserves for the $1,000 deposit. The remaining $800 are excess reserves, and Bank A can increase its loans and other investments by that amount. Bank A makes a loan of $800 and creates a deposit of $800. To keep the illustration simple, assume the borrower checks out the entire amount to pay a bill and the $800 is deposited in Bank B. The result is that reserves of Bank B are increased $800, of which $160 are required as backing for the added $800 of deposits, leaving $640 of excess reserves for loans or other investments. Bank B makes a loan of $640 and creates a deposit of $640. The $640 plus the $800 makes a total of $1,440 created by Banks A and B. If the $640 is checked out and deposited in Bank C, Bank C would have $512 of excess reserves for loans after deducting its 20 per cent required reserve, raising the total amount of funds created to $1,952. The amounts of excess reserves available as each successive loan is checked out and deposited in another bank, together with related figures, are shown in Table 17.1.

Assuming deposits newly created through the making of loans are withdrawn and redeposited in other banks, as illustrated in Table 17.1, the process can continue until the whole of the initial $1,000 deposit has been absorbed by the 20 per cent reserve requirement. Maximum potential deposits total $5,000 or five times the original deposit, and the amount loaned totals $4,000.

This example illustrates how commercial banks as a group are able to create deposits. It also illustrates the fact that when *maximum* deposit expansion is accomplished, the initial deposit becomes entirely "tied up" within the banking system as required reserves. All the credit extended has been created. It should be noted, however, that for this expansion process to take place, the initial deposit

TABLE 17.1

ILLUSTRATION OF THE POTENTIAL MULTIPLYING POWER OF FRACTIONAL RESERVES, ASSUMING 20 PER CENT REQUIRED RESERVES

Bank	Amount Deposited	Reserves Gained	Excess Reserves	Amount Loaned	Cumulative Deposits Created
(1)	(2)	(3)	(4)	(5)	(6)
A....................	$1,000	$1,000	$ 800	$ 800	$ 800
B....................	800	800	640	640	1,440
C....................	640	640	512	512	1,952
D....................	512	512	410	410	2,362
E....................	410	410	328	328	2,690
F....................	328	328	262	262	2,952
G....................	262	262	210	210	3,162
H....................	210	210	168	168	3,330
I....................	168	168	134	134	3,464
J....................	134	134	107	107	3,571
Total, ten banks shown....	$4,464	...	...	$3,571	...
Total, other banks........	536	536	429	429	$4,000
Total, all banks..........	$5,000	...	...	$4,000	...

must represent truly *new* reserves and not merely a deposit transfer between businesses or individuals. Moreover, the expansion illustrated is the *maximum* which can take place with the assumed 20 per cent reserve requirement. In actual practice the multiple normally is not as constant nor as large as used in the example, due to differences in reserve requirements, cash needed for day-to-day transactions, and policies of various banks.

It may be well to note that a multiple contraction of deposits can occur as well as a multiple expansion. Assuming there are no excess reserves, withdrawal of funds from the banking system generally causes a multiple contraction of deposits in much the same way that addition of new funds permits a multiple expansion.

If money is withdrawn from a bank and lost through fire or flood, the reserves of the banking system are reduced and a multiple contraction of deposits may occur. Cashing a government bond and depositing the funds ordinarily would add *new* reserves to the banking system (since government bonds are redeemed with Federal Reserve Bank funds) and provide a basis for deposit expansion, offsetting the above loss.

Assets and liabilities of all commercial banks in the United States as of January 1, 1966, are summarized in Table 17.2. Assets are comprised primarily of investments in securities and loans, and reserves. Liabilities consist primarily of deposits: personal and busi-

TABLE 17.2

ASSETS AND LIABILITIES OF COMMERCIAL BANKS IN THE UNITED STATES,
JANUARY 1, 1966 *

ASSETS	Billions of Dollars
Cash, Balances With Other Banks, and Cash Collection Items	
Currency and coin.......................................	4.9
Reserve with Federal Reserve Bank (member banks)............	18.0
Other..	38.1
Total...	61.0
Securities	
United States Government obligations.......................	59.7
Other..	45.0
Total...	104.7
Loans and Discounts	
Farm real estate mortgage loans...........................	2.9
Other mortgage loans....................................	46.8
Nonreal-estate loans to farmers...........................	8.2
Other nonreal-estate loans................................	147.9
Total, less $3.0 billion of valuation reserves..................	202.8
Miscellaneous Assets, Total.................................	10.4
Total assets.......................................	378.9
LIABILITIES AND CAPITAL ACCOUNTS	
Deposits	
Demand..	185.3
Time..	148.5
Total...	333.8
Miscellaneous Liabilities, Total.............................	14.7
Total liabilities (excluding capital accounts).................	348.5
Capital Accounts	
Stock..	10.4
Surplus..	13.6
Undivided profits.......................................	6.4
Total capital funds...................................	30.4
Total liabilities and capital..............................	378.9

* Source: *Assets, Liabilities, and Capital Accounts, Commercial and Mutual Saving Banks, December 31, 1965*, Report of Call No. 74, Fed. Dep. Ins. Corp., Washington, D.C.

ness deposits, Government deposits, and interbank deposits. About 55 per cent of the deposits are payable on demand and the remaining 45 per cent are time or savings deposits.

Note the relative amounts of loans and investments compared with the volume of deposits. As was shown by the illustration of how deposits are created, individual banks receive deposits which increase their excess reserves and permit them to make loans and investments. Thus, the line of causation for individual banks runs from the amount of excess reserves to the amount which may be safely loaned if the deposit which is created should be checked out. For the banking system the line of causation is from the excess reserves to the multiple effect in deposit creation through new loans and investments. Thus, the total volume of deposits of all banks combined is governed primarily by the amount of loans and investments made by the banking system.

Further insight into commercial bank lending can be gained by analyzing a series of statements for an individual bank. A year-to-year study of bank statements, as is evident from this example, provides an excellent record of the interactions between farm conditions and the ability of banks to meet the farmers' need for credit. Moreover, such a study brings out the primary position and importance of deposits in determining loan volume. Before a banker makes a farm loan he is likely to ask himself whether the bank's reserve position warrants such a loan. For purposes of illustration, the principal balance sheet items for a bank in a small community serving a rural area are shown in Table 17.3. The first item to observe is deposits, appearing in the sixth column in the table. Only slight changes occurred in deposits between 1921 and 1931, as shown by the June 30 statements. A peak, it is true, was reached in 1925, and a continual decline set in at this time which lasted until 1932. But the important drop in deposits occurred between 1931 and 1932. Up to this time there were three banks in the community, the one shown being the smallest. Between 1931 and 1932 one of the other banks failed. This and other failures had a profound effect on the bank in question. To meet deposit withdrawals, three important steps were taken: First, the loan total was reduced from $142 to $96 thousand; second, the bank borrowed $16 thousand from other banks; and third, the bank reduced the capital from $50 to $25 thousand. The bank was unable to sell government securities to meet the crisis because these securities had been sold between 1929 and 1930. The bank weathered the storm, however, and the deposits continued to gain steadily after 1932, one reason being that there were now only two instead of three banks in the community, and

TABLE 17.3

PRINCIPAL BALANCE SHEET ITEMS FOR A COUNTRY BANK IN IOWA, JUNE 30, 1921,
1925, 1930–1967, IN THOUSANDS OF DOLLARS*

Year as of June 30†	Loans and Discounts	Securities	Cash Items	Total Assets	Deposits	Other Liab.	Capital Items
1921	$ 163	$ 40	$ 20	$ 236	$ 159	$ 8	$ 69
1925	172	63	24	273	208	0	65
1930	149	0	43	230	174	0	56
1931	142	0	50	228	171	0	57
1932	96	0	20	164	92	16	56
1933	80	0	61	152	125	0	27
1934	27	20	263	320	293	0	27
1935	44	7	388	449	422	0	27
1936	186	55	275	528	500	0	28
1937	238	30	343	618	590	0	28
1938	304	45	247	602	571	0	31
1939	462	55	163	685	648	0	37
1940	475	50	173	702	640	0	62
1941	446	50	301	800	729	0	71
1942	407	96	510	1,016	940	0	76
1943	416	648	435	1,501	1,422	0	79
1944	305	1,310	847	2,464	2,376	0	88
1945	330	1,759	285	2,376	2,266	0	110
1946	336	2,305	366	3,008	2,878	0	130
1947	382	2,782	476	3,641	3,502	0	139
1948	597	2,557	383	3,537	3,369	0	168
1949	877	1,986	357	3,222	3,015	0	207
1950	1,024	1,697	327	3,048	2,817	0	231
1951	1,062	1,619	431	3,113	2,862	0	251
1952	1,279	1,418	439	3,137	2,851	0	286
1953	1,280	1,690	409	3,379	3,072	0	307
1954	1,250	1,662	835	3,749	3,432	0	317
1955	948	1,670	389	3,679	3,337	0	342
1956	1,250	1,648	240	3,607	3,235	0	372
1957	1,353	1,339	461	3,608	3,228	0	380
1958	1,492	1,130	586	3,667	3,263	0	404
1959	1,848	1,544	194	3,579	3,157	8	414
1960	1,635	1,725	404	3,774	3,341	7	426
1961	1,763	1,885	563	4,224	3,793	0	431
1962	1,994	1,756	377	4,141	3,703	8	430
1963	2,313	1,785	605	4,714	4,266	9	439
1964	2,905	1,663	323	4,910	4,459	11	440
1965	2,946	1,982	495	5,434	4,966	14	454
1966	3,221	2,655	391	6,280	5,766	27	487
1967‡	3,654	2,434	363	6,457	5,907	29	521

* Bank is located in town of less than 2,000 population. Capital stock was reduced from $50,000 to $25,000 in 1933 and increased from $25,000 to $40,000 in 1940, to $80,000 in 1952, and to $100,000 in 1954.
† Either June 30 or earlier in June.
‡ March, 1967.

another reason being the increased confidence in banks resulting from the deposit guarantee.

The secondary position which loans occupy is indicated by the continued liquidation of loans which took place in this bank between 1932 and 1934. In spite of the increase in deposits from $92 to $293 thousand, loans actually declined from $96 to $27 thousand. The huge increase in cash items indicates the availability of funds to lend. Since there were only two instead of three banks in the community during this period, it is evident that farmers were either not wanting to borrow or the bank was not interested in lending. The bank, on the other hand, was building up its cash reserve and buying government securities. As time passed without agricultural prices dropping drastically, the bank increased its loans. In short, deposits expanded rapidly between 1932 and 1935 and slowly afterward, while loans declined until 1934 but expanded rapidly afterward.

The effect of World War II on the bank is strikingly shown in the spectacular rise in deposits and in United States bonds. These two items increased approximately two million dollars in each case, while loans were less at the end of the war than at the beginning.

A spectacular increase in loans took place between 1947 and 1950, and also between 1962 and 1967. The first loan increase was supported entirely by sale of United States bonds, and the second mainly by increased deposits. The increase which took place in this bank in capital, surplus, and undivided profits is clearly evident in the last column of Table 17.3.

SIGNIFICANCE OF THE MONEY-CREATING POWER

The ability of the commercial banking system to create loan funds has great economic significance. By regulating the volume of reserves available to banks, the Federal Reserve System imparts an elasticity to the nation's credit system essential for economic progress and stability. Without such flexibility farmers and other businessmen would have to maintain more permanent operating capital to meet fluctuating and uncertain financial requirements. Large sums might be held idle for extended periods, while at other times available funds would prove insufficient to meet seasonal needs or other peak requirements.

The money-creating power of the commercial banking system affects the credit supply available to agriculture both directly and indirectly. It influences commercial bank loans to farmers as well as bank financing of merchants, dealers, processors, and the like, through which farmers obtain considerable credit. At the same time it influences investment policies of commercial banks and, thereby, the flow of credit to farmers through other lending institutions. Consider, for example, the source of funds for Production Credit Association loans to farmers. Production Credit Associations obtain most of their loan funds from the Federal Intermediate Credit Banks, which, in turn, obtain their funds by selling Federal Intermediate Credit Bank debentures to investors. Commercial banks purchase a substantial volume of these debentures. When commercial banks have excess reserves they are anxious to buy Credit Bank debentures even though the rate of return may be quite low. However, when bank reserves are short and money is "tight" it will not pay commercial banks to invest in Federal Intermediate Credit Bank debentures unless the rate of return is much higher. Thus it is evident that the reserve position (and money-creating power) of commercial banks has an influence not only on loans made to farmers by commercial banks themselves, but also on credit which farmers obtain from other sources.

The influence of the money-creating power of commercial banks on the economy of the country and general price level has great significance for agriculture. These considerations fall largely in the study of policy but are mentioned here since they are closely associated with credit extended to farmers. The financing of agriculture is an integral part of financing the entire economy. During periods of prosperity when resources of the country are fully employed, increasing the money supply does not increase the supply of goods and services available. Creating more money at such times merely provides people and business with more money with which to bid against one another for the scarce goods and services. As a result prices rise and the resulting inflation causes maladjustments in the economy. While farmers who are in debt might benefit from inflation, as a group they may come out on the short end of the deal if their costs of operation rise more than prices they receive. Consequently, the interests of agriculture may be best served by limiting the money-creating power of commercial banks to that needed to maintain a fairly stable price level even though that may mean somewhat higher interest costs.

Arrangements To Increase Lending Capacity

Lending capacity of commercial banks is limited by two primary factors: (1) reserves, as outlined above, and (2) bank capital.

Reserves limit the aggregate volume of loans and investments a bank can carry, whereas bank capital limits the size of individual loans. Section 5200 of the National Bank Act limits the size of loan which a national bank may grant to any one customer to a given percentage of the bank's unimpaired capital and surplus. Feeder-cattle loans are limited to 25 per cent, and farm real estate and other agricultural loans to 10 per cent of the bank's capital and surplus. Some state laws are more restrictive while others are more liberal than the National Bank Act regulations.

Limitations on size of loans often are important to smaller country banks in a community of larger farms, since loan requirements of such farms often exceed the lending limit of the bank. The rapid and continuing growth in size of farms has accentuated the problem, since the capital structure of many country banks has not grown as fast, relatively, as the size of farms. The problem is encountered most frequently in the western half of the United States. Moreover, with the trend being toward larger farm units it appears that the problem of farm loan size relative to bank capital loan limitations will become increasingly acute.

Commercial banks have developed a number of ways or methods which facilitate increasing their lending capacity and handling larger lines of credit. One of the most important of these is bank mergers and development of branch banking systems. During the year 1966, a total of 137 commercial banks in the United States were consolidated with or absorbed by other commercial banks, and banks were converted into branches in 113 of the mergers.[1]

Branch Banking

As a means of expanding their business and of providing more adequate and convenient service to the public, banks frequently establish branch offices known as *branch banks*. State laws vary widely in this regard; whereas some states permit branch banking without restriction or with certain limitations, some others practically prohibit branches entirely. The National Bank Act, under which national banks are chartered, permits establishment of branches according to state law where the bank is located. Branches, like new banks, may not be established without approval of the appropriate supervising authority.

Other things being equal, branch banking facilitates handling

---

[1] *Federal Reserve Bulletin,* Board of Governors of the Federal Reserve System, Washington, D.C., Feb., 1967, p. 310.

a larger total volume of loans relative to reserves, by being more economical of bank reserves—shifting them from one area to another as the need arises. Consider, for example, two banks in a community with approximately the same volume of deposits, one an independent bank and the other a branch bank office. The independent bank is limited in its loan volume (excluding loans carried on a correspondent basis, and the like, to be discussed later) by its own reserves. On the other hand, the branch bank office has the benefit of all reserves in the banking institution of which it is a part. It is evident, therefore, that the branch office may have a very large volume of reserves at its disposal. Of course, all branches must be served from the "pot of reserves" and, therefore, when money is tight (reserves are scarce) the branch bank office will be restricted in the volume of loans it can carry, the same as the independent bank. In fact, a branch banking operation could draw funds from a local community to head office loan customers. When a branch bank has a number of offices serving a fairly large area, all communities served by the institution seldom have simultaneous peak demands for loans, even in periods of prosperity. This helps make funds available for individual branches according to their needs.

Branch banking also facilitates making larger individual loans since branch banking institutions generally have more capital and surplus than independent country banks serving agriculture. Referring to the independent and branch bank example used in the preceding paragraph, the independent bank is limited in the size of individual loans it can make by its own capital and surplus. In contrast, the size of individual loans the branch bank office can make depends upon the capital and surplus of the entire banking institution of which it is a part. Thus, it is probable that the branch bank office could make larger individual loans than the unit bank.

Chain Banking and Group Banking

Another type of relationship used by banks to augment their loan funds and to facilitate handling larger loans, particularly in Minnesota and the Dakotas, is referred to as chain banking and group banking. These are forms of multiple-office banking (similar to branch banking) in which a number of independently incorporated banks are brought under the same control by ownership, by common directors, or by some other means. *Chain banking* refers to arrangements where control rests in the hands of one or more individuals, while *group banking* describes arrangements in which control is vested in a holding company, corporation, business trust, or the like.

Chain or group banking arrangements are similar to branch banking in that control is centralized. However, being comprised of separate banking corporations, mutual lending activity must be carried out on somewhat of a correspondent bank basis. Central control facilitates these relationships, of course. Even though individual banks of the group are separate corporations, they have the advantage of strength derived from the parent organization and of diversification over a large area. In other words, individual banks are relieved of full dependence upon their own resources. Smaller banks benefit in this regard particularly by spreading their risks and possibly by having access to services of specialized personnel in credit analyses, management of bond portfolios, and in carrying out other specialized functions. Moreover, proponents of chain or group banking generally believe that the management of individual banks improves, following their becoming a part of a chain or group. These advantages are similar to those usually given for branch banking. On the other hand, there also are some disadvantages to chain and group banking, and again these are similar to those generally given for branch banking. With strict central control, some independence of action and flexibility may be forfeited, which may serve to dampen local initiative and progressive action in the community. Conversely, too loose control and supervision may contribute to inefficient operations, including weak credit analysis and an inadequate loan and service policy.

Correspondent Bank Relationships

Business arrangements by which commercial banks in the United States coordinate their efforts in rendering bank services are referred to as *correspondent bank relationships*. Through correspondent relationships, two or more banks can team up to provide funds for loans and to handle large loans. In addition, correspondent bank relationships facilitate many other operations and services essential in banking and needed in rural areas, including bank management assistance for country banks, transfer of funds, check clearance, bond and stock portfolio counseling, and servicing of rural accounts held by city banks.

Banks of any size can have correspondent relationships with

other banks. In practice, however, a smaller bank usually becomes a correspondent of a larger bank or banks.

REASONS FOR CORRESPONDENT BANK RELATIONSHIPS

Correspondent bank relationships constitute a method of economizing on bank reserves, or of making fuller use of reserves, similar to branch banking. Loan requirements in some agricultural areas may double during peak lending seasons and reserves of local banks often are inadequate to meet such demands. Excess reserves of city banks can be made available through correspondent relationships, and used to supplement those of the country bank. Thus, as branch banking provides a means of using excess reserves for loans anywhere in the area served by the branch bank, correspondent bank relationships similarly facilitate making use of excess reserves for loans in any part of the area served by the correspondent banks. Of course, with both branch banking and correspondent banking, this benefit to the smaller bank is dependent upon reserves being available. If a city correspondent bank has no excess reserves, it can be of little help to the country bank.

Country banks use correspondent relationships to help provide loans larger than they are permitted to make on the basis of their own capital and surplus. A small local bank, in a state that limits the size of loan that can be made to an individual or a business, often cannot meet the credit requirements of large farms, farmer cooperatives, machinery dealers, and the like. Through correspondent relationships even the smallest commercial bank can take care of any credit requirement of good quality in the community except possibly for long-term real estate loans.

Correspondent relationships also provide a method of spreading risks associated with credit extension. Whereas the lending authority of a country bank may permit carrying a certain line of credit, the risk involved may be such that the bank would rather provide only part of the funds. Similarly, some loans may be "bankable," but involve enough risk so that the local bank is reluctant to carry too many in its loan portfolio. By participating with one another on such loans, commercial banks are able to meet more of the credit needs of agriculture without individually incurring excessive risk.

CORRESPONDENT BANK LOAN PROCEDURES

There are several methods used by correspondent banks in making and servicing loans, depending upon the general agreement between the banks and circumstances of each transaction. Edgar T. Savidge, Secretary of the Agricultural Commission of the American Bankers Association, made a survey of commercial banks and outlined these methods as follows:

1. The country bank takes the entire loan in its name, even though the amount exceeds the bank's legal limit. A participation certificate is issued to the city bank for that share of the loan being sold. The collateral is pledged to the country bank where it is retained. The country bank services the loan and collects principal and interest payments and remits to the city bank its portion.

2. The loan is written in the names of both the country and the city bank with separate notes for the share that each is to carry. The instrument pledging the collateral is likewise drawn to indicate the respective interest that each bank has. This procedure is used generally when the transaction involves a deed of trust or a mortgage which becomes a matter of public record. Normally, the country bank is responsible for servicing the entire loan but, in some cases, payments are made by the borrower to each of the two banks involved.

3. The country bank takes all notes in its name and transfers all or a portion of them to the city bank, depending on whether the country bank is selling all or only part of the loan. If the city bank purchases only part of the loan, the collateral is shared by the two banks in direct proportion to their respective interests. The bank to service the loan and collect the payments will vary, but normally this would be done by the country bank as it is in direct contact with the borrowers.

4. In cases where country bank borrowers need amounts of credit beyond the capacity of these banks, they are referred to city banks. If the transaction is completed, it is essentially a direct loan by the city bank. In most situations, city banks prefer that their correspondent carry a small portion of the loan since, by so doing, the country bank will watch the borrower's condition more closely.

About 70 per cent of the banks reporting participate in making original credit examinations of the borrower and appraisals. In some instances, the country bank will service the loan while, in other cases, inspections are made by the city bank. If the latter is done, copies of inspectors' reports are submitted to the country bank. City banks with agriculturally trained men on their staffs are in a better position to make inspections than those without them.

Practically all banks reported that they would participate in renewals. Forty per cent of them limit their participation in loans to helping country banks meet seasonal loan

requirements, whereas 60 per cent will participate on a continuous, year-round basis.[2]

Loans From Other Banks

Another method used by commercial banks to increase their
loan funds is to borrow from other banks. An unusual or unexpected withdrawal of deposits, or demand for loans, for example,
may deplete a bank's reserves. Under such circumstances a bank may
find it necessary to borrow. Generally, a bank that is a member of
the Federal Reserve System borrows from its Federal Reserve Bank,
while a nonmember bank borrows from its correspondent bank.
Note that such borrowings provide loan funds by augmenting the
borrowing bank's reserves. Commercial bank borrowing from Federal Reserve Banks will be considered further in the next chapter.

Arrangements With Life Insurance Companies

A number of commercial banks have arrangements with life
insurance companies whereby farm mortgage real estate loans made
by the bank are subsequently taken over by an insurance company.
These arrangements have increased considerably in importance in
recent years. Over $1 billion of farm credit outstanding January 1,
1960, had resulted from bank-insurance company collaboration of
one kind or another. In recent years bank-insurance company relationships have been instrumental in bringing over twenty times as
much additional credit to farmers as have correspondent bank relationships.[3]

Many bank-insurance company arrangements are informal,
while others are handled on a more or less formal basis. For example, under an "Approved Mortgage Plan" used by some life insurance companies, the company signs an agreement with the bank to
make the real estate appraisal and to purchase the loan any time
within two years; and the bank agrees to assign the loan to the
insurance company within that time. The insurance company's
form of note and mortgage is used, and where the bank cannot
legally make the loan for the term of years desired, an *extension and*

---

[2] Edgar T. Savidge, "Interbank Relations in Financing Agriculture," *Jour.
of the American Bankers Association,* July, 1954.
[3] Personal correspondence with Lawrence E. Kreider, American Bankers
Assoc.

modification agreement is executed wherein the insurance company agrees that it will extend the term after purchasing the loan.

Arrangements with life insurance companies provide commercial banks, in effect, with an important type of loan funds. The nature of bank deposits makes it desirable for banks to specialize in short-term rather than long-term loans. If a large portion of bank deposits were used for long-term loans, banks might be unable to remain solvent under heavy deposit withdrawals. With resources largely in short-term loans and investments, a continuous flow of cash is available in case it is needed to meet deposit withdrawals. Moreover, real estate loans of national banks are limited by law to the larger of paid-in capital plus unimpaired surplus, or sixty per cent of time and savings deposits. Thus, arrangements with insurance companies enable commercial banks to broaden their credit service by providing a source of long-term loan funds for real estate mortgages.

QUESTIONS AND PROBLEMS

1. Explain the nature of a commercial bank. By what authority does a bank operate?
2. Who owns commercial banks? Discuss the significance of ownership in operation of a bank.
3. Discuss the role of directors in affairs of a bank.
4. Explain how bank reserve requirements limit the amount of loans a bank may make.
5. How does the source of commercial bank loan funds differ from those of other lenders?
6. Explain how the commercial banking system creates deposits. Can one bank alone create deposits?
7. Compare branch banking and correspondent bank relationships as a means of providing loan services.
8. Outline the various ways in which loans made on a correspondent bank basis may be handled.
9. Compare chain or group banking with branch and correspondent banking from the viewpoint of financing agriculture.
10. Discuss commercial bank arrangements with insurance companies as a means of broadening bank loan service to agriculture.

REFERENCES

Doll, R. J., and Castle, E. N., *Financing Agriculture Through Commercial Banks,* Fed. Res. Bank of Kansas City, 1954.

The Federal Reserve System, Purposes and Functions, Board of Governors, Fed. Res. System, Washington, D.C.

How Our Reserve Banking System Operates, Monetary Study No. 2, rev. ed., Economic Policy Commission, Amer. Bankers Assoc.

Our Financial System at Work, Monetary Study No. 1, rev. ed., Economic Policy Commission, Amer. Bankers Assoc.

Savidge, Edgar T., "Interbank Relations in Financing Agriculture," *Jour. of the ABA,* July, 1954.

Chapter 18

COMMERCIAL BANKS AND THE FEDERAL RESERVE SYSTEM

THE Federal Reserve System is comprised of the Board of Governors and the twelve Federal Reserve Banks. The Board of Governors of the Federal Reserve System is a governmental agency in Washington, D.C., consisting of seven men appointed for fourteen-year terms by the President of the United States, with the advice and consent of the Senate. The Board is responsible for supervising the Federal Reserve System and has a major hand in formulating national monetary and credit policies. The twelve Federal Reserve Banks (with a total of twenty-four branches) are corporations chartered by the Congress of the United States. The fifty states are divided into twelve districts, each with its own Reserve Bank. The capital stock of each Federal Reserve Bank is owned by member banks in the district. However, the Federal Reserve Banks are operated, not for profit of stockholders, but in the public service.[1] Each of the twelve banks has its own board of directors.

The Federal Reserve System constitutes the primary monetary regulatory authority of the nation. Through power entrusted to it

---

[1] The return to member banks is limited by law to a 6 per cent annual dividend on stock owned. Income above amounts needed to cover dividends, expenses, and any additions to surplus necessary to maintain a capital-surplus ratio of 2 to 1 is paid to the Treasury. (Source: *The Federal Reserve System, Purposes and Functions,* Board of Governors of the Federal Reserve System, Washington, D.C., 1963, pp. 196–97.)

by the Congress of the United States, the System exerts very significant influence on commercial banks and on the supply of credit.
Practically all the larger banks in the country are members of the
Federal Reserve System. Member banks have over 80 per cent of the
commercial banking assets. The System exerts direct influence on
policies of these banks, primarily through actions which affect bank
reserves. Some of these actions also influence credit policies of
nonmember banks. Moreover, member bank policies, in turn, affect
nonmember banks since member banks typically perform many of
the same functions for nonmember correspondents that the Federal
Reserve Banks perform for members. Reflecting the impact of monetary policy on the credit supply of the economy in general, Federal
Reserve policy also affects other lenders, such as merchants, dealers,
Federal Intermediate Credit Banks, Federal Land Banks, and insurance companies. The nature of this influence was indicated in the
preceding chapter.

Functions of the Federal Reserve System

Since the Federal Reserve System exerts such a significant
influence upon financial affairs of the country, an understanding of
its functions is needed to understand fully the role of commercial
banks in financing agriculture. The intent here is not to give a
complete picture of all phases of the Federal Reserve System—that
constitutes a complete course of study in itself—but rather to give a
summary picture of the System's function as it relates to credit, and
of the more important means employed to influence credit extension by commercial banks.

The basic function of the Federal Reserve System is to use its
broad powers "to foster growth at high levels of employment, with a
stable dollar in the domestic economy and overall balance in our
international payments."[2] This means that the Federal Reserve
System has a responsibility to the nation's economy as a whole, and
not to any one segment alone. It means that the System should
develop and maintain a national monetary policy supported by
financial machinery as needed to provide an economic climate in
which private enterprise will develop, grow, and prosper. To facilitate achieving this objective, authorities should take action to help
counteract both inflationary and deflationary movements.

---

[2] *Ibid.,* p. 2.

In carrying out this basic function the Federal Reserve System relies primarily on its power to regulate the supply of credit. The job is to allow an adequate flow of credit to "foster growth at high levels of employment" without going too far so that inflation develops. The following paragraphs from a publication of the Board of Governors of the System are pertinent.

> In a dynamic and growing economy, enough credit and money is that amount which will help to maintain high and steadily rising levels of production, employment, incomes, and consumption, and to foster a stable value for the dollar. When credit, including bank credit, becomes excessively hard to get and costs too much, factories and stores may curtail operations and lay off employees. Smaller payrolls mean hardship for workers, who curtail their purchases; merchants feel the decline in trade and reduce their orders for goods. Manufacturers in turn find it necessary to lay off more workers. A serious depression, unemployment, and distress may follow.
>
> When credit is excessively abundant and cheap, the reverse of these developments—an inflationary boom—may develop. An increase in the volume and flow of money resulting from an increase in the supply and availability of credit, coupled with a lowering of its cost, cannot in itself add to the country's output. If consumers have or can borrow so much money that they try to buy more goods than can be produced by plants running at capacity, this spending only bids up prices and makes the same amount of goods cost more. If merchants and others try to increase their stocks so as to profit by the rise in prices, they bid up prices further. Manufacturers may try to expand their plants in order to produce more. If so, they bid up interest rates, wages, and the prices of materials. In the end they raise their own costs.[3]

Since such a large part of the Federal Reserve System's primary function depends upon regulating the supply of credit, commercial banks of the nation play an important role in the undertaking. This is because commercial banks are the financial institutions through which credit can be created, so it is through them that the credit supply of the nation is controlled.

MEANS OF INFLUENCING CREDIT EXPANSION

There are a number of means which the Federal Reserve System can use to control credit expansion, but the three most important are:

---

[3] *Ibid.*, p. 11.

1. Adjusting reserve requirements of commercial banks
2. Open market operations
3. Changing the Federal Reserve discount rate

These methods constitute *active* means of control since the System takes initiative in bringing about desired changes through their use. All three are effective through their influence on bank reserves.

Adjusting Reserve Requirements

The Board of Governors of the Federal Reserve System has authority to change reserve requirements of member banks within limits set by law. The reserve maximum and minimum requirements, given as a percentage of deposits, are shown in Table 18.1.

TABLE 18.1

MAXIMUM AND MINIMUM RESERVE REQUIREMENTS OF FEDERAL RESERVE SYSTEM MEMBER BANKS *

Reserve Requirement	Demand Deposits		Time Deposits
	Country banks	Reserve city banks	All banks
	(per cent)	*(per cent)*	*(per cent)*
Minimum...................................... 7		10	3
Maximum......................................14		22	10

* Source: *Federal Reserve Bulletin*, Board of Governors, Fed. Res. System, Washington, D.C., Feb., 1967, p. 252.

Authority to change reserve requirements gives the Federal Reserve System a powerful tool to use in controlling bank credit since the amount of reserves a bank has, compared with the required reserves, governs its potential loan volume. As long as a bank has excess reserves it may make additional loans—assuming there is a demand for more credit. However, if the bank has a reserve deficiency it must make up the deficiency by borrowing, selling securities, allowing repayments to exceed loan extensions, acquiring additional deposits without offsetting loan increases, or by a combination of these means. Thus, if the Federal Reserve System wants to encourage an increase in the amount of credit, it can do so by lowering the reserve requirements (within the range provided by law), thereby giving banks more excess reserves for loans. On the other hand if the Federal Reserve System wants to restrict the supply of credit, it can achieve this end by increasing the reserve requirements.

An example will help clarify the effect of a change in reserve requirements. Since the creation of deposits is accomplished by the banking system as a whole, all commercial banks are considered as a unit in the example and it is assumed that their combined assets and liabilities are as shown in Table 18.2.

TABLE 18.2

ASSETS AND LIABILITIES OF ALL COMMERCIAL BANKS IN THE UNITED STATES
(Hypothetical data with all dollar amounts in billions)

ASSETS			LIABILITIES		
Loans.........................$ 96			Deposits (demand)............$200		
Bonds....................... 100			Capital and surplus........... 20		
Reserves.................... 24					
Total....................$220			Total......................$220		

Memo:	Situation I	Situation II	Situation III
Reserve requirement........	12%	10%	14%
Actual reserves............	$24	$24	$24
Required reserves..........	$24	$20	$28
Excess reserves............	$ 0	$ 4	$ 0
Reserve deficiency.........	$ 0	$ 0	$ 4

Starting with Situation I shown in Table 18.2, the reserve requirement is assumed to be 12 per cent, giving a dollar reserve requirement of $24 billion, the same as reserves assumed to be available. In other words, with conditions assumed in Situation I the banking system has no excess reserves. Under such circumstances the commercial banking system is not in position to expand loans or investments.

Now assume that the Federal Reserve System believes additional funds are needed to meet credit needs of the country and that it, therefore, lowers the reserve requirement to 10 per cent as shown in Situation II. This action lowers the amount of required reserves to $20 billion, leaving $4 billion of excess reserves. The banks are then free to expand their loans and investments, as illustrated in the preceding chapter, until all their excess reserves are "used up." With the assumed 10 per cent reserve requirement, loans and investments can be increased by $40 billion. To keep the illustration simple, assume the entire $40 billion deposit expansion takes place through making new loans and that all the proceeds of the loans are kept on deposit. Loans shown in Table 18.2 would then total $136 billion and deposits $240 billion. It is evident that lowering the legal reserve requirement releases a given amount of reserves which can lead to an increase of several times that amount in loans.

Comparison of Situations I and III in Table 18.2 illustrates the effect of an increase in reserve requirements. In Situation I the reserve requirement is 12 per cent and the dollar amount of reserves available is just equal the required reserves. Increasing the reserve requirement to 14 per cent of deposits raises the amount of reserves required to $28 billion, which causes a reserve deficiency of $4 billion. The banking system could remove this deficiency by one or a combination of methods: reducing the volume of loans (probably as payments are received), selling bonds, or borrowing from the Federal Reserve. Assume the system decides to reduce the volume of loans and thus absorb deposits. With the reserve requirement at 14 per cent, the $24 billion of available reserves will support appproximately $171 billion of deposits. In other words, deposits have to be reduced by about $29 billion to remove the $4 billion reserve deficiency. Thus, with a 14 per cent reserve requirement the ratio is about 7 to 1. Again the powerful impact of action by the Federal Reserve System is evident, this time in the direction of contraction rather than expansion. By adjusting reserve requirements the System can exert great influence over credit conditions. Reserve requirements along with open market operations and discount rate changes lie at the heart of monetary control.

Open Market Operations

The term *open market operations* generally refers to buying and selling of securities—mostly short-term Government issues—by the Federal Reserve System in public financial markets of the nation. Open market transactions, which all take place at the New York Federal Reserve bank, are conducted under direction of the Federal Open Market Committee, composed of seven members of the Board of Governors and five of the Federal Reserve Bank presidents. Broad powers have been given this committee.

The primary influence of open market operations on credit extension is exercised through their effect on reserves of commercial banks. When analyses made by the Federal Reserve System indicate that increased availability of credit would help achieve desired expansion of economic activity, the Open Market Committee buys securities. Purchases of Government securities by the Open Market Committee increase bank reserves and enable the banking system to increase loans and investments, thereby creating more deposits. For example, assume the Open Market Committee buys securities from a bank, insurance company, broker, or individual and gives in payment a check drawn on a Federal Reserve Bank. The seller of the securities deposits the check in his account at a member bank, and the bank in turn receives a credit to its reserve balance at its Reserve Bank when the check is collected. Reserve funds created by this transaction are *newly created* by the Federal Reserve System. While the receiving bank's reserve balance is increased in exactly the same way that a draft drawn on another commercial bank would add to its reserves, the difference is that the check drawn on a Reserve Bank does not produce an offsetting reduction in the reserve balance of another commercial bank. Thus, the net result is an increase in reserves of the commercial banking system and an equal addition to Federal Reserve System holdings of Government securities.

When analysis of the Federal Reserve System indicates inflationary pressures are developing and that the rate of growth in the supply of money should be restricted, the Open Market Committee sells securities, which reverses the above procedure. Sale of Government securities by the Federal Reserve System reduces member bank reserves and thereby curtails credit extension.

The way in which open market operations affect commercial bank lending might be further clarified by referring again to Table 18.2. Assume that excess reserves are nil as in Situation I. Having no excess reserves, the banking system is unable to create additional deposits through loans. Now suppose the Open Market Committee concludes credit should be eased and directs that $1.0 billion of Government securities be purchased in the open market. The effect of this action on reserves of "All Commercial Banks" considered in Table 18.2 is shown by comparing Situations I and IV in Table 18.2 Continued.

Federal Reserve purchase of $1.0 billion of securities increases the dollar reserves of commercial banks by $1.0 billion (to $25 billion), thereby creating a billion of excess reserves. If all the

excess reserves are used for credit expansion, a *maximum* of about
$8.3 billion of new loans could be made with reserve requirements
at 12 per cent.

Comparison of Situations I and V illustrates the effect of a sale
of $1.0 billion of securities in the open market by the Federal
Reserve System. Reserves of commercial banks are reduced by $1.0
billion, causing a reserve deficiency of $1.0 billion. If this deficiency
is removed by reducing loans, the total volume of loans outstanding
in Table 18.2 would be reduced by about $8.3 billion with the
assumed 12 per cent reserve requirement.

TABLE 18.2 CONTINUED

(Dollar amounts in billions)

	Situation I (From Table 18.2)	Situation IV	Situation V
Reserve requirement.......	12%	12%	12%
Actual reserves............	$24	$25	$23
Required reserves..........	$24	$24	$24
Excess reserves............	$ 0	$ 1	$ 0
Reserve deficiency.........	$ 0	$ 0	$ 1

Changing reserve requirements of commercial banks and open
market operations by the Federal Reserve System are merely two
different methods of accomplishing the same objective: changing
the amount of reserves held by commercial banks and thereby
influencing their loan and investment policies. In practice the two
methods are used to supplement each other. Generally reserve requirements are not changed often and only when fairly substantial
changes are needed in reserves. On the other hand, open market
operations are used to adjust reserves for daily and seasonal variations in requirements.

In passing it should be noted that for open market operations
and changes in reserve requirements to be effective, a free market
must be maintained for Government securities. As is shown by
Table 17.2, Government securities constitute a large proportion of
commercial bank assets. Since these securities can be sold to acquire
additional reserves, it is evident that commercial banks have a very
large dollar reserve potential. If the price of Government securities
were supported, as it was for a period following World War II,

commercial banks could sell securities without penalty (of a lower price) and acquire reserves to permit a huge expansion in loans. Under these conditions the Federal Reserve System would have little control over the total supply of credit. On the other hand, with a free market for Government securities, interest rates tend to increase as inflationary tendencies develop. As a result Government security prices drop. Under such circumstances commercial banks are less inclined to sell Government securities, both because a loss will be realized and because, with a lower price, the rate of return is higher. With commercial banks reluctant to sell securities, Federal Reserve open market operations and changes in reserve requirements can have an effective influence on reserves.

Changing the Discount Rate

With approval of the Board of Governors of the Federal Reserve System, the Federal Reserve Banks can adjust the discount rate (the rate of interest charged member banks on loans from the Reserve Bank) as a means of influencing extension of credit to the public. Member banks may borrow from Reserve Banks to a modest degree under usual conditions (and to a considerably greater degree in extreme circumstances) on the basis of Government securities and customers' notes which are eligible and acceptable. (Nonmember banks may also borrow from and discount paper with the Federal Reserve Banks in emergency situations.) When banks are borrowing, an increase in the discount rate increases their costs and thereby tends to discourage borrowing. But, more important, it serves as a warning that credit extension needs watching, and banks know that if such warnings are not heeded, the more positive and forceful tools of adjusting reserve requirements and open market operations may follow. Thus, a major influence of adjusting the discount rate is psychological, and as such it is a potent influence not only on commercial banks, but on business generally.

Adjustments in the discount rate may serve also as a signal of easier credit conditions. A reduction of the rate lowers the cost of commercial bank borrowing and, in turn, encourages commercial banks to make business loans. It also provides a psychological effect in that business may feel more inclined to undertake expansion plans if credit promises to be adequate and lower in cost.

While changes in the discount rate are directly effective only on member banks, the effect is passed on indirectly to nonmember banks through correspondent relationships, and to the economy in general through the effect on the general interest rate structure.

Example of Federal Reserve Action

The way in which the three methods of controlling credit extension through the commercial banking system was used during the period from late 1965 to early 1967 is portrayed by the following quotation taken from the *Federal Reserve Bulletin*.

The Federal Reserve provided reserves generously in late 1965 and in early 1966 to smooth credit market adjustments to the December 1965 increases in the discount rate and in ceiling rates on time deposits under Regulation Q, and to the burgeoning credit demands. Open market operations over the balance of the first half of 1966 were conducted so as to increase pressure on banks' reserve positions. Nonborrowed reserves grew at a reduced pace after January, although they were supplied liberally in early spring and again around midyear to lessen the credit market pressures being generated by strong business borrowing demands to accommodate accelerated tax payments. Member bank borrowings from the Federal Reserve increased as banks adjusted to the gradually increasing monetary restraint. Primarily as a result of the increase in borrowings, total member bank reserves rose by 4.1 per cent (annual rate) from February through June, about the same as their rate of expansion from mid-1965 through January 1966.

Banks bid actively for time deposits in the first half of 1966, and the expansion of such deposits helped to sustain growth in bank credit at a 9.8 per cent annual rate over the first 6 months of 1966, a little above the pace of the second half of 1965. Demands for credit, especially by the business sector, increased further. Higher market interest rates, together with intensified bank competition for funds, led to a sizable reduction in net inflows of savings to nonbank savings institutions and thence to the mortgage market. As a result the homebuilding industry was feeling the impact of monetary restraint, whereas industrial and other business concerns were still obtaining credit, though at rising interest rates, to finance their increasing outlays for fixed capital and inventories.

During the summer, the Federal Reserve took a variety of steps to redress the balance in the flow of funds between business borrowers and the housing industry and to help prevent rate competition for savings among financial institutions from adding to the upward thrust of interest rates.

In July the Regulation Q ceiling on new multiple-maturity time deposits was reduced to 5 per cent for deposits with maturities of 90 days and over, and to 4 per cent for those of less than 90 days. Between July and September reserve requirements on time deposits in excess of $5 million at each member bank were raised from 4 to 5 and then from 5 to 6 per cent. Bank issues of promissory notes maturing in less than 2 years also were brought under reserve-requirement and interest-ceiling regulations. As a result of these actions, required reserves of member banks were increased by an estimated $900 million.

In a letter on September 1, the Presidents of the Federal Reserve Banks requested member bank cooperation in curtailing expansion in loans to business. The letter indicated that member banks experiencing deposit losses which made efforts to adjust by reducing their business loan expansion instead of cutting further into their holdings of securities, especially municipal securities, would be extended credit through the discount window for longer periods than usual. This action was taken in an effort not only to exert more restraint on business loans, but also to ease credit market pressures that would be generated if banks—faced with potentially large run-offs of large-denomination certificates of deposit (CD's) — were to liquidate substantial amounts of securities in order to adjust their positions.

In late September, new temporary authority was enacted by Congress which broadened the basis for setting interest rate ceilings on time and savings deposits. The Board of Governors promptly reduced to 5 per cent from $5\frac{1}{2}$ per cent the maximum rate of interest member banks could pay on time deposits of less than $100,000. Federal agencies that regulate savings and loan associations and mutual savings banks also established similar ceilings under this new authority.

Starting around midsummer the advanced levels of market rates in combination with the ceilings on time deposit rates led to a sharply reduced expansion in commercial bank time deposits. In particular there were sizable declines in outstanding negotiable CD's as banks were unable to roll over all the CD's maturing. These CD runoffs, together with a continued restrictive open market policy, resulted in a net decline in outstanding bank credit in late summer and early fall.

Expansion in bank credit resumed, however, in the last few weeks of 1966 and accelerated in early 1967. From November 1966 through January 1967, nonborrowed reserves of banks increased rapidly after declining at a 4 per cent rate from July through October. Net borrowed reserves declined to an average of $20 million in January 1967 from the October high of $430 million. Late in December the special discount arrangements established in the September letter were terminated.[4]

---

[4] *Federal Reserve Bulletin,* Board of Governors of the Federal Reserve System, Washington, D.C., Feb., 1967, pp. 189–92.

It is interesting to note the joint use of two monetary control measures in late 1965 and early 1966; i.e. open market operations "to smooth credit market adjustments to the December 1965 increases in the discount rate. . . ." It is also interesting to note the use of other monetary control measures in conjunction with the standard methods. Adjustments in interest rate ceilings were very effective due to the relatively high rate structure prevailing in the economy. In the above discussion of changing the discount rate the point was made that if such warning is not heeded more positive and forceful tools would be used. The September 1 letter to member banks was such a tool. It requested commercial banks to limit their loans to business. "The letter indicated that the discount windows at the Federal Reserve Banks were open to banks conforming to these guidelines."[5] Such a letter undoubtedly is very effective in obtaining cooperation from commercial banks, particularly in a period when net borrowed reserves are at or near their peak, and there is real danger of substantial run-off in deposits.

QUESTIONS AND PROBLEMS

1. What is the Federal Reserve System? Obtain a copy of the Federal Reserve Pulletin and outline the boundaries of the twelve districts.
2. Outline the objectives of the Federal Reserve System.
3. Give the three primary methods used by the Federal Reserve System to influence credit extension.
4. Explain how a change in reserve requirements can affect the loan volume of commercial banks.
5. Explain how open market operations affect commercial bank loan volume.
6. Explain how adjusting the discount rate affects extension of credit by commercial banks.
7. Compare changing reserve requirements, open market operations, and changing the discount rate in their effect on commercial bank loans.
8. Outline how the Federal Reserve System employed reserve requirements, open market operations, and the discount rate to influence business conditions and loans during 1965 and 1966.
9. What is the current policy of the Federal Reserve System with regard to commercial bank loans?

---

[5] Economic Research Division, *Business in Brief,* The Chase Manhattan Bank, New York, N.Y. Feb., 1967, p. 3.

REFERENCES

Annual Reports of the Federal Reserve System, Board of Governors, Washington, D.C.

Davis, Carlisle R., *Credit Administration,* Amer. Inst. of Banking, Amer. Bankers Assoc., Chap. 16.

The Federal Reserve System, Purposes and Functions, Board of Governors, Fed. Res. System, Washington, D.C., 1963.

How Our Reserve Banking System Operates, Monetary Study No. 2, rev. ed., Economic Policy Commission, Amer. Bankers Assoc.

Roosa, Robert V., *Federal Reserve Operations in the Money and Government Securities Markets,* Fed. Res. Bank of New York.

Chapter *19*

COMMERCIAL BANK FARM LOAN
POLICY AND PROCEDURE

COMMERCIAL banks develop policies to guide operations of the institution somewhat as a rudder is used to guide a ship. If it were not for the rudder, the ship would drift aimlessly with winds and tides. Likewise, without a policy a banking institution would drift aimlessly with economic pressures and views of individual officials.

Bank policy is necessary since a number of different individuals are involved or affected by the way the bank is operated. Depositors are concerned with safety of their funds, stockholders with a safe, profitable investment, and borrowers with the bank's loan policy. Interests of these three groups must be molded into a single policy.

The framework of a bank's policy is established by legislation under which it is chartered and by regulations issued by supervisory agencies. Within this framework general policy outlines are formulated by the bank's board of directors. Officers and supervisory personnel, in turn, fill in the details as necessary to facilitate operations. The bank's loan committee has considerable to do with formulating loan policies.

Since banks are independent corporations organized by people, their policies naturally vary greatly. Two banks may look alike to the public, but in reality they may be very different institutions. This is an important fact to keep in mind in selecting a lender. One bank may have a progressive farm policy and be interested in making loans, while another bank may invest the bulk of its assets in securities. Some banks maintain a flexible policy designed to meet needs of the community, while others make few changes.

From the viewpoint of credit extension, two of the more important policy considerations pertain to:

1. The distribution of the bank's earning assets
2. The policy followed in making and servicing loans

Policy with regard to the bank's earning assets determines the amount of funds put into loans, and loan policy indicates the way or terms upon which those funds are made available to borrowers.

EFFECT OF EARNING-ASSET DISTRIBUTION ON LOANS

Assets of banks often are grouped on the balance sheet as cash, loans, investments, and other assets. Of these, loans and investments generally are the largest items. These two groups comprise the major earning assets of banks and the allocation of funds between them indicates the relative importance of the bank's loan program.

Table 19.1 portrays the dollar volume of loans and investments of all commercial banks in the United States over a period of several decades. Note the relative decrease in importance of loans from the 1920's to the 1940's, and the reversal of this trend in the

TABLE 19.1

LOANS, INVESTMENTS, AND DEPOSITS OF ALL COMMERCIAL BANKS IN THE
UNITED STATES FOR GIVEN DATES*

| June 29 or 30 | Total Loans and Investments | Loans | | Investments | | Total Deposits | Loan-Deposit Ratio | Invest-ment-Deposit Ratio |
		Amount	Per cent of total	Amount	Per cent of total			
	(millions)	(millions)		(millions)		(millions)		
1920	$ 36,294	$ 28,103	77.4	$ 8,191	22.6	$ n.a.†	n.a.†	n.a.†
1930	48,892	34,539	70.6	14,353	29.4	54,954	62.8	26.1
1940	41,148	17,414	42.3	23,734	57.7	60,325	28.9	39.3
1950	121,768	44,796	36.8	76,972	63.2	143,827	31.1	53.5
1960	188,900	114,840	60.8	74,060	39.2	209,010	54.9	35.4
1966‡	369,920	259,330	70.1	110,590	29.9	330,880	78.4	33.4

* Source: Data for 1966, 1960, and 1950 are from the Fed. Res. Bul. Loan and investment data for earlier years are from *Banking and Monetary Statistics*, Board of Governors, Fed. Res. System, 1943, p. 19. Deposits for 1940 are from the Ann. Rept. of the Fed. Dep. Ins. Corp. for the year ended December 31, 1940, p. 140. Deposits for 1930 are from the Fed. Res. Bul. for that year (p. 650) and are for all banks, exclusive of interbank deposits.
  † n.a. = not available.
  ‡ Preliminary.

1950's. Traditional theory of commercial banking, evidenced to a degree in the original Federal Reserve Act, held that the banking system should adjust its earning assets to needs of the business world. The commercial banking system was considered merely an adjunct to the productive process. However, during the decades between the two World Wars, and particularly during and following World War II, revolutionary changes occurred in commercial banking. Among other things, investments of commercial banks in securities (primarily United States Government obligations) grew much faster than loan volume.

Investments in securities provide commercial banks flexibility to adjust to changing conditions. They provide secondary reserves for deposits to supplement required reserves, enabling a bank to readily adjust to a run-off in deposits if such should occur. They can also be liquidated to provide funds for loans should a favorable opportunity arise. The latter often occurs in prosperous times when interest rates are relatively high and security prices relatively low. Thus, such flexibility may carry a fairly high price tag if securities have to be sold below cost. When this is the case, a bank's management may decide to place funds from new deposits or maturing securities in loans but be unwilling to sell securities at a loss in order to accommodate additional credit demands.

The amount of flexibility provided by securities naturally varies with the amount of securities owned by commercial banks. When securities comprise a relatively unimportant item in the balance sheet, the flexibility provided is limited, and vice versa. It is evident, therefore, that the flexibility of the commercial banking system has been declining for a number of years. The relative importance of investments in securities has declined considerably since 1950, while the relative amount of loans has increased (see Table 19.1). Concomitantly, the loan-deposit ratio has increased to a record level. Under such circumstances, many banks may be operating at or above their preferred loan-deposit ratios, somewhat as manufacturing concerns operate above their preferred capacity-utilization ratios in periods of strong demand. Consequently, a high level of loans to deposits generally becomes a constraining factor in bank lending.

A high loan-deposit ratio does not necessarily mean, however, that banks in general are overextended. The changing composition of commercial bank liabilities in the 1960's has contributed to the acceptability of higher loan-deposit ratios. Time and savings deposits, as well as bank capital accounts, have grown far more rapidly than demand liabilities. Savings deposits generally have good stability, as do also many time deposits. However, marketable certificates of deposit may be unstable should available rates on other money market instruments become relatively more attractive.

The upward trend in the loan-deposit ratio during the 1950's and 1960's was accompanied by a decline in the investment-deposit ratio to a near record low. Under such circumstances many banks may be operating below their preferred investment-deposit ratios. In other words, they may not have as many securities as they would like to have in order to provide secondary reserves for deposits. Consequently, a further reduction in holdings of securities relative to deposits is resisted. This appears to have been the case in the early 1960's. The investment-deposit ratio of commercial banks did not decline materially from 1960 to 1966 even though demand for loans was exceptionally strong. Thus, when the investment-deposit ratio is low the volume of loans made by commercial banks is governed primarily by the amount of excess reserves generated by current operations.

Banks vary greatly in their loan-investment policies. Country banks tend to have a smaller proportion of their earning assets in loans than larger city banks. In mid-1966, for example, loans accounted for 62.6 per cent of total loans and investments of country member banks (of the Federal Reserve System). In comparison, Reserve city member banks averaged 78.3 per cent in loans in New York and 74.6 per cent in loans in Chicago. Other Reserve city member banks averaged 73.1 per cent in loans.[1]

A further indication of the variation in loan ratios is provided by a study of rural Iowa banks.[2] Loans were compared with deposits for two different periods, at the beginning of 1957 and nine years later at the beginning of 1966. The comparison was expressed in terms of the loan-deposit ratio, which indicates the extent to which the banks were "loaned up." In 1957 the typical rural bank in Iowa had loans equal to 40 to 49 per cent of its deposits, while in 1966 the typical bank had loans equal to 50 to 59 per cent of its deposits. Variation in the loan-deposit ratio of the rural banks in the two periods was as follows:

[1] *Federal Reserve Bulletin,* Board of Governors of the Federal Reserve System, Washington, D.C., Nov., 1966, pp. 1662–63.
[2] A rural bank was arbitrarily classified as any bank in a town with less than 5,000 population. In 1957 all rural banks were included, while in 1966 a sample totaling one-third of the rural banks was used.

Loan-deposit ratio

Year	10–19	20–29	30–39	40–49	50–59	60–69	70–79	80–89	Total
				Per cent of banks					
1957	2	8	21	30	25	11	3	0	100
1966	...	4	9	26	30	23	8	...	100

The variation in both 1957 and 1966 was extremely wide. In 1957 there were 2 per cent of the banks with loans amounting to less than 20 per cent of deposits and at the other extreme 3 per cent of the banks with loans amounting to 70 per cent or more of deposits. In 1966 less than 1 per cent were in the bottom group, while the 70–79 per cent group had jumped from 3 to 8 per cent. The banks with a low loan-deposit ratio probably did not have an aggressive loan program. Loans which such banks make often are conservative, while most banks with an average or higher loan-deposit ratio probably have an aggressive loan program. Such banks often do a better job in credit extension than more conservative banks. However, a bank should not have an excessive loan-deposit ratio. A bank which is "loaned up" may have to reduce its loan volume in case something happens in the community to cause a reduction in deposits. Also, a bank which is loaned up may be unable to provide additional credit needed to meet seasonal loan requirements.

The credit service of a bank to farmers in the community is indicated not only by its distribution of earning assets between loans and investments, but also by its policy regarding farm versus nonfarm loans. A bank may have a satisfactory loan-deposit ratio and still make few farm loans. Progressive banks generally are interested in the entire community and, in periods when credit is tight, allocate a portion of their funds to each type of loan in accordance with demand. However, banks vary greatly in this regard and a farmer would do well to inquire regarding the bank's policy. Published bank statements generally do not show a farm and nonfarm breakdown of loans.

FARM LOAN CHARACTERISTICS

Two primary considerations of commercial banks in making farm loans are: (1) service to borrowers, and (2) risk involved in making loans. Banks make loans to all types of farmers, but some farmers merit more credit than others. Bankers must be able to discriminate among applications for loans and decide whether to make the loan or discourage the applicant from borrowing. Success of the banker in handling this task determines to a large degree how successful the bank is in serving the farm community and the stockholders.

Bankers usually have a knowledge of their customers that is distinctly helpful in handling farm loans. The banker is in an excellent position to know the credit standing of the farmer who has been carrying a checking account and doing business with him for several years. If the farmer pays his bills promptly, has no long-standing debts, is accumulating property, and is a man of high moral standards, the local banker generally knows it. If the reverse situation exists, the banker usually is likewise aware of it. This information is only a part of that desired for a long-term loan, but it is a major requirement in making short-term advances. If an individual customer with a good record asks for a 2-month loan to pay taxes because his livestock are not ready to market, the banker is able to act promptly on such a request. On the other hand, the customer who has all his property mortgaged and fails to measure up on other counts is likely to be refused. Short-term credit agencies not having the local knowledge which bankers possess, are forced to safeguard themselves against losses by more restrictions. They must obtain security interests, waivers from landlords, nondisturbance agreements from other lenders, and make inspections, some of which would not be necessary if they were in a position to know the local conditions as well as the local banker.

The local bank has the added advantage of being close to the farmer. Other short-term credit agencies may be located only at county seat towns or in larger cities, and consequently many farmers have to make a special trip to see them. Where there is a bank in the local trading area, the farmer can drop in when he is in town for other purposes. The bank is the logical place for the farmer to apply for short- and intermediate-term credit, particularly when he is using a checking account and other bank services. Since the bank has to have a certain amount of income to operate, farmers may actually lower the cost of other services by borrowing from the bank. Moreover, the service the bank may be giving him and the knowledge his banker has about his financial standing make it easy for the farmer to give the additional information needed in the balance sheet and income statement required for a loan.

The general policies of commercial banks in making farm loans are indicated by the various characteristics of loans they make. Five primary characteristics are discussed briefly in the following paragraphs.

Types of Loans

The most important type of farm loans made by commercial banks is production loans to provide funds for current farm operations, items such as seed, fertilizer, tractor fuel, repairs, labor, feed, and feeder livestock. Loans for intermediate-term purposes, such as machinery and equipment, milk cows, and breeding livestock, rank second in importance. Real estate loans rank third.

According to material presented in Chapter 16, short- and intermediate-term loans account for about three-fourths of the total volume of commercial bank credit outstanding January 1, and real estate loans account for the balance. This comparison probably understates the relative importance of commercial bank production loans since many of them are made and repaid within the year and, therefore, are not reflected in January 1 data.

Loans for intermediate-term purposes comprise an important part of nonreal-estate loans made by commercial banks. A survey by the Federal Reserve System showed that loans made for such purposes comprised 44 per cent of the number and 47 per cent of the amount of total nonreal-estate loans held by commercial banks June 30, 1956.[3] Considering the increasing importance of machinery in farming, intermediate-term loans may well be relatively more important now than at the time of the survey.

Maturity of Loans

Maturity of farm loans made by commercial banks naturally vary considerably with the type or purpose of the loan. Current operating loans generally are payable on demand or in less than one year. The phrase "payable on demand" is sometimes used in extending credit to established customers when the period of time the

---

[3] "Farm Loans at Commercial Banks," *Federal Reserve Bulletin,* Board of Governors of the Federal Reserve System, Washington, D.C., Nov., 1956, Jan., Feb., and March, 1957. While survey was taken a few years ago it still is generally applicable since basic policy of commercial banks changes rather slowly. The basic legal framework is not changed very often and boards of directors and officers generally serve a bank for an extended period. New board members and officers tend to be "trained" by older associates which adds stability to policy. Moreover, changes which are made currently, such as in the interest rate, generally affect all loans in about the same way, so relative differences shown by the survey still hold.

funds will be needed is uncertain. However, its use is of question-able merit since it reflects lack of planning in use of credit. More-over, while bankers generally do not expect to "demand" payment of such loans, such a provision in a note should not be lightly dismissed. Conditions beyond the control of the banker may force him to exercise legal prerogatives.

Loans made for intermediate-term purposes are frequently written for short terms. The Federal Reserve survey, referred to above, showed that two-thirds of the loans for these purposes were financed with renewals of short-term notes. As would be expected, loans for purchase of farm real estate had longer maturities. How-ever, 31 per cent of such loans reported in the Federal Reserve survey matured within one year or less, and another 57 per cent within one to ten years. Only 12 per cent of the loans for purchase of farm real estate had maturities in excess of ten years.

Interest Rates

Interest rates charged by commercial banks vary from time to time, depending upon demand for credit, general economic condi-tions, policy of the Federal Reserve System, and rates charged by other lenders. Thus, rates charged at one time may be considerably different from those charged at another time. However, the relative level of interest rates for different types and sizes of loans remains relatively constant over time, and it is this aspect of interest rates that is primarily considered in this section.

Interest rates on commercial bank operating loans typically have a range of about 2.0 percentage points, such as from 5.0 to 7.0 per cent or from 6.0 to 8.0 per cent. The modal rate customarily is not quite one-half the way up the range. For example, if the range is 6.0 to 8.0 per cent, the modal rate is a little less than 7.0 per cent. This structure is typical of commercial farming areas with a rela-tively large number of commercial farms. However, in areas of predominantly small farms, the modal interest rate is somewhat higher in the rate range.[4]

Type of loan has an influence on the interest rate. The Federal Reserve survey showed that the rate on commercial bank operating loans averaged 6.2 per cent in mid-1956, compared with 6.9 per cent for intermediate-term loans. The average interest rate on bank loans

---

[4] James O. Wise, *Commercial Bank Loans of Georgia Farmers*, Ga. Agr. Exp. Sta. Mimeo. Series N.S. 208, 1964, p. 9.

secured by real estate was about one percentage point less than on other loans. However, this difference was due in part to size of loan. For loans of comparable size the rate difference was about one-half percentage point.

Size of loan is a major factor affecting the interest rate. The cost of making, managing, and servicing a loan does not increase materially with size. In fact, small loans often require more service than large loans. As a result, the interest rate on large loans typically is considerably lower than on small loans. The Federal Reserve survey referred to above showed that the interest rate varied from 7.4 per cent for loans under $500 to 5.3 per cent for loans over $25,000. The average for all farm operating loans at that time was 6.2 per cent. A study made in Georgia in 1964 showed that the modal rate of interest was 8 per cent on production loans of $5,000 and under, but decreased to 6 per cent on loans for $10,000.[5]

Factors other than type and size of loan influence the interest rate charged individual borrowers, as indicated by the following statement from the Federal Reserve report.

> As between different borrowers, rates varied most with size of note. They also varied considerably with creditworthiness as measured by net worth, with method of repayment, and security of loan. Smaller variations appeared for other loan characteristics—purpose, maturity, and renewal status—and for such borrower characteristics as tenure.
>
> Some rate differences related to general economic and institutional characteristics of the various regions of the country, for which the Survey provided no measures. In areas where agriculture is characterized by small units and variable incomes, as in some regions of the South, rates may have been higher, because of poorer risks, than in areas with larger farms and more stable incomes, like the Corn Belt. Sharp fluctuations in demand for loans in areas with highly seasonal farming activities may have been reflected in higher rates on loans. In some regions relative scarcity of capital funds contributed to higher rates of interest generally, including those on farm loans.
>
> Bank rates on farm loans are influenced by competition with other lenders, primarily the agencies supervised by the Farm Credit Administration (the production credit associations and the Federal land banks), insurance companies, and individuals. The degree of competition varies from one locality to another and among different types of loans. Prevailing rates on obligations in broader markets indirectly affect the rates that farmers pay, through competition for funds which otherwise might be invested in farm loans.[6]

---

[5] *Ibid.*, p. 9.
[6] "Farm Loans at Commercial Banks," p. 12.

Security for Loans

A primary consideration of commercial banks, as well as of all lenders, is the risk involved in making a loan. Lenders make only loans they feel are sure to be repaid. However, the certainty of repayment varies. Some loans are practically riskless, some involve a small amount of risk, and some are moderately risky. Moreover, unforeseen developments often arise which lower the quality of loans after they have been made.

Policy relative to requiring security naturally varies among banks. Although all loans need a signed note to provide evidence that an obligation exists between the borrower and the bank, many banks prefer unsecured loans since they involve less "red tape." This is the case particularly where relatively little risk is involved. Other bankers follow the practice of obtaining security for practically all loans. Moreover, some state laws require security for loans above a certain size if financial statements are not available.

The Federal Reserve survey, already referred to, showed that 73 per cent of all loans were backed by security, and an additional 5 per cent were endorsed. The remaining 22 per cent were unsecured. A study made in Georgia showed that 93 per cent of all loans were secured, and an additional 3 per cent were endorsed, leaving only 4 per cent of the loans unsecured.[7]

In many instances, banks (and other lenders) obtain security as a protection for the borrower as well as the bank, for a bank must make sure the farmer will continue to have his income-producing assets to work with. In other words, a banker may require security to insure the farmer against outside disturbances. Where such a possibility exists, a bank often obtains a mortgage or security interest in livestock and equipment—sometimes even on hay, grain, and ensilage—to make sure the borrower will continue to have these "tools" to use in the business throughout the life of the loan.

Repayment Plans

Single payment notes represent the dominant repayment method used by commercial banks except for real estate loans. The Federal Reserve survey indicated single payment notes were used for

---

[7] Wise, p. 7.

practically all current expense loans and for a majority of the intermediate-term loans. Only about 40 per cent of the intermediate-term loans were set up on an installment basis. However, it should be recognized that renewals are widely used by commercial banks in farm lending as indicated by the following statement taken from the Federal Reserve survey report.

> Of all farm loans outstanding at banks at midyear, 35 per cent had been renewed one or more times. This proportion must be considered in the light of the fact that some loans were made too recently to have been the subject of renewal, and that some loans are long-term amortized loans.
>
> One-fourth of the outstanding loans had been renewed by "plan," in that they were the subject of written or oral understandings between lenders and borrowers at the time the original credits were extended. An arrangement of this kind could be considered as taking the place of giving the credit a longer initial maturity, perhaps repayable in installments. Thirty per cent of outstanding loans to finance intermediate-term investments, and 24 per cent of loans for current expenses, had been renewed by plan.
>
> Unplanned renewals, which had occurred in 10 per cent of the outstanding loans, were equally frequent among loans for current expenses and those to finance intermediate-term investments. Regionally, they were most frequent in the Dallas District, where weather conditions were unfavorable in 1956.[8]

Greater Emphasis on Intermediate-term Loans

Intermediate-term loans made by commercial banks have been increasing in recent years in response to changes in farm technology and the rapid increase in capital requirements. Among other things intermediate-term financing is needed for farm improvements, breeding livestock, machinery, and equipment. Recognizing the increased need for such credit, commercial bank supervisory authorities and leading commercial bankers have encouraged expansion of this type of credit. Note the statement signed by the Chairman of the Board of Governors of the Federal Reserve System, the Comptroller of the Currency, and the Chairman of the Federal Deposit Insurance Corporation reproduced in Figure 19.1.[9] In this statement, reference is made to the need for careful farm planning when

---

[8] "Farm Loans at Commercial Banks," p. 12.
[9] Foreword of *Intermediate-term Bank Credit for Farmers,* Agr. Commission, American Bankers Assoc., 1957.

longer repayment programs are used, and it is pointed out that no federal law or regulation prevents commercial banks from extending credit to farmers on an intermediate-term basis. This is a significant statement pertaining to loan policy of commercial banks, particularly in light of the increased ability of commercial banks to safely make such loans due to their larger holdings of government securities (see Table 19.1) and the associated potential liquidity which these provide.

Washington, D. C.

The June 30, 1956 Agricultural Loan Survey administered by the Federal Reserve System in co-operation with the Office of the Comptroller of the Currency and the Federal Deposit Insurance Corporation showed that one-third of all bank notes to finance intermediate-term farm investments had maturities longer than one year. However, renewals of shorter term notes were also used to facilitate many intermediate type investments.

While approximately two-thirds of those shorter term renewals were reported to have been made on an advanced commitment basis, the survey revealed no information as to the adequacy of the planning on which the commitments were based. Other available information indicates that, in all too many cases, intermediate-term farm financial programs are inadequately planned.

It is important that all concerned realize the advantages to be derived from careful farm planning when longer repayment programs are expected. In loans of this type, it is generally advisable that a plan of farm operations, for the period of the line of credit, become a major part of the loan folder. The plan should include a schedule of estimated income, expenses, and loan repayment capacity, and should provide for periodic reviews of the farm financial program.

No Federal law or regulation prevents commercial banks from extending credit to farmers on an intermediate-term repayment basis. Like all classes of loans, each loan of this type should be evalu-

ated on the basis of its own characteristics—the risk involved, the character, ability, financial reponsibility and record of the borrower, value and character of collateral, and *the feasibility and probability of its orderly liquidation in accordance with the repayment plan.*

It is the belief of the Federal supervisory agencies that intermediate-term credit by commercial banks on a sound and prudent basis contributes greatly to the growth and strength of American agriculture.

WM. McC. MARTIN, JR.
Chairman
Board of Governors
Federal Reserve System

RAY M. GIDNEY
Comptroller of the Currency

H. E. COOK
Chairman
Federal Deposit
Insurance Corporation

Fig. 19.1—Statement pertaining to intermediate-term loans by commercial banks. (Source: **Intermediate-term Bank Credit for Farmers,** Agricultural Commission, The American Bankers Association, 1957, p. 3.)

FARM LOAN REPRESENTATIVES

With the increasing use of capital in agriculture and the growing complexity of farming as a business, directors and officers of commercial banks have felt the need of having on their staffs men trained in agriculture who could provide adequate banking service for their farm customers. The men employed to do this work are not only adapting bank loans to fit the needs of farm borrowers but also are spending time with borrowers out on their farms, assisting them in obtaining the kind of credit they need, and providing information or management service which the borrowers find helpful. A banker in a county seat town of 5,000 population recently established an agricultural department in the bank and employed a farm-reared, agricultural college graduate to take charge, stating that the purpose was "to promote a relationship between the banker and the farmer which is mutually profitable."

A survey conducted by the American Bankers Association gives, among other things, information on training needed by and duties and responsibilities of an agricultural representative.[10] The majority of agricultural representatives responding to the survey questionnaire were in their 30's and 40's, and had a variety of experience in other positions before joining the bank's staff. The group as a whole was well educated, but they believed their academic training had been too narrow. For example, 57 per cent felt that, in addition to technical training in agriculture, business courses such as banking, finance, business administration, law, and accounting would be most helpful to those planning to enter bank agricultural work, whereas only 11 per cent had extensive training along these lines. Similarly, 61 per cent mentioned the need for training in agricultural economics and 15 per cent mentioned speech, English, journalism, and other communication-type courses. The report points out that "Not only was there a disparity between general business or other broadening courses taken and those needed, the problem will likely become more acute. Increasingly, it is important that bankers serving rural areas have more than an understanding of the details of specialized farm enterprises. As farms take on more and more of the characteristics of efficient-sized business organizations, financial management and other business factors increase in relative importance."[11]

Agriculturally trained men in commercial banks perform a variety of services as shown by the following quotation:

> The most prevalent responsibilities fall in the category of loan services—analyzing financial statements, making appraisals, farm loan administrative details, making and servicing real estate and nonreal-estate secured farm loans in their bank,

---

[10] *Agriculturally Trained Men in Banking*, Agr. Commission, American Bankers Assoc., New York, 1959.
[11] *Ibid.*, p. 8.

and working with an insurance company or correspondent bank on farm loan cases.

However, their services go beyond this. For example, they actively work with public relations programs or nontangible services not of direct or immediate benefit to their banks. This group of activities includes (1) attendance or speaking at 4-H, FFA, and other youth group meetings, (2) farm visits to potential customers, (3) meeting with farm-related businessmen, organizations, and various public agencies, and (4) promotional and advertising work.

Agricultural representatives also provided many types of tangible services for farmers. These include soil testing, income tax counsel, farm planning, farm management, farm appraisals on a nonfee basis, and counseling on diverse financial and technical matters. Over 90 per cent of them believed agriculturally trained bankers should counsel with borrowers on farm financial matters. Over two-thirds of them expressed the same opinion relative to farm technical matters.[12]

LOAN PROCEDURE

The procedure followed by commercial banks in making loans varies from bank to bank but in general follows the pattern outlined in Chapter 15. A summary of the steps recommended by the American Bankers Association is as follows:

1. As the farmer is making known his credit needs, many banks find it desirable to fill out an application form or the application section of a financial statement (see Figs. 15.1a and 15.1b suggested by the ABA).
2. If initial conversation and application information indicate the possibility of closing a loan, then obtain a credit statement and at least a listing of his more important receipts and expenses.
3. Become thoroughly acquainted with the farmer's plans for the coming year.
4. Help the farmer prepare a budget of anticipated expenses and income and a schedule of advancing the credit as needed (see Figs. 19.2 and 19.3).
5. Develop a repayment plan for the loan.
6. After analysis, three alternatives are available:
   a. If collateral descriptions are available, secured as well as unsecured loans can be closed promptly.
   b. If necessary, submit available data to the loan committee for its action.
   c. Investigate further.

[12] *Ibid.*, pp. 13–14.

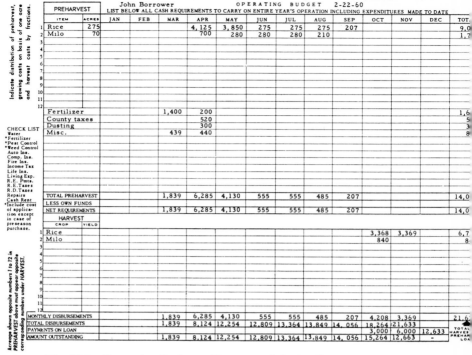

Fig. 19.2—Operating Budget. (Courtesy of the Wells Fargo Bank—American Trust Company, San Francisco.)

   (1) Visit the farm.
   (2) Check his reputation for paying debts.
   (3) Check the public records for all liens.
  7. Close the loan or submit it to the loan committee for its final action.
  8. Final action.
   a. Arrange insurance coverage.
   b. Promptly file or record lien instruments (if any).
   c. Organize and complete the credit file.
   If a loan is declined, the farmer should be advised why his application was not acceptable to the bank.[13]

This loan procedure advocated by the ABA brings out a number of good points. The emphasis on budgeting is a noteworthy feature which is becoming commoner. One phase of the loan procedure which banks still do not emphasize enough is that of marginal analysis, which was treated in Chapter 5. This step, which involves

---

[13] *Agricultural Production Financing,* Agr. Commission, American Bankers Assoc., New York, 1951, p. 7.

<table>
<tr><td colspan="4">

BUDGET LOAN

Note Number ___91693___ __ __ _____

Due Date _____December 15, 1959____

</td><td colspan="3">

John Borrower
R. R. 3
Shelbyville,   INDIANA

</td></tr>
</table>

$ 2,794.00 _____   SHELBYVILLE, INDIANA, ___March 7_____, 19 59

On or before___ December 15 _____, 19 59 for value received, I (or we, and each of us) promise to pay
to the order of The **NATIONAL STATE BANK** Shelbyville, Indiana, negotiable and payable at the office of the payee,

_____Two Thousand Seven Hundred Ninety-Four and no/100 - - - - - - - - - - - -_____Dollars,

and attorney's fees and without any relief whatever from valuation or appraisement laws of the State of Indiana, with
interest at the rate of___six___ per cent per annum from date of disbursement until paid.

In case of failure to perform any of the terms or conditions of any mortgage securing said indebtedness, the entire balance of principal and interest shall, at the option of the holder hereof, be immediately due and payable.

The makers and endorsers severally waive demand, presentment for payment, protest, notice of protest, and notice
of non-payment of this note. The note is secured by a chattel mortgage of even date herewith.

_____John Borrower_____

| Date | Principal | | Balance | | Schedule of Payments | |
	Disbursements	Repayments		Date Due	Amount	
Mar. 7, 1959	1,507.00		1,507.00	May 1 '59	500	00
Apr. 3 1959		700.00	807.00	Aug. 1 '59	600	00
May 1, 1959	200.00		1,007.00	Nov. 1 '59	125	00
Aug 3, 1959	DRAFT 1,087.00		2,094 00	Dec. 15 '59	300	00
Sep. 24, 1959		200.00	1,894 00	Balance Renewed if approxi-		
Sep. 29, 1959		200.00	1,694 00	mate schedule made.		
Sept 22, 1959		200.00	1,494 00			
Oct. 9, 1959		300.00	1,194.00			
Nov. 13, 1959		200.00	994.00			

Fig. 19.3—Budget-Loan Note. (Courtesy of The American Bankers Association.)

the comparison of net income resulting from the expansion of different enterprises on the farm, could be included in No. 3 or No. 6 in
the ABA plan outlined above. Use of the comment record would be a
valuable aid, along with balance sheets and income statements, in
determining the best use to be made of credit on a given farm.

QUESTIONS AND PROBLEMS

1. What is meant by bank policy? Why is it needed?
2. What or who determines a bank's policy?
3. Discuss the factors a bank might consider in determining the
   amount of farm loans to make.
4. Outline the things considered by commercial banks in developing a farm loan policy.
5. Discuss the types of loans made by commercial banks and to
   whom these are made.

6. Discuss the term of loans made by commercial banks. What term do loans for intermediate-term purposes carry?
7. How are commercial bank loans secured?
8. Interest rates charged vary by size and type of loan. Why? Are these differences justifiable?
9. Outline the methods of repayment for various types of bank loans.
10. Discuss the reasons for greater emphasis on intermediate-term loans by commercial banks. Can banks do a better job financing intermediate-term credit needs of farmers with intermediate-term loans than with renewable short-term loans?
11. Outline the procedure recommended by the American Bankers Association for commercial banks to follow in making loans.
12. Prepare an appraisal of commercial banks as a source of credit for farmers.

REFERENCES

Agricultural Credit, Amer. Inst. of Banking, Amer. Bankers Assoc., 1954.
Agricultural Production Financing, Agr. Commission, Amer. Bankers Assoc., 1951.
Agriculturally Trained Men in Banking, Agr. Commission, Amer. Bankers Assoc., 1959.
Christiansen, R. A., Hartwig, P. A., and Staniforth, S. D., *Bank Credit for Agriculture in Wisconsin,* Wisc. Agr. Exp. Sta. and Farm Econ. Div., ERS, USDA, cooperating, Bul. 557, June, 1962.
Correspondent Agribanking, Agricultural Committee, Amer. Bankers Assoc., 1963.
Farm Loans at Commercial Banks, Board of Governors, Fed. Res. System, Washington, D.C., 1957.
Farm Real Estate Financing, Amer. Bankers Assoc., 1949.
Hesser, Leon F., "Bank and PCA Lending to Farmers," *Federal Reserve Bulletin,* Board of Governors, Fed. Res. System, Washington, D.C., Sept., 1963, pp. 1224–34.
Intermediate-term Bank Credit for Farmers, Agr. Commission, Amer. Bankers Assoc., 1957.
Wise, James O., *Commercial Bank Loans to Georgia Farmers,* Ga. Agr. Exp. Sta. Mimeo. Ser. NS 208, Aug., 1964.

Chapter 20

INSURANCE COMPANIES
AND THEIR LOAN FUNDS

LIFE insurance companies are an important source of long-term mortgage credit for farmers, being the largest institutional lender in the farm mortgage field.[1] Of the $21,196 million of farm mortgage loans outstanding January 1, 1966, insurance companies held $4,813 million, or 23 per cent (see Table 16.3, Chapter 16).

Life insurance companies are among the largest financial institutions in the nation, their group assets totaling about $160 billion. Moreover, their growth has been very rapid. Except for the Great Depression of the 1930's, their assets each decade have nearly doubled. With such a rate of growth it appears likely that life insurance companies will continue to be important in the farm mortgage field. However, their activity in this area will depend also upon company management and alternative uses for investment funds.

OWNERSHIP AND CONTROL OF INSURANCE COMPANIES

Life insurance companies are of two types: stock companies and mutual companies. *Stock companies* are owned by the stock-

---

[1] Life insurance companies make practically all the farm mortgage loans which are made by insurance companies. Property and casualty insurance generally represents short-term contracts which do not require that long-run policy reserves be accumulated. For this reason reserves of such companies generally are put in short-term investments.

holders who provide the capital required by the company. Policy premiums for such companies are calculated to cover as closely as possible the anticipated actual cost of the insurance protection which is sold, so dividends paid to policyholders are usually small. Stockholders carry the risk of loss which might be sustained, and also receive any profit which is realized the same as in any stock corporation.

Mutual insurance companies are cooperative associations of persons established to provide insurance on their own lives. Policyholders are "members" corresponding to stockholders in the stock company. Thus, mutual insurance companies are owned by the policyholders. Insurance written by mutual companies is generally participating insurance, which means that policyholders participate in earnings of the company. Since there is no stock ownership, as in the stock company, to absorb unusual losses, premiums collected are set high enough to cover almost any eventuality, and then the excess of premiums over costs is returned to policyholders as dividends.

Insurance companies are corporations organized under state law and are controlled by the board of directors of the corporation. Directors of stock companies are elected by the stockholders, usually on the basis of one vote for each share of stock owned. Directors of mutual companies are elected by member-policyholders.[2]

The board of directors, in turn, elects officers and employs a staff to carry on affairs of the company in accordance with the company's charter and general policy established by the board.

Insurance companies are supervised by the state insurance department, which is headed by an official generally referred to as Commissioner of Insurance, Superintendent of Insurance, or Director of Insurance. This official has general control, supervision, and direction over all affairs of insurance companies operating in the state. Each company is required to submit an annual report giving certain specified information to the state department of insurance. These reports enable the commissioner to keep currently informed on operations of companies. Moreover, the commissioner may at any time deemed advisable examine a company or inquire otherwise into its affairs. Most states require that all insurance companies be examined every two or three years. Expert examiners having special

---

[2] This statement is technically correct, but it may not portray the actual procedure in some states. In New York, for example, an "administration ticket" consisting of only one candidate for each position on the board of the class that is up for reelection is nominated by the company. An independent ticket may be nominated by the policyholders, but such a ticket must be submitted five months prior to the election. Thus, the election usually is in reality only "ceremonial."

training and knowledge not possessed by regular examiners of the insurance department may be employed where necessary to facilitate a thorough examination. The costs of all examinations are charged to the company examined.

Ownership and control of insurance companies have an important bearing upon their function as farm mortgage lenders. To grow and prosper they must operate on the basis of sound business principles, which involves fair treatment of both policyholders and borrowers. Lending policies must be such that needs of borrowers are met without incurring excessive risk which subsequently might lead to serious financial problems or foreclosure, and loans generally are distributed so as to contribute most to public goodwill. It should be kept in mind that the primary responsibility of an insurance company is to its policyholders. A stock company is organized for the purpose of selling insurance to make a profit. Mutual insurance companies are organized to provide insurance protection for policyholders. Responsibility to borrowers is of secondary importance since loans serve only as a means of profitably utilizing reserves associated with insuring of policyholders.

LOAN FUNDS

Life insurance companies issue, for the most part, long-term policies on which reserve funds are slowly accumulated as the insured grows older and the policy matures. When an insured dies, his survivor may request that proceeds of the policy be paid in installments rather than in a lump sum. Thus, life insurance companies accumulate large sums of money in connection with their insurance program which they hold for long periods of time. These funds are invested and, in turn, produce income which adds additional assets for investments.

Policy of an insurance company regarding allocation of funds to various types of investments is established, subject to provisions of law, by the board of directors, with the advice of officers of the company. Three principal considerations usually are involved: (1) security of principal, (2) adequacy of yield, and (3) diversification of investments.

Security of principal is important since the primary object of a life insurance company is to pay claims. Insurance obligations generally are fixed in terms of a given number of dollars, and a company's ability to meet its fixed claims is of paramount importance. For this reason insurance companies generally give more importance to security than to either of the other two considerations in selecting investments.

While security is important, *adequacy of yield* must also be considered to facilitate reducing the cost of insurance to policyholders. Competition is keen in the insurance field, and the rate earned on investments plays an important role in determining the company's competitive position. Thus, an insurance company may sacrifice some security on a small percentage of its investments in order to increase the average yield.

The practice of *diversification of investments* is followed to reduce risks and to develop goodwill. It is considered sound policy to limit size of individual loans and to spread investments among different businesses or classes of investments as well as geographically. Such a policy reduces the probability of a large loss and also makes funds available for financing more homes, farm purchases and improvements, business developments, and the like, as a means of creating goodwill for the company.

Mortgage loans as a class generally satisfy very well the investment requirements of life insurance companies, as more than one-third of their assets are now invested in such loans (see Table 20.1). Mortgage loans provide a relatively high degree of security, particularly since almost all types are now amortized. Periodic loan payments, therefore, gradually strengthen the security position of the

TABLE 20.1

DISTRIBUTION OF ASSETS OF LIFE INSURANCE COMPANIES IN THE UNITED STATES*

Item	1940	1950	1960	1966
Total Assets, Jan. 1 (millions of dollars)..	$29,243	$59,630	$113,650	$158,884
Per Cent Invested in:				
Government securities.............	26.7	29.8	10.0	7.2
Securities of business and industry...	29.2	39.0	43.9	42.7
Mortgages:				
Farm........................	3.0	1.9	2.5	3.0
Nonfarm.....................	16.4	19.7	32.0	34.8
Policy loans.....................	11.1	3.7	4.1	4.8
Miscellaneous...................	13.6	5.9	7.5	7.5
Total.....................	100.0	100.0	100.0	100.0

* Source: *Life Insurance Fact Book, 1966*, Institute of Life Insurance, New York, N.Y.; also *Spectator Life Insurance Year Book*, a Chilton publication. Figures in the table represent total assets, both in and out of the United States, of companies incorporated in the United States.

investment. As a group, mortgage loans also provide a fairly satisfactory yield, and they probably are the most effective type of investment from the viewpoint of creating goodwill.

Farm mortgage loans, however, do not seem to be so generally acceptable as nonfarm mortgages. During the past two decades only 2 to 3 per cent of life insurance company assets have been invested in farm mortgages (see Table 20.1). A number of factors probably are involved. Making farm mortgage loans is a relatively specialized business. Earning capacity of the farm must be considered along with value and permanency of the security, and a specialized staff is needed to make and handle such loans. Moreover, interest income tends to be lower on farm than on city loans, and more expense is involved in obtaining an adequate appraisal of farm property, and in travel and time due to the greater distances. For such reasons many companies make no farm mortgage loans and this, of course, lowers the overall average.

The following paragraph taken from a private communication indicates the approach followed by insurance companies in determining farm loan policy.

> The total amount of farm loans made by our company is determined in the long run by the opportunity for investment in such loans relative to the opportunities for investment in other sectors of the capital market that are open to us. The state statutes under which we operate permit investment in a variety of securities. Federal, state, and local government bonds, Canadian bonds, utility bonds, bonds of industrial corporations, mortgages on urban real estate, title to urban real estate, and preferred and common stock of qualifying corporations are some of these permitted securities. At any point of time one of these will be more attractive than others from a standpoint of net yield after costs of acquisition and servicing and the risk involved are given proper weight. Company management is constantly weighing these factors and selecting the investments producing the most satisfactory return. This consideration does not completely control as the need for diversification compels the selection of a variety of investments, but the emphasis will tend to be on the most attractive outlet. It is also true that some permitted investments are not used due to considerations other than net yields. An example is commercial paper which is perfectly acceptable from a risk standpoint but is too short-term to attract our funds which are essentially long-term. This process of selection will, in the long run, determine the amount of funds invested in farm mortgages. It is a market process and is essentially the same as any other market mechanism.

As is indicated by this quotation and by the above material, funds of life insurance companies available for farm loans depend primarily upon company policy. It is true, as some contend, that farm loan funds are influenced by reserves available for investment. Insurance companies cannot create loan funds. During periods of severe financial strain, growth of reserves may be slow and policy loans and policy surrender demands are high. Under such circumstances, it may be necessary to curtail loans and other investments. It should be noted that under such difficult conditions other lenders also are forced to curtail their loans. Federal Land Bank loans were expanded during the 1930's only by help from the United States Treasury. Without such help they undoubtedly would have been forced to sharply curtail their loans. It should be noted also that since farm loans comprise only a relatively small proportion of insurance company assets, reserves could drop sharply without influencing farm loans to any great extent, particularly if company officials felt it advisable to allocate funds to that purpose.

Company officials customarily make an allotment of funds to the various types of investments early in the year, based upon an estimate of the amount of assets which will be available. As a result, farm loans may be restricted at times. For example, a farm loan department may be allocated $25,000,000 for loans during the year. If demand for loans is strong, this amount may all be loaned out by September or October, in which case the company would be out of the farm loan field for the balance of the year. In practice, however, a company farm loan department generally does not run itself entirely out of funds. If demand is strong, the company is a little more "choosy" in the loans it makes, and by this means conserves some funds for good loans throughout the year. Company officials may, if conditions warrant, make some additional funds available in the interest of maintaining a reputation of being a dependable source of credit.

LOAN POLICY

Insurance companies provide a strong competitive source of credit in areas where they concentrate their lending activity. They usually give farm mortgage credit to farmers in these areas on favorable terms and at rates as low as they would to comparable borrowers in business or other lines of activity. The farmer who has a good farm mortgage to offer for a long-term loan is in a position to benefit from the competition among insurance companies, and between insurance companies and other lenders eager to make this type of farm mortgage loan.

Life insurance companies generally make only first mortgage loans on farm and ranch property. In some states they are prohibited by law from making short-term loans. Furthermore, they generally have little interest in short-term loans because of the character of their reserves and the extensive supervision required by such loans.

Insurance companies which are active in the farm mortgage field choose the territory in which they lend. Smaller companies with limited farm loan funds concentrate their lending activity in selected areas to facilitate economy of operations and to obtain maximum returns. Larger companies also choose their areas of operations with a view to obtaining the greatest return possible with the smallest amount of expense and risk consistent with other company objectives. Having no obligation to serve all farmers, they select those areas where safety is combined with a large volume of business at a rate as high as possible under these conditions. Preference is given to areas where commercial farms predominate in number, where soils are fairly uniform, where precipitation or irrigation water is dependable, and where investment return is consistent with risk. The proportion of farm mortgage debt held by insurance companies in each state on January 1, 1966, is shown in Figure 20.1.

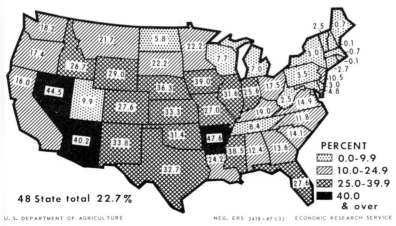

Fig. 20.1—Proportion of farm mortgage debt held by life insurance companies, January 1, 1966. (Courtesy of the Economic Research Service, USDA.)

There is little incentive for an insurance company to provide loan service in areas which are "spotty," or where there are few good loans. Expense of making and servicing loans is higher relative to income in such areas. An official of a leading insurance company expressed it as follows in a personal communication.

> The reason we are not spread universally throughout the country is the limited number of loans available in some sections of the type and size desirable for our portfolio. Many areas of the country are spotty, and particularly in some areas marginal farms are the rule rather than the exception. This type of farm is not the security we are seeking for our loans.

Insurance companies choose the loans they make in areas where they operate. The same type of considerations are involved in selecting individual loans as in selecting areas. While considerable variation exists among companies, two primary considerations are *type* and *size* of unit. In general, insurance companies prefer to loan on typical or modal types of farms. Their loans run for a long period of time, during which ownership or operation of the farm may change and the probability of getting a good operator on a typical type of farm is greater than on a specialty operation. Moreover, while management is very important, the primary security back of a farm mortgage loan is the farm itself, and typical types of farms generally provide relatively more security than specialty operations. Thus, some companies do not make loans on specialized operations such as feed lots, poultry operations, packing plants, and the like, where there is a predominance of buildings, and where extremely specialized management is required. As indicated, success of such operations generally depends upon management to a great degree and should it be disrupted for one reason or another, the specialized facilities securing the loan may have little value. Markets for products of such businesses may also be less certain in the long run, or at least the company may have to make special studies to adequately appraise the long-run market potential. Such special work adds to expense of operations. Moreover, to thoroughly analyze and properly service loans on such farms may be beyond the training and experience of the company's staff and ordinarily the return on such loans is not sufficient to warrant bringing in specialized consultants.

What has been said should not be interpreted as meaning insurance companies ignore management in making loans. In general, they only consider financially responsible applicants with a desirable credit reputation. Insurance companies want their borrowers to have good habits and good health, to be familiar with farming, to have a financially sound operation, and to be making financial progress. By looking at the operator, his accomplishments, and his financial statement, a company can give the better, more efficient operator the benefit of a larger loan.

This raises a question that has always plagued farm mortgage lenders: If a better operator is given a larger loan, in what position is the lender if the operator dies or sells the farm? One insurance company official expressed his views as follows in a letter to the authors.

> First, we are in the business of insuring lives. Therefore, we know pretty well what the life expectancy is for people of any given age, and this is taken into consideration. The odds are that our loan will be reduced by the better, more efficient operator before he passes away.
>
> Second, the better, more efficient operator usually has a more valuable class of security, and cares for his farm better than the "average operator." Invariably, such property will have a higher resale value, if that becomes necessary, than the farm that is cared for in an average way. From our past experience, we know that losses are negligible on the better classes of security, compared with those sustained on lower grade farms which generally attract poorer operators.

To protect themselves should the farm be sold, a number of insurance companies put an accelerator clause in the mortgage. The following clause was taken from a mortgage recorded in Iowa.

> Mortgagor agrees to reduce principal of said note to $15,000 before conveying said premises and further agrees that this mortgage shall become due and payable forthwith at the option of the mortgagee, if the mortgagor shall convey said premises, or if the title thereto shall become vested in any person or persons in any manner whatsoever before the principal amount of said note is reduced to said amount.

Such a clause fairly well protects the company since it gives them the right to call for payment of the mortgage should the farm be sold.

As to size of farm, except for part-time farms, insurance companies make loans only on economic-sized units for the area in which the farm is located. The policy statement of a leading life insurance company in the farm mortgage field carries the following paragraph.

> No loan should be considered on units of such limited acreage that under normal conditions will not provide suffi-

cient income to support a family in reasonable comfort and leave the necessary margin for the payment of first mortgage indebtedness. The size will vary with the location, type of farming and crops grown, productivity of the land and economy of operation.

Insurance companies make quite a number of loans on part-time farms adjoining residential areas of cities and larger towns. They generally do not loan on large estates with costly pretentious buildings which have a limited sales field, but rather on moderately valued farms with useful buildings which have appeal to many within a practical price range. Their interest centers on property located on good roads and within easy commuting distance to business and retail shopping centers, schools, churches, and the like.

SIZE OF LOANS

There are no limits on the size of insurance company loans except for a self-imposed minimum and a maximum based upon the appraised value of the security. The minimum generally is set in the range of $5,000 to $10,000, depending upon individual company policy, with a view to avoiding the relatively high expense and possible risk associated with such loans. One insurance company official explained it this way in a personal letter to the authors.

> There are two very good reasons why insurance companies have a minimum size of loan they are willing to make. One is that most loans below $10,000 are on small, marginal, inefficient units. Regardless of the interest rate charged or the safety of the investment from a sale of the security standpoint, because of the limited volume of business and the limited income produced by the security, there is a substantial amount of servicing required with such small loans. The other reason is that the cost for handling each dollar invested on a small loan is pretty high and, therefore, the larger loans are somewhat more desirable. The first reason, however, is the most pressing.

The maximum amount which insurance companies can loan is limited by law in most states to two-thirds of the appraised value of the security as established by the company's appraisers or loan representatives. Except for this restriction, there is no maximum dollar limit on the size of loan which a company may make. They have made quite a number of loans in excess of one million dollars, and one company reported a loan for as much as $4.5 million.

As was indicated in Chapter 16, life insurance company loans are larger, on the average, than farm mortgage loans made by other lenders. The average size of farm mortgages recorded by life insurance companies in 1965 was $40,150, compared with $21,320 for Federal Land Bank loans, and an average of $16,920 for all farm mortgages recorded. There are a number of reasons for this, but a primary one is the fact that insurance companies operate on a profit motive and there is more money in larger loans. Expenses involved in making and servicing loans do not increase nearly in proportion to size. Commercial banks also operate on a profit basis, of course, but the average size of their loans tends to be relatively small since many of them are of an "accommodation" type to meet relatively short-term requirements of borrowers. Moreover, since the banker generally knows farmers in his territory and is able to maintain first-hand contact with them, he can net more from small farm mortgage loans than can the insurance company operating from a distance. Insurance company loans average larger than Federal Land Bank loans since the land banks provide credit service to all farmers who can qualify for a loan, regardless of the size of farm.

Term of Loans and Repayment Plans

Insurance company loans generally range in terms from five to 25 years, with most of them being written currently for a 20-year term.[3] A few loans are written for longer terms of up to 33 years, and in some instances up to 40 years. The determining factor is quality of the security. Where the security is exceptional the term may be extended to 25 years or more, depending on company policy. Similarly, where the security is subject to an unusual hazard, such as soil erosion or an uncertain supply of irrigation water, a shorter term may be used to give the company latitude to periodically review each individual loan and thereby reduce the risk involved.

While the majority of insurance company loans are written for about 20 years, they often are amortized at a somewhat slower rate. On good farms with no unusual hazards, principal payments may be set as low as 3 per cent and possibly as low as 2 per cent of the face amount of the loan, depending upon company policy. In such cases the balance is due as a balloon payment at maturity. Interest is in addition to the principal payments and gradually decreases as the loan is repaid.

---

[3] Betty A. Case, *Farm Mortgage Loans Held by Life Insurance Companies,* USDA, ARS 43–58, Oct.. 1957, p. 7.

In response to an inquiry from the authors, an insurance company official gave these views on why this practice is followed:

> There is no real good sound reason why mortgages are not written for thirty to forty years, to more closely coincide with the amortization of the loan. However, there is no great pressure for this to happen, inasmuch as our average loans are on the books for just a little over ten years. Usually they are either rewritten or paid off long before the maturity date. Loans that carry through to maturity are very much the exception rather than the rule.
>
> You must appreciate that the insurance industry as a business makes its contractual arrangements over a long period of years, and there is no great haste for change of some things. Looking back over the last twenty-five years, maturities on farm mortgages have lengthened from five years with no amortization to a standard pattern pretty much of twenty years, with some thirty to forty year amortizations. The lengthening process is continuing, but without an urgency of demand, this takes a long time.

In recent years some insurance companies have developed noteworthy modifications in the amortization schedule. The policy of one company provides that if the loan does not exceed 50 per cent of the appraised value, annual principal payments may be as follows:

a. First five years—3 per cent of the face amount of the loan
b. Second five years—2 per cent of the face amount of the loan
c. After ten years—no principal payments

When a larger proportion of the appraised value is loaned, amortization payments the first five years are increased to 5 per cent.

A "Double Diminishing" repayment plan used for some time by another major insurance company accomplishes about the same objective. With this plan, principal payments are set at a fixed percentage of the *unpaid* balance of the loan rather than of the original face amount of the loan. Thus, both the principal and interest payments diminish as the loan is repaid. And after the loan is reduced to 50 per cent of the original amount, no further principal payments are required until the loan matures.

Both of these plans have desirable features. They enable an insurance company to amortize a loan at a relatively rapid rate until it is reduced to an unquestionably safe amount, and to then retain the loan as an investment. They also may be of help to the farmer by encouraging him to reduce his loan to a safe amount through larger payments in the earlier years. Moreover, the option of discontinuing principal payments when the loan is partially repaid has the advantage of letting the farmer choose whether he should continue to accumulate savings through principal payments on the farm or whether he would gain more satisfaction by using his funds in other ways.

Insurance companies generally restrict prepayments (payments ahead of schedule) during any one year to 20 per cent of the original amount of the loan. Some companies permit a larger payment if the funds are derived from farm income. Most companies also permit a larger prepayment upon payment of a premium equal to, say, 2 per cent of the amount of the payment. The restriction on prepayments arises because of the large costs involved in placing a loan on the books. Life insurance companies generally do not charge loan-closing fees except to cover direct cash outlays for legal services, recording the mortgage, and the like, and, therefore, major costs of putting the loan on the books must be covered by interest income. Thus, insurance companies feel it is necessary to be assured that loans will stay in their portfolio a reasonable length of time or that they will be reimbursed for loan acquisition costs in the event of premature payment in full.

Some companies allow additional prepayment privileges up to, say, 20 per cent of the principal amount of the loan to build a reserve payment fund to meet future loan payments if needed. Such payments ordinarily are not subject to withdrawal. Interest generally is allowed on such funds at the rate paid on the loan.

QUESTIONS AND PROBLEMS

1. What type of loans do insurance companies make?
2. How important are insurance companies as farm lenders in your state? In the nation? Is their volume of loans increasing or decreasing? Are they increasing or decreasing in importance relative to other lenders?
3. Who owns and controls insurance companies? What significance does this have from the viewpoint of the farmer wanting to obtain a loan?
4. What is the primary source of insurance company loan funds? Evaluate this source of funds from the viewpoint of dependability of loan service. Compare this source of funds with the primary source of commercial bank loan funds.
5. What factors do insurance companies consider in determining how much of their assets to put into farm loans?

6. Are insurance companies a source of credit for all farmers? Discuss.
7. Outline the loan policy generally followed by insurance companies. Do they give much consideration to the operator?
8. Are insurance companies limited in the size of loan they may make? How does the size of insurance company loans compare with those of other lenders? Of what significance is this for farmers?
9. Outline the policy of insurance companies with regard to term of loan.
10. Explain the repayment plans used by insurance companies. Appraise their repayment policy.
11. Assume that a farmer obtains a $10,000, 5 per cent, 20-year amortized loan with annual principal payments of 3 per cent of the face amount of the loan. Set up a table showing principal and interest payments, and the total payment due each year. How much will the balloon payment be at maturity? Set up a similar table on a Double-Diminishing repayment plan basis assuming annual principal payments are 3 per cent of the unpaid balance. Compare and appraise the two plans.
12. Appraise the advisability of discontinuing principal payments when the loan is, say, one-half repaid.
13. Is it possible to have too much competition in the farm mortgage loan business? What may be the consequences?

REFERENCES

Agricultural Finance Review, ARS, USDA (gives statistical data).

Case, Betty A., *Farm Mortgage Loans Held by Life Insurance Companies,* ARS, USDA, 43–58, Oct., 1957.

Krause, K. R., Atkinson, J. H., and Snyder, J. C., *Specialized Illinois and Indiana Farm Mutual Insurance Companies in a Changing Competitive Environment,* Purdue Univ. Agr. Exp. Sta. Res. Bul. 771, Dec., 1963.

Life Insurance Fact Book, Inst. of Life Ins., 1958, pp. 80–83.

Maclean, Joseph B., *Life Insurance,* McGraw-Hill, New York, 1958, Chaps. 12 and 19.

Mehr, R. I., and Cammack, Emerson, *Principles of Insurance,* Richard D. Irwin, Inc., Homewood, Ill., 1958, Chap. 23.

Chapter 21

INSURANCE COMPANY
LOAN AND SERVICE PROCEDURE

THE organization or method by which the company maintains contact with farmers is a basic part of an insurance company's loan and service procedure. Most insurance companies are located in centers of population some distance from major farming areas. Many companies have their headquarters in cities in the eastern part of the United States. Some are located in larger cities of the Midwest, and along the Pacific coast. Under such circumstances insurance companies make farm loans through their own branch offices or salaried field representatives reporting directly to the home office, or through correspondents who negotiate and close the loans and assign them to the insurance company. Some companies have their own branch offices or field representatives in part of the country and use correspondents in other parts. Most companies which have their own field organization use middlemen such as banks, realtors, insurance agents, and attorneys who originate loan applications. These middlemen also are often called brokers or correspondents.

BRANCH OFFICES AND FIELD REPRESENTATIVES

Insurance companies generally locate their branch (or district) offices and field representatives in the centers of good agricultural areas where there are prospects for a relatively large volume of high quality loans. Companies which operate pretty much throughout the entire country generally use branch or district offices to facilitate operations and management, whereas companies which operate in only certain parts of the country use field representatives without district offices. For example, one major insurance company has six district offices which serve thirty-eight states. The remaining states are served from the home office of the company. Another company which makes farm loans in only a part of the country has eleven field representatives in the Corn Belt, five in the Rocky Mountains, and five in Texas. Each branch office or field representative is assigned a specific territory in which to work.

Each branch or district office is supervised by a manager who is responsible to the farm loan department of the home office of the company. The branch manager employs a staff, often in consultation with the home office, to carry on functions of the office. The staff includes fieldmen well trained in farm and business management, and in appraisal to develop farm loan business for the company. Field representatives of companies which do not maintain branch offices perform about the same function as these fieldmen.

While procedures vary considerably among insurance companies, activities of branch offices and field representatives can be classified into three general groups: (1) loan procurement, (2) loan investigation and closing, and (3) loan servicing. The first two of these groups are discussed here and the third pertaining to servicing loans in the territory is covered later in the chapter.

Regarding *loan procurement,* branch office personnel and field representatives develop some business on their own, but with most companies the majority comes from contacts with parties who have financial dealings with farmers and farm owners and are in position to know when long-term real estate financing is needed. A large percentage of loans results from farm real estate sales and, therefore, a primary contact is with real estate brokers. Other contacts include loan offices, banks located usually in small and medium-sized towns, attorneys, tax accountants, and the like. With most companies these contacts direct business to the attention of the company, and for this service a commission is paid on loans which are closed. The loans are negotiated by the company's branch office fieldman or field representative, depending upon the type of field organization.

The second phase of the field operation pertaining to *investigation and closing of the loan* follows in general the procedure outlined in Chapter 15. It includes a thorough investigation of the applicant as to financial progress and responsibility, credit reputation, age, health, family financial requirements, and the like. It includes an appraisal of the property to determine its normal productivity and related factors, and whether net income produced under normal circumstances will be sufficient to support the operator and his family and leave an adequate surplus to cover interest and principal payments. It includes the "loan closing," a term which covers all the activities attending the actual making of the loan. Notes and mortgages have to be signed and acknowledged, previous mortgages paid and released, and the new mortgages recorded. Any slip in the loan-closing negotiations may be costly, as illustrated by the local agent who allowed a day to intervene between the release of the old mortgage and the recording of the new. During that intervening day, a bank which had an unrecorded second mortgage put that mortgage on record at the courthouse thus making it a first mortgage ahead of the agent's mortgage.

A company with a branch office field organization which closes its loans through attorneys or title insurance companies generally proceeds as follows:

a. The branch office sends the *Advice of Loan Approval* to the borrower, and a copy to a local attorney or title company in the community where the farm is situated. Blank mortgage forms are also sent to the attorney or title company.
b. The local attorney or title company examines the title and, if everything is in order, prepares the mortgage and authorizes the branch office to disburse the loan proceeds (funds). If any imperfection is found in the title, it is called to the attention of the branch office.
c. The branch office escrows the loan proceeds with the local attorney or title company who pays out the funds when any defects in the title have been removed and any other conditions stipulated by the company have been complied with.

Companies which have a field representative type of farm loan organization follow a somewhat similar procedure. The field representative sends the loan application, appraisal report, and financial statements, along with his recommendations to the home office of the company where they are considered by the farm loan department. When the application is approved, loan papers generally are sent out to a local attorney who represents the company in the actual closing of the loan.

Agreements With Commercial Banks

Some insurance companies have developed arrangements with commercial banks whereby the bank does more than merely direct attention of the company to a loan prospect. Some of these arrangements are informal. On the other hand, some are formal business contracts. For example, under a mortgage purchase plan used by several major insurance companies, the bank originates the application and makes the loan on the basis of an appraisal made by the insurance company. The agreement between insurance company and bank provides that the bank will sell and the company will buy the loan within two years after it is closed. Where the bank cannot legally make a loan for the length of time desired, an agreement is executed whereby the company agrees to extend the term after purchasing the loan.

Plans such as these have an advantage for the commercial bank of providing short-term loan outlets for funds, and at the same time provide the contracting insurance company with a source of long-term investments. The borrower may also benefit by having a source of long-term credit available from his local bank, particularly if the bank is providing his short- and intermediate-term credit. The bank and farmer can then work out an overall financial plan for the farm which is a sounder financing procedure than using two independent lenders. Since both the bank and insurance company have interests in the loan, however, the borrower should be sure of what is involved, loan service procedures, and the like, to facilitate making intelligent decisions.

Farm Mortgage Correspondents

Other than commercial banks, which have already been discussed, farm mortgage correspondents of insurance companies generally are mortgage brokers, or individuals associated with mortgage companies, real estate offices, and the like. They are not always easy to recognize because they combine their loan business with other business endeavors. A mortgage company, for example, may make many different types of loans, with farm loans representing only a small segment of the business. A real estate agent may arrange to be a correspondent for an insurance company to provide a source of long-term financing as a means of facilitating farm sales. Lawyers, insurance agents, tax accountants, and abstractors sometimes act as loan correspondents as an accommodation for their customers and to expand their business.

The term "correspondent" has come to have a rather broad meaning in connection with the making of farm mortgage loans by insurance companies. Originally it referred to some local mortgage company which originated loans for an insurance company and continued to service them on a fee basis throughout their life. Some insurance companies use this type of correspondent today in place of a field organization. Companies with a field organization use middlemen or loan brokers who procure loan applications but do not negotiate the loan, and these are now also commonly called correspondents.

Note that while the correspondent and the insurance company together do all the negotiating and servicing of loans, a wide difference exists in the role played by the correspondent. At one extreme the correspondent actually makes the loan himself and sells it to the insurance company. At the other extreme the correspondent merely brings the prospective borrower or his application to the attention of the company who does all the remaining work in negotiating and servicing the loan.

Three different types of arrangements may be used to illustrate the variation in the role of correspondents. Consider first the situation where the correspondent plays a major role in making and servicing the loan. In this situation the correspondent finds the prospect, obtains an application, and appraises the property. Some correspondents then make the loan and sell it to the insurance company. Other correspondents submit the papers direct to the home office of the company and the company then negotiates the loan. In either case the correspondent services the loan on a fee basis. In some situations the borrower makes payments to the correspondent, while in others he sends them direct to the home office. In this connection it might be noted that the arrangement whereby the borrower sends payments to the correspondent has the advantage of enabling him to keep more currently informed on status of the loan. On the other hand, arrangements whereby loan payments are sent direct to the insurance company enable the company to use punch cards and mechanical equipment to prepare payment notices and to keep records.

With a second type of situation the correspondent plays a similar but reduced role compared with that outlined above, since a fieldman of the insurance company enters the picture and takes over some of the functions. The correspondent still finds the prospect, obtains the application, and makes the appraisal, but submits these papers to a salaried fieldman of the company working in the area. This fieldman inspects the prospective loan and then submits it to his home office. After the loan is placed on the books, this same fieldman services it and the correspondent no longer has any obligation to the insurance company.

With the third type of situation, the correspondent serves only as a loan "finder." The only function these finders perform is to find prospective borrowers for insurance companies. The insurance company through its salaried field and home office personnel performs all the functions associated with making and servicing loans. It might be pointed out that finders are associated primarily with insurance companies who have salaried field personnel. The first two types of correspondents referred to above seldom if ever use finders as a source of loan applications.

Insurance companies uniformly reserve the right to accept or reject loans. In other words, the insurance company decides whether or not it will make or buy a loan. For loans which it makes or buys, the insurance company carries all the risk. Correspondents do not carry any risk on loans they originate except for expenses associated with extra services they might render on problem loans.

A correspondent may act as an agent for more than one insurance company, particularly if he has different types of loans. Some insurance companies specialize in the type and quality of loan they will make, and to properly service his clients, the correspondent may represent more than one company.

Insurance companies usually give their correspondents exclusive right to make loans in a given territory, such as a state or a number of contiguous counties. This means that if a loan application is submitted to the company by some other agent, the commission or a portion of it will be paid to the company's correspondent who has exclusive right to the territory.

LOAN SERVICING

With profit being their motive for operation, insurance companies give careful attention to loan service as a means of building goodwill for the company generally and to help build their loan volume. Competition between profit-motivated companies encourages superior service in many instances. They recognize that well-satisfied customers are their best advertisement for new loans, as well as for their insurance business generally.

Servicing of loans involves a number of things which may be grouped into three general categories: (1) checking to see that the loan continues in good standing, (2) working with problem loans which may develop, and (3) performing general services such as processing partial releases. Note the following statement, taken from a letter to the authors from a major company with a branch office field organization.

> Our loan servicing includes the following:
>
> a. We check annually on all of our loans to see that the real estate taxes are paid since they are a prior lien. In some offices we check with the county tax collector and in other offices we engage a special tax searching service who makes the tax search for us.
>
> b. We hold fire insurance policies on buildings where needed, and we follow up on expirations to see that the insurance is continued.
>
> c. When a loan becomes delinquent, we follow up by correspondence and personal contact to see that it is paid. Our philosophy is that if a borrower can pay without unreasonable sacrifice, he must pay. If he can't pay, we analyze his situation to see if he can work it out or if we must foreclose as a last alternative.
>
> d. We process partial releases and modifications as requested. The principle involved in partial releases is that the remaining security must adequately secure the loan regardless of the value of the land being released.

The following statement is taken from the originating and servicing agreement of a major insurance company with its farm mortgage correspondents:

> In servicing such loans, Correspondent undertakes to perform under the Company's direction, all acts and duties which a reasonably prudent mortgage lender would perform with respect to its own mortgages. Without limiting the generality of the foregoing: . . .
>
> Correspondent will keep adequate records respecting the mortgages, which records shall be the property of the Company and shall be open to inspection and audit by the Company, and Correspondent will furnish reports on request regarding the status of mortgages. Once a year, Correspondent will furnish proof acceptable to the Company of the payment of all

taxes, assessments or other public charges affecting the mortgaged premises. Correspondent will at all times use due diligence to keep buildings and other improvements on the mortgaged premises adequately insured as required by the mortgage, and to prevent liens superior to the mortgages from attaching to the mortgaged premises. It will promptly notify the Company of any facts coming to its attention which might have an adverse bearing on the Company's investment. It will make inspections of the mortgaged premises at reasonable intervals as requested from time to time by the Company and, in any event, at least once a year, filing reports with the Company on forms approved by the Company. It will, in the event of casualty, assist in collecting insurance moneys and, if requested by the Company, in having the properties restored and will cooperate with the Company in any legal proceedings affecting the loans or the mortgaged premises. It will not accept sums in reduction of principal in excess of the amounts permitted by the loan terms.

To protect its investment an insurance company must make certain that real estate taxes, assessments, or other public charges are paid, since they become a prior lien against the property ahead of the mortgage. Attention must be given to keeping insurance on buildings in force and to seeing that they and the farm generally are kept in repair, otherwise the company's security could deteriorate and the loan might become impaired. In addition to impairment of the security, such defaults often serve as a warning of possible loan weakness from other causes. For example, a temporary tax delinquency increases the borrower's operating costs and may be an indication of a careless attitude toward his obligations. Similarly, a lapse of an insurance policy may indicate carelessness and may prove to be a disaster financially to the borrower, should fire or natural forces destroy the improvement.

Servicing delinquent loans generally is not much of a problem during periods of economic prosperity. The relatively few borrowers who become involved financially often find a better situation in nonfarm employment, with the result that their farms generally are taken over by financially stronger operators in the community. However, during less prosperous times delinquency can become quite a problem.

The procedure involved in dealing with delinquent loans varies somewhat from company to company, but in general the pattern is as follows. When payment is not received in response to the initial notice, a second reminder notice is sent. If no response to the reminder notice is received, the case is turned over to a member of the company's service group who analyzes the case and decides whether collection should be attempted by further correspondence or whether it should be turned over to the branch office or company correspondent. A quotation from personal correspondence with a major insurance company indicates the general procedure a correspondent should follow in servicing delinquent loans:

> In servicing loans, the correspondent should give the same attention to the Company's investment that he would follow if it were his personal loan. At the same time, he should remember that in most instances he is the Company's sole personal contact with the borrower and from that relationship the borrower will form his opinion of the attitude and policy of the Company. The protection of the Company's investment is paramount, but a substantial contribution can be made in that respect by impressing upon the worthy borrower that the Company has a sympathetic interest in his progress and desires his confidence with respect to any financial problems that he may have. A proper regard for his obligations will command the full cooperation of the Company.

Insurance companies generally are as lenient as possible with worthy borrowers during periods of difficulty. Loans are made with the understanding that they will be repaid, of course, and the prospective borrower should fully realize that an insurance company's first responsibility is to its policyholders. However, insurance companies also realize that because of the dynamic character of the farm business, income fluctuates widely. To help offset the effect of income fluctuations some companies have set up reserve payment plans, as referred to above, through which borrowers can build reserves to help meet payments in low income periods. And insurance companies generally realize that some deviation may be necessary in their regular and planned collection policy. Interest payments generally are insisted upon, if at all possible, to keep the loan from building up to an unwarranted amount. But principal payments often are extended or deferred, or the loan is rewritten, when it is felt that such action is justified, and when the borrower has a reasonable prospect of working out of his difficulty. Insurance companies generally have no desire to force a farmer out of business. Foreclosure action is taken only as a last resort when careless management, misuse of funds, and the like, lead the company to believe a loan extension would merely postpone the day of reckoning.

Referring to partial releases, subordination agreements, and the like, insurance companies make an effort to cooperate with and accommodate the borrower in such matters. Whenever the release involves a loss of a substantial portion of the security, the field office or correspondent usually is asked to study the situation and to obtain a new appraisal as a basis for determining the amount which should be paid on the loan. In making this determination, the company considers not only the value of the remaining security but also what the earning capacity of the unit will be after the release is effected.

QUESTIONS AND PROBLEMS

1. Does the loan and service procedure followed by a lender make any difference to the borrower? Discuss.
2. Is there an insurance company loan office or representative in your locality? How would you go about making contact with an insurance company about a loan?
3. Why do insurance companies have branch or district offices? Field representatives? Correspondents? Compare these and discuss their functions.
4. Discuss and appraise the arrangement some insurance companies have with commercial banks for making loans. Inquire of your banker whether he has such an arrangement and, if so, how it works.
5. Discuss and appraise the procedures used by insurance companies in making loans; in servicing loans.

Chapter 22

MERCHANTS AND DEALERS

MERCHANTS, dealers, processors, and other types of middlemen comprised the original sources of credit for agriculture. They extended credit to farmers long before lending institutions evolved. Colonial planters, for example, depended on merchants in England to furnish supplies on credit and to sell their crops. As the Colonies developed, local merchants gradually expanded their activities and played a dominant role in financing agriculture. Even after establishment of banks and other financial institutions, merchant and dealer financing continued to be used extensively, particularly in the South.

Sales promotion usually is the primary reason why merchants and dealers extend credit to farmers. It facilitates sales of gasoline, feed, fertilizer, supplies, and the like, particularly when these items are delivered and the farmer is not at hand to make payment. It also helps in selling items where large amounts are involved. Machinery dealers often extend credit to help close a sale; livestock commission companies make loans to farmers for purchasing livestock.

Credit is also used as a magnet by marketing firms. Dealers who contract to buy fruits and vegetables from farmers sometimes make advances for operating expenses; cotton gins provide financing for cotton farmers as a means of increasing their ginning business; farm cooperatives provide credit in some cases to their members for whom they process and sell products or purchase supplies. Some manufacturers of farm implements, and particularly their

dealers, extend credit not only to increase their sales but also because of the profit they realize on the lending itself.

Development of the technological revolution tends to cause
the volume of merchant-dealer credit used by farmers to expand. As
purchased inputs become increasingly important in operation of the
farm business, the amount of merchant and dealer credit used
probably increases. This trend is likely for two reasons: First, credit
extension is a natural by-product of the merchant's primary line of
business, and use of such credit is convenient for the farmer; second,
the continued use of a substantial amount of merchant-dealer credit
in agriculture suggests that both creditors and debtors benefit mutually from its use.

Extent of Merchant-Dealer Credit

As was indicated in Chapter 16, nonreal-estate debt held by
merchants, dealers, and other nonreporting creditors totaled $7.9
billion January 1, 1966. The 1960 Sample Survey of Agriculture
indicates merchants and dealers probably held about two-thirds of
this amount, or about 25 per cent of the total nonreal-estate debt
outstanding.[1] Thus, it is evident that merchants and dealers play an
important role in financing agriculture. Moreover, the volume of
nonreal-estate loans outstanding January 1 represents only a part of
the credit used during the year. Operating loans typically are outstanding for less than twelve months, and in most types of farming a
substantial portion of the short-term credit employed is repaid
before the end of the year.

Further information on the relative importance of merchant-
dealer credit is provided by a comprehensive summary and analysis
of the 1960 Sample Survey of Agriculture, published by the Board of
Governors of the Federal Reserve System.[2] Table 22.1 summarizes
data from this report on the proportion of farmers *using nonreal-
estate credit* who were borrowing from merchants and dealers, and
the proportion of the nonreal-estate debt owed to merchants and

---

[1] Wilellyn Morelle, Leon Hesser, and Emanuel Melichar, *Merchant and
Dealer Credit in Agriculture*, Board of Governors of the Federal Reserve System,
Washington, D.C., 1966. The 1960 Sample Survey of Agriculture, summarized in
this report, showed that merchants and dealers held 65 per cent of the nonreal-
estate debt owed to nonreporting creditors (merchants, dealers, individuals, and
miscellaneous).

[2] *Ibid.*

TABLE 22.1

RELATIVE IMPORTANCE OF MERCHANTS AND DEALERS AS A SOURCE
OF NONREAL-ESTATE CREDIT IN THE UNITED STATES, 1960.*

Classification	Per Cent of Farmers Using Nonreal-estate Credit Borrowing From[†]		Per Cent of Nonreal-estate Debt Owed to[‡]	
	Merchants and dealers	Commercial banks	Merchants and dealers	Commercial banks
All Operators............. 60	43		22	39
Area§				
North..................... 64	51		20	42
South..................... 56	27		30	27
West...................... 57	47		21	41
Economic Class‖				
Commercial				
Large (I–II)............ 58	53		19	43
Medium-sized (III–IV)...... 66	48		23	35
Small (V–VI)............ 53	36		24	40
Noncommercial............. 57	36		29	38
Type of Commercial Farm				
Cash grain................. 64	55		24	40
Cotton.................... 57	24		32	28
Tobacco................... 50	29		39	21
Dairy..................... 69	46		21	31
Livestock.................. 54	54		15	49
Other..................... 62	41		26	35
Tenure of Operator				
Full owner................. 58	40		22	37
Part owner................. 63	45		22	40
Tenant.................... 61	47		24	41
Age of Operator				
Under 35.................. 67	52		22	43
35–54.................... 60	44		22	39
55 and over............... 56	40		23	39

* Source: Wilellyn Morelle, Leon Hesser, and Emanuel Melichar, *Merchant and Dealer Credit in Agriculture*, Board of Governors, Fed. Res. System, Washington, D.C., 1966, pp. 19–20.

† Since many farmers borrow from more than one source, the percentages of farmers using nonreal-estate credit who borrow from the various sources add to more than 100.

‡ The percentages of the volume of nonreal-estate debt owed to the various sources add to 100.

§ In tabulations of the Sample Survey, the West was defined to include North Dakota, South Dakota, Nebraska, Kansas, Oklahoma, Texas, and all states to the west of these except Hawaii and Alaska, which were not included in the Survey. The South included Arkansas, Tennessee, Kentucky, Virginia, Maryland, Delaware, and states to the south. The North encompassed the remaining states.

‖ These are U.S. Census classifications. In general, commercial farms are farms with annual sales of $2,500 and over. Classes I and II represent commercial farms with annual sales of $20,000 and over, classes III and IV commercial farms with annual sales of $5,000 to $19,999, and classes V and VI commercial farms with annual sales of under $5,000.

dealers. Data for commercial banks, generally considered the major source of nonreal-estate credit, also are given in the table to provide a basis for judgment and comparison in considering the merchant-dealer figures.

Of the sources of nonreal-estate credit, merchants and dealers ranked first in *number* of farmers financed. Three out of every five farm operators *using nonreal-estate credit* owed at least some of it to merchants and dealers. The corresponding ratio for commercial banks was 2 out of 5.

Merchants and dealers are also important in terms of *volume* of credit extended, ranking second only to commercial banks. They accounted for 22 per cent of the nonreal-estate debt reported in the Sample Survey compared with 39 per cent for commercial banks. However, it is evident that the average amount of credit extended per borrower by merchants and dealers is substantially less than the average loan extended by commercial banks.

Considered by geographic area, the Survey showed merchants and dealers to be the most widely used source of nonreal-estate credit in all three regions of the country. They stand out particularly in the northern states where they provide at least some credit to nearly two-thirds of the farmers using nonreal-estate credit. They also stand out in the South, not particularly in the proportion of borrowers financed, but in the fact that they provide credit for twice as many farmers as commercial banks.

The proportion of the nonreal-estate debt owed to merchants and dealers also indicates that they play a relatively important role in financing agriculture in the South. Whereas, in the North and West, merchants and dealers held only about 20 per cent of the nonreal-estate debt, in the South they accounted for 30 per cent. Among the small cash-crop farmers, and particularly the tenants, the proportion of credit provided by merchants and dealers was even higher. Thus, the Survey indicated that this segment of southern agriculture continues its long tradition of relatively heavy dependence on merchant-dealer credit.

All sizes of farms are major users of merchant and dealer credit. Within each farm size-group, more operators were indebted to merchants and dealers than to any other source. Use of merchant-dealer credit was most common among borrowers on medium-sized farms, two-thirds of which reported such debt, whereas only a little more than half the borrowers on small and large farms had merchant debt. The proportion of nonreal-estate credit supplied by merchants and dealers was highest on the small farms and declined somewhat as size of farm increased.

Use of merchant-dealer credit was widespread among farmers having nonreal-estate debt on all types of farms, with the proportion ranging from 50 per cent on tobacco farms to 69 per cent on dairy farms. More variation was found in the relative proportion of the nonreal-estate credit supplied by merchants and dealers, the range being from a low of 15 per cent on livestock farms to a high of 39 per cent on tobacco farms. In general, on the types of farms where merchant-dealer credit was relatively important, bank credit was relatively less important, and vice versa. The particularly large proportion of credit supplied by commercial banks on livestock farms indicates their important role in financing purchases of feeder cattle, which were at a seasonal peak when the Survey was made. The lesser role of commercial banks in financing operations of cotton and tobacco farms may, in part, have reflected the fact that crop production loans were largely repaid by the time the Survey was taken.

Only minor variation existed among the three principal types of tenure—full owners, part owners, and tenants—in the proportion of borrowers using merchant-dealer credit and in the proportion of the nonreal-estate debt owed to merchants and dealers. A joint classification of borrowers by tenure and area, however, revealed a great dependence of tenants in the South on merchant and dealer credit. Southern tenant farmers were more indebted to merchants and dealers than to commercial banks and Production Credit Associations combined. In contrast, full owners and part owners in the South owed approximately equal amounts to each of these three types of lenders. Such differences among tenures were not found in the North and West. In these areas banks were supplying each tenure group with about twice as much credit as merchants and dealers.

All ages of farmers make substantial use of merchant-dealer credit. However, the Survey showed that the proportion of farmers using nonreal-estate credit who were indebted to merchants and dealers declined substantially with advancing age. The proportion borrowing from commercial banks also declined with advancing age. This dual decline was caused by the fact that the proportion of borrowers indebted to more than one source declined substantially with advancing age. The relative amount of debt owed to the various sources did not vary greatly by age group.

Types of Merchant-Dealer Credit Arrangements

Credit extended by merchants, dealers, processors, some manufacturers, and other types of middlemen takes many forms. The form may vary considerably from one type of dealer to another. For example, feed dealers generally offer different credit arrangements from machinery dealers. Moreover, a given merchant may have a different form of credit arrangement with one customer than with another. When vertical integration is involved, funds provided by the middleman may be more in the nature of an investment of equity capital in the farm venture than of a loan to the farmer.

The various arrangements under which credit is extended by merchants and dealers may be generally classified into three groups: open account credit, extended open account credit, and credit extended under formal contract. In addition to these, vertical integration and financial leases constitute means whereby a farmer can obtain use of capital.

Open Account Credit

Open account credit is extended by many retailers, including some manufacturers who sell direct to farmers, when frequent sales are made for relatively small amounts. Customers usually are billed once each month. This procedure is more convenient than cash payment for each purchase, particularly when supplies are delivered to the farm and the farmer is not at hand to pay for them.

Many feed, fertilizer, machinery, and similar manufacturers also provide open account financing for farmers through their local distributor. Manufacturers often are involved with the larger accounts, which they may carry in entirety or in conjunction with a local distributor.

Extended Open Account Credit

Open account credit carried more than thirty days is customarily referred to as extended open account credit. Oil dealers customarily extend credit to farmers for 90 days, and in some cases for longer periods. Some dealers in seed, fertilizer, and other supplies provide extended open account credit to farmers, with payment to be made at harvest time when crops are sold. Similarly, some feed dealers provide extended open account credit with payment to be made when livestock are sold. Some manufacturers also provide extended open account credit either alone or on a participation basis with local dealers.

Formal Contracts

Formal written contracts, such as promissory notes and conditional sales contracts, are used by some merchants and dealers, and by some manufacturers, to secure credit transactions with farm customers. These may or may not involve vertical integration. Firms with "past-due" extended open account credit lines usually require customers to sign promissory notes. Merchants and dealers needing financing themselves use formal written contracts in extending credit and, in turn, use the formal written contracts as a basis for securing credit from a lending institution, the manufacturer, or an acceptance company. When vertical integration enters the picture, contracts involved in the transaction go beyond those customarily used in credit extension.

Vertical Integration

Vertical integration, as was pointed out in Chapter 4, involves the *linking* together of two or more stages of the production-marketing process. The form and degree of associated financing varies widely within agriculture. With many farmer-dealer and farmer-processor links, the dealer or processor (whom we refer to as the integrator) sells supplies to affiliated farmers on terms very similar to those customarily used by merchants and dealers. Relatively small amounts of financing are involved. Under such arrangements the integrator may provide for the producer a variety of operating capital items such as seeds, plants, baskets, and specialized cultural and harvesting services as a way of assuring quality and uniformity of product. Quality specifications for hybrid seed corn, peas for canning, and similar products are important in processing and marketing the finished product. The integrator may advance the inputs on credit and deduct payment upon delivery of the product; or the inputs may constitute an investment by the integrator, the cost of which is considered in setting the contract price. But whether they are credit advances or investments, financing in this kind of contract is primarily a means of implementing terms of the contract. With these types of arrangements, the farmer carries all the risk involved—which usually is not excessive, due to either the nature of the venture or the size of the enterprise involved.

Integration involving heavy financing has evolved, notably in broiler and egg production, due to the high risks associated with price and production, particularly with the size of enterprise needed for efficient production. Even those farmers who could raise the money to produce independently have been reluctant to accept the hazards. Thus, integrators have found it necessary to provide the bulk of the variable inputs as one of the incentives to farmers. Under these types of contracts, the integrator provides a variety of operating capital items such as feed, chicks, pigs, medicine, and equipment. He also provides a number of services, including specific managerial guidance and specialized services such as those of a veterinarian. The integrator usually retains ownership of the capital he furnishes and becomes a joint operator with the farmer, rather than a creditor. Some contracts provide for income to be shared by the parties involved, while with others the farmer is guaranteed a minimum return. The guaranty may be in the form of a stipulated payment per bird, animal, or pound or per month. Incentive payments for good feed conversion rates are sometimes added.

In instances such as those where title is held by the integrator, the advances or items which he provides do not constitute extension of credit. The farmer receives additional capital to work with, however, which enables him to increase the size of his operation and thereby his income. In this way, the capital provided by the integrator performs a function similar to that of credit.

Lease Arrangements

There are two basic types of leases: (1) the *operating* lease, where the lessor stocks and maintains the equipment which is leased for relatively short periods at relatively high rates; and (2) the *financial* lease, where the machine or equipment is provided by the lessor to meet the specifications of a customer who leases the item for a specific period under terms which return to the lessor his capital plus a return on his investment.[3] The latter type of lease, with which we are concerned in this chapter, is relatively new to agriculture. However, use of this type of lease is expanding at a fairly rapid rate and indications are that both dealers and financial institutions will use it increasingly in the future.

While financial leasing does not involve credit extension as such, it constitutes a means whereby dealers provide capital (in the form of machinery and equipment) for farmer use, employing the lease in place of credit in some cases to facilitate the "sale" of the machinery or equipment involved. As will become evident, financial lease arrangements used with machinery and equipment are more closely related to credit extension than are typical farm real estate leases, since the contract provides for adequate payments to cover the purchase price of the item plus interest.

Financial lease plans usually are available only to farmers with a favorable and proved credit record who can display a good future-earnings potential. These qualifications are required in order that the dealer and manufacturer can be sure lease payments will be made promptly.

Because of wide variations in types of equipment, intensity of use, and potential obsolescence, as well as differences in the physical and financial needs of the farmer, the terms, conditions, and rental rates are negotiated in each case. Thus, it is not feasible to give specific terms and conditions of lease contracts. However, they can be outlined in a general way to indicate the nature of the leases involved.

With a financial lease, the farmer selects the machine he wants. The term of lease is always less than the anticipated life of the machine. However, it is varied according to the farmer's needs, credit status, type of equipment being leased, and the use to which the equipment will be put. One major manufacturer has a minimum term of 24 months and a maximum term of 60 months for agricultural equipment.

As indicated above, financial lease payments typically are scheduled so that the lessor's original investment will be returned to him, with interest, during the term of the lease. Rental payments may be made by the month, quarterly, semiannually, or annually. For example, assume equipment with a retail value of $6,500 is leased for a period of four years on a semiannual payment basis.

---

[3] John A. Hopkin, *Leasing vs. Buying of Agricultural Equipment,* an unpublished talk presented in 1964. Dr. Hopkin is Vice-President, Bank of America, San Francisco, Calif.

Eight payments will be involved, the first to be made at the time the contract is signed. With the schedule used by one major manufacturer, each payment would amount to $993.85, which means that the aggregate value of the lease would be $7,950.80.

The lessee ordinarily may not sublease the machines or assign any of his rights under the contract. However, the lease may be terminated after a specified period, such as twelve months, by selling the machine at a bona fide sale in the open market. Such sale is subject to prior written approval of the lessor and all proceeds of the sale after deduction of expenses incurred by the farmer in connection with the sale must be delivered to the lessor. If the amount thus received exceeds the *present value* of the rentals due under the contract, the excess is returned to the lessee. However, if the proceeds are less than the present value of the rentals, the lessee is obligated to pay the difference unless other alternatives are provided in the contract.

At the expiration of the term of the lease the contract may be renewed, or the equipment may be returned to the lessor, or it may be sold as outlined in the preceding paragraph.

The lessee is responsible for normal repair and maintenance of the equipment, and for payment of property taxes, license fees, and any other charges assessed against the equipment. The warranty provided by the lessor is similar to that provided by a dealer on equipment sold. The lessee assumes full liability for property damage and personal injury or death caused by the equipment or its use. The lessor customarily requires that the lessee carry insurance to cover such liability. The lessee also assumes all risk of loss or damage to the equipment during the term of the lease.

Financial leases, properly used, have some advantages from the standpoint of financing a farm business. They can be used to "stretch" limited capital. Through leasing, assets can be acquired without tying up limited capital for a down payment. Moreover, some advantage may arise out of *delayed* income tax payments, since lease rental payments are deductible from income as a direct expense while a cash payment on a purchased machine is not. Depreciation and interest are tax deductions allowable on purchased items. However, most leases are written for terms shorter than those normally used for depreciation of purchased machines. These possible advantages should not be allowed to lead one blindly into using financial leases. All factors should be considered, including the relative overall costs of leasing versus ownership.

COST OF MERCHANT-DEALER CREDIT

Farmers using merchant and dealer credit may find it extremely costly, moderately priced, or relatively cheap, depending on the policy of the lender and the type of credit arrangement. Usually a formal interest charge is not made for *open account credit,* although frequently a cash discount may be forfeited. Rogers found in studying merchant credit in the Corn Belt that nearly one-half of the feed dealers included in the survey offered a cash discount ranging from 1 to 5 per cent. More than two-thirds of the fertilizer dealers offered cash discounts ranging from 1 to 8 per cent, the most common discount falling within the range of 5 to 6.9 per cent. However, only one-sixth of the petroleum dealers offered cash discounts on gasoline purchases and these ranged from 1 cent to 2 cents per gallon. The machinery dealers included in the survey typically gave cash discounts but no regular pattern was evident, the size of the discount depending upon individual circumstances such as size of purchase, the trade-in, and the cash position of the firm at the time. To qualify for the cash discount some merchants required payment at the time of delivery, while others allowed 10, 15, or 30 days. One fertilizer dealer in the survey allowed up to 90 days from date of delivery.[4]

Interest may or may not be charged on *extended open account credit,* depending on the amount of credit involved and the term, and also on the policy and bargaining position of the dealer. However, an interest charge typically is imposed on interest-free accounts if payment is not received by the due date. When a charge is made on an open account, it may be effective from the beginning, or after thirty days, or from the beginning if the account is not paid in thirty days.

Credit extended under *formal contracts* usually carries an interest charge.

Interest charged by merchants and dealers is commonly higher than that charged by financial institutions extending credit for the same purpose. Nominal rates varying from 12 to 15 and even to 18 per cent are common. Some farmers probably are unaware of the relatively high cost of this type of credit. They may not have taken

---

[4] LeRoy F. Rogers, "Effects of Merchant Credit on Farm Organization," Ph.D. thesis, Univ. of Ill., 1963, pp. 56–71.

time to compare the alternative costs. Other farmers use it because they cannot obtain credit elsewhere, or think they cannot, at lower rates. However, some farmers use merchant-dealer credit in spite of its high cost because of the convenience, the relatively liberal terms provided, and the like. From the farmer's standpoint, the relevant consideration is the total cost—the sale price plus the cost of credit measured in terms of money, inconvenience, and time required— with one arrangement compared with another.

A number of factors contribute to the comparatively high cost of merchant-dealer credit. Expenses per dollar of credit granted tend to be high compared with those of financial institutions serving farmers. Many small advances to customers by merchants without an efficient method of handling accounts adds to costs of extending and collecting credit. In some cases additional time is required on the part of sales personnel to explain the credit policy to customers. Collection costs and bad debt losses tend to be heavier than for financing institutions since merchants often are less thorough in credit analysis, items sold on credit such as feed and fuel cannot be repossessed when they have been used, and the security is often inadequate or nonexistent. Moreover, if the merchant must borrow the money which he, in turn, lends to his customers, his cost for loan funds may well be higher than the corresponding cost of financial institutions.

An illustration of the relative importance of the various items of cost in extending merchant credit is provided by a study made by the Farmer Cooperative Service.[5] The cost of credit extended was obtained from sixteen cooperative associations and classified as interest, bookkeeping, extension, collection, and bad debts. Credit costs as a per cent of accounts receivable were as follows:

	Accounts Receivable (per cent of average)
Interest	6.0
Extension	1.2
Bookkeeping	3.6
Collection	2.2
Bad debts	0.4
Total	13.4

As these figures indicate, the relatively high cost of merchant credit arises not from excessive interest charges on the part of the

[5] T. R. Eichers, *Credit Control in Selected Retail Farm Supply Cooperatives*, Area III, Farmer Cooperative Service, USDA, General Report 43, 1958, p. 19.

merchant but from the other costs associated with extension of such credit. In many cases these noninterest costs are greater relative to the total cost than indicated by this example. Collection and bad debt costs often run substantially higher.

SOURCE OF MERCHANT-DEALER LOAN FUNDS

Merchants and dealers who extend credit to farmers usually must be financed themselves. Major sources of this financing are local commercial banks, larger city banks, banks for cooperatives, and manufacturers. If the merchant or dealer is a cooperative institution with farmers owning shares, the financing is likely to come from a bank for cooperatives or a commercial bank. Other merchants and dealers are quite likely to be financed by local commercial banks. However, if the merchant or dealer is a large operator and uses an extensive line of credit, he may go direct to a large city bank for his financing. Manufacturers may provide dealer financing for a wide variety of items such as machinery and equipment, machine repair and overhaul, fertilizer, feed, and the like. In such cases the manufacturer may obtain financing either by retaining earnings or by borrowing from a large city bank.

Dealer-Feed Manufacturer Arrangements

Financing arrangements between dealers and feed manufacturers vary considerably. With some arrangements the dealer is fully liable for defaulted contracts, while with others he carries no financial responsibility. With some financing plans the dealer pays part of the finance charges, while with other arrangements the farmer carries the full load. Finance charges may be in the form of a nominal interest charge or, more commonly, in the form of a flat fee per ton in addition to the cash price.[6]

Dealer-Machinery Manufacturer Arrangements

Financing arrangements between dealers and machine manufacturers also vary, but to a somewhat lesser extent than in the feed industry. The general provisions of a contract used by a major machinery manufacturer are outlined to indicate what is involved.

[6] Rogers, p. 74.

A merchant or dealer who obtains financing from a machinery manufacturer enters into a contract with the manufacturer which spells out the terms and conditions under which the credit is obtained. Credit normally is extended on the basis of customers' notes and leases, which must meet the requirements specified by the manufacturer. Notes include finance charges, computed as prescribed by the manufacturer. All payments on the note and all rental payments on leases are made by the note maker or lessee directly to the manufacturer. The dealer is liable for the payments if the customer defaults. To insure that funds are available to meet this obligation, a "dealer's reserve account" is set up by the manufacturer. This account is separate and distinct from the dealer's regular account or statement which reflects indebtedness of the dealer to the manufacturer. When any note or lease is accepted by the manufacturer, 1 per cent of the face amount of the note, or of the aggregate rentals in the case of a lease, is credited to the dealer's reserve account. The manufacturer credits the dealer's reserve account with interest on the average month-end balance at a specified rate. Any "activity bonus" earned by the dealer is also credited to this account. When the amount accumulated in the dealer's reserve account exceeds 3 per cent of the dealer's indebtedness to the manufacturer, the excess is applied to the currently due obligations of the dealer or paid to him in cash.

If any note or lease accepted by the manufacturer is not paid in full, the loss is charged to the dealer's reserve account, together with related expenses incurred by the manufacturer. However, under certain conditions the manufacturer may stand part of the loss.

Dealer-Lending Institution Arrangements

Merchants and dealers also have used various financing arrangements with lending institutions to provide customer credit without having to carry it on their own books. For example, machinery dealers and commercial banks have worked out plans whereby the bank purchases the farmer's note from the dealer. The most common arrangements are: (a) the full-endorsement plan, (b) the limited-recourse plan, (c) the repurchase plan, (d) the nonrecourse plan, and (e) the mutual reserve plan.[7]

[7] *Farm Equipment Financing by Banks,* American Bankers Assoc., New York, 1956.

The *full-endorsement plan* provides that the dealer is fully liable to the bank for all defaulted obligations. The responsibility of making collections generally is transferred to the bank, but the dealer continues as the primary creditor. This plan is not looked upon with favor by representatives of dealers and farm equipment manufacturers. Their view is that the dealer should be relieved largely from the credit aspects of the business. Moreover, their belief is that banks may tend to lean too heavily upon the recourse crutch and give too little attention to quality of the credit. A full-recourse arrangement can easily lull the lender into a false sense of security which, in turn, can lead to bad credit practices on the part of both the dealer and the lending institution.

The *limited-recourse plan* limits the liability of the dealer as to time or amount on individual or aggregate sales contracts bought by the bank. Thus, with this plan the bank assumes some direct liability on loans and, in return, the plan provides for building specified reserves to cover losses incurred. Generally, to encourage making sound sales, the dealer is relieved of full liability only after a specified number of payments have been made on the sales contract.

The *repurchase plan* provides that the dealer repurchase farm equipment repossessed by the bank for the unpaid balance of the contract. Various types of arrangements can be made under this plan. The bank can assume responsibility for any legal action which becomes necessary. Reserves similar to those with the limited-recourse plan can be built to cover losses. This plan, as well as the limited-recourse plan, puts the dealer on a participation basis with the bank, which tends to facilitate fuller cooperation.

The *nonrecourse plan* provides for the bank to buy the equipment sales contract and become the primary creditor. The bank has no recourse to the dealer if the purchaser of the equipment defaults on payments. Naturally banks are quite selective in contracts which they buy on a nonrecourse basis and, therefore, such arrangements are not very popular.

With the *mutual reserve plan* the dealer sells his paper to the bank without recourse, but a sufficiently large reserve is created to protect the bank against losses. One method of building the reserve is for the bank to retain a certain percentage of the net proceeds on each contract purchased. Manufacturers' cash discounts to dealers for prompt payment vary, but often run as high as 5 per cent. Therefore, the dealer can permit the bank to retain an amount up to 5 per cent of the contract without having to draw on his own cash to create the reserves. The reserve may also be built by setting aside part of the finance charges. For example, if the equipment dealer charged the buyer 8 per cent annual interest, 2 per cent may be placed in the reserve, leaving a net yield of 6 per cent for the bank. Sometimes the two methods are combined to facilitate building the required reserve at a more rapid rate. When the minimum stipulated reserve is reached, the bank then remits the amount of the excess to the dealer. When and if the dealer's paper pays out in full, he receives the entire amount in the reserve. The major difference between this plan and the repurchase plan is that the dealer is not obligated to repurchase repossessed equipment with the mutual reserve plan.

Through arrangements with sales finance companies and other organizations, such as General Motors Acceptance Corporation, and C.I.T. (Commercial Investment Trust), Financial Corporation, merchants and dealers make a substantial amount of credit available to their customers without having to provide it themselves. Such companies finance credit transactions by purchasing customer notes or accounts from the merchant or dealer. Another device used by merchants and dealers is to establish a separate credit corporation. In such cases the initial capital is ordinarily furnished by the parent firm, and loan funds are obtained by discounting customer notes with, or borrowing through, regular banking channels. Where the financing agency is organized by a farmer cooperative, it may obtain loan funds by discounting with a Federal Intermediate Credit Bank. Under certain conditions it may also borrow from a Bank for Cooperatives.

Credit Arrangements of Farm Cooperatives

Farm cooperatives have made credit sales for years and carried the credit themselves as an account or note receivable. With the expansion in use of merchant credit in recent years, these receivables have tended to tie up working capital needed for other purposes. As a result, farm cooperatives are turning to other methods of financing patron credit requirements. Arrangements with Production Credit Associations, rural credit unions, and commercial banks are briefly outlined in this section.

Arrangements between supply cooperatives and Production Credit Associations can be illustrated by two general types of plans referred to as the guaranty plan and the reserve plan. With the *guaranty plan* the Production Credit Association agrees to accept all loans below some specified size, such as $1,000. The cooperative guarantees the association against loss on such loans. Larger loans are handled on an individual basis. The *reserve plan* is similar to the guaranty plan except that a reserve fund is established by the cooperative to cover losses. The amount of the reserve is agreed upon by the PCA and the cooperative, and any losses in excess of the reserve are borne by the association. The PCA services these loans and collects principal and interest payments the same as with its regular loans. A primary advantage of these arrangements from the patron's point of view is that he can arrange for credit at the time he buys his supplies without the necessity of a separate trip to the PCA office.

A number of farm cooperatives have sponsored formation of rural credit unions to assist in financing sales. The credit union frequently is housed with the cooperative and, therefore, is readily accessible to consider credit requirements of those doing business with the cooperative. In some cases a fieldman is employed to help farmers with their farm plans and to help service loans which are made. Loan funds of rural credit unions are derived from various sources including savings of members, deposits by the sponsoring cooperatives, loans from local banks, and member notes discounted with a Federal Intermediate Credit Bank.

Many farmer cooperatives have developed arrangements with commercial banks for financing their patrons. Since at least one bank usually is located in the same town as the cooperative it is convenient to develop and operate with such arrangements. With one "open-account" financing plan the farmer estimates his seasonal credit needs and signs a note for the amount at the cooperative. The cooperative then turns the note over to the bank for servicing and collection. Throughout the season the cooperative extends accommodation credit to the farmer and periodically transfers the balance in the account to the bank to be charged against the patron's note. Interest is charged by the bank only for the time the patron uses the money. Thus, the plan provides patrons with a ready source of credit without the cooperative having to provide the loan funds. Moreover, it transfers to the bank the servicing and collection of the loan. However, it should be kept in mind that the cooperative fully guarantees repayment of the note to the bank and, therefore, must make the credit investigation and carry all the risk associated with the loan.

Cooperatives have worked out other plans with commercial

banks for production financing, financing machinery and equipment purchases, and the like. The arrangements vary widely but in general the cooperative continues as the primary lender. In most cases the plans provide a source of credit for patrons but do not relieve the cooperative of risk involved in the loan.

QUESTIONS AND PROBLEMS

1. Is extension of credit by merchants and dealers an innovation? Discuss.
2. Discuss the importance of merchants and dealers as a source of credit for farmers.
3. Why do merchants and dealers offer credit?
4. What types of credit do merchants and dealers extend?
5. Is leasing of farm equipment a form of credit extension? Discuss.
6. Outline the major provisions of a farm equipment lease.
7. Does merchant credit cost the farmer more than other credit? If so, why does he use it?
8. Are merchants justified in the rates they charge for credit? What are the main items of cost?
9. Why do merchants tend to have relatively heavy losses?
10. Where do merchants and dealers obtain the funds they loan to farmers?
11. Are merchants and dealers a dependable source of credit? Discuss.
12. Appraise merchant credit as a source of financing. Does it contribute to optimum balance in use of capital in the farm business as outlined in Chapter 2?

REFERENCES

"Accounts Receivable Lending—Credit at the Margin," *Business Conditions,* Fed. Res. Bank of Chicago, Mar., 1958, pp. 5–11.
Bailey, J. M., Pursell, A. H., and Engberg, R. C., *How Cooperatives Use Credit Agencies To Meet Patron's Needs,* Farmer Cooperative Serv., USDA, Gen. Rept. 52, 1958.
Davis, Lynn H., and Korzan, Gerald E., *Contract Farming in Oregon,* Oreg. Agr. Exp. Sta. Bul. 580, June, 1961.
Engberg, R. C., "Credit Implications of Integration in Agriculture," *Jour. Farm Econ.,* No. 5, Dec., 1958, pp. 1370–79.
Feedmen and Bankers Working Together To Serve Today's Farmers, Amer. Bankers Assoc. and the Amer. Feed Manuf. Assoc.
Mighell, Ronald L., and Jones, Lawrence A., *Vertical Coordination in Agriculture,* Agr. Econ. Rept. 19, ERS, USDA, Feb., 1963.
———, and Gavett, Earle E., *Contract Production of Truck Crops, 12 Selected Areas, United States,* Farm Econ. Div., ERS-152, Mar., 1964.

Morelle, Wilellyn; Hesser, Leon; and Melichar, Emanuel, *Merchant and Dealer Credit in Agriculture,* Board of Governors, Fed. Res. System, Washington, D.C., 1966.

Phillips, Richard, *Feed Industry Financing and Contract Programs in Iowa and Surrounding States,* Iowa Agr. Exp. Sta. Spec. Rept. 28, Apr., 1961.

Rickey, L. F., and Robbins, C. B., *Controlling Open Account Credit in Feed Cooperatives,* Farmer Cooperative Serv., USDA, FCS Circ. 24, 1957.

Rogers, LeRoy F., *Effects of Merchant Credit on Farm Organization,* unpublished Ph.D. thesis, Univ. of Ill., 1963.

Chapter 23

FARM CREDIT SYSTEM

THE Farm Credit System is composed of the Farm Credit Administration and the cooperative banks and associations which were organized and put into operation by the United States Government as a means of helping farmers to help themselves. The various banks and associations are discussed in the three following chapters. The purpose of this chapter is to give an overall picture of the Farm Credit System, including a brief review of conditions which brought about such an ambitious undertaking by the Federal Government on behalf of one segment of the economy, and to explain the organization and function of the Farm Credit Administration.

THE FARMERS' CAMPAIGN FOR CREDIT

A demand for more adequate credit was an important and enduring factor in farmers' movements from Colonial times. As the economy of the country developed, more and more capital was needed for land, farm improvements, machinery, livestock, and the like. But credit facilities were far from adequate to meet these growing needs. The relatively few existing commercial financial institutions were accustomed to financing the faster turnover of urban business and displayed little interest in lengthening their loan terms to accommodate the slower turnover in agriculture. Moreover, the financial institutions were concentrated in the eastern industrial centers and loans were made to farmers through agents and middlemen.

This situation caused problems for farmers in use of both long- and short-term credit. Real estate loan terms rarely exceeded three to five years, and when money became tight, renewals often were refused. Agents and middlemen customarily charged relatively high commissions and renewal fees in addition to interest. With loans being for such short terms, these charges added a heavy financing burden and were a major factor contributing to loan breakdown and foreclosure. Shortage of production credit forced many farmers, particularly in the South, to use merchant credit. As pointed out in Chapter 22, this is a relatively expensive source of financing due to the extra costs involved in extending such credit.

Many attempts were made to provide more suitable credit facilities. A number of banks were organized by the Grange, and various states took steps to provide credit for agriculture. However, the amount provided was inadequate. Fed by gradually declining prices during the thirty years following the Civil War, the farmers' campaign for credit reached a high pitch by the close of the nineteenth century. The Northwest Alliance called for mortgage loans up to 50 per cent of the value of the land for periods of twenty years at 2 per cent interest. A Populist representative speaking in 1890 stated: ". . . we want the power to make loans direct from the Government. We want the accursed foreclosure system wiped out. . . . We will stand by our homes and stay by our firesides by force if necessary, and we will not pay our debts to the loan shark companies until the Government pays its debt to us. The people are at bay, let the bloodhounds of money who have dogged us thus beware."[1]

The farmers' long and arduous fight for Federal governmental credit finally bore fruit in the Federal Farm Loan Act of 1916. While not providing direct government credit, as demanded, the Act laid the groundwork whereby farmers could build a credit system of their own to provide agriculture with "tailor-made" farm loans.

The Farm Loan Act proved to be the first in a long chain of federal credit legislation for the benefit of agriculture. The 1920's and particularly the 1930's were indeed difficult for agriculture. These two 10-year periods might very appropriately be called the "farm foreclosure decades." Fed by difficult times in agriculture, an

---

[1] J. D. Hicks, *The Populist Revolt,* Minn. State Univ. Press, Minneapolis, 1931, p. 160.

attitude of concern and helpfulness in the urban population, and a change in attitude of the Government from a "hands off" policy to one of assistance and leadership, the farmers' campaign for credit produced considerable legislation and a number of executive orders designed to aid the credit position of agriculture. An understanding of the Farm Credit System, as it exists today, and of the Farmers Home Administration, discussed in a later chapter, may be furthered by a historical portrayal of these acts and executive orders (see Table 23.1).

EVOLUTION OF THE FARM CREDIT SYSTEM

As the economy of the country reached its lowest ebb in the Great Depression of the 1930's, wise and foresighted men in government and agriculture moved to complete the Farm Credit System, thereby laying the groundwork of a complete credit system farmers could cooperatively own and operate to provide for their credit needs. The Farm Credit Administration, created in 1933, brought together under one administrative agency almost all federally sponsored farm credit agencies and activities existing at the time. The new organization included the Seed Loan Agency from the Department of Agriculture; the Federal Land Banks, and Federal Intermediate Credit Banks from the Federal Farm Loan Board which was under the Treasury Department; the Regional Agricultural Credit Corporations from the Reconstruction Finance Corporation; and the Federal Farm Board, an independent agency. The Production Credit System and the Banks for Cooperatives, created by the Farm Credit Act of June 16, 1933, rounded out the Farm Credit System. With these facilities the System could finance the entire range of farmers' needs for real estate, production, marketing, and purchasing operations. From May 27, 1933, the date of organization, until 1939, the Farm Credit Administration was an independent agency of the Federal government responsible to the President. In 1939, it was placed in the Department of Agriculture where it remained until 1953.

The Farm Credit Act of 1953 reestablished the Farm Credit Administration as an independent agency and provided that "It shall be housed in the Department of Agriculture in the District of Columbia and it may, with the consent of the Secretary of Agriculture, utilize the services and facilities of the Department of Agriculture." The Farm Credit Act of 1956 merged the Production Credit

TABLE 23.1

Date	Description of Act or Order	Agency Created or Major Provisions
1916, July 17	Federal Farm Loan Act	1. Federal Land Banks 2. Joint Stock Land Banks
1921, March 3	First seed loan appropriation. (A few loans made earlier in 1918.)	1. Seed Loan Agency in USDA
1923, March 4	Amendment to Federal Farm Loan Act	1. Federal Intermediate Credit Banks
1929, June 15	Agricultural Marketing Act	1. Federal Farm Board 2. Stabilization corporations
1932, Jan. 23	Amendment to Federal Farm Loan Act	1. Added 125 million of Government capital to Federal Land Banks
1932, July 21	Emergency Relief Act	1. Regional agricultural credit corporations
1933, March 27	Executive Order creating Farm Credit Administration	1. Farm Credit Administration
1933, May 12	Emergency Farm Mortgage Act	1. Land Bank Commissioner loans
1933, June 16	Farm Credit Act	1. Production Credit System 2. Banks for Cooperatives
1933, Oct. 16	National Recovery Act and Executive Order	1. Commodity Credit Corporation
1934, Jan. 31	Federal Farm Mortgage Corporation Act	1. Federal Farm Mortgage Corporation
1935, Apr. 30	Executive Order	1. Resettlement Administration—later changed to Farm Security Administration
1935, May 11	Executive Order and REA Act of May 20, 1936	1. Rural Electrification Administration
1937, July 22	Bankhead-Jones Act providing for tenant-purchase loans	1. Tenant-Purchase Loans—Division of Farm Security Administration
1937, Aug. 28	Water Facilities Act	1. Direct loans in 17 western states by Farm Security Administration
1939, June 24	Executive Order	1. Placed FCA, REA, and CCC in USDA
1944, June 22	Service Men's Readjustment Act	1. G. I. (veterans) loan guarantee 2. G. I. (veterans) loan insurance
1944, Dec. 20	Act to Compromise, Adjust or Cancel Certain Indebtedness	1. Administered by Farm Security Administration
1945, June 30	Amendment to Farm Loan Act	1. Increased loan limit on FLB loans to 65 per cent
1946, Aug. 14	Farmers Home Administration Act of 1946	1. Farm Security Administration changed to Farmers Home Administration 2. Mortgage insurance program for farm purchase or improvement
1949, Apr. 6	Act to Provide Emergency Credit	1. Administered by Farmers Home Administration 2. Amended July, 1953, to include Special Livestock loans
1949, July 15	Housing Act	1. Farm housing loans (Farmers Home Admin.)

TABLE 23.1 (Contd.)

Date	Description of Act or Order	Agency Created or Major Provisions
1949, Oct. 19	Act to Extend Financial Assistance to Homestead Entrymen	1. Administered by Farmers Home Administration
1949, Oct. 28	Amendment to REA Act	1. Rural telephone credit program (REA)
1953, Aug. 6	Farm Credit Act of 1953	1. Farm Credit Board created to manage FCA 2. Approved PCA class C preferred stock
1954, Aug. 17	Amendment to Water Facilities Act	1. Added Soil Conservation loans under Farmers Home Administration—became known as Soil and Water Conservation loans 2. Extended program to all states 3. Loans either direct or insured
1954, Aug. 31	Act to Provide Special Emergency Credit	1. Farmers Home Administration loans to farmers whose credit needs are not met by commercial lenders or Farmers Home Administration under regular or other emergency loan authorities
1955, Aug. 11	Farm Credit Act of 1955	1. Provided plan for systematic retirement of Government capital in Banks for Cooperatives, for their increased ownership and control by borrowing cooperatives, and for their operation on a cooperative basis
1956, July 26	Farm Credit Act of 1956	1. Merged Production Credit Corporation in each District with Federal Intermediate Credit Bank 2. Purchase of FICB's by PCA's
1959, Dec. 31	Farm Credit Act of 1959	1. Gave FLB's authority to make unamortized loans 2. Changed name of NFLA's to FLBA's 3. Transferred responsibility for appraisals from FCA to FLB's
1961, Jan. 1	The 1960 amendment to the Farm Credit Act of 1933	1. Central Bank for Cooperatives board increased from 7 to 13
1961, June 30	Housing Act of 1961	1. Extended Farmers Home Administration housing loans to families living in rural areas and small communities 2. Authorized Farmers Home Administration loans for farm labor housing

TABLE 23.1 (Contd.)

Date	Description of Act or Order	Agency Created or Major Provisions
1961, Aug. 8	Agricultural Act of 1961	1. Increased Farmers Home Administration operating and farm ownership loan limits 2. Authorized Farmers Home Administration loans for rural community water systems
1961, Oct. 3	Amendments to the Federal Farm Loan Act and the Farm Credit Act of 1933	1. Permitted installment payments on FLB loans to be scheduled more frequently than semiannually 2. Permitted FLB loans to be made to a farming corporation if owners of its stock assume personal liability to the extent prescribed by FCA 3. Extended from 5 to 7 years the maximum maturity of loans made or discounted by FICB's 4. Provided formula for creation and maintenance of PCA reserve for bad debts 5. Permitted retirement of interests in any BC held by a cooperative which is liquidated or dissolves
1962, Sept. 27	Food and Agriculture Act of 1962	1. Authorized Farmers Home Administration loans for development of rural recreation enterprises 2. Authorized Farmers Home Administration loans for rural renewal
1962, Sept. 28	Senior Citizen Housing Act	1. Authorized Farmers Home Administration rural senior citizen housing loans 2. Authorized Farmers Home Administration grants for emergency repairs to houses owned by low income rural families
1964, Aug. 20	Economic Opportunity Act	1. Authorized Farmers Home Administration economic opportunity loans to individuals and to cooperatives
1964, Aug. 31	Amendment to Farm Credit Act of 1933	1. Required BC to pay in money after it retires Government capital such part of its patronage dividends as would permit them to qualify for the same tax treatment as do such dividends paid by organizations operating on a cooperative basis
1965, Aug. 10	Housing and Urban Development Act of 1965	1. Authorized Farmers Home Administration to make insured rural housing loans

TABLE 23.1 (Contd.)

Date	Description of Act or Order	Agency Created or Major Provisions
		2. Authorized Farmers Home Administration rural housing loans in communities up to 5,500 population
1965, Oct. 4	Amendments to Federal Farm Loan Act and Farm Credit Act of 1933	1. Provided for unsecured loans or advances to PCA's by FICB's
		2. Increased the FICB debt to capital and surplus ratio
		3. Authorized FICB to require additional investments in its stock by PCA's
		4. Authorized FICB's to allocate amounts applied to reserve account
		5. Authorized PCA's to require borrowers to invest in an equity reserve
		6. Permitted PCA's to allocate on a patronage basis earnings applied to surplus account
1965, Oct. 7	Rural Community Facilities Act	1. Authorized Farmers Home Administration loans for rural community sewer systems
		2. Authorized Farmers Home Administration grants for rural community water and sewer systems
1966, Aug. 2	Amendments to Federal Farm Loan Act, Farm Credit Act of 1933, 1937, and 1953, and the Agricultural Marketing Act	1. Authorized FLB's to make loans on farm land located in other districts
		2. Authorized FICB's to purchase FLB, BC, and U.S. agency obligations for investment
		3. Made it unnecessary to look to Agricultural Marketing Act for purposes, conditions, and limitations on BC loans
1966, Sept. 20	Amendment to Federal Farm Loan Act	1. Deleted interest rate limitation on FICB debentures
1966, Oct. 15	Act to Provide for Commemoration Medal	1. Authorized the Secretary of Treasury to strike FLB medals commemorating FLB fiftieth anniversary
1966, Nov. 3	Demonstration Cities and Metropolitan Development Act	1. Authorized Farmers Home Administration rural housing loans to buy newly constructed buildings
		2. Authorized Farmers Home Administration loans for rental housing for low and moderate income rural families

Corporations in the Federal Intermediate Credit Banks, which gave the Farm Credit System the organization it has today.

The Farm Credit System is made up of the Farm Credit Administration in Washington, D.C., and the banks and associations in the twelve Farm Credit Districts. Organization of the System is portrayed in Figure 23.1. Each District has three banks which are housed together in the district offices: a Federal Land Bank, a Federal Intermediate Credit Bank, and a Bank for Cooperatives. A Central Bank for Cooperatives is located in Washington, D.C.

Two of the banks in each District have local affiliated organizations. The Federal Land Bank Associations (FLBA's) are composed of farmers who borrow from the Federal Land Banks. The Federal Intermediate Credit Banks have two types of affiliates: The Production Credit Associations (PCA's), and "other financing institutions" (OFI's). The PCA's are farmer owned cooperatives. The OFI's are mostly agricultural and livestock loan companies or credit corporations which rediscount endorsed agricultural loans with the Federal Intermediate Credit Banks as provided for by law. The Production Credit Associations are the primary affiliates of the credit banks, there being relatively few OFI's.

THE FARM CREDIT ADMINISTRATION

The Farm Credit Administration consists of the Federal Farm Credit Board, the Governor, and personnel who make up the Governor's staff. The Governor and his staff comprise the "Washington Office." Note that the Farm Credit Administration does not include the Farm Credit Districts. Prior to passage of the Act of 1953, the Farm Credit Administration was generally considered to include the entire system across the nation.

The Farm Credit Administration is a supervisory organization. It is not a lending institution—it makes no loans. Loans are made by the banks and associations of the Farm Credit System which are supervised by the Farm Credit Administration.

Federal Farm Credit Board

The Farm Credit Act of 1953, which took the Farm Credit System out of the Department of Agriculture, established a 13-member, part-time, policy-making Federal Farm Credit Board. The declared policy of Congress in the 1953 Act was to encourage and

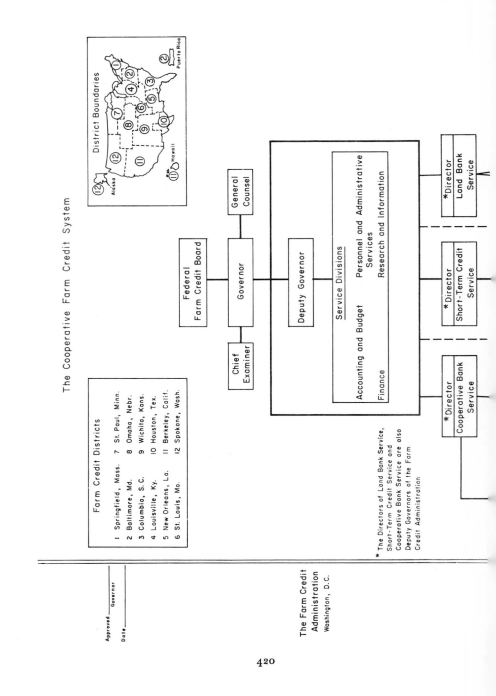

The Cooperative Farm Credit System

District Boundaries

Puerto Rico

Alaska

Hawaii

Farm Credit Districts

1 Springfield, Mass.
2 Baltimore, Md.
3 Columbia, S.C.
4 Louisville, Ky.
5 New Orleans, La.
6 St. Louis, Mo.
7 St. Paul, Minn.
8 Omaha, Nebr.
9 Wichita, Kans.
10 Houston, Tex.
11 Berkeley, Calif.
12 Spokane, Wash.

Federal Farm Credit Board

General Counsel

Governor

Chief Examiner

Deputy Governor

Service Divisions

Accounting and Budget

Finance

Personnel and Administrative Services

Research and Information

*Director Land Bank Service

*Director Short-Term Credit Service

*Director Cooperative Bank Service

* The Directors of Land Bank Service, Short-Term Credit Service and Cooperative Bank Service are also Deputy Governors of the Farm Credit Administration

The Farm Credit Administration
Washington, D.C.

Approved _____ Governor

Date _____

420

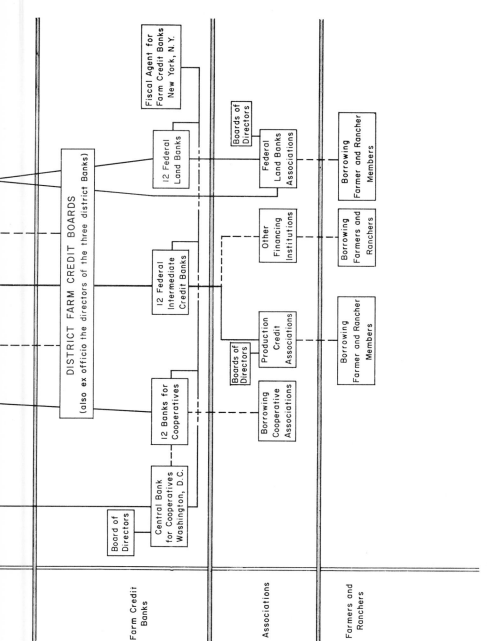

Fig. 23.1—Organization of the Farm Credit System. (Courtesy of the Farm Credit Administration.)

facilitate increased borrower participation in the management, control, and ultimate ownership of the System. Twelve members of the Board, one from each of the Farm Credit Districts, are appointed (on a staggered basis—two each year) for 6-year terms by the President of the United States, with the advice and consent of the Senate, after giving consideration to nominations made by borrowers of the District banks and associations. The three groups of borrowers (the Federal Land Banks, the Production Credit Associations and the cooperatives borrowing from the district Banks for Cooperatives) each nominate twelve men, making a total of thirty-six. To date, the selection has been made from these men, on a bipartisan basis, to provide approximately equal representation for each of the three borrowing groups. The thirteenth member of the Board is appointed by the Secretary of Agriculture as his representative.

Each member of the Board must have been a resident of the Farm Credit District from which appointed for a minimum of ten years prior to appointment. A member of the Federal Farm Credit Board is not permitted to simultaneously be a member of a District Board, or an officer or employee of the Farm Credit Administration or of any corporation operating under its supervision. Members are eligible to serve only one full term, plus any portion of an unexpired term to which they may be appointed.

The Federal Farm Credit Board holds regular 3-day meetings every other month and special meetings as needed. Each board member is paid $100.00 per day, plus expenses, for time spent in performance of official duties, up to a maximum of seventy-five days per year.

The function of the Board is to direct, supervise, and control the Farm Credit Administration as provided for by law. It works closely with District Farm Credit Boards, farm organizations, and others interested in providing effective credit service for agriculture.

The Board is required to make annual reports to Congress, including recommendations for amendments to laws pertaining to Federal Agricultural Credit. This function constitutes a standing invitation for any recommendations which would improve credit facilities for agriculture.

The Washington Office

The Federal Farm Credit Board appoints a Governor to administer affairs of the Farm Credit Administration. The Governor is in charge of the Washington Office, which is divided into three major operating divisions called "Services": the Land Bank Service, the Short-term Credit Service, and the Cooperative Bank Service.

The *Land Bank Service* has responsibility for supervision of the Federal Land Banks and Federal Land Bank Associations. It establishes appraisal standards for their use and reviews appraisals and loans to see that they conform to established standards. Its duties also include coordinating the operating and financial policies of the banks and associations, including planning for issuance and marketing of consolidated farm loan bonds.

The *Short-term Credit Service* supervises and coordinates the operations of the Federal Intermediate Credit Banks and the Production Credit Associations. It counsels with the Banks on major phases of operations, including matters of capitalization, development of credit standards, investment of funds, and disposition of earnings. The Short-term Credit Service participates in planning for the issuance and marketing of consolidated debentures of the Intermediate Credit Banks.

The *Cooperative Bank Service* supervises the thirteen Banks for Cooperatives. It participates in planning for issuance and marketing of consolidated debentures of the Banks for Cooperatives, analyzes applications for certain loans submitted by the Banks for review and counsel, and develops policies and regulations to facilitate carrying out provisions of the laws under which the Banks are chartered. The Cooperative Bank Service also advises on and participates in programs to develop and strengthen farmers' cooperatives. In addition, it handles matters relating to the Agricultural Marketing Act Revolving Fund, which is available to the Governor of the Farm Credit Administration for investment in capital stock of the Banks for Cooperatives.

The Washington Office includes a number of "Staff" executives and "Service Divisions," as shown on the organization chart, to assist with carrying out responsibilities of the Farm Credit Administration. One of these is the *Chief Examiner* who is responsible for examination of the Banks and Associations as required by law. All Banks and Production Credit Associations must be examined at least annually. Federal Land Bank Associations are examined as directed by the Governor—presently about every eighteen months. Examinations are made to determine (a) whether the institution is operating in accordance with the law and established policies and procedures, (b) whether there are operational weaknesses which should be corrected, and (c) whether there are any irregularities such as defalcations and embezzlements. The function is very similar to that performed by public accounting firms in auditing books of private corporations and by national bank examiners in auditing national banks. The Farm Credit examiners are Federal Civil Service employees responsible solely to the Washington Office. A resident examiner is located in each District and also serves as Farm Loan Registrar, who functions as part of the Personnel and Administrative Services Division.

The *Farm Loan Registrar* in each District holds in trust the collateral for the bonds and debentures sold to the investing public by the Farm Credit Banks. The Registrars, in effect, serve as representatives of the people and institutions who buy the bonds and debentures, certifying that adequate collateral is pledged as security as provided for by law.

All operating expenses of the Farm Credit Administration are paid from assessments upon the banks of the System within the limits set by annual appropriations by Congress. These expenses include the per diem salaries and expenses of the Federal Farm Credit Board, and the salaries, wages, retirement benefits, and expenses of the Governor and his staff. Since the 1953 Act directed that the Farm Credit Administration be housed in the Department of Agriculture, no rent is paid for office space which it occupies.

The Fiscal Agent

The Fiscal Agent, with an office and small staff in New York City, handles the sale of bonds and debentures sold by banks of the Farm Credit System. The sale of bonds and debentures will be covered in the following chapters in connection with the discussion of source of loan funds for each of the banks.

The Fiscal Agent is not a part of the Farm Credit Administration but is jointly employed by the Federal Land Banks, the Federal Intermediate Credit Banks, and the Banks for Cooperatives. His function is to maintain contact with leading financial institutions and to keep informed on the supply and demand forces operating in the money markets. The supply of investment funds emanates from many different sources: insurance companies, commercial banks, individuals, corporations, trust funds, endowment funds, municipalities, and the like. Demand for funds comes from sources such as federal, state, and local governments, school districts, business, and government corporations. Funds available for investment do not constitute an even flow. Neither do the demands for investment funds. The money market, including the cost of money, is in a continuing state of change. The Fiscal Agent attempts to keep abreast of these trends and to analyze the various aspects of the money market to determine the most opportune time to sell bonds and debentures, the length of term which likely will sell best, and the interest cost which can be anticipated. He keeps the Governor and the Bank presidents, or their designated committees, currently informed on such matters, counsels with them, collaborates on committee meetings, and the like. When decisions have been arrived at he arranges for and carries out the sale of the securities.

FARM CREDIT DISTRICTS

The twelve Farm Credit Districts of the Farm Credit System are each made up of the District Farm Credit Board, and the Banks and Associations, together with their boards of directors, and the borrowing farmers and their borrowing cooperative associations. The twelve Districts encompass the entire United States and Puerto Rico. They are designated by number and by the name of the headquarters city, as shown in Figure 23.1. The Banks and Associations make loans to farmers and to their cooperative associations as provided for by law and by policies established by their respective boards of directors. Policies for the three Banks in each district are formulated by the District Farm Credit Board.

District Farm Credit Boards

Each of the twelve Farm Credit Districts has a part-time Board made up of seven members. The law provides that six of the directors shall be elected, two by borrowers from the Federal Land Bank, two by borrowers from the Production Credit Associations, and two by borrowers from the Bank for Cooperatives; provided, however, that two-thirds of the capital, surplus, and reserves of these institutions is farmer owned. Until such ownership is achieved, the number of elected directors by each of the borrower groups is limited to one. The Land Bank System is completely farmer owned so two directors are elected by Land Bank borrowers in each District. PCA's likewise elect two directors since member-owned capital makes up more than two-thirds of the net worth. Borrowing cooperative associations of the Banks for Cooperatives in ten of the districts elect two directors and are qualified under the law in the remaining two districts to elect a second director, effective January

1, 1968. The law provides for the seventh director, and any of the six directors which are not eligible for election, to be appointed by the Governor of the Farm Credit Administration with the advice and consent of the Federal Board.

To be eligible for election or appointment, District Farm Credit Board members must have been residents of the District for at least two years. Officers and employees of the District Banks are ineligible for election or appointment. The term of District directors is three years and they are eligible for reelection and reappointment.

District Boards customarily hold one regular 3-day meeting each month. A national meeting is held annually of all District Board members in the twelve Districts, together with the Federal Farm Credit Board members and members of the Board of Directors of the Central Bank for Cooperatives. District Board members receive compensation on a basis somewhat comparable with that of Federal Board members, and are reimbursed for expenses incurred in connection with official duties.

District Farm Credit Offices

In each of the twelve Districts an organization somewhat similar to that of the Farm Credit Administration operates under the District Farm Credit Board. A big difference is that the District does not have an administrator with authority similar to the Governor of the Farm Credit Administration. Instead, the District office is headed by a "Presidents Committee," comprised of the three bank presidents. The member of this committee selected as chairman acts in a liaison capacity between the Governor of the Farm Credit Administration and the three banks. Another major difference is that in place of the three Services in the Washington Office, the Districts have the three Banks as shown on the organization chart. Most of the Districts have a bare minimum of auxiliary services such as those provided by the "Service Divisions" of the Washington Office.

RELATIONSHIP OF THE FARM CREDIT ADMINISTRATION TO THE FARM CREDIT DISTRICTS

The Farm Credit Act of 1953 provided that the Farm Credit Administration "shall be an independent agency in the executive branch of the Government." As an independent agency in the "executive branch of the Government," the Farm Credit Administration is responsible directly to the President as any other department of the Government. It is also subject to direction, supervision, and control of the President as is any other executive agency of the Government. The Farm Credit Administration is "independent" only in the sense that there is no intervening department or executive agency between it and the President, such as there was during the time the Farm Credit Administration was in the United States Department of Agriculture. Being "independent," the Administration is relatively free to chart its own course of action in accordance with the law.

The Banks and Associations of the Farm Credit System are federally chartered corporations. In the language of the law, they are instrumentalities of the Government vested with a public interest. Thus, Congress has appropriately provided for their supervision through an "agency in the executive branch of the Government."

The supervisory powers of the Farm Credit Administration are provided by the basic laws under which the Farm Credit Banks and Associations were organized. By assigning certain duties to the Farm Credit Administration, the Congress gave it responsibility for supervision of the various institutions to assure that they operate according to the applicable statutory provisions. The exercise of such supervision is subject to the judgment and discretion of the Governor and the Federal Board. Whether less supervision is required over District Banks and Associations when all Government capital has been retired is an administrative decision. The present law provides for no change in the legal powers of supervision with retirement of Government capital.

The supervisory authority of the Farm Credit Administration does not encompass management of the District institution. Management of any corporation is vested in its board of directors and officers, and the District Banks and Associations are no exceptions. While the dividing line between supervision and management is not always sharp, under the Farm Credit System, management is vested in the Board of Directors and officers of the various corporations while supervision is vested in the Farm Credit Administration.

GOVERNMENT CONTROL OF THE FARM CREDIT SYSTEM

The degree of control over the Farm Credit System exercised by the Government is fairly self evident from the preceding discussion. To summarize, it is exercised through the following means.

1. The Farm Credit Administration is a Government bureau which has certain authority and responsibility of a supervisory nature, authorized and specified by law. This supervision includes determination as to whether the Banks and Associations are operating in accordance with the law.
2. Policies of the FCA are determined by the Federal Farm Credit Board which is appointed by the President with Senate confirmation except for one member who is selected by the Secretary of Agriculture.
3. Personnel appointments and policies in the FCA are in accordance with regular Government procedure.
4. The FCA operating funds are appropriated by the Congress, but the actual funds come from assessments upon the thirty-seven banks of the System.

In addition to these controls, the President of the United States and the Treasury Department exercise certain control over the system, including its issuance of bonds and debentures. The law requires that as long as the Federal Intermediate Credit Banks and the Banks for Cooperatives have Government capital, they shall consult with the Treasury Department before selling debentures. Although not required by law, the Federal Land Banks follow a similar practice of consultation with the Treasury before selling bonds.

In the summer and fall of 1966, the money supply in the United States was extremely tight and interest rates moved up sharply. The President, in a memorandum dated September 9, 1966, asked the heads of departments and all Federal lending agencies to review their operations to assure that loans made were for essential and nonpostponable needs. He also asked them to examine policies and operations with a view to reducing their borrowings in the market.

The general policy, applied to all agencies that obtain funds in the market, was to limit public offerings of securities for the balance of the year to amounts not exceeding maturing issues. Any additional funds were to be obtained from the U.S. Treasury. In conformity with this policy, all three banks of the System reduced their public offerings in September. The Federal Land Banks and Banks for Cooperatives reduced their total offerings of securities below estimated needs under normal lending procedures. The Federal Intermediate Credit Banks had a normal seasonal pay-down so were not asked to reduce their total offerings, but the Treasury took about one-third, leaving two-thirds for the public market. The Farm Credit Administration developed procedures with Treasury officials whereby necessary credit for agricultural production and marketing would have a very high priority—next to national defense.

QUESTIONS AND PROBLEMS

1. Do you recognize any similarity in economic conditions in the years in which farm credit agencies were organized? Explain.
2. Outline the organization of the Farm Credit System.
3. What is the chief function of the Farm Credit Administration?
4. Compare and contrast the Federal and District Farm Credit Boards.
5. What is the function of the fiscal agent? Who employs him? Where are his headquarters located?
6. Explain the relationship of the Farm Credit Administration and the Farm Credit Districts.
7. Is an unusual amount of supervision carried on in the Farm Credit System?
8. To what extent is the Farm Credit System controlled by the Government?
9. How would you appraise the organization of the Farm Credit System?

REFERENCES

Farm Credit Administration, *Annual Reports.*
——, *The Cooperative Farm Credit System,* FCA Circ. 36-A.
——, *Laws Administered by the Farm Credit Administration,* as amended to Jan. 1, 1957, FCA Circ. 20, rev., and 1964 Supplement.
Tootell, Robert B., *The Role of the Farm Credit Administration in the Farm Credit System,* FCA Circ. 38, Jan., 1965.
von Tungeln, George R., *Cooperative Farm Credit, Description and Analysis, Georgia, North Carolina, and South Carolina,* S.C. Agr. Exp. Sta. Bul. 505, June, 1963.

Chapter 24

FEDERAL LAND BANK SYSTEM

THE Federal Land Bank System comprises that part of the Farm Credit System through which farmers obtain real estate mortgage loans. The System, which is supervised by the Farm Credit Administration, is made up of the twelve Federal Land Banks, and about 700 Federal Land Bank Associations in the twelve Farm Credit Districts. Through the System, farmers and ranchers throughout the nation can pool their credit needs, obtain funds by sale of bonds in the investment centers, and make loans at cost which are adapted especially to their needs. The System provides the rancher 100 miles from a railroad or a farmer in any part of the United States or Puerto Rico about the same bargaining power in borrowing funds which is available to major businesses such as General Motors, American Telephone and Telegraph, or the Union Pacific Railroad. Features of Federal Land Bank loans are their uniform appraisals, uniform interest rates throughout each Farm Credit District, and their long-term amortization plan of repayment. Interest rates vary somewhat among Districts, depending upon the cost of operating the Land Bank and Associations in the District.

FEDERAL LAND BANKS

Each Federal Land Bank is a corporation chartered as a permanent institution under the Federal Farm Loan Act of 1916. All twelve Land Banks were chartered in 1917, and immediately began operations. The charter of the Wichita Bank, the first issued, is shown in Figure 24.1.

Policies of the Federal Land Banks are determined by the respective District Farm Credit Boards. The Board is authorized,

Fig. 24.1—A sample Federal Land Bank charter. (Courtesy of the Farm Credit Administration.)

subject to provisions of law under which the Bank is chartered and supervision of the Farm Credit Administration, to exercise all such powers as are necessary to carry on business of the Land Bank.

Each District Farm Credit Board employs a president, vice-president (s), treasurer, and secretary, and other employees to manage and operate the Federal Land Bank in the District. The primary function and responsibility of the Land Bank is the making of farm mortgage loans through the local Federal Land Bank Associations and the servicing of such loans. Land Bank personnel analyze all loan applications submitted by the Associations. Most of the servicing of loans is carried on by the Associations. The procedure followed in making and servicing of loans is discussed later in this chapter.

Since each Federal Land Bank loan is made direct from the Bank to the borrower, the Bank itself or through the Association maintains a financial record for each individual loan, together with various summary records for use of the officers and Board, and as prescribed by the Farm Credit Administration in Washington, D.C. Through the Treasurer's Department, the Bank keeps a running record of funds available for loans. The Bank must keep tab on its position and probable requirements for loan funds as a basis for determining the extent of its participation in the periodic sale of consolidated bonds by the twelve Land Banks. This phase of operations is discussed later in the chapter in the section on bonds.

The Federal Land Bank in each District has certain responsibilities for supervising the FLBA's in the District. The Banks, by mutual agreement with the Associations, have delegated many functions involved in making and servicing loans to the Associations. Thus, the Associations have authority to handle many transactions. Some of these are final and binding upon the Bank, such as the "firm loan commitment" authority delegated to some Associations. Delegation of authority does not transfer responsibility, however. Therefore, the Banks have a responsibility to supervise the Associations as necessary to make certain that delegated authority is properly exercised. In addition, the Farm Credit Administration has authorized the Land Banks to perform a number of its powers and duties in supervision of the Associations.

FEDERAL LAND BANK ASSOCIATIONS

Each Federal Land Bank Association is a corporation, organized by borrowers from a Federal Land Bank, which operates in a specified area under a Federal charter authorized by the Farm Loan Act of 1916. Charters of the early associations were granted by the Federal Farm Loan Board. The charter of the first Association, the Pawnee County National Farm Loan Association, Larned, Kansas, is portrayed in Figure 24.2. The names of all National Farm Loan Associations were changed to Federal Land Bank Associations effective January 1, 1960.

The entire country has long since been covered by Associations. In fact, too many Associations were chartered to facilitate efficient businesslike operation. The number reached a peak of 5,034 as of January 1, 1936, and consolidation has been going on since that time. Today, Associations are chartered by the Farm Credit Administration upon the recommendation of the Federal Land Bank in the District where the Association is located. Association territories ordinarily do not overlap.

As is the case with all corporations, each FLBA is controlled by a Board of Directors. The Board may have not less than five nor more than seven members, who are elected by members of the Association for 3-year terms. The Board employs a manager who serves as the executive officer of the Association. The manager cannot be a member of the Board, and in nearly all cases is a full-time employee.

The volume of loans made by the Land Bank in an area depends in large degree upon the Association serving the area. The Association is the unit of the system which originates the business and maintains firsthand contact with the public.

OWNERSHIP OF THE SYSTEM

The Federal Land Banks have been completely owned by the FLBA's since 1947, and the FLBA's have always been entirely owned by borrowing farmers. When the System was first organized in 1917 practically all the capital of the Land Banks was provided by the Federal Government. The initial capital of each Land Bank was $750,000, making an aggregate of $9,000,000. Of this amount, the Federal Government provided $8,892,130 and the investing public provided $107,870.[1] Nearly all the Government capital was

---

[1] Subscription to capital stock of the twelve Federal Land Banks was open to the public for only thirty days. This was the only time in history that the public was allowed to subscribe for the stock. The short period, plus the fact the investor was put on notice that dividends probably would not be paid the first year at least, that they would never exceed 6 per cent, and that the stock would be redeemed at par, helps account for the small public subscription.

CHARTER

OF

NATIONAL FARM LOAN ASSOCIATION
No. _1 — 9_

TREASURY DEPARTMENT
OFFICE OF THE FEDERAL FARM LOAN BOARD

Washington, D. C., *March 27th*, 1917

Whereas, by satisfactory evidence presented to the Federal Farm Loan Board, it has been made to appear that, The *Pawnee County* National Farm Loan Association of *Larned*, County of *Pawnee* and State of *Kansas*, and in the *Ninth* Federal Land Bank District, has complied with all of the provisions of "The Federal Farm Loan Act," required to be complied with before a national farm loan association shall be granted a charter; and

Whereas, The Federal Land Bank of *Wichita*, situated in the city of *Wichita*, County of *Sedgwick*, and State of *Kansas*, and for the *Ninth* Federal Land Bank District, has recommended that said National Farm Loan Association be granted a charter;

Now, therefore, the Federal Farm Loan Board does hereby grant a Charter to the *Pawnee County* National Farm Loan Association of *Larned*, County of *Pawnee*, and State of *Kansas*, and said association is hereby authorized and empowered to receive from the Federal Land Bank of *Wichita*, sums to be loaned to its members, and to do all other things provided for, and in accordance with the provisions of the Act of Congress approved July 17, 1916, known as "The Federal Farm Loan Act," and to do all other things implied or incidental thereto, within the following-described territory :— *Pawnee County Kansas*

In witness whereof, the Federal Farm Loan Board has caused this charter to be signed by its executive officer, the Farm Loan Commissioner, attested by its Secretary, and has caused its seal to be hereunto affixed this *27th* day of *March*, 1917

FEDERAL FARM LOAN BOARD,

By *Geo. W. Norris*
Farm Loan Commissioner.

Attest:
W. W. Flannagan
Secretary.

Fig. 24.2—A sample Federal Land Bank Association charter. (Courtesy of the Farm Credit Administration.)

repaid during the 1920's, but with the Great Depression of the 1930's, the Government again put money into the System. This subscription to capital stock in 1932 totaled $125,000,000. Additional subscriptions to paid-in surplus of the Banks in the following years raised the Government's investment to a peak of $313,942,505 as of June 30, 1939. The last of this Government capital in the System was repaid in 1947.

The present capital of the Land Banks and of the Associations is made up of member-owned stock and reserves and surplus. Each borrower buys stock in the FLBA equal to 5 per cent of the amount of his loan. The FLBA, in turn, buys an equal amount of stock in the Land Bank of the District. Thus, the FLBA's are owned by the borrowing farmers, and the Federal Land Banks are owned by the Associations. Both the Associations and the Land Banks have accumulated substantial reserves and surplus. Summary data for the Associations and Banks of the System are given in Table 24.1.

TABLE 24.1

MEMBER-OWNED STOCK AND RESERVES AND SURPLUS OF THE FEDERAL LAND BANKS AND THE FEDERAL LAND BANK ASSOCIATIONS AS OF JUNE 30, 1966*

	Land Banks	FLBA's
	(millions)	(millions)
Member-owned Stock	$272.9 †	$273.1 †
Reserves and Surplus	354.2	129.3
Total	$627.1	$402.4

* Courtesy of the Farm Credit Admin.
† The slight difference in these figures is due to the fact that loans of the System were increasing at the time and there is a slight lag between the time the farmer buys stock in the Association and the Association buys stock in the Land Bank.

The relationship of reserves and surplus to member-owned stock is worth noting, especially since some critics have implied at times that farmer-owned stock in the System may become worthless because it is held as collateral security for loans. The FLBA's have, as a group, accumulated reserves and surplus equal to 47 per cent of the value of member-owned stock, while the reserves and surplus of the twelve Land Banks exceed the value of the stock by 30 per cent. The combined reserves and surplus of the Banks and Associations are about 75 per cent greater than the value of the member-owned stock. In other words, the Banks and Associations together have about $8.85 of reserves and surplus for every $5.00 share of stock owned by borrowing farmers.

The Banks as well as the Associations in each District have adopted long-range financial plans to provide for the accumulation and maintenance of a net worth position adequate to reasonably assure continued financial solvency and the continuity of credit services to farmers, but avoiding the accumulation of net worth in excess of these needs. These plans are designed to accumulate net worth which will provide cost-free funds to protect the Banks' earning position when money costs are abnormally high, to carry worthy borrowers in times of distress, and to absorb losses in excess of valuation reserves. Reserves accumulated vary greatly among Districts, however (see Table 24.2).

TABLE 24.2

EARNED NET WORTH (RESERVES AND SURPLUS) OF THE ASSOCIATIONS AND
THE LAND BANKS PER SHARE OF CAPITAL STOCK OUTSTANDING
JUNE 30, 1966.*

	FLBA's (dollars)	Land Bank (dollars)	Total (dollars)
Springfield	$2.21	$8.09	$10.30
Baltimore	1.48	6.12	7.60
Columbia	1.90	3.69	5.59
Louisville	1.46	5.60	7.06
New Orleans	3.39	11.04	14.43
St. Louis	2.26	6.19	8.45
St. Paul	1.82	7.92	9.74
Omaha	2.80	5.41	8.21
Wichita	1.66	6.61	8.27
Houston	6.05	9.44	15.49
Berkeley	2.06	5.21	7.27
Spokane	1.43	4.96	6.39
Total	2.37	6.49	8.86

* Source: Farm Credit Admin., Washington, D.C.

While the earned net worth for the System is nearly double the stock outstanding, earned net worth per share in the Columbia and Spokane Districts is not much more than the value of the stock outstanding. Within the Districts variation also exists. Some Associations have accumulated a relatively small amount of reserves and surplus to protect member-owned stock from impairment or to help the Association withstand adverse conditions. Often this situation is the result of a too liberal dividend policy, but other factors, such as a small Association having a small volume of loans and relatively high operating expenses, also make accumulation of earned net worth difficult.

MAKING AND SERVICING OF LOANS

The Federal Land Bank Association is the local contact point or office through which farmers obtain Land Bank loans. The Association receives the application, makes an investigation as to the character and financial condition of the applicant and adequacy of the security, and prepares a written inspection report. An appraisal of the property is also required.

The appraisal is made by a Land Bank Appraiser or by an Association employee authorized to make appraisals by a Federal Land Bank in accordance with standards prescribed by the Farm Credit Administration. A staff of federally appointed Farm Credit Appraisers is maintained in each district to review the appraisals and the quality of the loans made to assure compliance with adopted appraisal and lending standards.

Federal Land Bank appraisals are based upon the long-term normal value of the farm. Normal earning power of the farm is a principal factor in the appraisal. The 1955 Act permits recognition also of earnings from dependable sources outside the farm. Normal earning power is based upon a set of normal prices of farm products and normal farm operating costs established by the Farm Credit Administration. These prices and costs are adjusted from time to time to bring them into line with conditions anticipated to prevail during the life of the loan. The procedure followed in making the appraisal was outlined in general terms in Chapter 15.

On the basis of their inspection and the appraisal report, the Association determines whether they wish to approve the loan. Unanimous approval by the Association Loan Committee, composed of three members of the Board of Directors or two Directors and the Association manager, is required for consideration of the application. Association approval signifies their willingness to pledge resources of the Association as collateral security supplementing a first mortgage on the farm. An agreement between eleven of the Land Banks and their Associations provides that in the event a loan breaks down, any loss will be shared equally by the Bank and the Association. The Farm Credit Administration permits each District to develop its own policy if it does not conflict with the law, so in one District, provisions have been made whereby the Associations assume full responsibility for losses.

Consideration of the application by the Federal Land Bank is based primarily upon the appraisal report, supplemented by the Association investigator's report. The law limits the size of loan to 65 per cent of the normal value of the farm as specified in the appraisal report, plus the amount of stock required. The total amount of the loan thus may not exceed 68.42 per cent of the normal agricultural value. If major weakness is evident, the loan commitment may be limited to less than the maximum. The Loan Committee of the Land Bank has final responsibility for action taken on the application. It cannot, however, approve a loan in excess of that recommended by the Association.

The making or closing of Land Bank loans largely follows conventional lines except that the procedure is split between the Bank and the Association. Land Bank attorneys consider the abstract of title to the property and determine whether the applicant has proper title to the farm. In parts of the country where title insurance is used in place of abstracts, the Bank's legal staff examines any exceptions specified in the preliminary report of the title insurance company to determine adequacy of the title. Usually the note and mortgage are drafted in the Bank, and a "remittance statement" is prepared setting forth requirements to be met before the loan proceeds are released, and the way in which the money is to be paid out. If part of the funds are to be used for buildings or other improvements, that part of the funds may be held in trust until all the costs are known. At this point in the closing process, the Association takes over and completes the remaining steps. This involves carrying out the requirements specified in the remittance statement, having the applicants sign the note and mortgage, and recording the mortgage in the county recorder's office.

Federal Land Bank loans can be made for any constructive purpose. Practically the only limitation is that the applicant must be engaged in farming or derive the principal part of his income from farming. An applicant is considered to be engaged in farming if as operator or landlord he personally or through an agent actively participates to a substantial degree in management or operation of the farm. Most landlords and many part-time farmers, as well as family-type corporations engaged in farming qualify for Land Bank loans.

Most Land Bank loans are made for terms ranging from twenty to thirty-five years. Legislation permits making loans for not less than five nor more than forty years. So far the Land Banks generally have not taken advantage of the maximum term. Most loans are amortized, either on the even or decreasing payment plan basis, to fully liquidate the loan during the term for which it is written. Under the 1959 Farm Credit Act the banks now have authority to make loans with no amortization or with partial amortization.

Servicing of Land Bank loans is carried out by the Bank and the Association along lines similar to those discussed in Chapter 15. Checking on payment of real estate taxes and keeping insurance on buildings in force is done by the Association. Services involving partial releases and the like are handled jointly by the Bank and the Association. Delinquency problems are also a joint responsibility, though the Association does most of the "leg work" in normal times. Generally, the Bank is directly involved only in the more difficult cases.

The Land Banks have developed a number of policies to help borrowers get by in hard times. Reserves may be built by depositing money in the "future payment fund" to be held until needed to make payments on the loan. Interest is paid by the Bank on money in the future payment fund. If necessary, the Bank will also defer payments on loans, or extend the term of loan to help the borrower with a good credit rating. As is generally true of all reputable lenders, every effort is made to avoid foreclosure proceedings against worthy borrowers who are doing their honest best and have a reasonable prospect of working out of the difficulty. Generally, the large majority of loan delinquency occurs as a result of drouth, low prices, or other misfortunes over which the borrower has no control. Under such circumstances the Land Bank considers it is as well off with the present borrower on the farm, even though loan payments may not exceed the crop share rental (which may be nil in the case of drouth) as it would be by foreclosing and renting the farm to the borrower or another farmer. Foreclosure is only the last resort.

INTEREST RATES AND DIVIDENDS

Interest rates paid by Land Bank borrowers vary over time with general interest rates and the rate the Banks have to pay on their bonds. As of January 1, 1967, all Banks had a contract rate—the rate specified in the note and mortgage—of 6 per cent and were billing at that rate on new loans. The contract rate on Land Bank loans has ranged between 4 and 6 per cent, the legal maximum. Between 1917 and 1935, the contract rate fluctuated between 5 and 6 per cent. During 1935, the Federal Land Bank rate on new loans was uniformly reduced over the country from 5 to $4\frac{1}{2}$, to $4\frac{1}{4}$, to 4. The uniform contract rate of 4 per cent for all Banks was broken when the Columbia Bank went to $4\frac{1}{2}$ per cent in 1948 and to 5 per cent in 1951. Some other Banks raised their rates after 1948 but the majority held to the 4 per cent contract rate until the mid-1950's.

Congress provided reductions in interest rates from 1933 to 1944 to Federal Land Bank borrowers, which brought the net rate below the contract rate specified on the note and mortgage. These reductions resulted in a net $4\frac{1}{2}$ per cent rate between July 11, 1933, and June 30, 1935, to all Federal Land Bank borrowers with loans made through associations. Congress provided, from June 30, 1935, to July 1, 1944, that the net rate on these loans be reduced to $3\frac{1}{2}$ per cent. Congress further provided that the Treasury Department make up the difference between the net rate paid by the borrower and the contract rate specified on the original loan. This difference was paid by the Treasury Department directly to the Federal Land Banks. Thus Federal Land Bank borrowers who paid an average of $5\frac{1}{4}$ per cent interest during the 1917–33 period paid only $3\frac{1}{2}$ per cent between 1935 and 1944, and the Government made up the difference between $3\frac{1}{2}$ and $5\frac{1}{4}$ per cent or whatever the contract rate was on the existing Federal Land Bank mortgage. From 1933 through 1944 the Government subsidy for interest rate reduction amounted to $277 million. When the Government discontinued the interest rate subsidy on July 1, 1944, the Federal Land Banks reduced the contract rate on all mortgages made through Associations to 4 per cent. The Banks were able to do this because they refinanced their outstanding bonds at lower interest rates.

When the total income of a Land Bank is higher than necessary to cover costs and to provide adequate reserves and surplus, dividends are paid to the borrower-members on the basis of stock ownership. The Land Bank pays dividends to the FLBA's and the FLBA, in turn, pays dividends to the farmer-members. Usually, not all the dividends paid by the Land Bank are paid to the farmer. Through arrangements between the Banks and the Associations, each Association receives substantial compensation for its part in making and servicing loans. In most Districts, however, this is inadequate to pay all operating expenses of the Association and to build adequate legal reserves and net worth. Therefore, most Associations use part of their dividend income for these purposes. During the year ended June 30, 1966, ten Federal Land Banks paid dividends totaling $18.4 million, and the Associations paid dividends to farmer-members totaling $12.7 million.

LAND BANK BONDS

The primary source of Federal Land Bank loan funds is from sale of consolidated Federal Farm Loan bonds to the investing public. These bonds are sold in denominations ranging from $1,000 to $100,000. Consolidated Federal Farm Loan bonds are the joint and several obligations of the twelve Land Banks. They are not guaranteed by the United States Government either as to principal or interest, and this fact is emphasized in literature advertising Land Bank bonds. However, the philosophy prevails among the investing public that the Government would act to avoid any default on the Banks' bond obligations since the System was created by the Government, and since the Government came to its rescue in the Great Depression of the 1930's.

The size of each bond issue sold is determined by the twelve banks individually estimating how much money they will need to refund maturing bonds and to provide for new loans until the next issue of bonds is sold. Banks generally obtain some funds between bond issues by borrowing from commercial banks. They sometimes borrow also from other Land Banks, from the Federal Intermediate Credit Banks, and from the Banks for Cooperatives when temporarily surplus funds are available from those sources.

Consolidated Federal farm loan bonds outstanding January 1, 1967, are given in Table 24.3. Bonds outstanding at that time totaled $4.4 billion compared with $5.0 billion of loans outstanding, indicating the importance of bonds in providing loan funds for the System. Note the term of the bonds and the interest rate. In financing long-term loans with short-term bonds, the Land Banks run the risk of collecting insufficient interest to cover interest on the bonds and loan service costs.

While the Federal Land Banks experienced difficulty in issuing bonds during the period 1917–20 and during the Great Depression of the 1930's, the bonds have enjoyed a good market for a number of years. Competition from Federal, state, and local governments, and business has generally been a factor in determining the term of some issues and, of course, in the interest rate paid, but the Land Banks have been able to sell the bonds needed to fund their loans. A number of factors help create the favorable market which prevails. One of the most important is the uniform appraisal standards used as a basis for making Federal Land Bank loans. Another factor is the substantial amount of surplus and reserves

TABLE 24.3

CONSOLIDATED FEDERAL FARM LOAN BONDS OUTSTANDING JANUARY 1, 1967, AND RELATED DATA*

Issued	Terms†	Maturity	Face Rate	Amount Outstanding (Net)
			(per cent)	*(millions)*
4/20/65	1 5/6 years	2/20/67	4 1/4	$126.0
6/20/66	8 months	2/20/67	5.60	125.0
5/1/62	5 years	5/22/67	4	180.0
9/20/66	10 months	7/20/67	6.05	302.3
12/20/65	1 2/3 years	8/21/67	4 3/4	179.0
7/20/66	1 1/4 years	10/23/67	5 3/4	150.0
10/22/63	4 years	10/23/67	4 1/8	174.0
12/20/66	1 year	12/20/67	5 7/8	329.0
2/21/66	1 11/12 years	1/22/68	5 1/8	130.0
4/1/59	9 years	3/20/68	4 1/4	86.0
8/20/64	3 1/2 years	3/20/68	4 1/4	25.0
5/2/66	2 years	5/20/68	5 1/4	242.0
5/1/63	5 years	6/20/68	4	186.0
8/20/64	4 years	8/20/68	4 1/4	160.0
2/2/59	10 years	3/20/69	4 3/8	100.0
7/15/57	12 years	7/15/69	4 5/8	60.0
2/23/65	4 1/3 years	7/15/69	4 1/4	129.5
10/20/64	5 years	10/20/69	4 1/4	209.0
2/1/60	10 years	2/20/70	5 1/8	82.0
2/14/58	12 years	4/1/70	3 1/2	83.0
1/5/60	10 1/2 years	7/20/70	5 1/8	85.0
10/1/57	10–13 years	10/1/67–70	4 1/2	75.0
5/1/56	15 years	5/1/71	3 1/2	60.0
2/15/57	10–15 years	2/15/67–72	4 1/8	72.0
9/14/56	16 years	9/15/72	3 7/8	109.3
2/20/62	12 years	2/20/74	4 1/2	155.0
4/20/65	10 years	4/21/75	4 3/8	200.0
2/21/66	10 years	2/24/76	5	123.0
7/20/66	10 years	7/20/76	5 3/8	150.0
2/20/63	10–15 years	2/20/73–78	4 1/8	148.0
5/2/66	12 years	4/20/78	5 1/8	150.0
	Total			$4,385.1

* Source: Farm Credit Admin.
† Approximate.

which has been accumulated in the Land Bank System. Supervision provided by the Farm Credit Administration and its review of Land Bank appraisals also are contributing factors.

QUESTIONS AND PROBLEMS

1. Outline the organization of the Federal Land Bank system.
2. Who determines the policies of the Federal Land Bank? The FLBA?

3. What is the function of the Federal Land Bank? The FLBA?
4. Explain the procedure by which a farmer obtains an FLB loan.
5. Where do Federal Land Banks obtain loan funds?
6. Who owns the Federal Land Banks? The FLBA's?
7. In contrast to other lenders, each FLB and FLBA has an assigned territory. Why do you think the system has been set up on this basis? Would it be better if territories were not assigned?
8. Whereas other lenders vary the interest rate according to size of loan and risk involved, the Land Bank interest rate is the same for all farmers within the district. Is this a good thing? Is it economically defensible?
9. Dividends are paid according to stock ownership. Is this an equitable basis for paying dividends? Does it conform with cooperative principles?
10. What is the difference between a consolidated and an individual bond issue? What is the relationship between bond rates and interest rates paid by borrowers?
11. What is your opinion regarding the capital stock requirements of a system like the Federal Land Banks?
12. Obtain quotations on prices of Federal Land Bank bonds from the financial page of a newspaper or from a financial periodical. How do current prices and interest rates compare with those given in this Chapter?

REFERENCES

Farm Credit Administration, *The Cooperative Farm Credit System*, FCA Circ. 36, rev. Dec., 1965.
———, *1917–57—Years of Progress With the Cooperative Land Bank System*, FCA Circ. E-43, Jan., 1957.
———, *Annual Reports*.
———, *Laws Administered by the Farm Credit Administration*, as amended to Jan. 1, 1957, FCA Circ. 20, rev., and 1964 Supplement.
———, *Federal Land Bank System . . . How It Operates*, FCA Circ. 35, rev. 1965.

Chapter 25

PRODUCTION CREDIT SYSTEM

THE production credit system is made up of about 465 Production Credit Associations (PCA's) and 12 Federal Intermediate Credit Banks (FICB's). The PCA's make both short- and intermediate-term loans to farmers and obtain the funds for making such loans by borrowing from or rediscounting farmers' notes with the FICB's. These banks also discount loans made to farmers by a number of "other financing institutions" (OFI's) such as commercial banks, livestock loan companies, and agricultural credit corporations. The Federal Intermediate Credit Banks obtain loan funds by selling debenture bonds to the investing public. Credit services are provided in the United States and Puerto Rico.

FEDERAL INTERMEDIATE CREDIT BANKS

The twelve Federal Intermediate Credit Banks were organized and chartered in 1923, each as a permanent institution, under the Federal Farm Loan Act of 1916, as amended.

The District Farm Credit Board establishes the policy of the Federal Intermediate Credit Bank in the District the same as they do for the Federal Land Banks. Likewise, they employ a president, vice-president (s), treasurer, and secretary, and other employees as necessary to manage and operate the Credit Bank. The Credit Banks do not loan directly to farmers, and do not engage in a

444

general banking business. They are "wholesalers" of credit and, as such, are authorized to discount loans for, and make loans to, lending institutions which finance credit needs of farmers. The Production Credit Associations are the primary local outlets for Federal Intermediate Credit Bank funds, though "other financing institutions" discount a substantial amount of loans with the Credit Banks. The Federal Intermediate Credit Banks are also authorized to loan to each other, to any Federal Land Bank, or to any Bank for Cooperatives.

The Farm Credit Act of 1956 merged the Production Credit Corporation with the Federal Intermediate Credit Bank in each of the twelve Districts. The Production Credit Corporations were wholly owned by the Government and one was established in each District in 1933 to organize and supervise the Production Credit Associations. In merging the two, the 1956 Act provided that the new Federal Intermediate Credit Banks assume the function of supervising and assisting the Production Credit Associations "in a manner which will enable them to make sound credit available to farmers and ranchers." This function involves, among other things, working with the Associations on loan standards and on servicing of problem cases. The Credit Banks also perform certain delegated supervisory functions for the Farm Credit Administration.

PRODUCTION CREDIT ASSOCIATIONS

Each Production Credit Association is an individual corporation chartered under the Farm Credit Act of 1933 by the Governor of the Farm Credit Administration. As in the Federal Land Bank Associations, members of a PCA elect a part-time board of directors from among their own members. This board establishes policies of the Association and employs a secretary-treasurer to conduct the affairs of the Association. The secretary-treasurer cannot be a member of the board and usually is a full-time employee.

Most PCA's serve fairly large areas including several counties and one or more trade centers. Some Associations cover a whole state. Generally, territories do not overlap, although in some instances Associations financing specialized or large operations duplicate other Association territories. As one means of making their services more readily accessible, many Associations have established field or branch offices. Most of these are operated on a full-time basis, but some may be serviced only one or two days each week. In some cases the field and branch offices are housed with the FLBA, in which case the FLBA manager may serve as the PCA field representative.

OTHER FINANCING INSTITUTIONS

The law under which the Federal Intermediate Credit Banks operate authorizes them to discount or purchase agricultural loans from commercial banks, trust companies, savings institutions, credit unions, and any association of agricultural producers engaged in making loans to farmers and ranchers. These lenders are commonly referred to as "other financing institutions," OFI's, and sometimes as "private financing institutions," PFI's. The term, OFI, is considered somewhat more descriptive since most of the PCA's are now also privately capitalized.

The OFI's constitute one feature which distinguishes the Production Credit System from the Land Bank System and a little history will help explain how this difference developed. When the Federal Intermediate Credit Banks were organized in 1923 the belief prevailed that there were sufficient local credit facilities available to serve agriculture if they only had a source of wholesale funds where they could discount their loans. As a result, the Federal Intermediate Credit Banks were established as "bankers-banks," to serve as sources of loan funds for the existing agricultural lending agencies and new ones which might be organized. Subsequent experience was largely disappointing in this regard, however. Only a limited number of farmers were reached with Federal Intermediate Credit Bank funds because of lack of local financing institutions designed to make sound credit available at the farm level. Loans discounted were few in number and unusually large in amount; for the most part they were cattle and sheep loans made in the western states. Funds from the Credit Banks generally did not reach the average and smaller farmer.

Many of the lenders who discounted loans with the Federal Intermediate Credit Banks became insolvent and failed as the Great Depression of the 1930's settled on the country, adding impetus to the need for new local credit outlets; but some of them survived and some new lenders qualified to discount loans with the Credit Banks. As of January 1, 1967, there were 109 OFI's distributed among the twelve Farm Credit Districts as follows:

Federal Intermediate Credit Bank	Number of OFI's	Federal Intermediate Credit Bank	Number of OFI's
Springfield	6	St. Paul	22
Baltimore	6	Omaha	27
Columbia	3	Wichita	14
Louisville	5	Houston	10
New Orleans	3	Berkeley	7
St. Louis	4	Spokane	2

The number of OFI's doing business with the Credit Banks fluctuates some from month to month and year to year since those which qualify can start and stop discounting loans at will.

A financing institution wanting to discount loans with, or borrow from, a Federal Intermediate Credit Bank files an application with the Bank and furnishes complete information about its financial condition and business. The institution may be required to pledge with the Credit Bank a certain amount of capital, usually in the form of United States Government bonds, as general collateral for its discounted loans or other obligations. The majority of the OFI's discounting loans with the Credit Banks make agricultural loans exclusively, though the law does not make such a specific requirement. However, only loans made "for any agricultural purpose" are eligible for discount.

Legislation permitting lenders to discount loans with the Federal Intermediate Credit Banks does not liberalize their lending authority. OFI's continue to be governed by the laws of the jurisdiction under which they are chartered.

OWNERSHIP OF THE PRODUCTION CREDIT SYSTEM

The Production Credit System is a mixed-ownership system. Part of the capital is owned by the Federal Government and part by farmers who own stock in the System. The Government capital is gradually being retired and eventually the System will be entirely farmer owned.

Most of the capital in the Federal Intermediate Credit Banks, part of the Production Credit System, belongs to the Government. Being organized in 1923 as wholly owned Government corporations, no provision was made for retirement of the Government capital until passage of the Farm Credit Act of 1956. This Act provided a long-range plan for farmer ownership of the Bank through gradual acquisition of Credit Bank stock by the Production Credit Associations.

The 1956 Act provided for the Credit Banks to issue two classes of stock. Class A stock is issued to and held by the Governor of the Farm Credit Administration, on behalf of the United States Government, and has prior claim on assets of the Banks in the event of liquidation or dissolution. Class B stock is issued to and held only by the PCA's.

The Farm Credit Act of 1956 became effective January 1, 1957, and on that date the twelve Federal Intermediate Credit Banks had a combined net worth of $150.5 million, consisting of:

Capital stock owned by the United States.........$ 87,405,000
Surplus.. 63,066,704
　　　Total................................. $150,471,704

The $87.4 million of capital stock was composed of the original Government subscription of $60 million to capitalize the twelve Credit Banks, and $27.4 million of Government capital remaining in the Production Credit Corporations when they were merged with the Credit Banks. Of the $63.1 million surplus, $50.3 million had been accumulated by the Credit Banks during the period 1923–56 and the remaining $12.8 million had been accumulated by the Production Credit Corporations and turned over to the Credit Banks as part of the merger.

The law provided for the Credit Banks to issue Class A stock to the Governor for only the $87,405,000 of Government capital. In other words, the PCA's will be required to retire this amount of Government funds, together with any additional capital that may be obtained from the Revolving Fund. The $63.1 million of surplus was given to the System.[1]

The plan for retirement of the $87.4 million of Government capital set forth in the 1956 Act provided for the PCA's to purchase

---

[1] No provision was made for retirement of the $63 million of surplus. Thus, while the Credit Banks were wholly owned by the Government during the period 1923–56, and Production Credit Corporations during the period 1933–56, the entire earnings on the Government capital and earnings of the Credit Banks—over and above the franchise tax amounting to 25 per cent of net earnings—were left in the Production Credit System for the continuing benefit of borrowing farmers. Prior to passage of the 1956 Act, some persons felt the Production Credit System had not received the same "break" as the Land Bank System. Their view was that the Land Banks had enjoyed free use of Government capital—accumulated earnings on Government capital used by the Land Banks belonged to the Banks—while in the Credit Banks and Production Credit Corporations, accumulated earnings belonged to the Government. However, provisions of the 1956 Act really gave the Production Credit System the superior "break." It had free use of Government capital for a longer time and was awarded the accumulated earnings for the entire period.

Class B stock in the Banks equal to 15 per cent of the Government-owned Class A stock in all the Banks, or a total of $13.1 million. This purchase, in effect, constituted a down payment by the PCA's on the Credit Banks. The remaining Class A stock may be retired with Class B stock acquired by the PCA's in payment of patronage refunds made by the Credit Banks out of their earnings. However, the law does not provide for retirement of Class A stock as Class B stock is issued on a dollar-for-dollar basis, and experience so far indicates it may be many years before the Government capital is completely retired.

Patronage refunds to the OFI's are paid in participation certificates. No dividends are to be paid on Class A stock.

The Production Credit Associations, the other part of the Production Credit System, are almost entirely farmer owned. On January 1, 1967, $307.2 million or about 99.8 per cent of the $307.8 million total capital stock of the Associations was owned by members. Of the 465 Associations in the country, 453 were fully member owned. In addition, the Associations had accumulated earnings of $224 million.

Production Credit Associations have three types of capital stock: Classes A, B, and C. Class A stock is held by the Governor on behalf of the Federal Government, or owned by investors who usually are farmers or ranchers. Class B stock is owned by borrowing farmers and ranchers. Class C stock normally is held by the Governor, but also may be held by investors.

Class B stock is acquired by members in connection with their loans. Borrowers are required by law to own Class B stock equal to 5 per cent of their loan, the same as in the FLBA's. If a borrower owns Class A stock it may be converted to Class B stock to meet this requirement. Any Class B stock owned by a farmer who has not borrowed from the Association for a period of two years automatically becomes Class A stock. Only Class B stock has voting rights on most business matters. Dividends may be paid on both Class A and B stock without preference, or on Class A stock alone, as determined by the Association's Board of Directors. Dividends may also be paid on Class C stock.

PRODUCTION CREDIT SYSTEM LOANS

Loans obtained through the Production Credit System are made by the PCA. The PCA then uses the farmers' notes and mortgages as collateral to obtain a similar amount of credit from the Federal Intermediate Credit Bank of the District. PCA's with adequate capital of their own may make some loans and carry them in their own portfolio as a means of investing their own funds.

This arrangement in making loans constitutes a major difference compared with the Land Bank System. Whereas Land Bank loans run direct from the Bank to the borrower—with the FLBA endorsing the loan and sharing any risk involved—Production Credit System loans are made outright by the PCA, with the PCA carrying all the primary risk involved on a loan.

Production Credit Association loans may be made for any agricultural purpose, including financing of operating expense, capital requirements connected with crop and livestock production, living expenses, and family needs. Except for loans made on the basis of an open note, most are secured by a first mortgage on chattel property. However, real estate mortgages are also taken as supplementary or full security for PCA loans. During the year ending June 30, 1962, the latest year for which data are available, the percentage of their loans thus secured ranged from 2.7 per cent in the Omaha District to 58.3 per cent in the Columbia District.

To obtain a loan, the applicant contacts the PCA serving his territory. In making application for a loan, special consideration is given to credit needs and to a plan for repaying the loan. A majority of PCA loans are made on the budget basis whereby the applicant and the PCA together work out a financial plan for the farm, covering the entire season. PCA's encourage that such budget plans be made prior to the rush of farm work, so money will be available as needed without delaying other important activities.

Most Associations give immediate service to old members who have a good credit rating. The general practice is for a PCA representative to visit the applicant's farm and make an inspection of the business and security. When a member has handled his previous credit in a satisfactory manner, and his application is consistent with earlier borrowings, the farm visit may be deferred and the loan disbursed immediately.

The large majority of PCA loans are made to mature within a year. In budgeting the repayment schedule, special consideration is given to when income will be available. Advances to meet current or annually recurring expenses are expected to be paid from current income. Loans for capital or semicapital purposes, such as loans for purchase of breeding livestock or machinery, frequently are written with a maturity in excess of one year. PCA's throughout the country now make intermediate-term loans for periods up to seven years, the maximum term permitted by law. Intermediate-term loans accounted for about 15 per cent of the total amount of PCA loans outstanding on June 30, 1962, the latest year for which data are available.

A loan or line of credit to an individual in excess of 15 per cent of the capital and surplus of the Association must have prior approval of the Federal Intermediate Credit Bank. Those in excess of 35 per cent must also have prior approval of the Farm Credit Administration.

When the PCA has completed making the loan it sends the note and, if required, papers related to the loan to the Federal Intermediate Credit Bank. The Credit Bank, if it accepts the loan, will advance the Association the full amount of the loan. If the loan is for $1,000, the PCA receives the full $1,000. In this way the PCA replenishes its funds for making other loans. The OFI's follow a similar procedure.

The terms *discount, rediscount,* and *purchase* are commonly used in connection with loans made by the Credit Banks. The law provides that the Credit Banks shall "discount for, or purchase from, any Production Credit Association . . . with its endorsement, any note, draft, or such other obligation presented by such Association." In this connection it might be helpful to give some definitions of these terms, in the strict sense, and then indicate the present procedure in the Production Credit System.

Discounts. As applied to a note or other obligation acquired by one person or concern from another, the term "discount" in its stricter sense means an obligation acquired for a consideration less than the face amount of the instrument. Ordinarily, it is a note from the face amount of which the one purchasing or acquiring the instrument has deducted interest and for which only the remaining net proceeds were advanced or remitted.

Purchases. As applied to a negotiable instrument, such as to a note or similar obligation, the term "purchase" ordinarily means to acquire at face value.

Rediscounts. As applied to the business of a bank, the term "rediscount" should be understood to mean negotiate or sell (a note or other negotiable instrument) with the endorsement of the seller; an obligation so negotiated; or, in a financial statement, the liability of the person or concern which negotiated such an obligation.

Originally the Intermediate Credit Banks discounted most of their paper, but following the development of the Production Credit Associations, the Banks shifted to the practice of purchasing with interest to accrue, and with very few exceptions that is the present procedure in all districts.

Interest Rates, Fees, and Dividends

Interest rates on PCA loans depend upon operating expenses, the amount Associations are required to pay for loan funds obtained from the Credit Banks, and the need for accumulating reserves in order to further strengthen their financial position. Rates charged vary somewhat over time, a major factor being the cost of money obtained from the Credit Banks. Rates vary among Associations, primarily because of differences in operating expenses which, in turn, depend to a large degree upon the volume of loans made by the Association. On January 1, 1967, 194 PCA's were charging 7 per cent interest, 121 were charging less than 7 per cent; and rates of the remaining 150 were above 7 per cent, the highest being 8¾ per cent. Thirty-six PCA's charged more than one rate January 1, 1967. These Associations were classified in the above tabulation according to their predominant rate.

Most of the Associations also charge moderate loan service fees, the amount of which depends upon local conditions and the size of loans made. These fees are true service charges, not a "loading" or "commission" charge camouflaged as a service charge. They are charged to help meet the expenses incurred by the Association in making loans, such as visits to farms, searching lien records, and recording mortgages.

During the calendar year 1966, 383 PCA's declared dividends amounting to $2,789,000, including $593 declared by one Association on Class C stock to the United States Government. In addition to dividends on Class A and B stock, member borrowers of 38 Production Credit Associations received $841,000 in refunds of interest on a patronage basis. Provision for patronage refunds by the PCA's distinguishes them from the FLBA's who are authorized to make refunds only on the basis of stock ownership.

The interest and discount rates charged the PCA's and OFI's by the Credit Banks depend to a large degree upon the rates the Credit Banks have to pay on debentures sold. Rates paid by the Banks have varied widely in recent years and as a result the discount rates also have varied from time to time. On January 1, 1967, seven Banks were charging 6½ per cent, four 6¼ per cent, and one Bank, in which the rate changed monthly with the cost of money, charged 6.07 per cent on loans outstanding during December, 1966.

The Credit Banks are prohibited from paying dividends on Class B stock or on participation certificates held by the OFI's as long as any Class A stock remains outstanding. When a Bank has retired all its Class A stock it may then pay like dividends on Class B stock and participation certificates not to exceed 5 per cent. The Credit Banks pay patronage refunds in the form of Class B stock to the Associations and participation certificates to the OFI's as outlined above in the section explaining ownership of the Credit Banks.

FEDERAL INTERMEDIATE CREDIT BANK DEBENTURES

The twelve Credit Banks obtain funds for their lending operations principally through sale of consolidated collateral trust debentures to the investing public. These debenture bonds are similar to bonds sold by Federal Land Banks in that they are fully collateralized. However, there are some differences in other respects. One difference is in term of years; Federal Land Bank bonds tend to have longer terms, although some bonds are issued with terms of one year or less. FICB debentures usually are for a term of nine months but sometimes less. Maturities of debentures issued during the year 1966 ranged from two to nine months. Federal Land Bank bonds always have an interest rate coupon and may be offered at par, at a discount, or at a premium, depending on the market. Federal Intermediate Credit Bank debentures merely carry a stated rate of interest, are sold at par, and at maturity the principal is paid with accrued interest.

Debenture bonds sold are the joint and several obligations of the twelve Federal Intermediate Credit Banks and are secured by at least a like face amount of collateral consisting principally of loans and discounts of the Credit Banks. United States Government obligations and cash may also be used as security. Collateral security pledged in support of Credit Bank debentures is certified as adequate and held by the Registrar of the Farm Credit District. The Government assumes no liability, direct or indirect, for Credit Bank debentures.

Individual Credit Banks which run short of funds between

monthly debenture sales borrow from other Credit Banks, Land Banks, or Banks for Cooperatives, or from commerical banks.

Questions and Problems

1. Explain what is meant by the Production Credit System.
2. What is the relationship of the Production Credit System to the Farm Credit System? To the Farm Credit Administration?
3. Appraise the significance of the System to farmers.
4. Who establishes the policy of the Federal Intermediate Credit Banks?
5. Who owns the Credit Banks?
6. Who owns the PCA's? The OFI's? Contrast the two when both are entirely owned by private individuals.
7. Who establishes the policy for PCA's? For OFI's?
8. Explain the relationship between the FICB and the PCA's and OFI's.
9. Do PCA's and OFI's compete for the same loans? How did it happen that both were provided for in the law?
10. Where do the Credit Banks obtain the funds they loan?
11. Using data given in the Agricultural Finance Review, determine the proportion of the nonreal-estate loan volume extended by the PCA's in your state. In the United States.
12. Explain the procedure whereby PCA's and OFI's obtain funds from the Credit Bank.
13. What determines the interest rate charged by a PCA? Why is the PCA rate higher than the FLB rate?
14. From your local paper or from a financial newspaper, such as the *Wall Street Journal,* find the quotations of FICB debentures. Determine how many issues are outstanding and what interest they are earning.

References

Arnold, C. R., *Farmers Build Their Own Production Credit System, 1933–1958,* FCA Circ. E-45, Aug., 1958.
Farm Credit Administration, *Annual Reports.*
———, *The Cooperative Farm Credit System . . . Functions and Organization,* FCA Circ. 36, Dec., 1965.
———, *Federal Intermediate Credit Banks . . . How They Operate,* FCA Circ. 7, rev. 1963.
Hepp, Ralph E., Staniforth, Sydney D., Peterson, Gustaf A., and Christiansen, Rudolph A., *The Role of Farm and Financial Management in Production Credit Associations in Wisconsin,* Wisc. Agr. Exp. Sta. and USDA, cooperating, Bul. 565, June, 1963.
Hill, F. F., Aull, G. H., Butz, E. L., Gans, A. R., Murray, W. G., and Saulnier, R. J., *Risk Problems of Production Credit Associations,* FCA Bul. CR-5, Jan., 1952.

Research and Information Division, *PCA Members and Their Loans*, FCA
Bul. CR-8, May, 1957.
————, *Production Credit Association . . . Characteristics of Loans and
Member Borrowers*, FCA Bul. CR-9, July, 1963.
Taylor, Marlowe M., *Farm Credit in a Southern Great Plains Drouth Area*,
USDA, ARS 43–12, June, 1955. (Mimeo.)

Chapter 26

BANKS FOR COOPERATIVES
AND FINANCING FARM COOPERATIVES

MANY farmers and ranchers carry on part of their business through cooperatives. To facilitate efficient operation, the cooperative usually is organized as a corporation, with a board of directors and officers. Capital is provided by the members, though in many cases the cooperative borrows part of the funds used in the business.

The purpose of this chapter is twofold: to outline the organization and operation of the Banks for Cooperatives, and to discuss the financing of cooperatives in general. Discussion of the Banks for Cooperatives will show their place in the Farm Credit System, including their ownership, types of loans, and loan procedures. The part on financing of cooperatives in general will show the sources of their capital, and the types of lenders from whom they obtain credit.

THE BANKS FOR COOPERATIVES

The thirteen Banks for Cooperatives—twelve District Banks and the Central Bank in Washington, D.C.—comprise that part of the Farm Credit System through which farmers can obtain credit for their cooperatives. Each Bank for Cooperatives is a separate corporation chartered under the Farm Credit Act of 1933 as a permanent institution.

Policies of each Bank are determined by its board of directors.

456

Each District Bank is served by the District Farm Credit Board. As indicated in earlier chapters, members of the District Board are ex officio directors of each of the three Farm Credit Banks in the District. The Central Bank for Cooperatives has its own board of directors, one from each of the twelve Farm Credit Districts and a director-at-large. Present law provides that when the Central Bank is two-thirds or more borrower owned, twelve of the directors will be elected by the District boards of directors and one will be appointed by the Governor of the Farm Credit Administration, with the advice and consent of the Federal Farm Credit Board. The position of two-thirds borrower ownership was reached in 1965, and as terms of the appointed directors expire they will be succeeded by elected directors. The directors of each Bank employ a staff of officers and other help as necessary to carry on the affairs of the Bank.

The Central Bank for Cooperatives, the thirteenth Bank in the Cooperative Bank System, does not have its parallel in either the Land Bank System or the Production Credit System. One of its functions under the 1933 Act was to facilitate financing large cooperatives doing business in more than one District. Architects of the system visualized that these large cooperatives would need larger loans than the District Banks could handle. Under the Farm Credit Act of 1955 the Central Bank makes loans directly to cooperative associations only in cases where it is not practicable for the loan to be made by a District Bank. The Central Bank now serves the credit needs of cooperatives primarily by purchasing participations in certain larger loans made by the District Banks and by making loans to the District Banks for Cooperatives.

Ownership of the Banks for Cooperatives

The Farm Credit Act of 1955 provided a comprehensive plan whereby the thirteen Banks for Cooperatives can become completely farmer owned. Provision was made for three types of capital stock: Class A, Class B, and Class C. Class A stock is owned by the United States Government. It is nonvoting and no dividends are paid thereon. Class B stock is of an investment type which any farmers' cooperative may purchase and on which noncumulative dividends of from 2 to 4 per cent per annum may be paid. Class C stock, which receives no dividends, is acquired by borrowing cooperatives in three ways:

1. By purchase of at least one (voting) share to qualify for a loan.
2. By investing regularly in Class C stock a certain percentage of the interest paid to the Bank. Each borrowing cooperative is required to invest regularly in Class C stock from 10 to 25 per cent of the amount of interest paid on its loans. The exact percentage is established by the District Board, with approval of the Farm Credit Administration. If, for example, required purchases are set at 15 per cent, the borrowing cooperative purchases $15 of Class C stock for each $100 of interest it pays to the Bank for Cooperatives.
3. Through patronage refunds paid in the form of Class C stock. Patronage refunds can be paid from part of the Bank's annual net savings or by distributing in Class C stock surplus previously allocated to borrowers upon a patronage basis.

Complete ownership by cooperatives of the District Banks for Cooperatives will eventually be achieved by retirement of all Class A stock in each Bank. As of January 1, 1967, this goal had been reached in four of the Districts. Similarly, the Central Bank will be owned ultimately by the District Banks. The law provides for retirement of Government-owned Class A stock in each Bank annually in an amount substantially equivalent to the Class C capital stock acquired by borrowers during the year. When Class A stock is retired the funds are paid into the Agricultural Marketing Act Revolving Fund and are available for repurchasing of Class A stock if necessary.

The amount of capital stock outstanding, together with reserves and surplus accumulated, on January 1, 1956 (the effective date of the 1955 Act), and on January 1, 1967, are as follows:

	January 1, 1956	January 1, 1967
	(millions)	(millions)
Class A Stock—U.S. Government	$150.0	$ 41.2
Class B Stock—Cooperative Associations and others	...	4.2
Class C Stock—Cooperative Associations	...	113.1
Other—Cooperative Associations	20.6	.028[1]
Total	$170.6	$158.5
Reserves, Surplus and undistributed earnings	$ 88.1	$118.2

---

[1] $28,100.

The item "other" represents the old type of capital stock purchased by borrowing cooperatives as provided by the Farm

Credit Act of 1933. Under the 1955 Act, at the option of the cooperative, practically all of this stock was converted to new Class B stock and Class C stock. Since January 1, 1956, the borrowing cooperatives have acquired additional Class C stock and the Banks have retired Class A stock as shown by the figures.

Under the provisions of the Farm Credit Act of 1955, the accumulated surplus and reserves of approximately $88 million on the effective date of the Act, January 1, 1956, became permanent capital of the Banks. This followed the precedent set with the Land Banks, and subsequently followed with the Federal Intermediate Credit Banks. Such surplus and reserves may not be distributed as patronage refunds.

During the year ended June 30, 1966, combined net earnings of the thirteen Banks were $11.1 million. In accordance with the law these were applied as follows:

(millions)

1. Credited to a surplus account and allocated to
   patrons on the books of the Banks, 25 per cent.......$ 2.4
2. Federal franchise tax paid.........................   1.4
3. Dividends of from 3 to 4 per cent per year paid
   on Class B stock..................................   .3
4. Net savings distributed as patronage refunds to
   borrowers in the form of Class C stock.............   7.0

   Total...$11.1

All allocations of surplus and all payments of patronage refunds are directly proportionate to the amount of interest paid by each borrower. When the surplus account of a Bank exceeds 25 per cent of the sum of all its outstanding capital stock, the Bank may issue additional Class C stock to cooperatives for the oldest allocations of surplus. After all Class A stock of a Bank has been retired, the Class B and Class C stock may also be retired at par in the order in which it was issued. Thus, the Banks will eventually be on a revolving capital plan similar to that used by many other types of cooperatives.

Types of Loans

To be legally eligible to borrow from a Bank for Cooperatives, a cooperative must be made up of farmers and must be operated for the mutual benefit of its members. The cooperative must be one in which members act together to process or market their products, to purchase or distribute farm supplies, or to furnish farm services. In addition the law provides that in order to be eligible for a loan from a Bank for Cooperatives, the cooperative may not do more business with nonmembers than with members. Moreover, business of the cooperative must be conducted on the basis of one vote per member or else dividends on stock or membership capital must be limited to not more than 8 per cent annually. A further requirement is that, except for mutual fire insurance companies, at least 90 per cent of the voting rights of a cooperative must be held either by farmer-members or by associations owned and controlled by farmers. In the case of farmers' mutual fire insurance companies, at least 75 per cent of the voting control must be held by its producer members. These requirements may seem like major hurdles to obtaining a loan from the Banks for Cooperatives, but in actual practice an agricultural cooperative organized and operated in accordance with generally accepted cooperative principles usually can qualify. The cooperative must, of course, meet the credit requirements of the Bank.

The Banks for Cooperatives provide credit to meet all the needs of a farm cooperative to establish and maintain a modern, efficient operation of the size required to carry on the business of its members. Included is credit to buy or expand plant sites, buildings, and equipment, and to provide capital for operating the business. In addition, the Banks provide credit for inventories of farm supply and service cooperatives and for storing and marketing commodities of farm marketing cooperatives. (Thus, in passing, it may be noted that the Banks for Cooperatives alone provide a credit service for cooperatives comparable to that which the Federal Land Banks and the Federal Intermediate Credit Banks combined provide for individual farmers through the local credit associations.) Inventory loans permit the cooperative to extend credit to members on supplies purchased, although, as explained in the discussion of merchant-dealer credit, farm cooperatives generally prefer not to extend this type of credit. Commodity loans assist cooperatives in making immediate payments to members on commodities delivered to the Association. Loans generally are secured by a first lien on items involved in the loan or on other acceptable collateral.

Repayment plans are adapted to the type and requirements of the cooperative financed. Loans to finance commodities in storage generally are repaid from sales proceeds of the collateral. Inventory loans are repaid when the supplies are sold, or when payment is received. Seasonal or short-term operating loans are payable during the year. Term loans to finance plant sites, buildings, and equipment generally are repaid in installments over a period of years, the period varying according to the type of collateral involved and the needs of the borrower. There is no legal limitation as to maximum maturity of term loans.

Interest rates are established by the board of directors of a Bank with the approval of the Farm Credit Administration and by law may not exceed 6 per cent per annum. Interest rates vary among Banks, depending on the type and term of loan involved and the cost of loan funds which are obtained primarily through sale of debentures. Generally, short-term loans carry a lower rate than long-term loans. This converse relationship compared with rates on loans to an individual farmer is due primarily to the size of loans involved. Short-term loans to farm cooperatives usually are sufficiently large that management and service costs per dollar of credit extended is relatively low compared with individual farm loans. Interest is charged only on the amount advanced under the loan and for the time the funds are used by the cooperative. There is no penalty for prepayment.

Loan Procedure

A cooperative desiring a loan from a Bank for Cooperatives should contact the Bank in the Farm Credit District in which the headquarters of the Association is located. Loan applications are referred to the business analysts and appraisers of the Bank who review the operations, make credit investigations, and appraise the facilities or other properties to be pledged as security for the loan. The information so obtained, together with a credit report prepared by an analyst, are considered by the Executive or Loan Committee of the Bank when action is taken on the application.

The same general type of information is needed in making a loan to a cooperative as in making a loan to an individual. However, in place of dealing with the farmer and his wife, the Bank in making a loan to a cooperative deals with a corporation which operates under policies established by a board of directors elected by the members. In considering an application for a loan, the articles or certificate of incorporation, with all amendments thereto, certified by the Secretary of State must be considered to make sure the cooperative is a legal entity. The bylaws also are considered. Among other things they provide a basis for determining the eligibility of the cooperative to borrow from the Bank. Audit reports, balance sheets, and operating statements for recent years are analyzed to determine the trend and present financial status of the cooperative. Through these reports and consultation with the manager and board of directors the Bank for Cooperatives seeks answers to questions such as:

What has been the earnings history of the cooperative for the past three to five years?

Has it strengthened its financial structure during this period?

What is the capability of the manager?

Does the board of directors work as a team?

Do they truly represent the membership and are they good businessmen as well as good cooperators?

Is the membership loyal and cooperative?

Will the territory and volume of business the cooperative can anticipate support an efficient operation?

Are the facilities adequate and efficient, or will some be acquired which are?

Will the loan help the cooperative make or save money for its members?

Will the cooperative be able to repay the loan?

Can the cooperative stand the risk added by the additional loan? This type of information is considered in making new loans. Where the cooperative has been doing business with the Bank, the business analysts already have much of this information either from direct contact or from reports in Bank files. In such cases, where the cooperative has developed a good credit rating, the credit transaction is relatively simple and can be handled with dispatch.

Source of Loan Funds

Funds loaned by the Banks for Cooperatives come from several sources. Data for selected years are given in Table 26.1.

In addition to funds available from their capital and surplus, the banks obtain a large amount of funds by sale of consolidated collateral trust debentures to investors. These are the joint and several obligations of all the Banks for Cooperatives. Debentures outstanding January 1, 1967, together with those issued and retired during 1966, are given in Table 26.2.

Debentures sold by the Banks for Cooperatives are very similar

TABLE 26.1

SOURCE OF FUNDS FOR BANKS FOR COOPERATIVES ON SELECTED DATES *

Type of Funds	June 30, 1960	June 30, 1965	January 1, 1967
	(*millions*)	(*millions*)	(*millions*)
Government-owned Stock.........$ 118.3		$ 52.1	$ 41.2
Coop-owned Stock............... 45.9		105.0	117.3
Surplus and Reserves............ 98.1		111.9	118.2
Borrowed Money................ 1200.4		2455.3	1100.0
Total $1462.7		$2724.3	$1376.7

* Source: Farm Credit Admin.

TABLE 26.2

BANKS FOR COOPERATIVES CONSOLIDATED DEBENTURES ISSUED AND RETIRED DURING
CALENDAR YEAR 1966, AND OUTSTANDING JANUARY 1, 1967 *

Date of Issue	Term	Rate	Date of Maturity	Issued During Year	Retired During Year	Outstanding January 1, 1967
		(*per cent*)		(*millions*)	(*millions*)	(*millions*)
8/2/65	5 mos. 29 days	4.30	2/1/66		$ 228.5	
10/4/65	6 mos.	4.35	4/4/66		230.5	
11/1/65	6 mos. 1 day	4.30	5/2/66		164.5	
12/1/65	6 mos.	4.50	6/1/66		228.0	
2/1/66	6 mos.	4.95	8/1/66	$ 238.0	238.0	
4/4/66	5 mos. 29 days	5.30	10/3/66	230.0	230.0	
5/2/66	5 mos. 29 days	5.25	11/1/66	157.5	157.5	
6/1/66	6 mos.	5.40	12/1/66	242.5	242.5	
8/1/66	6 mos.	5.90	2/1/67	276.0		$ 276.0
10/3/66	6 mos.	6.25	4/3/67	295.0		295.0
11/1/66	6 mos.	5.90	5/1/67	255.8		255.8
12/1/66	6 mos.	6.05	6/1/67	247.4		247.4
				$1,942.2	$1,719.5	$1,074.2

* Source: Farm Credit Admin.

to those sold by the Federal Intermediate Credit Banks. Banks for
Cooperatives debentures have varied in term from six months to
three years but most issues have been for terms of one year or less.
They bear coupons only if the term is one year or longer. Otherwise
they merely carry a stated rate of interest, are sold at par, and at
maturity both the principal and accrued interest are paid to the
investor. The security behind debentures consists of borrowers'
notes pledged with the district's registrar. The United States Government does not guarantee the debentures either as to principal or
interest.

In addition to obtaining funds by selling debentures, the
Banks for Cooperatives borrow directly from Federal Intermediate
Credit Banks, Federal Land Banks, and commercial banks. Such
direct loans are used primarily to meet needs between debenture
issues. Also the District Banks borrow from each other and from the
Central Bank which helps alleviate the need for borrowing from
other sources.

Financing Farmer Cooperatives

Farmers finance their cooperatively owned businesses by using all the standard methods employed by other business corporations as well as some distinctive methods of their own. These methods include memberships, various types of certificates, common stock, preferred stock, bonds, reserves and surplus, and borrowed capital.

Most of the *equity capital*—capital which does not involve a legal obligation of repayment or redemption at a stated time or under stated conditions—required by a farmer cooperative comes from the members who own and use the cooperative to obtain farm supplies, to furnish various farm services, or to market their crops. This conforms with the general principle that the individuals who stand to gain from a venture should assume the primary risks. In addition to members, some equity capital may be obtained from nonmember patrons; other cooperatives; marketing and supply companies; and individuals, firms, and organizations interested in promoting the cooperative.

Cooperatives obtain *debt capital*—that is, incur legal liability to repay the funds under specified conditions—from the same sources as they obtain equity capital. They also borrow from Banks for Cooperatives, commercial banks, insurance companies, and others. About half the farm cooperative associations operating in the mid-sixties were using borrowed funds.[2] Banks for Cooperatives are the major source of debt capital, supplying well over half of the borrowed funds.

Revolving Fund Plan of Financing

An effective method used by many cooperatives to raise capital from members is called the *revolving fund plan of financing*. In addition to providing a plan for effectively raising capital in a relatively "painless" way, it facilitates cooperative practices and materially aids in keeping control of a cooperative in the hands of its current members or patrons.

The revolving fund plan provides for a cooperative to retain funds and build a surplus reserve as a means of providing capital for

---

[2] David Volkin, "Financing Cooperatives" in *Farmer Cooperatives in the United States*, Farmer Cooperative Service, FCS Bul. 1, revised 1965, p. 30.

the Association. The funds retained may be net earnings realized in normal operations or specific amounts authorized to be deducted from sales proceeds. Some marketing cooperatives retain both authorized deductions as well as earnings realized in operations and revolve them as a unit. The amounts retained are allocated to members on the books of the cooperative on a patronage basis. Retained earnings and authorized deductions, therefore, comprise contributions of capital by individual members.

The "revolving" part of the plan enters the picture when the cooperative has accumulated adequate capital, at which time the retained net earnings and authorized deductions are paid to members on a "first retained—first paid" basis. Thus, the revolving fund plan provides for the cooperative to retain earnings and authorized deductions for its use, and to allocate them on its books as patron's contributions of capital, to be returned at a later date. In most cases the date is not specified, though some cooperatives give a specific date. Some cooperatives also sell preferred stock, certificate and debenture bonds that are redeemed on a revolving fund basis.

The way the revolving plan works is illustrated by Figure 26.1. The cooperative used in the illustration started operation in 1951 with an initial capital of $30,000, of which half had been subscribed

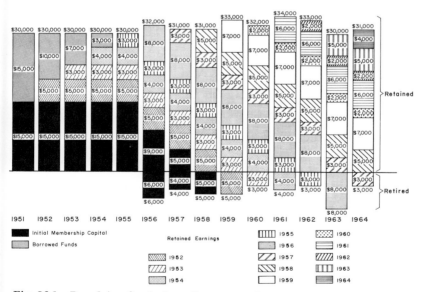

Fig. 26.1—Revolving fund plan of a cooperative. (Courtesy of the Farmer Cooperative Service, USDA.)

by the members and half borrowed. The initial membership capital was left in the cooperative for the first few years, and borrowed funds were repaid as earnings accumulated. In 1952 retained earnings of $5,000 enabled the cooperative to pay a like amount on the loan. Additional retained earnings in 1953, 1954, and 1955 made possible full repayment of the loan. The next step was retirement of initial membership capital, which was accomplished during the years 1956 to 1958 through use of annual retained earnings in the manner described for repayment of borrowed funds. The cooperative was then in position to begin the capital revolving process, i.e. repaying its oldest outstanding capital contributions acquired through retained earnings with current retained earnings. For example, in 1959, the $5,000 of capital derived from earnings retained in 1952 were retired. In 1960, the $3,000 retained in 1953 were retired, and so on. By this revolving process, current patrons of the cooperative gradually take over capital ownership of the cooperative by retiring the oldest outstanding capital. Retired farmers and others who no longer use services of the cooperative thus are able to have their capital for other uses. The plan also permits expanding the capital structure of the cooperative if the membership desires to do so and are willing to postpone the revolving feature for a year or so.

Financing Rural Electric and Telephone Cooperatives

Farmer cooperatives which provide electric and telephone service to rural areas are financed in a different way from other cooperatives. They obtain direct Government loans through the Rural Electrification Administration (REA), an agency of the U.S. Department of Agriculture. Congress annually determines the amount of money REA may lend, and funds are made available from the Treasury to REA as needed. As borrowers make principal and interest payments to REA, this money is returned to the Treasury.

The 1935 census indicated only 11 per cent of the farms in the United States were receiving central station electric service. Sparsely populated rural areas and the comparatively large initial investment required for constructing rural lines effectively discouraged private business from widespread investments in this field. The Rural Electrification Administration was established by Executive

Order in 1935, and in 1936 the Congress enacted the Rural Electrification Act. The initial act provided only for financing electric systems, but the rural telephone loan program was added by Congress in 1949 to meet the need of rural people for adequate telephone service. As of July 1, 1966, more than 98 per cent of the farms in the United States had electric service, and about 80 per cent had telephone service.

The REA is permitted to make electric loans to cooperatives, public and privately owned utility companies, and to states and territories. About 93 per cent of such loans have been to cooperatives, all of them locally owned enterprises incorporated under the laws of the states in which they operate. As of July 1, 1966, REA had approved over $5.9 billion in electric loans to 1,103 borrowers, which included 993 cooperatives, 53 public power districts, 32 other public bodies, and 25 electric companies.

As of July 1, 1966, electric borrowers had repaid $1.4 billion on principal, which included $279 million paid ahead of schedule. A total of 105 borrowers had repaid their obligations in full. Seven borrowers were overdue in payments amounting to $559,012. Loans to two small systems were foreclosed in the early days of the REA program at a loss of $44,478.

Under the Telephone Amendment, REA is empowered to make loans to existing companies and to cooperative, nonprofit, limited-dividend, or mutual associations for the improvement and expansion of rural telephone service. As of July 1, 1966, telephone loans totaling about $1.3 billion had been approved to 625 independent telephone companies and 230 cooperatives.

As of July 1, 1966, telephone borrowers had repaid $116.0 million of principal on their loans, including $11.0 million ahead of schedule. Four borrowers were behind in payments as of July 1, 1966, for a total amount of $129,895.

Loan terms provided by REA are distinctly favorable. Electric loans cover the full cost of constructing the power lines and other facilities. Both electric and telephone loans bear only 2 per cent interest and are repaid over a maximum period of 35 years. Payments on principal generally begin 3 years from the date of the note, to permit borrowers adequate time to complete construction and produce revenue from operations to meet payments.

Security for REA loans consists of a first mortgage on the equipment and facilities financed. To facilitate obtaining and maintaining adequate security, the REA promulgates regulations and material specifications through the terms of the loan contract and mortgage. Engineering and managerial advisory service is provided borrowing cooperatives as a further aid to success of the undertaking.

The major portion of REA loans has been made for installing electric and telephone lines and related facilities for providing electric power and telephone service to rural people.

About one-fourth of the REA loans have been used for financing of electric generating plants and transmission lines. Loans are also made to electric borrowers to enable them to finance installation of consumer facilities, including wiring of buildings, electrically operated water systems, light fixtures, appliances, and the like. Under this type of financing, REA makes loans to existing borrowers, who, in turn, make loans to the farmers. However, such loans account for only 1 per cent of the total amount of loans approved.

QUESTIONS AND PROBLEMS

1. What is the relationship of the Banks for Cooperatives to the Farm Credit System?
2. What is the function of the District Banks for Cooperatives? The Central Bank for Cooperatives?
3. Who determines the policy of each of the thirteen Banks?
4. Who owns each of the thirteen Banks?
5. What are the requirements to borrow from the Banks for Cooperatives?
6. What types of loans are made by the Banks for Cooperatives?
7. Where do the Banks for Cooperatives obtain the money they loan?
8. What determines the interest rate charged on loans by a BC?
9. Outline the procedure a cooperative should follow to obtain a BC loan.
10. What methods do cooperatives use to obtain capital?
11. Explain the revolving fund method of financing a cooperative.
12. Farmer cooperatives generally have a high proportion of equity capital. With the increasing amount of capital required to farm, financing cooperative business in addition to "on-the-farm" business puts an added financial strain on the farmer. It is not uncommon for farmers to borrow personally in order to subscribe capital for their cooperative. From an economic viewpoint, how much capital should patrons subscribe and how much should the cooperative borrow?
13. What is the Rural Electrification Administration?
14. Why was it organized? What are its functions?
15. What is the source of funds loaned by REA?

REFERENCES

Engberg, Russell C., *Financing Farmer Cooperatives,* Banks for Cooperatives, 1965.

Erdman, Henry E., and Larsen, Grace H., *Revolving Finance in Agricultural Cooperatives,* Mimir Publishers, Inc., Madison, Wisc., 1965.

Farm Credit Administration, *A Statistical Handbook of Farmer Cooperatives,* FCA Bul. 26, Nov., 1938. (This report is the first broad study of financing cooperatives. It shows amounts borrowed and sources of credit by types of cooperatives, by states, and the like. Currently it is out of print.)

————, and Rural Electrification Administration, *Annual Reports.*

Farmer Cooperative Service, *Revolving Fund Method of Financing Farmer Cooperatives,* Gen. Rept. 41, Mar., 1958.

Griffin, Nelda, *Financial Structure of Regional Farm Supply Cooperatives,* Farmer Cooperative Serv., USDA, Gen. Rept. 124, 1965.

————, *Financial Structure of Regional Farmer Cooperatives,* Farmer Cooperative Serv., USDA, Gen. Rept. 133, 1966.

Henning, G. F., and Burkes, Marshall, *Changes in the Financial Structure of Agricultural Business Organizations,* Ohio Agr. Exp. Sta. Res. Bul. 952, Oct., 1963.

Hulbert, Helim H., Griffin, Nelda, and Gardner, Kelsey B., *Methods of Financing Cooperatives,* Farmer Cooperative Serv., USDA, Gen. Rept. 32, June, 1957.

Knapp, Joseph G., and staff, *Farmer Cooperatives in the United States,* Farmer Cooperative Serv., USDA, Bul. 1, revised, 1965.

Korzan, Gerald E., and Gray, Edward L., *Capital Growth and Adjustment of Agricultural Cooperatives,* Oreg. Agr. Exp. Sta. Bul. 596, Nov., 1964.

Person, H. S., *The Rural Electrification Administration in Perspective,* REA, Washington, D.C., 1950.

Purcell, Arthur H., *Rural Credit Unions in Southern Indiana,* U.S. Dept. of Agr., Farmer Cooperative Serv., Gen. Rept. 116, July, 1963.

Chapter 27

FARMERS HOME ADMINISTRATION

THE farmers' campaign for credit, as outlined in Chapter 23, called for low cost direct loans from the Government. In response, the Farm Credit System, including the Federal Land Bank System, the Production Credit System, and the system of the Banks for Cooperatives, was sponsored by the Government as a means whereby farmers could, through cooperative action, provide for their own credit needs. However, the demand for direct loans from the Government was not ignored. Government credit assistance was provided from time to time through temporary Government agencies to meet emergency credit needs. The Federal Farm Mortgage Corporation, referred to in the Chronological Record of Federal Acts and Executive Orders Relating to Agricultural Credit Agencies, given in Chapter 23, is an example of such an agency.

The Government also took direct steps to help beginning farmers and other farmers with limited resources. Commercial lenders, including the Farm Credit System, generally have not provided adequately for credit needs of this group. The situation was particularly acute in the Great Depression of the 1930's. The Resettlement Administration, later called the Farm Security Administration, was created in 1935 to help rehabilitate destitute farm families by extension of supervised credit and limited financial relief, commonly called *grants*. This use of grants combined with farm operating loans made it possible for many farm families to continue operating their farms rather than having to go on already swollen relief rolls.

As economic conditions improved in the 1940's the need for emergency financing diminished, but progress of the technological revolution accentuated the problems of beginning farmers and of other farmers with limited capital. It became increasingly difficult to acquire the minimum amount of capital required to farm. As a result, the Farmers Home Administration Act of 1946 was passed which created the Farmers Home Administration (FHA), and abolished the Farm Security Administration and the Emergency Crop and Feed Loan Division of the Farm Credit Administration. The new Act continued and broadened the loan services of these two agencies to enable the FHA to provide the financial assistance needed at that time. During the decades which followed, the lending authority of FHA was further broadened several times, with the greatest expansion, in terms of both new loan programs and increased lending authority, occurring following 1961. The increase in farm capital requirements associated with development of the technological revolution, together with higher operating costs and land prices, were major factors in the expansion of FHA. However, two new factors were involved: (1) a marked change in U.S. Department of Agriculture policy from the traditional position of concern solely with problems of agriculture to a concern that included the entire rural community, and (2) added emphasis on use of credit to aid in economic development of farms and communities.

ORGANIZATION

The Farmers Home Administration, an agency of the U.S. Department of Agriculture, is made up of the National Office located in Washington, D.C., the National Finance Office located in St. Louis, Missouri, 43 state offices, and some 1,600 county offices, together with the associated state and county FHA committees, as shown in Figure 27.1.

The National Office under the direction of an Administrator determines policies within the framework of the laws set up by Congress, issues procedures, controls budgets, and directs and gives technical training to field staffs. The National Finance Office located at St. Louis handles the fiscal, business management, and accounting services. It keeps records and accounts for all funds disbursed, insured, and collected by the agency. Also, it maintains records and inventories of the agency's property.

The 43 state offices, each under a state director, serve all 50

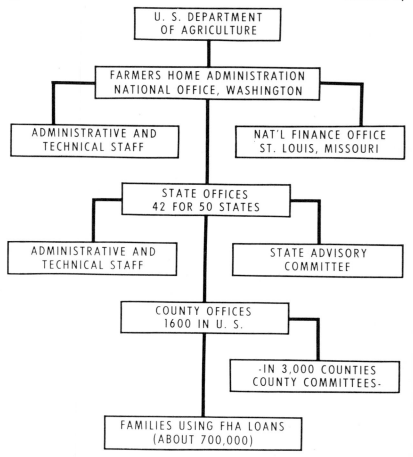

Fig. 27.1—Organization chart of the Farmers Home Administration. (Courtesy of the Farmers Home Administration.)

states, Puerto Rico, and the Virgin Islands. The California, Maine, Maryland, and Oregon state offices serve more than one state and the Puerto Rico office also serves the Virgin Islands.

The state director has been delegated broad authority and responsibility by the Administrator to carry out the loan program in his state. He and his staff direct and train county office staffs, analyze loan programs, and administer the budgets allotted to his state for loans and administrative expenses. He also approves certain types of loans, authority for which is not delegated to county supervisors. In most states the state director appoints selected leading farmers and businessmen interested in farmers' problems to a state advisory committee. From time to time he consults with this committee on the credit needs in the state and on the adapting of national policies to state problems.

The 1,600 county offices strategically located throughout the country usually are in county seat towns, with some offices serving more than one county. All applications for loans are made through these county offices. The county supervisor in charge of each county office helps farm families prepare farm and home plans, approves most loans, gives technical advice to borrowers during on-the-farm visits, and accepts payments from borrowers. He also gives technical assistance, long-range development planning assistance, and general supervision in connection with other types of loans.

A Farmers Home Administration Committee consisting of three members is appointed by the state director for each county or county office area. At least two members of the committee must be farmers. The third member may be a local businessman familiar with local farmers and their needs. These committees determine the eligibility of applicants, certify the value of farms where real estate loans are being made, review borrowers' progress, and make recommendations concerning certain loan approval and loan servicing actions.

Objectives

The lending authority of the Farmers Home Administration as it exists today involves three principal objectives, all of which are supplementary to the services of commercial lenders. The first objective is to strengthen the economic position of individual family farmers. Providing supervised credit to individual farmers who are unable to obtain adequate credit from commercial lenders at reasonable rates and terms continues as a major function of the agency. This objective includes extension of credit to eligible farmers for those things that will improve the level of agricultural income and living standards. We are primarily concerned with this objective in this chapter.

The second principal objective of FHA is to improve rural communities, including towns with a population of less than 5,500. This objective has evolved in recent years as the scope of U.S. Department of Agriculture activities has broadened to include the entire rural community. Lending authority includes extension of credit and accompanying counsel and supervision for items such as resource conservation and development, rural renewal, rural community water and sewer systems, watershed protection, development of recreation areas, and rural housing.

The third principal objective of FHA is to alleviate rural poverty. This is a part of the Federal Government's Economic Opportunity program. It involves providing Economic Opportunity loans to both individuals and cooperatives to help improve family incomes of low income rural people.

The types of loans extended under each of these objectives are discussed later in the chapter.

SOURCE OF LOAN FUNDS

The Farmers Home Administration is a government credit agency. Money which FHA lends comes from three sources: (1) a *direct loan account* provided for by Congress, (2) a *revolving fund* set up by Congress primarily for emergency loans, and (3) funds furnished by commercial banks and other lenders for loans insured and serviced by FHA. Loans made from the first two sources are referred to as *direct loans,* those made from the latter are called *insured loans.*

Collections of principal and interest on direct loans are returned to the appropriate account or fund and are available for future loans. Hence, both the direct loan account and the revolving fund are operated on a revolving fund basis.

The maximum amount of direct loans which FHA may make from the direct loan account is determined by Congress. The amount may be reduced below this ceiling, however, by the Bureau of the Budget. The Bureau of the Budget specifies the maximum amount of direct loans which may be made from the revolving fund.

The objective of the insured loan program, which originated in the Farmers Home Administration Act of 1946, is to stimulate use of private capital in place of direct Government loans. Thus, it is the policy of FHA to use insured loan funds instead of direct loans whenever possible, up to the maximum prescribed by Congress. Through the insured loan program, private lenders can advance funds to eligible applicants for a number of different purposes, as will become evident later in the chapter. All loan-making and servicing operations are handled by FHA without cost to the lender. Interest paid investors and terms of the repurchase agreement are competitive with similar types of investments. Payments of principal and interest are fully guaranteed by the Government. If the borrower falls behind in his payments the Government issues a U.S. Treasury check to the lender for the amount due him. The Farmers Home Administration is responsible for handling delinquencies or foreclosures and bears the costs associated with liquidation.

Special Features of FHA Loans

In addition to the direct loan and insured loan features, FHA financing has a number of other special features. The Farmers Home Administration is authorized by law to make loans only to those farmers who are unable to obtain adequate credit from other sources on reasonable terms. Moreover, FHA borrowers agree to obtain their credit from other lenders when they reach or regain a position where they can do so. Every year thousands of farmers "graduate" to other lenders. During 1966 more than 28,000 farmers paid their loans in full to the Farmers Home Administration. The FHA credit program is designed to supplement rather than compete with other sources of credit. One of its real values to farmers lies in the fact that it operates in all farm sections of the country, providing a dependable source of loans to qualified farmers who have good character and experience but insufficient assets to qualify for adequate credit from commercial sources.

The Farmers Home Administration may make larger loans, relative to value of security, than commercial lenders. With direct farm ownership loans, for example, it may lend up to 100 per cent of the normal value of the farm as determined by appraisers. This provision is essential to achieving the main objective of the agency —that of helping farm families with limited means become established in farming, or if already established, to enlarge, reorganize, or develop and improve their farms to enable them to remain in farming on a sound basis. True, greater risk is involved in making such loans, but the public has decided through their elected representatives to shoulder this cost to help worthy farmers who are unable to obtain adequate capital from commercial lenders due to lack of security. Thus, FHA loans are made with the expectation that they will be repaid out of income to be received from a sound farming operation, rather than on the basis of the amount of security the borrower can provide. However, loans are secured by liens on real estate, or livestock, machinery, and crops, depending upon the type of loan.

As one means of reducing the risk involved and to help borrowers become established on a sound basis as quickly as possible, credit extended by FHA is backed with advice and technical assistance. For example, farm ownership borrowers receive planning and supervisory assistance through a systematic five-step process. The county supervisor is primarily responsible for furnishing this advice and assistance.

First, the county supervisor helps the borrower and his wife develop a *long-time* plan showing the system of farming to be followed and the major adjustments and improvements to be put into effect on the farm and in the home over a period of years. They then develop an *annual* Farm and Home plan to guide the year's operations and to facilitate progress in achieving the long-time plan. Both the annual and long-time plans take into consideration the problems, needs, and resources of the family and the farm.

Second, the county supervisor periodically visits the farm during the year to provide the family with technical advice and encouragement in carrying out the adjustments, improvements, and practices laid out in the farm and home plans.

Third, the county supervisor assists the family in carrying out a good system of record keeping to help evaluate management practices and financial progress.

Fourth, at the end of the year he assists the family in analyzing the outcome of their farm and home operations. Strong and weak points are pointed out and suggestions made for improvement.

Fifth, the county supervisor assists the family in developing an annual farm and home plan for the new year. The new annual plan is based on the results of the past years' farm operations, points brought out in the year-end analysis, and the resources and marketing prospects.

Thus, the FHA's supervised credit program consists of providing adequate credit and of assisting the borrowers to make effective use of the credit.

TYPES OF FHA LOANS

The various types of loans made by the Farmers Home Administration are shown in Table 27.1, and the data on loans obligated and outstanding indicate the relative importance of the different types.

TABLE 27.1

FARMERS HOME ADMINISTRATION LOANS OBLIGATED DURING FISCAL YEAR 1966
AND OUTSTANDING JUNE 30, 1966, UNITED STATES AND TERRITORIES,
CLASSIFIED BY TYPE *

	Obligations 1966 Fiscal Year		Loans Outstanding as of June 30, 1966	
	Number of borrowers	Amount (thousands)	Number of borrowers	Amount ‡ (thousands)
Operating Loans:				
Total........................	65,317	$ 276,030	113,215	$ 694,329
Farm Ownership Loans:				
Direct...........................	927	10,000	n.a.	329,317
Insured..........................	13,352	23,238	n.a.	899,556
Total..........................	14,279	233,238	84,422	1,228,873
Emergency Loans.....................	24,371	100,489	31,446	120,291
Rural Housing Loans:				
Farm:				
Direct........................	2,305	9,875	n.a.	279,275
Insured.......................	3,172	25,638	n.a.	27,998
Nonfarm:				
Direct........................	8,429	48,619	n.a.	400,810
Insured.......................	18,123	174,489	n.a.	111,453
Total rural housing............	32,029	258,621	106,263	819,536
Senior Citizen Rental Housing Loans:				
Direct........................	33	2,851	n.a.	3,124
Insured.......................	48	1,456	n.a.	2,519
Total rental housing	81	4,307	101	5,643
Farm Labor Housing:				
Insured loans....................	22	3,466	38	2,055
Grants in connection with loans......	4	2,156	...	...
Watershed Loans.....................	38	5,576	114	18,682
Rural Renewal Loans..................	4	882	12	1,590
Resource Conservation and Development Loans.......................	1	13	...	...
Association Loans and Grants:				
Water and waste disposal:				
Direct loans....................	224	27,684		
Insured loans...................	584	85,019		
Grants.........................	221	18,668		
Total water and waste..........	804 †	131,371		
Recreation loans:				
Direct.........................	3	250		
Insured........................	138	15,307		Breakdown of Association loans outstanding not available.
Total recreation.................	140 †	15,557		
Grazing loans:				
Direct.........................	2	58		
Insured........................	70	18,807		
Total grazing..................	70 †	18,865		
Irrigation, drainage and soil conservation loans:				
Direct.........................	3	7		
Insured........................	22	856		
Total—3 types..................	25	863		
All types of associations:				
Direct loans....................	232	27,999	n.a.	65,996
Insured loans...................	814	119,989	n.a.	154,269
Grants.........................	221	18,668	...	...
Total..........................	1,039†	166,656	1,715	220,265
Comprehensive Area Sewer and Water Planning Grants....................	101	1,329	...	...
Economic Opportunity Loans:				
To farmers.......................	9,993	15,238	n.a.	n.a.
To rural residents.................	7,080	12,026	n.a.	n.a.
Total..........................	17,073	27,264	25,033	41,166
To cooperatives....................	391	4,708	404	4,338
Soil and Water Loans to Individuals:				
Direct..........................	600	2,078	n.a.	8,638
Insured.........................	311	1,773	n.a.	12,053
Total soil and water.............	911	3,851	5,509	20,691
All types of loans and grants:				
Loans:				
Direct:........................119,721		516,384	n.a.	n.a.
Insured........................ 35,842		550,049	n.a.	n.a.
Total loans.................... 155,551 †		$1,066,433	308,663§	$3,177,459
Grants...........................	326	22,153	...	...

* Source: Farmers Home Administration.
† Unduplicated number; some associations received both direct and insured loans or both loans and grants.
‡ Amount outstanding on current programs. Excludes loans obligated but not advanced.
§ Unduplicated number of borrowers with unpaid loan balances.

It is evident that FHA makes a fairly large number of different types of loans. Or, put another way, FHA makes loans under a fairly large number of authorizations. Some of the authorizations stem from specific legislation pretaining to FHA. For example, authorization to make farm ownership loans emanates from the Consolidated Farmers Home Administration Act of 1961, as amended, and earlier, from the Farmers Home Administration Act of 1946. Other authorizations are derived from legislation which is broader in scope. For example, rural housing loans are made under provisions of Title V of the Housing Act of 1949, and economic opportunity loans are made under provisions of the Economic Opportunity Act of 1964. Since authorizations emanate from a number of different legislative Acts passed by Congress over a period of years, some overlapping has occurred. However, the various types of loans can be classified in a general way in three groups, as outlined in the discussion of objectives of the Farmers Home Administration, given above.

Loans To Aid Individual Farmers or Groups of Farmers

Loans to strengthen the economic position of individual farmers include those made to farmers individually and those made to groups of farmers. This distinction is obvious in the discussion of the various types of loans.

OPERATING LOANS

Operating loans are made primarily to enable farmers to obtain chattel resources essential to successful farm operation. They are made largely to help family-type farmers improve the use of their land and labor resources by making needed changes in their farming systems and by adopting improved farm practices. Funds may be advanced to pay for other farm and home operating needs; to make minor real estate improvements; and to refinance chattel debts. The distribution of active operating loans throughout the United States June 30, 1966, is indicated by Figure 27.2.

In order to qualify for an operating loan a farmer must have a *good* character rating. To go with the supplementary training and supervision provided by FHA, he must have the necessary experience, training, and managerial ability to operate a family-type farm. The income from his farming operations plus income from other sources must be sufficient to support his family and repay the loan. Both owners and tenants are eligible for these loans.

The size of operating loans depends upon the system of farming to be followed and the actual needs of the applicant. About 75 per cent of the initial operating loans to full-time farmers are made to enable the borrower to make a major change or reorganization in his farming program. The size of these adjustment type loans averaged approximately $10,000 during the year 1966. However, the size of operating loans varies widely. Loans range from a few thousand dollars up to $35,000. A borrower's total outstanding indebtedness for operating loans may not exceed $35,000.

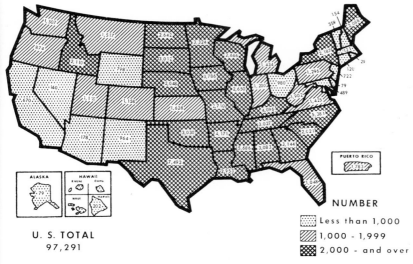

U. S. TOTAL
97,291

NUMBER

☷ Less than 1,000
▨ 1,000 - 1,999
▦ 2,000 - and over

Fig. 27.2—Number of operating loans outstanding, by states, June 30, 1966.
(Courtesy of the Farmers Home Administration.)

The repayment period for operating loans, which are made at 5 per cent interest, depends upon the use made of the funds. Loans are planned for specific purposes such as operating expenses and purchase of livestock and machinery necessary to put the farm and home plan in operation. Appropriate dates are arranged in advance for payments on each loan. Loan funds advanced to meet operating expenses during a crop year generally will be repaid when that year's income is received. Funds loaned to buy livestock and equipment are repaid over a period of years. The repayment schedule for these loans is based on income available after reasonable expenses are met, and consideration is given to making payments on the borrower's other debts. These livestock and equipment loans qualify as intermediate-term credit since the repayment period can be extended up to seven years. Where conditions warrant, deferments also can be granted, extending the period to a maximum of twelve years.

A cardinal principle in the operating loan program is that the farm and home plan must reflect enough income from the farm and other sources to provide an adequate living for the farm family, meet farm operating expenses, and enable the family to repay their debts and have a reasonable reserve to meet unforeseen emergencies.

FARM OWNERSHIP LOANS

Farm ownership loans of the Farmers Home Administration are for the purpose of helping farm families become successfully established on owner-operated farms. Having their origin in the Bankhead-Jones Farm Tenant Act of 1937, they are made under provisions of the Consolidated Farmers Home Administration Act of 1961, as amended, from funds advanced by private lenders and insured by the Farmers Home Administration, and from direct funds authorized by Congress. The same standards for farms and farmer's eligibility are followed for both insured and direct loans. The distribution of active farm ownership loans throughout the United States June 30, 1966, is indicated by Figure 27.3.

Farm ownership loans may be used for a wide range of items:

1. Purchase and enlargement of farms.
2. Development and improvement of farm land.
3. Carrying out basic land treatment practices such as liming, fertilizing, and seeding.
4. Construction, improvement, and repair of farm buildings and of the farm home.
5. Drilling wells and otherwise improving water supply systems for home use, livestock, and irrigation.
6. Providing drainage systems.
7. Establishing and improving farm forests, including clearing and preparing land for planting, buying seed or seedlings, and establishing approved forestry practices.
8. Providing facilities to produce fish under controlled conditions.
9. Financing recreational enterprises which will supplement farm income, including purchase and development of land, construction of buildings and other facilities, and purchase of equipment. Recreational enterprises which may be financed on family

farms include camping grounds, swimming facilities, tennis courts, riding stables, vacation cottages, lakes and ponds for boating, nature trails, and picnic grounds.
10. Refinancing debts.

A unique feature of the farm ownership program is the provision allowing direct or insured loans up to the normal value of the farm as determined by trained appraisers of the Farmers Home Administration. However, a farm ownership loan may not exceed the normal value of the farm and other security less any debts

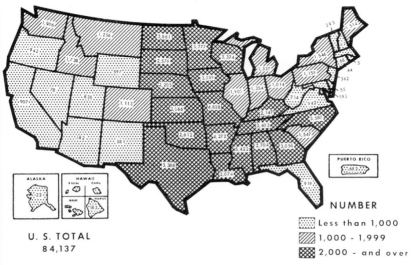

U. S. TOTAL
84,137

NUMBER

Less than 1,000
1,000 - 1,999
2,000 - and over

Fig. 27.3—Number of farm ownership loans outstanding, by states, June 30, 1966. (Courtesy of the Farmers Home Administration.)

against the property. Fears that this policy would encourage overborrowing have proved unfounded. The amount loaned may not exceed the amount certified by the county committee, and since the county committee is, in a sense, responsible for the success of the borrower, committees are not anxious to have borrowers loaded with debt they cannot repay.

A farm ownership loan, plus any other debts against the security, may not exceed $60,000. The interest rate is 5 per cent annually on the unpaid principal, except that the rate is 3 per cent on funds used for forestry purposes under an approved management plan. The maximum term is 40 years. When justified, the first payment of interest and principal on loans for approved forestry purposes may be deferred for up to 15 years. Loans are secured by a mortgage on the farm, including chattels and other suitable security. Just as with operating loans, supervision and assistance is provided by the FHA to help assure success of the loan.

Loan payments are due on January 1 each year. Borrowers are encouraged to build a reserve fund in years of good income to help keep the loan in good standing during low income years. This reserve fund plan has entirely replaced the variable payment plan specifically authorized in the 1937 Act.

The variable payment plan provided for payments to be based upon the amount of net cash income available after necessary living expenses were deducted. It was used on an optional basis for a period of years but was discontinued for a number of reasons. Among other things, it was hard to administer and a fully satisfactory basis could seldom be arrived at for determining payments which should be made.

RECREATION LOANS

The Farmers Home Administration may finance recreational enterprises as a part of operating and farm ownership loans. It also has authority to make loans for recreation development under the Food and Agriculture Act of 1962, as amended.

The motivating thrust behind this loan authorization is to shift unneeded and marginal cropland into other more useful and more profitable purposes and to provide rural communities with needed recreation facilities. Loans may also be made to individual farmers to develop marshes and swamps into profitable wildlife hunting areas; to dam creeks and to enlarge ponds and small lakes into fishing and swimming facilities; and to transform woodlands into profitable campsites. In this authorization, recreation was recognized as a new enterprise for farmers.

Loans can be made to individual farmers for this purpose, at 5 per cent annual interest, up to $35,000 on a short- or intermediate-term basis, and up to $60,000 on a long-term basis.

EMERGENCY LOANS

Emergency loans are made by the Farmers Home Administration in designated areas where farmers and ranchers temporarily are unable to obtain needed credit from other sources. An area is designated eligible for emergency credit by the Secretary of Agriculture when he determines that a production disaster such as a drouth or flood creates in the area a widespread need for agricultural credit which cannot be met for a temporary period from private and cooperative lenders or the regular FHA lending program. New legislation now makes it possible to make emergency loans to individual farmers, outside designated disaster areas, who are eligible for such credit.

Emergency loans are made by the FHA from a revolving fund established by Congress in 1949. They are made only to farmers or ranchers who are primarily engaged in farming, have reasonable prospects for success, and are unable temporarily to obtain needed credit from banks or other responsible sources. Applicants, to be eligible, must have suffered substantial production losses.

Loans may be made for the purchase of feed, seed, fertilizer, replacement equipment, and livestock; for other essential farm and home operating expenses; and for the replacement or repair of buildings, fences, and drainage and irrigation systems damaged or destroyed by a disaster. Loans may not be made for refinancing existing debts or to compensate applicants for their losses.

The interest rate is 3 per cent on emergency loans. Repayment schedules depend upon the purposes for which funds are advanced and upon the estimated income of the applicant. For example, loans for crop production are usually scheduled for repayment when income from the crops is normally received. Loans for replacement of livestock and equipment are repayable over periods from 1 to 5 years, while loans for the repair of buildings and other improvements to real estate are usually repayable over periods from 1 to 10 years.

In times of extreme emergency such as occurred with the aftermath of Hurricane Betsy in 1965, which devastated much of southern Louisiana, the Farmers Home Administration sets up special "emergency" offices and brings in additional personnel to handle the credit needs of the area.

RURAL HOUSING LOANS

Loans for housing can be made to individual farmers under the farm ownership lending authority, as outlined above. The Farmers Home Administration also makes and insures rural housing loans under Title V of the Housing Act of 1949, as amended in 1961 and 1962, and under the Housing Act of 1964. This legislation also makes provision for grants up to $1,000 for minor repairs and improvements to poverty level farmers.

These loans may be made to farmers and other residents in

rural areas and small communities with populations of not more than 5,500, which are not part of or closely associated with an urban area. The individual must satisfy certain specified requirements, including having sufficient income to pay operating and family living expenses, and meet interest and principal payments on debts, including the proposed rural housing loan. Special provisions are provided for rural senior citizens who are 62 years of age and over.

Funds may be used to finance building sites, and to construct adequate economically designed homes and essential farm improvements. In addition to major construction, funds are available to modernize homes—add bathrooms, central heating, modern kitchens, and other home improvements—as well as to enlarge or remodel farm service buildings and related facilities such as yard fences and driveways. A farmer may borrow funds to provide buildings for his own use or for the use of his tenants and laborers.

The maximum repayment term on rural housing loans is 33 years. The interest rate is 5 per cent for low and moderate income rural families and 5¾ per cent for families above the moderate income level. Rural housing loans are made only to applicants who are unable to obtain the credit they need from private and cooperative lenders on reasonable terms and conditions, a requirement that applies to all FHA loans. The FHA universal refinancing rule also applies, each borrower being expected to refinance the unpaid balance of the loan when able to obtain such refinancing at reasonable rates and terms from other lenders. Loans over $1,500 are generally secured by a mortgage on real estate or chattels, or other suitable property.

Rural housing insured loans and grants also may be made to associations of farmers to provide farm labor housing, including facilities for kitchens, dining halls, and appropriate health and recreational facilities. Terms are similar to those outlined above.

WATERSHED LOANS

Local organizations that are protecting and developing land and water resources in small watersheds can obtain loans from the Farmers Home Administration to help finance the projects. These loans are authorized by the Watershed Protection and Flood Prevention Act of 1954, as amended.

Eligible local organizations include soil conservation districts, irrigation districts, drainage districts, flood prevention or control districts, and similar organizations. The local organization must lack sufficient funds and be unable to borrow the needed funds at reasonable rates and terms from any other established source.

Loan funds may be used to install, repair, or improve facilities; store and convey irrigation water to farms; drain farm areas; stabilize annual stream flow; store water for such purposes as municipal water supply, recreation, fish and wildlife improvement, pollution abatement, and for similar purposes. Only watershed projects approved by the Soil Conservation Service are eligible for loans.

Loans are scheduled for repayment within the shortest period consistent with the borrowers' abilities to repay, but not to exceed 50 years. The interest rate is determined by the average rate paid by the United States Treasury on certain of its outstanding obligations at the beginning of the fiscal year in which the loan is made. Once the interest rate is set on a loan, it does not change during the life of the loan.

GRAZING ASSOCIATION LOANS

Under legislation enacted in 1962, the Farmers Home Administration is authorized to make loans to nonprofit associations of family farmers and ranchers up to $4 million. Funds can be used to purchase land; to secure grazing rights and leases; to construct necessary facilities; for water development; and for land and pasture improvement, including brush removal and necessary conservation programs. Shifting land and water resources to better uses, including the development of recreational areas and game and wildlife facilities, may also qualify for loans.

The term of the loan may not exceed 40 years and the interest rate is 5 per cent.

Loans To Improve Communities

Loans to help improve communities include some loans to individuals or groups of individuals, and loans to the communities themselves. The distinction is evident in the brief discussion given of the various types of loans.

HOUSING LOANS

Loans to farmers and other rural people for owner occupancy and for occupancy by tenants and laborers was discussed above. These loans improve rural communities. The Farmers Home Administration makes loans also under Title V of the Housing Act of 1949, as amended in 1962 and in 1966 to provide rental housing in rural communities (up to 5,500 population) for senior citizens 62 years of age and older, and farm families. Insured loans may be made to individuals, trusts, associations, partnerships, and corporations, including municipal corporations or other corporate agencies of a state or local government. Direct loans may be made to private nonprofit corporations or to cooperatives.

Applicants must be able to incur the obligations of the loan, give adequate security, and have sufficient income for repayment. They must also have the ability and intention of maintaining and operating the housing for the purposes for which the loan was made.

The interest rate is 3 per cent of the unpaid principal on direct loans and 5¾ per cent on insured loans. The maximum repayment period is 50 years for a direct loan and 40 years for an insured loan. A direct or insured loan may not exceed $300,000, or the development cost, or the value of the security, whichever is least. The appraised value of the security is determined by FHA. Ordinarily, a mortgage will be taken on the housing and the site as security for the loan. Additional security may be required.

WATER AND WASTE DISPOSAL LOANS

The Farmers Home Administration makes loans and grants to public bodies and nonprofit organizations primarily serving rural residents and towns (up to 5,500 population) to develop and install community irrigation and domestic water supply systems, and to install waste disposal systems.

A borrower's total indebtedness for these loans together with any assistance in the form of grants cannot exceed $4 million at any one time. The interest rate varies but may not exceed 5 per cent. The maximum term is 40 years. However, no repayment period will exceed the statutory limitation on the organization's borrowing authority nor the useful life of the improvement or facility to be financed. Loans are secured by bonds or notes pledging taxes, assessments or revenues, providing they meet statutory requirements. A mortgage may also be taken on the organization's facilities when state law permits.

RURAL COMMUNITY RECREATION LOANS

The Farmers Home Administration makes or insures loans to rural community groups to finance recreational facilities. To be eligible, the proposed facilities must be of service primarily to farmers and other rural residents by either direct use or economic benefits. The community group must have legal capacity to borrow and repay money, to pledge security for loans, and to operate the facilities. Recreational facilities financed include ponds, lakes, parks, picnic areas, athletic fields, golf courses, target ranges, ski slopes, camping facilities, dining halls, hunting areas, preserves, and the like.

A borrower's total indebtedness for these loans cannot exceed $4 million. The interest rate is 5 per cent on the unpaid principal. The maximum term of loan is 40 years. However, loans are scheduled for repayment within the shortest time consistent with the borrower's ability to pay. No loan term may exceed the statutory limitation on the organization's borrowing authority nor the useful life of the improvement or facility financed. Bonds or notes pledging taxes, assessments, or revenues are accepted as security if they meet statutory requirements. A mortgage also is taken on the organization's facilities when state law permits.

Loans To Alleviate Rural Poverty

Under the Economic Opportunity Act of 1964, the Farmers Home Administration makes loans to rural families with low incomes and to cooperatives who furnish essential processing, purchasing, and marketing services; supplies; or facilities to low income rural families.

ECONOMIC OPPORTUNITY LOANS TO RURAL FAMILIES

Loans are made to low income farm and nonfarm rural families who need small amounts of capital to improve their earnings but are unable to obtain credit from other sources, including regular loan programs of the Farmers Home Administration, at reasonable rates and terms. Farmers may use economic opportunity loans for almost any farm business purpose. Farmers and nonfarmers may use these loan funds to finance such nonagricultural enterprises as well drilling, machinery repair, marketing services, guide services, trucking, carpentry, and clothing repair.

The total amount of loan to any one family may not exceed $3,500. The interest rate is $4\frac{1}{8}$ per cent annually on the unpaid principal. Each loan is scheduled for repayment within a period consistent with the borrower's ability to repay, with the maximum term being 15 years. Loans generally are secured with a promissory note and a loan agreement, plus a mortgage on property if such is available.

LOANS TO COOPERATIVES

Loans are made to cooperatives to provide services, supplies, or facilities not otherwise available and which serve to raise the income and living standards of low income rural families.

Each loan is scheduled for repayment over a period not exceeding 30 years. The interest rate is $4\frac{1}{8}$ per cent. In most cases a lien on real and personal property of the cooperative, including present and future inventory and assignment of income, will be taken as security for the loan.

QUESTIONS AND PROBLEMS

1. Outline and discuss the factors which brought the Farmers Home Administration lending program into being.
2. Outline the organization of FHA.
3. What are the objectives of the FHA?
4. What are the sources of funds for FHA loans?
5. What are the special features of FHA loans?
6. Outline the types of loans which are made by FHA. Are the various types necessary? Why not have just one broad type of loan that would include all the different types?
7. What are FHA operating loans? Discuss.
8. What are FHA farm ownership loans? What is their purpose? Discuss.
9. Compare farm ownership loans with insurance company and Federal Land Bank loans. Make comparisons in terms of interest rates, loan terms, payment plans, stock, availability, maximum loans, and loan procedure.
10. What are the dangers in making long-term loans for 100 per cent of farm value? What are the advantages?
11. Would a program similar to the farm ownership program be practical and profitable for a private agency? Discuss.
12. What are the social gains in the farm ownership program?
13. How does the FHA farm mortgage insurance program work? If the interest rates were higher would the loans expand rapidly?
14. Outline the features of the other FHA loans. Discuss each.

REFERENCES

Administrator of the Farmers Home Administration, *Annual Reports.*
Approaches to Income Improvement in Agriculture, ARS, USDA, Prod. Res. Rept. 33, Aug.. 1959.

Benedict, Murray, *Can We Solve The Farm Problem?* Twentieth Century Fund, Lord Baltimore Press, Inc., Baltimore, Md., 1955.

Christiansen, R. A., Staniforth, S. D., and Walton, Richard, *Effectiveness of Development Credit in Facilitating Rural Adjustments,* Dept. Agr. Econ., Univ. of Wisc. and Farm Econ. Div., ERS, USDA, cooperating, Ag. Ec. 45, Oct., 1965.

Collins, G. P., Neufeld, G. H., and Hunter, T. K., *Credit and Capital Growth: A Study of Farmers Home Administration Borrowers in Southeastern Oklahoma,* Okla. Exp. Sta. Processed Series P-490, Jan., 1965.

Hendrix, William E., *Approaches to Income Improvement in Agriculture—Experiences of Families Receiving Poduction Loans Under the Farmers Home Administration.* ARS, USDA, Rept. 33, Aug., 1959.

Holmberger, Peter, and Dahl, Reynold, *Financing Farms With 100 Percent Loans,* Minn. Agr. Exp. Sta. Bul. 447, 1958.

Loan Program of the Farmers Home Administration, Farmers Home Admin., USDA, PA 360, Dec., 1959.

Maris, Paul V., *The Land Is Mine—From Tenancy to Family Farm Ownership.* Agr. Monograph No. 8, USDA, Nov., 1950.

Saulnier, R. J., Halcrow, H. G., and Jacoby, N. H., *Federal Housing and Loan Insurance,* Princeton Univ. Press, Princeton, N.J., 1958.

Chapter 28

A SUMMARY COMPARISON AND ANALYSIS OF AGRICULTURAL LENDERS

THE objective of this chapter is to present a summary comparison of the items which comprise the basic framework of the major types of lenders and show how these characteristics influence their farm loans. The comparison will include the types of lending agencies discussed in Part II. Individuals who make loans will also be included in some of the comparisons. Some new material will be included to supplement that presented in earlier chapters.

OWNERSHIP AND CONTROL

A universal truism is that those in control, given the legal framework of the business, determine the policies and procedures under which it operates. The owners of a business are generally considered to exercise control. However, there is considerable variation from one lender to another in the amount of control exercised relative to ownership, and in the "remoteness" or indirectness of the control. Hence, in comparing lenders it is important to consider who is in control, together with the role of ownership in establishing control, since this has a bearing on loan policy and the service rendered in extending credit. Merchant and dealer firms owned by individuals or partnerships will be briefly considered first. Corporations will receive major attention, however, since they comprise the

490

dominant type of lending institution and since there is considerable variation among them in the relationship of ownership and control. Lending agencies owned by the government are not discussed in this section, it being sufficient to observe that they are instrumentalities of the government.

A merchant or dealer who owns the business he operates is typically in full control and establishes the policies and procedures in extending credit. He also has control over putting the policies and procedures into effect. The situation is similar when such a business is owned by a partnership. However, the control is not quite so direct since the owners must get together and determine the policies and procedures to be followed. The amount of control exercised by each of the owners depends upon the nature of the partnership and the interest, time, and ability of the individuals involved.

When a corporate form of business organization is involved, the control exercised by owners becomes somewhat more remote or indirect. The "chain of control" is lengthened since a board of directors, elected by the owners, is inserted. Thus, the stockholders of a corporation exercise indirect control through the board of directors.

While corporations are owned and indirectly controlled by their stockholders, or by the policyholders in the case of mutual life insurance companies, major differences prevail in the relative amount of control which may be exercised by individual owners due to differences in laws under which corporations are organized. Stockholders of commercial banks, stock insurance companies, and merchant-dealer corporations may exercise control in proportion to ownership; i.e. each share has one vote. On the other hand, owners (policyholders) of mutual insurance companies and "borrower stockholders" of the lending institutions comprising the Farm Credit System each have one vote irrespective of the degree of ownership. The term "borrower stockholders" is a generalization. The following, provided by the Farm Credit Administration, gives more detailed information regarding the voting strength of associations in electing district board members and in nominating persons for consideration of the President of the United States when he makes appointments to the Federal Farm Credit Board:

Federal Land Bank Associations—Each association is entitled to cast for one person a number of votes equal to the number of its stockholders, and the number of stockholders must be specified in the resolution adopted by the directors at the time of voting.

Production Credit Associations—Each association is entitled to cast for one person a number of votes equal to the number of its class B stockholders, and the number must be specified in the resolution adopted by the directors at the time of voting.

Cooperative Associations—Each cooperative association eligible to vote is entitled to one vote. An association is eligible to vote if (1) it is a holder of stock in the District Bank for Cooperatives issued before 1956; or (2) it is a holder of class C stock in the District Bank for Cooperatives, has been a borrower from the District Bank within the period April 1, ——— (date two years previous to election year), through March 31, ——— (date of election year), and continues to be eligible to borrow from the Bank.

Note that only "borrowing stockholders" have a right to vote in the latter type of lending institutions; i.e. stockholders who are not borrowers, including the Federal government, do not have a right to vote. Control exercised by the owners is further modified in the case of the banks in the Farm Credit System by appointment of one member of each board of directors by the Governor of the Farm Credit Administration with the advice and consent of the Federal Board.

Corporations organized under laws which provide that each share shall have one vote tend to be controlled by relatively few large stockholders. Substantial blocks of stock usually can elect at least one member of the board of directors. The stockholder himself may choose to serve or he may select someone else to represent his interests. Such directors often are also elected officers of the corporation by the board. Concentration of control in hands of large stockholders probably is a good thing, since such stockholders generally devote enough time and attention to affairs of the company to make it successful. Supervisory authorities for commercial banks encourage concentration of ownership in small banks to help assure success. The effect of such concentration of control on credit extension to farmers depends upon the policies established and the quality of management selected to put the policies into action. These points will be considered further in later sections of the chapter.

A final point to be considered in analyzing ownership and control of corporations from the viewpoint of credit extension is the relationship of the owners to the borrowers. In institutions comprising the Farm Credit System, the owners, who exercise control, and the borrowers are one and the same. This situation prevails to a limited degree with some country banks where farmers are major stockholders. But in most corporate lending institutions, including most commercial banks, the vast majority of the stockholders are not farmer borrowers. Obviously, when the borrowers are the owners they can, within limitations of their charter and regulations of supervisory authority, run the institution to provide themselves with maximum credit service. Moreover, the policies and procedures they adopt may have a beneficial influence on farm loan policies of other lenders. One note of caution should be kept in mind, however. Since the borrowers exercise control, they may unintentionally adopt policies which are in their own favor. Lending institutions which are owned and controlled by individuals representing various sectors of the economy (assuming such lenders exist) probably are in a better position to weigh the credit needs of agriculture in light of the needs of the community as a whole.

QUALITY OF MANAGEMENT

Quality of management probably is of greater significance in the finance field than in most other businesses because of the leverage associated with use of credit. The fruits of good management are multiplied through the financial leverage which credit provides. Similarly, poor lender management, at best, has a dilatory effect on borrowers and sometimes the leverage effect is sufficient to cause loan breakdown and foreclosure.

What characteristics identify a farm lender as having good management? The answer to this question, from the viewpoint of credit extension, is indicated by the discussion of finance principles in Part I. A good lender should have the economic training needed to effectively use the Three R's in extension of credit. First, he should be able to analyze a business and determine whether the *returns* associated with use of credit are sufficient to justify its use; i.e. whether use of credit will be profitable. A knowledge of marginal analysis is crucial in answering this question. A knowledge of agriculture, including new technological developments, also is essential in order to properly formulate the physical relationships which comprise the base for economic analysis. Second, he should be able to analyze the *repayment capacity* of a farm business to determine how much credit can be repaid. Ways of increasing repayment capacity should be considered in this analysis. Third, he should be able to analyze the *risk-bearing ability* of the business to determine whether it is adequate to carry the risk involved in using credit. Consideration should be given in this connection to ways of increasing risk-bearing ability.

How do lenders measure up in terms of these requirements? While material available is inadequate to fully answer this question observation indicates there is wide variation among lenders. Some managers are well qualified, or have employed well-qualified men to handle their agricultural loans. In contrast, some lenders have few of the needed qualifications. Definite progress is being made, but many men in responsible positions in lending institutions do not have a college or university degree.[1] Furthermore, many of those who have completed a formal education have not majored in subject matter areas which provide the needed training. Engineering firms, for example, generally employ graduates who have majored in engineering to do engineering work. However, many lenders, particularly those who are inadequately trained themselves, do not see the advantage of employing men with the specialized training which is needed to be an outstanding lender. In an analysis of commercial bank and PCA lending to farmers, Leon F. Hesser, agricultural economist, Federal Reserve Bank of Kansas City, concludes that "Banks that wish to compete more vigorously for business of farmers who use relatively large amounts of credit . . . may wish to consider the advisability of employing persons trained in agriculture and agricultural lending and equipping themselves to handle large farm loans through correspondent relationships if this is necessary. By the same token, as credit needs of individual farms continue to expand, large city banks may find increasing potentials for farm departments equipped to advise correspondents on credit needs and worthiness of operators of large farms, and to participate in loans as needed to permit their correspondents to engage in this business."[2]

MAJOR REASON FOR MAKING LOANS

The way in which a lender performs is dependent not only upon the level of management involved but also upon the objective the lender has for being in business. The latter has a major bearing upon the policies adopted and the loan procedures which are followed.

A lender usually is in business to maximize profits or to render

[1] For example, a study of 209 banks showed that only 69 per cent of the senior officers were college graduates. See: Frank S. Endicott, "College Men in Banking," in *Banking*, Jour. American Bankers Assoc., Feb., 1967, p. 43.
[2] Leon F. Hesser, "Bank and PCA Lending to Farmers," *Federal Reserve Bulletin*, Board of Governors of the Federal Reserve System, Washington, D.C., Sept., 1963, p. 1233.

maximum service, or to accomplish both objectives. The primary objective of commercial banks and life insurance companies probably is to maximize profits. However, considerable attention is given to service as a means of promoting their major line of business. A commercial bank strives to create a favorable image of itself in the public mind with a view of increasing its deposits, a major requisite for greater earnings. Similarly, an insurance company strives to create a favorable image to promote sales of life insurance. However, the better lenders also recognize the unique role they can play through credit extension in terms of fostering a prosperous and progressive community. Commercial banks that have capable directors, and management with broad and extended vision, typically give attention to promoting a balanced economy in the community. For example, when money is tight, one type of business is not favored at the expense of others in order to maximize interest income in the short run. Rather, the limited supply of funds available is allocated among customers according to their "need" as judged by the bank's management. Moreover, worthwhile and promising business ventures are often given major encouragement in terms of financing—which may involve relatively high risk—and through counsel and advice. Capably managed life insurance companies give some attention to this type of service but it is not so self-evident since the "community" in which they make loans is often considerably larger than that of commercial banks.

Merchants and dealers customarily extend credit to promote their principal business of selling inputs to farmers or of marketing their products. Thus, most merchants and dealers are in business to make money, but the money is made in their primary line of business. A few merchants and dealers, however, extend credit with a view of making money on the financing itself.

The lending agencies included in the Farm Credit System extend credit as a service to their borrower-owners. The borrower-owners are naturally interested in making money on their individual farms by using credit provided through the Farm Credit System. But the agencies themselves operate on a cost basis, returning any net residual interest collected to the borrowers in the form of dividends.

The objective of the Farmers Home Administration in making loans is to render service. Service is rendered not only in terms of financing but also in terms of counsel and advice, and more specific supervision than is typically provided by lenders. Some aspects of FHA loans and activities extend beyond the customary bounds of financial service to include a certain amount of subsidy in the form of favorable loan terms, including 100 per cent financing with relatively low interest rates.

SOURCE OF LOAN FUNDS

Agricultural lenders may be classified in two general groups: (1) those who have, or who generate through their operations, the major part of their loan funds, and (2) those who borrow the major part of the funds they loan. Commercial banks, life insurance companies, some merchants and dealers, and individuals fall in the first group. Commercial banks obtain most of their loan funds from deposits, which are created by the commercial banking system. They are unique in this respect. Insurance companies derive their loan funds primarily from reserves accumulated in connection with their major line of business, insuring lives. Merchants and dealers in this group use accumulated capital and internally generated funds derived from operations for extending credit. Individuals obtain their loan funds from inheritance and savings.

The second group of lenders includes merchants and dealers extending credit who do not fall in the first group, the lending institutions of the Farm Credit System, the "other financing institutions" which discount loans with the Federal Intermediate Credit Banks, and the Farmers Home Administration. Merchants and dealers who are short on equity capital obtain loan funds from their parent wholesalers and manufacturers, or by borrowing from lending institutions, particularly from commercial banks. Farm cooperative merchant-dealer firms also borrow from the Banks for Cooperatives and commerical banks. The Federal Land Banks, Federal Intermediate Credit Banks, and the Banks for Cooperatives obtain the major part of their loan funds by sale of bonds or debentures. The principal categories of investors in these securities, in the approximate order of their importance, are as follows:[3]

Short-term Securities	Long-term Securities
1. Commercial banks	1. Trust and pension funds
2. Corporations (industrial)	2. States and municipalities
3. Savings banks	3. Insurance companies
4. States and municipalities	4. Savings banks
5. Mutual funds	5. Mutual funds
6. Insurance companies	6. Corporations (industrial)
7. Trust and pension funds	7. Commercial banks
8. Individuals	8. Individuals

[3] Finance Division, Farm Credit Administration, Washington, D.C.

The Production Credit Associations and the "other financing institutions" obtain their loan funds from the Federal Intermediate Credit Banks. The Farmers Home Administration obtains its loan funds from private investors on an insured basis, and from funds provided by the Federal government.

DEPENDABILITY OF LOAN FUNDS

A number of factors are involved in considering the dependability of a lender's loan funds. The type, term, and size of loans made by a lender relate to the dependability of his loan service from these points of view. These aspects of the subject are considered in the following section. In this section attention is directed to dependability of loan funds in terms of the supply available and the ability of the lender, or of farm loans, to compete for use of the available funds. Lenders will be considered in two groups, according to the source of their loan funds, as outlined in the preceding section.

Lenders Who Have or Generate Their Own Loan Funds

Dependability of loan funds of lenders who have or generate their own funds naturally depends upon the supply of such funds which are available. The dependability of farm loan funds depends, in turn, on the ability of farm loans to compete with other loans and investments.

COMMERCIAL BANKS

Since commercial bank loan funds are derived primarily from deposits, their dependability is related to the volume of deposits. Deposits naturally fluctuate with the level of business activity, and bank loan volume fluctuates in a somewhat similar manner. The amount of farm loans held by commercial banks over a long period of years was portrayed in Figures 16.1 and 16.2 of Chapter 16. These charts dramatically portray the large changes which have occurred in the volume of farm loans held by banks. Changes in nonreal-estate loans have been particularly marked. During the Great Depression a sharp reduction occurred in bank loans, due, in part, to the large number of bank failures. The likelihood that such a sharp reduction will occur in the foreseeable future seems rather remote. Insurance provided by the Federal Deposit Insurance Corporation has a stabilizing effect on commercial bank deposits. The Federal Reserve System is currently a much more effective force in the economy than formerly. Moreover, Federal Reserve policy is to provide ample reserves in periods of recession or depression and to restrict the amount of reserves available in prosperous periods.

Within this framework of supply, good farm loans generally compete effectively for available bank loan funds. The policy of progressive bankers in promoting a balanced economy in the community may be a factor in the favorable treatment accorded farm loans. In many cases higher interest returns could be realized elsewhere, due in part to interest rate competition provided by Government-sponsored farm credit agencies.

INSURANCE COMPANIES

The volume of life insurance company funds available for loans and investments has shown a strong growth trend over a long period of years. Even during periods of depression the volume has expanded, albeit at a slower rate, since the volume of reserves continued to grow. Hence, the dependability of insurance company farm loan funds depends basically upon the ability of farm loans to compete with other loans and investments for the funds which are available. Policy loans have prior claim on funds since they constitute an obligation included in many company policies. The remainder of a company's funds usually is allocated to various types of loans and investments by management. Companies which allocate funds to agriculture are fairly consistent in their allocations. However, they also tend to be somewhat inflexible when demand for funds is strong, with the result that a farm loan representative may run out of funds before the end of the year. The situation was particularly acute in the latter part of 1966, for example, due to the exceptionally strong and widespread demand for loan funds, and the large expansion in policy loans (due to the tight money situation and the favorable interest rates on such loans) which necessitated some cutback in farm loan fund allocations by a number of companies. It should be recognized also that life insurance companies are in the business of insuring lives and, therefore, follow business practices in extending credit which will promote this endeavor. Thus, if a certain area is unprofitable, farm loan service likely is discontinued in that area. Similarly, if a certain size or type of loan proves unprofitable, the company probably will discontinue making such loans. For example, the low level of farm income was a major factor in the contraction of insurance company farm loans during the Great Depression (see Figure 16.1).

MERCHANTS AND DEALERS

Merchants and dealers who have or generate their own loan funds generally extend credit to customers with good credit ratings, if necessary, to facilitate sales or to increase the volume of products marketed. In this sense they constitute a dependable source of credit. However, they may have an inflexible policy of adjusting repayment terms if difficulties arise. Moreover, since most merchants and dealers extend credit only in connection with sales and marketing of products, they are not a normal source of credit for other purposes. There are, however, some exceptions to this generalization; e.g. cotton gins may extend a fairly broad line of credit to farmers as a means of increasing their ginning business.

INDIVIDUALS

Individuals vary widely in terms of dependability as a source of credit. Some constitute a dependable source. However, as a group, they are considered to be a comparatively undependable source of credit. Observe the large contraction in real estate loans held by "individuals and others" during the Great Depression, portrayed in Figure 16.1. Individuals often need their funds for family living or other purposes in difficult times—just at the time when the farmer often is also in great need of funds.

Lenders Who Borrow Their Loan Funds

Dependability of loan funds of lenders who borrow the major part of the money they loan naturally depends upon their ability to borrow. Ability to borrow in this context refers primarily to funds being available to borrow and to a lender's ability to bid successfully for them. However, the ability of a lender to qualify for a loan, and the position of supervisory authority, are also involved in some cases.

FARM CREDIT BANKS

As was indicated in the preceding section, the farm credit banks—the Federal Land Banks, the Federal Intermediate Credit

Banks, and the Banks for Cooperatives—borrow their loan funds from a wide range of sources. Economic forces at work in the economy affect these sources in much the same way that they affect the funds available to lenders in the first group. In fact, commercial banks and insurance companies, major lenders in the first group, also are major suppliers of funds for the farm credit banks. As a result, developments in the economy and actions of the Federal Reserve System which affect loan funds of commercial banks also affect loan funds of the farm credit banks. Similarly, management decisions of insurance companies have a direct bearing on farm credit bank loan funds. The economic forces which affect the supply of loan funds held by individuals also affect the amount of funds they have available for investment in farm credit bank securities.

Since the volume of loans held by the farm credit banks has increased over time, it is evident that they have been able to bid successfully for funds in the money markets. Purchases of farm credit bank securities by commercial banks and insurance companies pose interesting questions, however, since these lending institutions also are in the farm loan field. When the demand for loans is strong and money is tight, do these institutions restrict their purchases of farm credit bank securities? If so, how does this affect the supply, dependability, and cost of farm credit bank loan funds?

Farm Credit Administration officials indicate that purchases of farm credit bank securities by commercial banks and insurance companies vary considerably from time to time, particularly those made by banks. For example, while commercial banks typically rank first among purchasers of short-term farm credit bank securities, during 1966 they ranked second due to the tight money situation. The fact that they did not drop further is significant, however, since it indicates that commercial banks as a group have substantial funds for investment in securities even during tight money periods. All commercial banks maintain investments in securities to provide secondary reserves for deposits. While they usually concentrate on Government securities, commercial banks consider the return which can be realized on their investments. Hence, the farm credit banks usually can obtain commercial bank funds by providing an attractive yield. Moreover, some banks regularly maintain large holdings of securities, which adds to the flow of commercial bank funds available for investment in securities at all times.

The situation is somewhat similar with life insurance companies. Some companies put a small percentage of their funds in loans, preferring to concentrate on securities. Even those companies which concentrate on loans maintain a substantial security portfolio. Thus, a large amount of insurance company funds are usually available for investments in securities—Government bonds, and corporate bonds and stocks. Moreover, judging from the historical pattern of their investments, insurance companies prefer high quality issues which provide a good return. Being of high quality, farm credit bank securities probably could attract a considerable volume of insurance company funds, even when money is tight, providing the yields are sufficiently attractive.

Farm credit bank securities undoubtedly can also draw investment funds from other sources if the price is right. During 1966, for example, individuals were relatively heavy investors in these securities since the yield was relatively high compared with returns paid by building and loan associations, commercial banks, and similar institutions on savings accounts. There are limits to how far such bidding can go, however.

Proper perspective should be maintained regarding the overall volume of funds available in the economy compared with the credit demand. Credit is a commodity subject to forces of supply and demand the same as any other commodity marketed under free competition. Hence, in selling securities in the money market the farm credit banks compete with other users of funds and their success depends upon the price they are willing to pay for funds compared with other bidders. Obviously, when money is tight the price moves up sharply. This was the situation in the fall of 1966.

As a precaution against things getting out of hand, the Federal government entered the arena in the fall of 1966. The President asked heads of departments and all Federal lending agencies to review their operations to assure that loans made were for essential and nonpostponable needs. He also asked them to examine policies and operations with a view to reducing their borrowings in the money market. The general policy applied to all agencies that obtain funds in the market, was to limit public offerings of securities for the balance of the year to amounts not exceeding maturing issues. Any additional funds were to be obtained from the Treasury. In conformance with this policy, the Treasury purchased some farm credit bank securities in the latter part of 1966. Moreover, Treasury officials recognized the importance of credit in agricultural production and marketing and indicated that necessary requirements would have a very high priority—next to national defense.

Considering this and earlier history, it is evident that the Federal government is a significant factor in the supply and dependability of farm credit bank loan funds. During the period 1917–21, the Treasury purchased Federal Land Bank bonds because war financing interfered with normal functioning of the money markets. During the Great Depression of the 1930's the Federal government came to the rescue of the Federal Land Banks since, due to the depressed conditions in agriculture and in the economy generally, the price of the Banks' bonds had declined so much that additional public issues were not feasible. During the fall of 1966 the Treasury again gave direct support, as indicated above, by purchasing some farm credit bank securities and, also, by giving necessary credit for agricultural production and marketing a priority next to national defense. Hence, the Federal government has contributed directly to the supply and dependability of loan funds of the farm credit banks during both depression and tight money situations. Furthermore, while farm credit bank securities sold to the investing public are not guaranteed by the Government, assistance of the Government, coupled with its sponsorship and control of the System, provides indirect support for such issues. It should be recognized, however, that the control exercised by the Government basically serves only to limit the supply and dependability of loan funds during tight money periods to that necessary for essential agricultural purposes.

PCA'S AND OFI'S

Since *Production Credit Associations* obtain practically all the funds which they loan from the Federal Intermediate Credit Banks, the supply and dependability of their loan funds are directly related to the supply and dependability of loan funds of the FICB's. The situation is similar for funds which the *other financing institutions* obtain from the Federal Intermediate Credit Banks. These statements are based upon the assumption that the individual PCA's and OFI's are managed and operated in such a manner that they qualify to discount loans with a Federal Intermediate Credit Bank. This is not a particular problem as far as the PCA's are concerned since they are under the supervision of the Federal Intermediate Credit Banks, and since most PCA's have developed substantial surplus and reserves. More uncertainty is involved with some OFI's, however, in that they may qualify to discount loans with a Federal Intermediate Credit Bank for a period of time and then discontinue the affiliation. Obviously, the Federal Intermediate Credit Bank contributes to the supply and dependability of an OFI's loan funds only so long as it is qualified to discount loans.

MERCHANTS AND DEALERS

The dependability of loan funds of merchants and dealers who borrow the funds they lend is subject to the same limitations outlined above in the discussion of merchants and dealers who have or generate their own loan funds. In addition, loan funds of the borrowing merchant-dealer group are affected directly by policies of the lender from whom the funds are obtained, and indirectly by the forces which influence the loan funds of the lender.

FARMERS HOME ADMINISTRATION

Since this is a Government lending agency, the supply and dependability of its loan funds depend upon the Congress. Furthermore, loans can be made only to those unable to obtain credit from other sources on reasonable terms and conditions. Within this framework the supply and dependability of funds vary according to the policy of the administration in power and the lending authority involved. As a general rule, loan funds probably are inadequate to satisfy the demands. However, emergency loan funds have been adequate in most cases to meet the needs which have arisen.

Type, Term, and Size of Loans

The type and term of loans made by the various lenders are governed in large measure by the source of their loan funds. Since deposits of commercial banks are payable on demand, or on fairly short notice, commercial banks make short-term operating loans primarily. They also make quite a number of intermediate-term loans for working capital, and some long-term real estate loans. They are able to make some of these longer-term loans due to the high probability of always having a certain volume of deposits. The increase in recent years of time and savings deposits facilitates making more longer-term loans. Commercial banks make loans of all sizes, to all types of farmers. However, the capital structure of small country banks does not permit them to make as large loans as are required by some of the larger commercial farms. While large loans can be handled on a correspondent basis, commercial banks are sometimes reluctant to use this method. Thus, the operators of larger farms often look to larger commercial banks or to Production

Credit Associations for financing.[4] Since commercial banks usually make many small short-term loans to customers primarily as a service, the average size of commercial bank farm loans is somewhat smaller than those of other lenders.

Life insurance companies make long-term real estate loans since their loan funds are derived primarily from reserves accumulated on life insurance policies. Generally speaking, mortgage loans satisfy in a high degree the requirements of insurance companies as to security and yield. These companies typically choose to lend on large, well-managed farms in productive agricultural areas since returns realized are relatively high on such loans. They also select the areas in which they lend to minimize risk and achieve economy in making and servicing loans.

Since merchants and dealers typically extend credit only in connection with items sold or produce marketed, they usually make relatively small short- and intermediate-term chattel loans. Some merchants and dealers, however, extend large amounts of credit to finance sales of high-priced farm machinery, large farm operations, and the like.

The type of loan made by lending institutions in the Farm Credit System is determined by their respective charters. Federal Land Banks make long-term farm real estate loans. Having a responsibility to serve all credit-worthy types and sizes of farmers, the Federal Land Banks make loans of all sizes in all parts of the country. Their average size of loan is considerably smaller than that of life insurance companies, but substantially larger than real estate loans made by commercial banks. Production Credit Associations and the "other financing institutions" obtaining their funds from the Federal Intermediate Credit Banks make short- and intermediate-term chattel mortgage loans. The PCA's as a group provide credit service in all parts of the country, whereas the OFI's select the areas in which they operate. While PCA's have a responsibility to serve all farmers who qualify for a loan, there is some difference of opinion as to those who are suitable credit risks. Some have felt that certain PCA's tend to concentrate on the larger, more profitable loans and neglect or discourage smaller operators from using credit services of the association. Since each PCA is an independent credit agency responsible for meeting its own expenses and covering its own losses, members of a PCA naturally are interested in large, low-risk loans on which costs are low, since this enables the association to maintain

---

[4] Hesser, pp. 1224–33.

low interest and service charges. The OFI's generally finance relatively large, low-risk operations and, therefore, their loans average somewhat larger than those of PCA's operating in similar areas. The Banks for Cooperatives make all types and sizes of loans to farm cooperatives. Their real estate loans typically are for long-term periods, while chattel loans are for short or intermediate terms.

The Farmers Home Administration makes a wide range of types and sizes of loans to farmers, groups of farmers, and other people and groups in rural areas who are unable to obtain financing on reasonable rates and terms from commercial lenders. The size of FHA loans is governed by the amount required to provide sufficient income-producing capacity to support the family and repay the loan.

Loan Service in Light of the Three R's of Credit

Primary attention was given in Part I of the text to principles which serve as guides in extension and use of credit. These were considered in three groups, referred to as the Three R's of Credit. The objective of this section is to briefly analyze the major types of lenders in terms of this framework.

Returns

The first R of credit, it will be recalled, pertains to *returns produced* compared with the related costs. The question posed is, Will it pay to use credit and, if so, how much will it pay to employ? Three considerations are involved in this question: factor-factor relationships, factor-product relationships, and product-product relationships.

The economic objective in factor-factor considerations is to utilize relative amounts of factors which will minimize the cost of producing a product. As specified by Equation 5.6 given in Chapter 5, this condition is realized when

$$\frac{Py\frac{\Delta Y}{\Delta X_1}}{Px_1} = \frac{Py\frac{\Delta Y}{\Delta X_2}}{Px_2} = \cdots = \frac{Py\frac{\Delta Y}{\Delta X_n}}{Px_n} \tag{28.1}$$

where Y represents the product produced; Py is the price of the product; X_1, X_2, and X_n are the various factors of production used in producing product Y; and P_{x1}, P_{x2}, and P_{xn} are the prices of the various factors. To achieve these equalities, the manager obviously must be able to adjust the amount of the various factors utilized in producing the product. Credit extension by a single lender to acquire all factors facilitates adjusting the relative amounts of the various factors to achieve the desired balance.

How do the various lenders measure up when considered within this analytical framework? The Farmers Home Administration with its various lending authorities can provide a full line of credit; i.e. real estate credit, intermediate-term credit, and credit to acquire current production inputs. Moreover, these various lines of credit are obtained through the county office. This is important since the lender analyzes the entire business and gives managerial assistance in determining the amount of credit needed for various inputs to achieve maximum efficiency. Hence, the Farmers Home Administration ranks high in this regard. The same is true of the Banks for Cooperatives since they provide farm cooperatives with a full line of credit from a single source. It is also true for financing provided by some commercial banks; i.e. when the bank provides credit for all of a farmer's needs, including real estate, working capital, and current operations, through a single loan officer or department. Most commercial bank farm financing does not fall in this category, however, since the bulk of the credit provided by commercial banks is for current operations. Furthermore, some large banks extend farm credit through two or more departments. For example, machinery loans may be handled by the installment loan department, completely separate from the farm loan department which makes operating loans. Life insurance companies, the Federal Land Banks, the Production Credit Associations, and the "other financing institutions" all have similar weaknesses since each extends only a "partial" line of credit. Merchants and dealers, however, probably rank lowest in this respect since they usually extend credit only for certain items. Moreover, since credit is used as a vehicle to promote sales, it may well contribute directly to an imbalance in factor inputs; e.g. excessive farm machinery compared with other factors of production.

Equation 28.1 can also be written

$$\frac{\Delta Y P_y}{\Delta X_1 P_{x1}} = \frac{\Delta Y P_y}{\Delta X_2 P_{x2}} = \cdots = \frac{\Delta Y P_y}{\Delta X_n P_{xn}}. \tag{28.2}$$

Each $\Delta X P x$ in this equation represents a certain amount of capital, ΔC. Using i to represent the interest rate and subscripts $1, 2,$ and n

as relating to the different factors of production, Equation 28.2 may be written

$$\frac{\Delta Y P_y}{\Delta C_1 (1 + i_1)} = \frac{\Delta Y P_y}{\Delta C_2 (1 + i_2)} = \cdots = \frac{\Delta Y P_y}{\Delta C_n (1 + i_n)}. \qquad (28.3)$$

It is evident from this equation that the rate of interest charged has a direct bearing on the optimum amount of capital employed for various factors used in producing a product. Consider, for example, two farmers who use credit to finance purchase of fertilizer and machine parts. One farmer finances purchase of both types of factors with a 6 per cent commercial bank loan. In this case the optimum utilization of the two factors is achieved by using one dollar's worth of fertilizer for each dollar spent on machine parts. The second farmer also finances his fertilizer purchases with a 6 per cent bank loan, but uses dealer credit at 9 per cent interest for his machine parts. Under these circumstances, optimum utilization of the two factors is realized by using only about 97 cents' worth of machine parts for each dollar devoted to fertilizer. Hence, when one lender provides credit for a given factor of production and a second lender provides credit for another factor, any difference in interest rates charged by the two lenders will, theoretically, influence the relative amounts of capital used for the two types of factors.

Turning now to factor-product relationships, the objective is to increase the size of an enterprise to the point where marginal costs and marginal returns are equal. This relationship was expressed in Chapter 5 by Equation 5.7:

$$\Delta X_1 P_{x1} + \Delta X_2 P_{x2} + \cdots + \Delta X_n P_{xn} = \Delta Y P_y \qquad (28.4)$$

where ΔX_1, ΔX_2, and ΔX_n represent marginal inputs of factors used in producing product Y, the symbols P_{x1}, P_{x2}, and P_{xn} represent the prices of the various factors, and P_y represents the price of the product, Y. This equation was also written as

$$\Delta C(1 + i) = \Delta Y P_y \qquad (28.5)$$

with ΔC representing the marginal capital (exclusive of the cost of capital) and i representing the interest rate, to portray the optimum utilization of capital relative to its cost and the value of the associated product.

Considered in terms of this model, a lender who provides credit for all the inputs employed in producing a product is in the best position to assist the farmer in expanding the enterprise to the optimum size. Thus, the Farmers Home Administration, the Banks for Cooperatives, and commercial banks, which finance all of a farmer's requirements through a single loan department, rank high in this respect. Insurance companies, Federal Land Banks, Production Credit Associations, and "other financing institutions" are not in a position to render maximum credit service, in this sense, since they do not provide a full line of financing. Merchants and dealers rank lowest in terms of this model since they generally finance only certain inputs.

Considered from the point of view of product-product relationships, the objective is to balance use of credit so that the last (marginal) dollar used in each enterprise will produce the same amount of return. Farm income will be maximized, as indicated by Equation 5.9 of Chapter 5, when

$$\frac{\Delta Y_1 P_{y1}}{\Delta C(1 + i)} = \frac{\Delta Y_2 P_{y2}}{\Delta C(1 + i)} = \cdots = \frac{\Delta Y_n P_{yn}}{\Delta C(1 + i)} = 1 \, . \tag{28.6}$$

Obviously, a lender can be of maximum assistance to a farmer in achieving the equality indicated by this equation if he is in a position to provide all the financing required. With multiple lines of financing, the farmer derives little, if any, assistance from the lender in achieving an optimum balance in his business. In fact, when credit is used to promote sales, the lender may actually work against the farmer's interests of achieving the equality called for by Equation 28.6. Thus, the Farmers Home Administration ranks high in this respect. Theoretically, this permits FHA to achieve, subject to limitations on its size of loans to individual farmers, the optimum combination of resources indicated by Equation 28.6. The Banks for Cooperatives and commercial banks which provide a full line of credit through a single department also are in position to render a high level of service to farmers from the viewpoint of product-product relationships. On the other hand, most merchants and dealers probably are at the low end of the scale since they generally do not consider the overall aspects of the business in their financing.

Repayment Capacity

Four primary ways in which repayment capacity, the second R of credit, can be increased, as given in Chapter 9, are:

1. Building owner equity in the business
2. Organizing the business to increase net income
3. Using self-liquidating loans as far as possible
4. Planning the repayment schedule to conform with income

Organizing the business according to the principles outlined above in the discussion of *Returns* yields maximum net income and, in turn, facilitates building owner equity. Therefore, the analysis of lenders in terms of the first R of credit also applies to their contribution in terms of repayment capacity.

A loan is self-liquidating to the extent that the repayment schedule coincides with the rate at which proceeds of the loan are recouped as a part of gross farm income. Lenders who make operating loans generally schedule payments to coincide with sales of crops, livestock, or livestock products, so such loans generally are self-liquidating. However, lenders differ somewhat in this respect in financing working assets and fixed improvements. The Farmers Home Administration and the PCA's may now make intermediate-term loans for up to seven years. Thus, they are able to make self-liquidating loans on breeding livestock and milk cows, and on machinery and equipment which has a fairly short life. However, with normal use most machines will last for 10 to 15 years, with the result that the rate of depreciation may not be adequate to meet a seven-year repayment schedule. Commercial banks and merchants and dealers generally use a somewhat shorter-term repayment schedule on intermediate-term financing and, therefore, their loans for these purposes are somewhat less self-liquidating than those made by FHA and the PCA's. Farmers Home Administration and Federal Land Bank loans for fixed improvements generally are for fairly long terms and, therefore, generally are self-liquidating. This is the case particularly when the improvement loan is an integral part of a real estate loan. Insurance company loans generally are also amortized at a fairly low rate. However, since the term is often limited to approximately 20 years, loans for fixed improvements with a long life may not be fully self-liquidating. Commercial bank loans for fixed improvements generally are for relatively short terms and, therefore, generally are not fully self-liquidating.

Considered in terms of planning the repayment schedule to conform with income, the Farmers Home Administration probably ranks first, since this is a part of their procedure. It is their attention to planning the repayment schedule, coupled with long-term loans and increased income associated with management supervision and 100 per cent financing, which gives their borrowers the repayment capacity required to carry 100 per cent loans. PCA's and some commercial banks also rank high in this respect since they prepare budgets in cooperation with the borrower with this objective in mind. Other lenders also give attention to correlating the repayment schedule with income, but do so primarily on an informal or judgment basis.

Risk-bearing Ability

As was indicated in Chapter 11, a number of factors contribute to *risk-bearing ability,* the third R of credit. The factors to which a lender can most directly contribute are increasing income, enterprise selection, and ability to borrow. The first two of these were analyzed in some detail above in the discussion of loan service in terms of returns produced. Ability to borrow, from the standpoint of the lender's contribution to a borrower's risk-bearing ability, relates to the lender's ability to continue financing a borrower in difficult times. This, in turn, depends upon the dependability of a lender's loan funds, which was discussed at length in an earlier section of this chapter.

QUESTIONS AND PROBLEMS

1. Outline the ownership and control of the various types of lending institutions which extend credit to farmers. Explain how this affects their loan policy and service rendered.
2. How does management of a lending institution affect extension of credit to farmers? Analyze how management of the various lending institutions in your area affect their farm loan service.
3. Give the most important reasons why each of the major types of lenders make farm loans. How does this affect the loan service they provide?
4. Give the main source of loan funds of each of the major types of lenders.
5. What is meant by dependability of loan funds? Discuss.
6. Outline and discuss the dependability of loan funds of each of the major types of lenders.
7. Outline the type, term, and size of loans made by each of the major types of lenders.
8. Analyze the loan service of each of the major types of lenders in terms of the Three R's of Credit.

APPENDIX

APPENDIX TABLE 1

Amount of 1 at Compound Interest

$$s = (1 + i)^n$$

n	$\frac{1}{4}\%$	$\frac{7}{24}\%$	$\frac{1}{3}\%$	$\frac{5}{12}\%$	$\frac{1}{2}\%$
1	1.0025 0000	1.0029 1667	1.0033 3333	1.0041 6667	1.0050 0000
2	1.0050 0625	1.0058 4184	1.0066 7778	1.0083 5069	1.0100 2500
3	1.0075 1877	1.0087 7555	1.0100 3337	1.0125 5216	1.0150 7513
4	1.0100 3756	1.0117 1781	1.0134 0015	1.0167 7112	1.0201 5050
5	1.0125 6266	1.0146 6865	1.0167 7815	1.0210 0767	1.0252 5125
6	1.0150 9406	1.0176 2810	1.0201 6741	1.0252 6187	1.0303 7751
7	1.0176 3180	1.0205 9618	1.0235 6797	1.0295 3379	1.0355 2940
8	1,0201 7588	1.0235 7292	1.0269 7986	1.0338 2352	1.0407 0704
9	1.0227 2632	1.0265 5834	1.0304 0313	1.0381 3111	1.0459 1058
10	1.0252 8313	1.0295 5247	1.0338 3780	1.0424 5666	1.0511 4013
11	1.0278 4634	1.0325 5533	1.0372 8393	1.0468 0023	1.0563 9583
12	1.0304 1596	1.0355 6695	1.0407 4154	1.0511 6190	1.0616 7781
13	1.0329 9200	1.0385 8736	1.0442 1068	1.0555 4174	1.0669 8620
14	1.0355 7448	1.0416 1657	1.0476 9138	1.0599 3983	1.0723 2113
15	1.0381 6341	1.0446 5462	1.0511 8369	1.0643 5625	1.0776 8274
16	1.0407 5882	1.0477 0153	1.0546 8763	1.0687 9106	1.0830 7115
17	1.0433 6072	1.0507 5732	1.0582 0326	1.0732 4436	1.0884 8651
18	1.0459 6912	1.0538 2203	1.0617 3060	1.0777 1621	1.0939 2894
19	1.0485 8404	1.0568 9568	1.0652 6971	1.0822 0670	1.0993 9858
20	1.0512 0550	1.0599 7829	1.0688 2060	1.0867 1589	1.1048 9558
21	1.0538 3352	1.0630 6990	1.0723 8334	1.0912 4387	1.1104 2006
22	1.0564 6810	1.0661 7052	1.0759 5795	1.0957 9072	1.1159 7216
23	1.0591 0927	1.0692 8018	1.0795 4448	1.1003 5652	1.1215 5202
24	1.0617 5704	1.0723 9891	1.0831 4296	1.1049 4134	1.1271 5978
25	1.0644 1144	1.0755 2674	1.0867 5344	1.1095 4526	1.1327 9558
26	1.0670 7247	1.0786 6370	1.0903 7595	1.1141 6836	1.1384 5955
27	1.0697 4015	1.0818 0980	1.0940 1053	1.1188 1073	1.1441 5185
28	1.0724 1450	1.0849 6508	1.0976 5724	1.1234 7244	1.1498 7261
29	1.0750 9553	1.0881 2956	1.1013 1609	1.1281 5358	1.1556 2197
30	1.0777 8327	1.0913 0327	1.1049 8715	1.1328 5422	1.1614 0008
31	1.0804 7773	1.0944 8624	1.1086 7044	1.1375 7444	1.1672 0708
32	1.0831 7892	1.0976 7849	1.1123 6601	1.1423 1434	1.1730 4312
33	1.0858 8687	1.1008 8005	1.1160 7389	1.1470 7398	1.1789 0833
34	1.0886 0159	1.1040 9095	1.1197 9414	1.1518 5346	1.1848 0288
35	1.0913 2309	1.1073 1122	1.1235 2679	1.1566 5284	1.1907 2689
36	1.0940 5140	1.1105 4088	1.1272 7187	1.1614 7223	1.1966 8052
37	1.0967 8653	1.1137 7995	1.1310 2945	1.1663 1170	1.2026 6393
38	1.0995 2850	1.1170 2848	1.1347 9955	1.1711 7133	1.2086 7725
39	1.1022 7732	1.1202 8648	1.1385 8221	1.1760 5121	1.2147 2063
40	1.1050 3301	1.1235 5398	1.1423 7748	1.1809 5142	1.2207 9424
41	1.1077 9559	1.1268 3101	1.1461 8541	1.1858 7206	1.2268 9821
42	1.1105 6508	1.1301 1760	1.1500 0603	1.1908 1319	1.2330 3270
43	1.1133 4149	1.1334 1378	1.1538 3938	1.1957 7491	1.2391 9786
44	1.1161 2485	1.1367 1957	1.1576 8551	1.2007 5731	1.2453 9385
45	1.1189 1516	1.1400 3500	1.1615 4446	1.2057 6046	1.2516 2082
46	1.1217 1245	1.1433 6010	1.1654 1628	1.2107 8446	1.2578 7892
47	1.1245 1673	1.1466 9490	1.1693 0100	1.2158 2940	1.2641 6832
48	1.1273 2802	1.1500 3943	1.1731 9867	1.2208 9536	1.2704 8916
49	1.1301 4634	1.1533 9371	1.1771 0933	1.2259 8242	1.2768 4161
50	1.1329 7171	1.1567 5778	1.1810 3303	1.2310 9068	1.2832 2581

AMOUNT OF 1 AT COMPOUND INTEREST

$$S = (1 + i)^n$$

n	$\frac{1}{4}$ %	$\frac{7}{24}$ %	$\frac{1}{3}$ %	$\frac{5}{12}$ %	$\frac{1}{2}$ %
51	1.1358 0414	1.1601 3165	1.1849 6981	1.2362 2022	1.2896 4194
52	1.1386 4365	1.1635 1537	1.1889 1971	1.2413 7114	1.2960 9015
53	1.1414 9026	1.1669 0896	1.1928 8277	1.2465 4352	1.3025 7060
54	1.1443 4398	1.1703 1244	1.1968 5905	1.2517 3745	1.3090 8346
55	1.1472 0484	1.1737 2585	1.2008 4858	1.2569 5302	1.3156 2887
56	1.1500 7285	1.1771 4922	1.2048 5141	1.2621 9033	1.3222 0702
57	1.1529 4804	1.1805 8257	1.2088 6758	1.2674 4946	1.3288 1805
58	1.1558 3041	1.1840 2594	1.2128 9714	1.2727 3050	1.3354 6214
59	1.1587 1998	1.1874 7935	1.2169 4013	1.2780 3354	1.3421 3946
60	1.1616 1678	1.1909 4283	1.2209 9659	1.2833 5868	1.3488 5015
61	1.1645 2082	1.1944 1641	1.2250 6658	1.2887 0601	1.3555 9440
62	1.1674 3213	1.1979 0013	1.2291 5014	1.2940 7561	1.3623 7238
63	1.1703 5071	1.2013 9400	1.2332 4730	1.2994 6760	1.3691 8424
64	1.1732 7658	1.2048 9807	1.2373 5813	1.3048 8204	1.3760 3016
65	1.1762 0977	1.2084 1235	1.2414 8266	1.3103 1905	1.3829 1031
66	1.1791 5030	1.2119 3689	1.2456 2093	1.3157 7872	1.3898 2486
67	1.1820 9817	1.2154 7171	1.2497 7300	1.3212 6113	1.3967 7399
68	1.1850 5342	1.2190 1683	1.2539 3891	1.3267 6638	1.4037 5785
69	1.1880 1605	1.2225 7230	1.2581 1871	1.3322 9458	1.4107 7664
70	1.1909 8609	1.2261 3813	1.2623 1244	1.3378 4580	1.4178 3053
71	1.1939 6356	1.2297 1437	1.2665 2015	1.3434 2016	1.4249 1968
72	1.1969 4847	1.2333 0104	1.2707 4188	1.3490 1774	1.4320 4428
73	1.1999 4084	1.2368 9816	1.2749 7769	1.3546 3865	1.4392 0450
74	1.2029 4069	1.2405 0578	1.2792 2761	1.3602 8298	1.4464 0052
75	1.2059 4804	1.2441 2393	1.2834 9170	1.3659 5082	1.4536 3252
76	1.2089 6291	1.2477 5262	1.2877 7001	1.3716 4229	1.4609 0069
77	1.2119 8532	1.2513 9190	1.2920 6258	1.3773 5746	1.4682 0519
78	1.2150 1528	1.2550 4179	1.2963 6945	1.3830 9645	1.4755 4622
79	1.2180 5282	1.2587 0233	1.3006 9068	1.3888 5935	1.4829 2395
80	1.2210 9795	1.2623 7355	1.3050 2632	1.3946 4627	1.4903 3857
81	1.2241 5070	1.2660 5547	1.3093 7641	1.4004 5729	1.4977 9026
82	1.2272 1108	1.2697 4813	1.3137 4099	1.4062 9253	1.5052 7921
83	1.2302 7910	1.2734 5156	1.3181 2013	1.4121 5209	1.5128 0561
84	1.2333 5480	1.2771 6580	1.3225 1386	1.4180 3605	1.5203 6964
85	1.2364 3819	1.2808 9086	1.3269 2224	1.4239 4454	1.5279 7148
86	1.2395 2928	1.2846 2680	1.3313 4532	1.4298 7764	1.5356 1134
87	1.2426 2811	1.2883 7362	1.3357 8314	1.4358 3546	1.5432 8940
88	1.2457 3468	1.2921 3138	1.3402 3575	1.4418 1811	1.5510 0585
89	1.2488 4901	1.2959 0010	1.3447 0320	1.4478 2568	1.5587 6087
90	1.2519 7114	1.2996 7980	1.3491 8554	1.4538 5829	1.5665 5468
91	1.2551 0106	1.3034 7054	1.3536 8283	1.4599 1603	1.5743 8745
92	1.2582 3882	1.3072 7233	1.3581 9510	1.4659 9902	1.5822 5939
93	1.2613 8441	1.3110 8520	1.3627 2242	1.4721 0735	1.5901 7069
94	1.2645 3787	1.3149 0920	1.3672 6483	1.4782 4113	1.5981 2154
95	1.2676 9922	1.3187 4435	1.3718 2238	1.4844 0047	1.6061 1215
96	1.2708 6847	1.3225 9069	1.3763 9512	1.4905 8547	1.6141 4271
97	1.2740 4564	1.3264 4825	1.3809 8310	1.4967 9624	1.6222 1342
98	1.2772 3075	1.3303 1706	1.3855 8638	1.5030 3289	1.6303 2449
99	1.2804 2383	1.3341 9715	1.3902 0500	1.5092 9553	1.6384 7611
100	1.2836 2489	1.3380 8856	1.3948 3902	1.5155 8426	1.6466 6849

AMOUNT OF 1 AT COMPOUND INTEREST

$$s = (1 + i)^n$$

n	$\dfrac{7}{12}\%$	$\dfrac{2}{3}\%$	$\dfrac{3}{4}\%$	$\dfrac{7}{8}\%$	1%
1	1.0058 3333	1.0066 6667	1.0075 0000	1.0087 5000	1.0100 0000
2	1.0117 0069	1.0133 7778	1.0150 5625	1.0175 7656	1.0201 0000
3	1.0176 0228	1.0201 3363	1.0226 6917	1.0264 8036	1.0303 0100
4	1.0235 3830	1.0269 3452	1.0303 3919	1.0354 6206	1.0406 0401
5	1.0295 0894	1.0337 8075	1.0380 6673	1.0445 2235	1.0510 1005
6	1.0355 1440	1.0406 7262	1.0458 5224	1.0536 6192	1.0615 2015
7	1.0415 5490	1.0476 1044	1.0536 9613	1.0628 8147	1.0721 3535
8	1.0476 3064	1.0545 9451	1.0615 9885	1.0721 8168	1.0828 5671
9	1.0537 4182	1.0616 2514	1.0695 6084	1.0815 6327	1.0936 8527
10	1.0598 8865	1.0687 0264	1.0775 8255	1.0910 2695	1.1046 2213
11	1.0660 7133	1.0758 2732	1.0856 6441	1.1005 7343	1.1156 6835
12	1.0722 9008	1.0829 9951	1.0938 0690	1.1102 0345	1.1268 2503
13	1.0785 4511	1.0902 1950	1.1020 1045	1.1199 1773	1.1380 9328
14	1.0848 3662	1.0974 8763	1.1102 7553	1.1297 1701	1.1494 7421
15	1.0911 6483	1.1048 0422	1.1186 0259	1.1396 0203	1.1609 6896
16	1.0975 2996	1.1121 6958	1.1269 9211	1.1495 7355	1.1725 7864
17	1.1039 3222	1.1195 8404	1.1354 4455	1.1596 3232	1.1843 0443
18	1.1103 7182	1.1270 4794	1.1439 6039	1.1697 7910	1.1961 4748
19	1.1168 4899	1.1345 6159	1.1525 4009	1.1800 1467	1.2081 0895
20	1.1233 6395	1.1421 2533	1.1611 8414	1.1903 3980	1.2201 9004
21	1.1299 1690	1.1497 3950	1.1698 9302	1.2007 5527	1.2323 9194
22	1.1365 0808	1.1574 0443	1.1786 6722	1.2112 6188	1.2447 1586
23	1.1431 3771	1.1651 2046	1.1875 0723	1.2218 6042	1.2571 6302
24	1.1498 0602	1.1728 8793	1.1964 1353	1.2325 5170	1.2697 3465
25	1.1565 1322	1.1807 0718	1.2053 8663	1.2433 3653	1.2824 3200
26	1.1632 5955	1.1885 7857	1.2144 2703	1.2542 1572	1.2952 5631
27	1.1700 4523	1.1965 0242	1.2235 3523	1.2651 9011	1.3082 0888
28	1.1768 7049	1.2044 7911	1.2327 1175	1.2762 6052	1.3212 9097
29	1.1837 3557	1.2125 0897	1.2419 5709	1.2874 2780	1.3345 0388
30	1.1906 4069	1.2205 9236	1.2512 7176	1.2986 9280	1.3478 4892
31	1.1975 8610	1.2287 2964	1.2606 5630	1.3100 5636	1.3613 2740
32	1.2045 7202	1.2369 2117	1.2701 1122	1.3215 1935	1.3749 4068
33	1.2115 9869	1.2451 6731	1.2796 3706	1.3330 8265	1.3886 9009
34	1.2186 6634	1.2534 6843	1.2892 3434	1.3447 4712	1.4025 7699
35	1.2257 7523	1.2618 2489	1.2989 0359	1.3565 1366	1.4166 0276
36	1.2329 2559	1.2702 3705	1.3086 4537	1.3683 8315	1.4307 6878
37	1.2401 1765	1.2787 0530	1.3184 6021	1.3803 5650	1.4450 7647
38	1.2473 5167	1.2872 3000	1.3283 4866	1.3924 3462	1.4595 2724
39	1.2546 2789	1.2958 1153	1.3383 1128	1.4046 1843	1.4741 2251
40	1.2619 4655	1.3044 5028	1.3483 4861	1.4169 0884	1.4888 6373
41	1.2693 0791	1.3131 4661	1.3584 6123	1.4293 0679	1.5037 5237
42	1.2767 1220	1.3219 0092	1.3686 4969	1.4418 1322	1.5187 8989
43	1.2841 5969	1.3307 1360	1.3789 1456	1.4544 2909	1.5339 7779
44	1.2916 5062	1.3395 8502	1.3892 5642	1.4671 5534	1.5493 1757
45	1.2991 8525	1.3485 1559	1.3996 7584	1.4799 9295	1.5648 1075
46	1.3067 6383	1.3575 0569	1.4101 7341	1.4929 4289	1.5804 5885
47	1.3143 8662	1.3665 5573	1.4207 4971	1.5060 0614	1.5962 6344
48	1.3220 5388	1.3756 6610	1.4314 0533	1.5191 8370	1.6122 2608
49	1.3297 6586	1.3848 3721	1.4421 4087	1.5324 7655	1.6283 4834
50	1.3375 2283	1.3940 6946	1.4529 5693	1.5458 8572	1.6446 3182

AMOUNT OF 1 AT COMPOUND INTEREST

$$S = (1 + i)^n$$

n	$\dfrac{7}{12}\%$	$\dfrac{2}{3}\%$	$\dfrac{3}{4}\%$	$\dfrac{7}{8}\%$	1%
51	1.3453 2504	1.4033 6325	1.4638 5411	1.5594 1222	1.6610 7814
52	1.3531 7277	1.4127 1901	1.4748 3301	1.5730 5708	1.6776 8892
53	1.3610 6628	1.4221 3713	1.4858 9426	1.5868 2133	1.6944 6581
54	1.3690 0583	1.4316 1805	1.4970 3847	1.6007 0602	1.7114 1047
55	1.3769 9170	1.4411 6217	1.5082 6626	1.6147 1219	1.7285 2457
56	1.3850 2415	1.4507 6992	1.5195 7825	1.6288 4093	1.7458 0982
57	1.3931 0346	1.4604 4172	1.5309 7509	1.6430 9328	1.7632 6792
58	1.4012 2990	1.4701 7799	1.5424 5740	1.6574 7035	1.7809 0060
59	1.4094 0374	1.4799 7918	1.5540 2583	1.6719 7322	1.7987 0960
60	1.4176 2526	1.4898 4571	1.5656 8103	1.6866 0298	1.8166 9670
61	1.4258 9474	1.4997 7801	1.5774 2363	1.7013 6076	1.8348 6367
62	1.4342 1246	1.5097 7653	1.5892 5431	1.7162 4766	1.8532 1230
63	1.4425 7870	1.5198 4171	1.6011 7372	1.7312 6483	1.8717 4443
64	1.4509 9374	1.5299 7399	1.6131 8252	1.7464 1340	1.8904 6187
65	1.4594 5787	1.5401 7381	1.6252 8139	1.7616 9452	1.9093 6649
66	1.4679 7138	1.5504 4164	1.6374 7100	1.7771 0934	1.9284 6015
67	1.4765 3454	1.5607 7792	1.6497 5203	1.7926 5905	1.9477 4475
68	1.4851 4766	1.5711 8310	1.6621 2517	1.8083 4482	1.9672 2220
69	1.4938 1102	1.5816 5766	1.6745 9111	1.8241 6783	1.9868 9442
70	1.5025 2492	1.5922 0204	1.6871 5055	1.8401 2930	2.0067 6337
71	1.5112 8965	1.6028 1672	1.6998 0418	1.8562 3043	2.0268 3100
72	1.5201 0550	1.6135 0217	1.7125 5271	1.8724 7245	2.0470 9931
73	1.5289 7279	1.6242 5885	1.7253 9685	1.8888 5658	2.0675 7031
74	1.5378 9179	1.6350 8724	1.7383 3733	1.9053 8408	2.0882 4601
75	1.5468 6283	1.6459 8782	1.7513 7486	1.9220 5619	2.1091 2847
76	1.5558 8620	1.6569 6107	1.7645 1017	1.9388 7418	2.1302 1975
77	1.5649 6220	1.6680 0748	1.7777 4400	1.9558 3933	2.1515 2195
78	1.5740 9115	1.6791 2753	1.7910 7708	1.9729 5292	2.1730 3717
79	1.5832 7334	1.6903 2172	1.8045 1015	1.9902 1626	2.1947 6754
80	1.5925 0910	1.7015 9053	1.8180 4398	2.0076 3066	2.2167 1522
81	1.6017 9874	1.7129 3446	1.8316 7931	2.0251 9742	2.2388 8237
82	1.6111 4257	1.7243 5403	1.8454 1691	2.0429 1790	2.2612 7119
83	1.6205 4090	1.7358 4972	1.8592 5753	2.0607 9343	2.2838 8390
84	1.6299 9405	1.7474 2205	1.8732 0196	2.0788 2537	2.3067 2274
85	1.6395 0235	1.7590 7153	1.8872 5098	2.0970 1510	2.3297 8997
86	1.6490 6612	1.7707 9868	1.9014 0536	2.1153 6398	2.3530 8787
87	1.6586 8567	1.7826 0400	1.9156 6590	2.1338 7341	2.3766 1875
88	1.6683 6134	1.7944 8803	1.9300 3339	2.1525 4481	2.4003 8494
89	1.6780 9344	1.8064 5128	1.9445 0865	2.1713 7957	2.4243 8879
90	1.6878 8232	1.8184 9429	1.9590 9246	2.1903 7914	2.4486 3267
91	1.6977 2830	1.8306 1758	1.9737 8565	2.2095 4496	2.4731 1900
92	1.7076 3172	1.8428 2170	1.9885 8905	2.2288 7848	2.4978 5019
93	1.7175 9290	1.8551 0718	2.0035 0346	2.2483 8117	2.5228 2869
94	1.7276 1219	1.8674 7456	2.0185 2974	2.2680 5450	2.5480 5698
95	1.7376 8993	1.8799 2439	2.0336 6871	2.2878 9998	2.5735 3755
96	1.7478 2646	1.8924 5722	2.0489 2123	2.3079 1910	2.5992 7293
97	1.7580 2211	1.9050 7360	2.0642 8814	2.3281 1340	2.6252 6565
98	1.7682 7724	1.9177 7409	2.0797 7030	2.3484 8439	2.6515 1831
99	1.7785 9219	1.9305 5925	2.0953 6858	2.3690 3363	2.6780 3349
100	1.7889 6731	1.9434 2965	2.1110 8384	2.3897 6267	2.7048 1383

AMOUNT OF 1 AT COMPOUND INTEREST

$$s = (1 + i)^n$$

n	$1\frac{1}{8}\%$	$1\frac{1}{4}\%$	$1\frac{3}{8}\%$	$1\frac{1}{2}\%$	$1\frac{3}{4}\%$
1	1.0112 5000	1.0125 0000	1.0137 5000	1.0150 0000	1.0175 0000
2	1.0226 2656	1.0251 5625	1.0276 8906	1.0302 2500	1.0353 0625
3	1.0341 3111	1.0379 7070	1.0418 1979	1.0456 7838	1.0534 2411
4	1.0457 6509	1.0509 4534	1.0561 4481	1.0613 6355	1.0718 5903
5	1.0575 2994	1.0640 8215	1.0706 6680	1.0772 8400	1.0906 1656
6	1.0694 2716	1.0773 8318	1.0853 8847	1.0934 4326	1.1097 0235
7	1.0814 5821	1.0908 5047	1.1003 1256	1.1098 4491	1.1291 2215
8	1.0936 2462	1.1044 8610	1.1154 4186	1.1264 9259	1.1488 8178
9	1.1059 2789	1.1182 9218	1.1307 7918	1.1433 8998	1.1689 8721
10	1.1183 6958	1.1322 7083	1.1463 2740	1.1605 4083	1.1894 4449
11	1.1309 5124	1.1464 2422	1.1620 8940	1.1779 4894	1.2102 5977
12	1.1436 7444	1.1607 5452	1.1780 6813	1.1956 1817	1.2314 3931
13	1.1565 4078	1.1752 6395	1.1942 6656	1.2135 5244	1.2529 8950
14	1.1695 5186	1.1899 5475	1.2106 8773	1.2317 5573	1.2749 1682
15	1.1827 0932	1.2048 2918	1.2273 3469	1.2502 3207	1.2972 2786
16	1.1960 1480	1.2198 8955	1.2442 1054	1.2689 8555	1.3199 2935
17	1.2094 6997	1.2351 3817	1.2613 1843	1.2880 2033	1.3430 2811
18	1.2230 7650	1.2505 7739	1.2786 6156	1.3073 4064	1.3665 3111
19	1.2368 3611	1.2662 0961	1.2962 4316	1.3269 5075	1.3904 4540
20	1.2507 5052	1.2820 3723	1.3140 6650	1.3468 5501	1.4147 7820
21	1.2648 2146	1.2980 6270	1.3321 3492	1.3670 5783	1.4395 3681
22	1.2790 5071	1.3142 8848	1.3504 5177	1.3875 6370	1.4647 2871
23	1.2934 4003	1.3307 1709	1.3690 2048	1.4083 7715	1.4903 6146
24	1.3079 9123	1.3473 5105	1.3878 4451	1.4295 0281	1.5164 4279
25	1.3227 0613	1.3641 9294	1.4069 2738	1.4509 4535	1.5429 8054
26	1.3375 8657	1.3812 4535	1.4262 7263	1.4727 0953	1.5699 8269
27	1.3526 3442	1.3985 1092	1.4458 8388	1.4948 0018	1.5974 5739
28	1.3678 5156	1.4159 9230	1.4657 6478	1.5172 2218	1.6254 1290
29	1.3832 3989	1.4336 9221	1.4859 1905	1.5399 8051	1.6538 5762
30	1.3988 0134	1.4516 1336	1.5063 5043	1.5630 8022	1.6828 0013
31	1.4145 3785	1.4697 5853	1.5270 6275	1.5865 2642	1.7122 4913
32	1.4304 5140	1.4881 3051	1.5480 5986	1.6103 2432	1.7422 1349
33	1.4465 4398	1.5067 3214	1.5693 4569	1.6344 7918	1.7727 0223
34	1.4628 1760	1.5255 6629	1.5909 2419	1.6589 9637	1.8037 2452
35	1.4792 7430	1.5446 3587	1.6127 9940	1.6838 8132	1.8352 8970
36	1.4959 1613	1.5639 4382	1.6349 7539	1.7091 3954	1.8674 0727
37	1.5127 4519	1.5834 9312	1.6574 5630	1.7347 7663	1.9000 8689
38	1.5297 6357	1.6032 8678	1.6802 4633	1.7607 9828	1.9333 3841
39	1.5469 7341	1.6233 2787	1.7033 4971	1.7872 1025	1.9671 7184
40	1.5643 7687	1.6436 1946	1.7267 7077	1.8140 1841	2.0015 9734
41	1.5819 7611	1.6641 6471	1.7505 1387	1.8412 2868	2.0366 2530
42	1.5997 7334	1.6849 6677	1.7745 8343	1.8688 4712	2.0722 6624
43	1.6177 7079	1.7060 2885	1.7989 8396	1.8968 7982	2.1085 3090
44	1.6359 7071	1.7273 5421	1.8237 1999	1.9253 3302	2.1454 3019
45	1.6543 7538	1.7489 4614	1.8487 9614	1.9542 1301	2.1829 7522
46	1.6729 8710	1.7708 0797	1.8742 1708	1.9835 2621	2.2211 7728
47	1.6918 0821	1.7929 4306	1.8999 8757	2.0132 7910	2.2600 4789
48	1.7108 4105	1.8153 5485	1.9261 1240	2.0434 7829	2.2995 9872
49	1.7300 8801	1.8380 4679	1.9525 9644	2.0741 3046	2.3398 4170
50	1.7495 5150	1.8610 2237	1.9794 4464	2.1052 4242	2.3807 8893

AMOUNT OF 1 AT COMPOUND INTEREST

$$S = (1 + i)^n$$

n	$1\frac{1}{8}$ %	$1\frac{1}{4}$ %	$1\frac{3}{8}$ %	$1\frac{1}{2}$ %	$1\frac{3}{4}$ %
51	1.7692 3395	1.8842 8515	2.0066 6201	2.1368 2106	2.4224 5274
52	1.7891 3784	1.9078 3872	2.0342 5361	2.1688 7337	2.4648 4566
53	1.8092 6564	1.9316 8670	2.0622 2460	2.2014 0647	2.5079 8046
54	1.8296 1988	1.9558 3279	2.0905 8019	2.2344 2757	2.5518 7012
55	1.8502 0310	1.9802 8070	2.1193 2566	2.2679 4398	2.5965 2785
56	1.8710 1788	2.0050 3420	2.1484 6639	2.3019 6314	2.6419 6708
57	1.8920 6684	2.0300 9713	2.1780 0780	2.3364 9259	2.6882 0151
58	1.9133 5259	2.0554 7335	2.2079 5541	2.3715 3998	2.7352 4503
59	1.9348 7780	2.0811 6676	2.2383 1480	2.4071 1308	2.7831 1182
60	1.9566 4518	2.1071 8135	2.2690 9163	2.4432 1978	2.8318 1628
61	1.9786 5744	2.1335 2111	2.3002 9164	2.4798 6807	2.8813 7306
62	2.0009 1733	2.1601 9013	2.3319 2065	2.5170 6609	2.9317 9709
63	2.0234 2765	2.1871 9250	2.3639 8456	2.5548 2208	2.9831 0354
64	2.0461 9121	2.2145 3241	2.3964 8934	2.5931 4442	3.0353 0785
65	2.0692 1087	2.2422 1407	2.4294 4107	2.6320 4158	3.0884 2574
66	2.0924 8949	2.2702 4174	2.4628 4589	2.6715 2221	3.1424 7319
67	2.1160 2999	2.2986 1976	2.4967 1002	2.7115 9504	3.1974 6647
68	2.1398 3533	2.3273 5251	2.5310 3978	2.7522 6896	3.2534 2213
69	2.1639 0848	2.3564 4442	2.5658 4158	2.7935 5300	3.3103 5702
70	2.1882 5245	2.3858 9997	2.6011 2190	2.8354 5629	3.3682 8827
71	2.2128 7029	2.4157 2372	2.6368 8732	2.8779 8814	3.4272 3331
72	2.2377 6508	2.4459 2027	2.6731 4453	2.9211 5796	3.4872 0990
73	2.2629 3994	2.4764 9427	2.7099 0026	2.9649 7533	3.5482 3607
74	2.2883 9801	2.5074 5045	2.7471 6139	3.0094 4996	3.6103 3020
75	2.3141 4249	2.5387 9358	2.7849 3486	3.0545 9171	3.6735 1098
76	2.3401 7659	2.5705 2850	2.8232 2771	3.1004 1059	3.7377 9742
77	2.3665 0358	2.6026 6011	2.8620 4710	3.1469 1674	3.8032 0888
78	2.3931 2675	2.6351 9336	2.9014 0024	3.1941 2050	3.8697 6503
79	2.4200 4942	2.6681 3327	2.9412 9450	3.2420 3230	3.9374 8592
80	2.4472 7498	2.7014 8494	2.9817 3730	3.2906 6279	4.0063 9192
81	2.4748 0682	2.7352 5350	3.0227 3618	3.3400 2273	4.0765 0378
82	2.5026 4840	2.7694 4417	3.0642 9881	3.3901 2307	4.1478 4260
83	2.5308 0319	2.8040 6222	3.1064 3291	3.4409 7492	4.2204 2984
84	2.5592 7473	2.8391 1300	3.1491 4637	3.4925 8954	4.2942 8737
85	2.5880 6657	2.8746 0191	3.1924 4713	3.5449 7838	4.3694 3740
86	2.6171 8232	2.9105 3444	3.2363 4328	3.5981 5306	4.4459 0255
87	2.6466 2562	2.9469 1612	3.2808 4300	3.6521 2535	4.5237 0584
88	2.6764 0016	2.9837 5257	3.3259 5459	3.7069 0723	4.6028 7070
89	2.7065 0966	3.0210 4948	3.3716 8646	3.7625 1084	4.6834 2093
90	2.7369 5789	3.0588 1260	3.4180 4715	3.8189 4851	4.7653 8080
91	2.7677 4867	3.0970 4775	3.4650 4530	3.8762 3273	4.8487 7496
92	2.7988 8584	3.1357 6085	3.5126 8967	3.9343 7622	4.9336 2853
93	2.8303 7331	3.1749 5786	3.5609 8916	3.9933 9187	5.0199 6703
94	2.8622 1501	3.2146 4483	3.6099 5276	4.0532 9275	5.1078 1645
95	2.8944 1492	3.2548 2789	3.6595 8961	4.1140 9214	5.1972 0324
96	2.9269 7709	3.2955 1324	3.7099 0897	4.1758 0352	5.2881 5429
97	2.9599 0559	3.3367 0716	3.7609 2021	4.2384 4057	5.3806 9699
98	2.9932 0452	3.3784 1600	3.8126 3287	4.3020 1718	5.4748 5919
99	3.0268 7807	3.4206 4620	3.8650 5657	4.3665 4744	5.5706 6923
100	3.0609 3045	3.4634 0427	3.9182 0110	4.4320 4565	5.6681 5594

AMOUNT OF 1 AT COMPOUND INTEREST

$$s = (1 + i)^n$$

n	2 %	$2\frac{1}{4}$ %	$2\frac{1}{2}$ %	$2\frac{3}{4}$ %	3 %
1	1.0200 0000	1.0225 0000	1.0250 0000	1.0275 0000	1.0300 0000
2	1.0404 0000	1.0455 0625	1.0506 2500	1.0557 5625	1.0609 0000
3	1.0612 0800	1.0690 3014	1.0768 9063	1.0847 8955	1.0927 2700
4	1.0824 3216	1.0930 8332	1.1038 1289	1.1146 2126	1.1255 0881
5	1.1040 8080	1.1176 7769	1.1314 0821	1.1452 7334	1.1592 7407
6	1.1261 6242	1.1428 2544	1.1596 9342	1.1767 6836	1.1940 5230
7	1.1486 8567	1.1685 3901	1.1886 8575	1.2091 2949	1.2298 7387
8	1.1716 5938	1.1948 3114	1.2184 0290	1.2423 8055	1.2667 7008
9	1.1950 9257	1.2217 1484	1.2488 6297	1.2765 4602	1.3047 7318
10	1.2189 9442	1.2492 0343	1.2800 8454	1.3116 5103	1.3439 1638
11	1.2433 7431	1.2773 1050	1.3120 8666	1.3477 2144	1.3842 3387
12	1.2682 4179	1.3060 4999	1.3448 8882	1.3847 8378	1.4257 6089
13	1.2936 0663	1.3354 3611	1.3785 1104	1.4228 6533	1.4685 3371
14	1.3194 7876	1.3654 8343	1.4129 7382	1.4619 9413	1.5125 8972
15	1.3458 6834	1.3962 0680	1.4482 9817	1.5021 9896	1.5579 6742
16	1.3727 8571	1.4276 2146	1.4845 0562	1.5435 0944	1.6047 0644
17	1.4002 4142	1.4597 4294	1.5216 1826	1.5859 5595	1.6528 4763
18	1.4282 4625	1.4925 8716	1.5596 5872	1.6295 6973	1.7024 3306
19	1.4568 1117	1.5261 7037	1.5986 5019	1.6743 8290	1.7535 0605
20	1.4859 4740	1.5605 0920	1.6386 1644	1.7204 2843	1.8061 1123
21	1.5156 6634	1.5956 2066	1.6795 8185	1.7677 4021	1.8602 9457
22	1.5459 7967	1.6315 2212	1.7215 7140	1.8163 5307	1.9161 0341
23	1.5768 9926	1.6682 3137	1.7646 1068	1.8663 0278	1.9735 8651
24	1.6084 3725	1.7057 6658	1.8087 2595	1.9176 2610	2.0327 9411
25	1.6406 0599	1.7441 4632	1.8539 4410	1.9703 6082	2.0937 7793
26	1.6734 1811	1.7833 8962	1.9002 9270	2.0245 4575	2.1565 9127
27	1.7068 8648	1.8235 1588	1.9478 0002	2.0802 2075	2.2212 8901
28	1.7410 2421	1.8645 4499	1.9964 9502	2.1374 2682	2.2879 2768
29	1.7758 4469	1.9064 9725	2.0464 0739	2.1962 0606	2.3565 6551
30	1.8113 6158	1.9493 9344	2.0975 6758	2.2566 0173	2.4272 6247
31	1.8475 8882	1.9932 5479	2.1500 0677	2.3186 5828	2.5000 8035
32	1.8845 4059	2.0381 0303	2.2037 5694	2.3824 2138	2.5750 8276
33	1.9222 3140	2.0839 6034	2.2588 5086	2.4479 3797	2.6523 3524
34	1.9606 7603	2.1308 4945	2.3153 2213	2.5152 5626	2.7319 0530
35	1.9998 8955	2.1787 9356	2.3732 0519	2.5844 2581	2.8138 6245
36	2.0398 8734	2.2278 1642	2.4325 3532	2.6554 9752	2.8982 7833
37	2.0806 8509	2.2779 4229	2.4933 4870	2.7285 2370	2.9852 2668
38	2.1222 9879	2.3291 9599	2.5556 8242	2.8035 5810	3.0747 8348
39	2.1647 4477	2.3816 0290	2.6195 7448	2.8806 5595	3.1670 2698
40	2.2080 3966	2.4351 8897	2.6850 6384	2.9598 7399	3.2620 3779
41	2.2522 0046	2.4899 8072	2.7521 9043	3.0412 7052	3.3598 9893
42	2.2972 4447	2.5460 0528	2.8209 9520	3.1249 0546	3.4606 9589
43	2.3431 8936	2.6032 9040	2.8915 2008	3.2108 4036	3.5645 1677
44	2.3900 5314	2.6618 6444	2.9638 0808	3.2991 3847	3.6714 5227
45	2.4378 5421	2.7217 5639	3.0379 0328	3.3898 6478	3.7815 9584
46	2.4866 1129	2.7829 9590	3.1138 5086	3.4830 8606	3.8950 4372
47	2.5363 4351	2.8456 1331	3.1916 9713	3.5788 7093	4.0118 9503
48	2.5870 7039	2.9096 3961	3.2714 8956	3.6772 8988	4.1322 5188
49	2.6388 1179	2.9751 0650	3.3532 7680	3.7784 1535	4.2562 1944
50	2.6915 8803	3.0420 4640	3.4371 0872	3.8823 2177	4.3839 0602

AMOUNT OF 1 AT COMPOUND INTEREST

$$s = (1 + i)^n$$

n	2 %	$2\frac{1}{4}$ %	$2\frac{1}{2}$ %	$2\frac{3}{4}$ %	3 %
51	2.7454 1979	3.1104 9244	3.5230 3644	3.9890 8562	4.5154 2320
52	2.8003 2819	3.1804 7852	3.6111 1235	4.0987 8547	4.6508 8590
53	2.8563 3475	3.2520 3929	3.7013 9016	4.2115 0208	4.7904 1247
54	2.9134 6144	3.3252 1017	3.7939 2491	4.3273 1838	4.9341 2485
55	2.9717 3067	3.4000 2740	3.8887 7303	4.4463 1964	5.0821 4859
56	3.0311 6529	3.4765 2802	3.9859 9236	4.5685 9343	5.2346 1305
57	3.0917 8859	3.5547 4990	4.0856 4217	4.6942 2975	5.3916 5144
58	3.1536 2436	3.6347 3177	4.1877 8322	4.8233 2107	5.5534 0098
59	3.2166 9685	3.7165 1324	4.2924 7780	4.9559 6239	5.7200 0301
60	3.2810 3079	3.8001 3479	4.3997 8975	5.0922 5136	5.8916 0310
61	3.3466 5140	3.8856 3782	4.5097 8449	5.2322 8827	6.0683 5120
62	3.4135 8443	3.9730 6467	4.6225 2910	5.3761 7620	6.2504 0173
63	3.4818 5612	4.0624 5862	4.7380 9233	5.5240 2105	6.4379 1379
64	3.5514 9324	4.1538 6394	4.8565 4464	5.6759 3162	6.6310 5120
65	3.6225 2311	4.2473 2588	4.9779 5826	5.8320 1974	6.8299 8273
66	3.6949 7357	4.3428 9071	5.1024 0721	6.9924 0029	7.0348 8222
67	3.7688 7304	4.4406 0576	5.2299 6739	6.1571 9130	7.2459 2868
68	3.8442 5050	4.5405 1939	5.3607 1658	6.3265 1406	7.4633 0654
69	3.9211 3551	4.6426 8107	5.4947 3449	6.5004 9319	7.6872 0574
70	3.9995 5822	4.7471 4140	5.6321 0286	6.6792 5676	7.9178 2191
71	4.0795 4939	4.8539 5208	5.7729 0543	6.8629 3632	8.1553 5657
72	4.1611 4038	4.9631 6600	5.9172 2806	7.0516 6706	8.4000 1727
73	4.2443 6318	5.0748 3723	6.0651 5876	7.2455 8791	8.6520 1778
74	4.3292 5045	5.1890 2107	6.2167 8773	7.4448 4158	8.9115 7832
75	4.4158 3546	5.3057 7405	6.3722 0743	7.6495 7472	9.1789 2567
76	4.5041 5216	5.4251 5396	6.5315 1261	7.8599 3802	9.4542 9344
77	4.5942 3521	5.5472 1993	6.6948 0043	8.0760 8632	9.7379 2224
78	4.6861 1991	5.6720 3237	6.8621 7044	8.2981 7869	10.0300 5991
79	4.7798 4231	5.7996 5310	7.0337 2470	8.5263 7861	10.3309 6171
80	4.8754 3916	5.9301 4530	7.2095 6782	8.7608 5402	10.6408 9056
81	4.9729 4794	6.0635 7357	7.3898 0701	9.0017 7751	10.9601 1727
82	5.0724 0690	6.2000 0397	7.5745 5219	9.2493 2639	11.2889 2079
83	5.1738 5504	6.3395 0406	7.7639 1599	9.5036 8286	11.6275 8842
84	5.2773 3214	6.4821 4290	7.9580 1389	9.7650 3414	11.9764 1607
85	5.3828 7878	6.6279 9112	8.1569 6424	10.0335 7258	12.3357 0855
86	5.4905 3636	6.7771 2092	8.3608 8834	10.3094 9583	12.7057 7981
87	5.6003 4708	6.9296 0614	8.5699 1055	10.5930 0696	13.0869 5320
88	5.7123 5402	7.0855 2228	8.7841 5832	10.8843 1465	13.4795 6180
89	5.8266 0110	7.2449 4653	9.0037 6228	11.1836 3331	13.8839 4865
90	5.9431 3313	7.4079 5782	9.2288 5633	11.4911 8322	14.3004 6711
91	6.0619 9579	7.5746 3688	9.4595 7774	11.8071 9076	14.7294 8112
92	6.1832 3570	7.7450 6621	9.6960 6718	12.1318 8851	15.1713 6556
93	6.3069 0042	7.9193 3020	9.9384 6886	12.4655 1544	15.6265 0652
94	6.4330 3843	8.0975 1512	10.1869 3058	12.8083 1711	16.0953 0172
95	6.5616 9920	8.2797 0921	10.4416 0385	13.1605 4584	16.5781 6077
96	6.6929 3318	8.4660 0267	10.7026 4395	13.5224 6085	17.0755 0559
97	6.8267 9184	8.6564 8773	10.9702 1004	13.8943 2852	17.5877 7076
98	6.9633 2768	8.8512 5871	11.2444 6530	14.2764 2255	18.1154 0388
99	7.1025 9423	9.0504 1203	11.5255 7693	14.6690 2417	18.6588 6600
100	7.2446 4612	9.2540 4630	11.8137 1635	15.0724 2234	19.2186 3198

AMOUNT OF 1 AT COMPOUND INTEREST

$$s = (1 + i)^n$$

n	$3\frac{1}{2}$ %	4 %	$4\frac{1}{2}$ %	5 %	$5\frac{1}{2}$ %
1	1.0350 0000	1.0400 0000	1.0450 0000	1.0500 0000	1.0550 0000
2	1.0712 2500	1.0816 0000	1.0920 2500	1.1025 0000	1.1130 2500
3	1.1087 1788	1.1248 6400	1.1411 6613	1.1576 2500	1.1742 4138
4	1.1475 2300	1.1698 5856	1.1925 1860	1.2155 0625	1.2388 2465
5	1.1876 8631	1.2166 5290	1.2461 8194	1.2762 8156	1.3069 6001
6	1.2292 5533	1.2653 1902	1.3022 6012	1.3400 9564	1.3788 4281
7	1.2722 7926	1.3159 3178	1.3608 6183	1.4071 0042	1.4546 7916
8	1.3168 0904	1.3685 6905	1.4221 0061	1.4774 5544	1.5346 8651
9	1.3628 9735	1.4233 1181	1.4860 9514	1.5513 2822	1.6190 9427
10	1.4105 9876	1.4802 4428	1.5529 6942	1.6288 9463	1.7081 4446
11	1.4599 6972	1.5394 5406	1.6228 5305	1.7103 3936	1.8020 9240
12	1.5110 6866	1.6010 3222	1.6958 8143	1.7958 5633	1.9012 0749
13	1.5639 5606	1.6650 7351	1.7721 9610	1.8856 4914	2.0057 7390
14	1.6186 9452	1.7316 7645	1.8519 4492	1.9799 3160	2.1160 9146
15	1.6753 4883	1.8009 4351	1.9352 8244	2.0789 2818	2.2324 7649
16	1.7339 8604	1.8729 8125	2.0223 7015	2.1828 7459	2.3552 6270
17	1.7946 7555	1.9479 0050	2.1133 7681	2.2920 1832	2.4848 0215
18	1.8574 8920	2.0258 1652	2.2084 7877	2.4066 1923	2.6214 6627
19	1.9225 0132	2.1068 4918	2.3078 6031	2.5269 5020	2.7656 4691
20	1.9897 8886	2.1911 2314	2.4117 1402	2.6532 9771	2.9177 5749
21	2.0594 3147	2.2787 6807	2.5202 4116	2.7859 6259	3.0782 3415
22	2.1315 1158	2.3699 1879	2.6336 5201	2.9252 6072	3.2475 3703
23	2.2061 1448	2.4647 1554	2.7521 6635	3.0715 2376	3.4261 5157
24	2.2833 2849	2.5633 0416	2.8760 1383	3.2250 9994	3.6145 8990
25	2.3632 4498	2.6658 3633	3.0054 3446	3.3863 5494	3.8133 9235
26	2.4459 5856	2.7724 6978	3.1406 7901	3.5556 7269	4.0231 2893
27	2.5315 6711	2.8833 6858	3.2820 0956	3.7334 5632	4.2444 0102
28	2.6201 7196	2.9987 0332	3.4296 9999	3.9201 2914	4.4778 4307
29	2.7118 7798	3.1186 5145	3.5840 3649	4.1161 3560	4.7241 2444
30	2.8067 9370	3.2433 9751	3.7453 1813	4.3219 4238	4.9839 5129
31	2.9050 3148	3.3731 3341	3.9138 5745	4.5380 3949	5.2580 6861
32	3.0067 0759	3.5080 5875	4.0899 8104	4.7649 4147	5.5472 6238
33	3.1119 4235	3.6483 8110	4.2740 3018	5.0031 8854	5.8523 6181
34	3.2208 6033	3.7943 1634	4.4663 6154	5.2533 4797	6.1742 4171
35	3.3335 9045	3.9460 8899	4.6673 4781	5.5160 1537	6.5138 2501
36	3.4502 6611	4.1039 3255	4.8773 7846	5.7918 1614	6.8720 8538
37	3.5710 2543	4.2680 8986	5.0968 6049	6.0814 0694	7.2500 5008
38	3.6960 1132	4.4388 1345	5.3262 1921	6.3854 7729	7.6488 0283
39	3.8253 7171	4.6163 6599	5.5658 9908	6.7047 5115	8.0694 8699
40	3.9592 5972	4.8010 2063	5.8163 6454	7.0399 8871	8.5133 0877
41	4.0978 3381	4.9930 6145	6.0781 0094	7.3919 8815	8.9815 4076
42	4.2412 5799	5.1927 8391	6.3516 1548	7.7615 8756	9.4755 2550
43	4.3897 0202	5.4004 9527	6.6374 3818	8.1496 6693	9.9966 7940
44	4.5433 4160	5.6165 1508	6.9361 2290	8.5571 5028	10.5464 9677
45	4.7023 5855	5.8411 7568	7.2482 4843	8.9850 0779	11.1265 5409
46	4.8669 4110	6.0748 2271	7.5744 1961	9.4342 5818	11.7385 1456
47	5.0372 8404	6.3178 1562	7.9152 6849	9.9059 7109	12.3841 3287
48	5.2135 8898	6.5705 2824	8.2714 5557	10.4012 6965	13.0652 6017
49	5.3960 6459	6.8333 4937	8.6436 7107	10.9213 3313	13.7838 4948
50	5.5849 2686	7.1066 8335	9.0326 3627	11.4673 9979	14.5419 6120

AMOUNT OF 1 AT COMPOUND INTEREST

$$s = (1 + i)^n$$

n	$3\frac{1}{2}\%$	4%	$4\frac{1}{2}\%$	5%	$5\frac{1}{2}\%$
51	5.7803 9930	7.3909 5068	9.4391 0490	12.0407 6978	15.3417 6907
52	5.9827 1327	7.6865 8871	9.8638 6463	12.6428 0826	16.1855 6637
53	6.1921 0824	7.9940 5226	10.3077 3853	13.2749 4868	17.0757 7252
54	6.4088 3202	8.3138 1435	10.7715 8677	13.9386 9611	18.0149 4001
55	6.6331 4114	8.6463 6692	11.2563 0817	14.6356 3092	19.0057 6171
56	6.8653 0108	8.9922 2160	11.7628 4204	15.3674 1246	20.0510 7860
57	7.1055 8662	9.3519 1046	12.2921 6993	16.1357 8309	21.1538 8793
58	7.3542 8215	9.7259 8688	12.8453 1758	16.9425 7224	22.3173 5176
59	7.6116 8203	10.1150 2635	13.4233 5687	17.7897 0085	23.5448 0611
60	7.8780 9090	10.5196 2741	14.0274 0793	18.6791 8589	24.8397 7045
61	8.1538 2408	10.9404 1250	14.6586 4129	19.6131 4519	26.2059 5782
62	8.4392 0793	11.3780 2900	15.3182 8014	20.5938 0245	27.6472 8550
63	8.7345 8020	11.8331 5016	16.0076 0275	21.6234 9257	29.1678 8620
64	9.0402 9051	12.3064 7617	16.7279 4487	22.7046 6720	30.7721 1994
65	9.3567 0068	12.7987 3522	17.4807 0239	23.8399 0056	32.4645 8654
66	9.6841 8520	13.3106 8463	18.2673 3400	25.0318 9559	34.2501 3880
67	10.0231 3168	13.8431 1201	19.0893 6403	26.2834 9037	36.1338 9643
68	10.3739 4129	14.3968 3649	19.9483 8541	27.5976 6488	38.1212 6074
69	10.7370 2924	14.9727 0995	20.8460 6276	28.9775 4813	40.2179 3008
70	11.1128 2526	15.5716 1835	21.7841 3558	30.4264 2554	42.4299 1623
71	11.5017 7414	16.1944 8308	22.7644 2168	31.9477 4681	44.7635 6163
72	11.9043 3624	16.8422 6241	23.7888 2066	33.5451 3415	47.2255 5751
73	12.3209 8801	17.5159 5290	24.8593 1759	35.2223 9086	49.8229 6318
74	12.7522 2259	18.2165 9102	25.9779 8688	36.9835 1040	52.5632 2615
75	13.1985 5038	18.9452 5466	27.1469 9629	38.8326 8592	55.4542 0359
76	13.6604 9964	19.7030 6485	28.3686 1112	40.7743 2022	58.5041 8479
77	14.1386 1713	20.4911 8744	29.6451 9862	42.8130 3623	61.7219 1495
78	14.6334 6873	21.3108 3494	30.9792 3256	44.9536 8804	65.1166 2027
79	15.1456 4013	22.1632 6834	32.3732 9802	47.2013 7244	68.6980 3439
80	15.6757 3754	23.0497 9907	33.8300 9643	49.5614 4107	72.4764 2628
81	16.2243 8835	23.9717 9103	35.3524 5077	52.0395 1312	76.4626 2973
82	16.7922 4195	24.9306 6267	36.9433 1106	54.6414 8878	80.6680 7436
83	17.3799 7041	25.9278 8918	38.6057 6006	57.3735 6322	85.1048 1845
84	17.9882 6938	26.9650 0475	40.3430 1926	60.2422 4138	89.7855 8347
85	18.6178 5881	28.0436 0494	42.1584 5513	63.2543 5344	94.7237 9056
86	19.2694 8387	29.1653 4914	44.0555 8561	66.4170 7112	99.9335 9904
87	19.9439 1580	30.3319 6310	46.0380 8696	69.7379 2467	105.4299 4698
88	20.6419 5285	31.5452 4163	48.1098 0087	73.2248 2091	111.2285 9407
89	21.3644 2120	32.8070 5129	50.2747 4191	76.8860 6195	117.3461 6674
90	22.1121 7595	34.1193 3334	52.5371 0530	80.7303 6505	123.8002 0591
91	22.8861 0210	35.4841 0668	54.9012 7503	84.7668 8330	130.6092 1724
92	23.6871 1568	36.9034 7094	57.3718 3241	89.0052 2747	137.7927 2419
93	24.5161 6473	38.3796 0978	59.9535 6487	93.4554 8884	145.3713 2402
94	25.3742 3049	39.9147 9417	62.6514 7529	98.1282 6328	153.3667 4684
95	26.2623 2856	41.5113 8594	65.4707 9168	103.0346 7645	161.8019 1791
96	27.1815 1006	43.1718 4138	68.4169 7730	108.1864 1027	170.7010 2340
97	28.1328 6291	44.8987 1503	71.4957 4128	113.5957 3078	180.0895 7969
98	29.1175 1311	46.6946 6363	74.7130 4964	119.2755 1732	189.9945 0657
99	30.1366 2607	48.5624 5018	78.0751 3687	125.2392 9319	200.4442 0443
100	31.1914 0798	50.5049 4818	81.5885 1803	131.5012 5785	211.4686 3567

AMOUNT OF 1 AT COMPOUND INTEREST

$$s = (1 + i)^n$$

n	6 %	$6\frac{1}{2}$ %	7 %	$7\frac{1}{2}$ %	8 %
1	1.0600 0000	1.0650 0000	1.0700 0000	1.0750 0000	1.0800 0000
2	1.1236 0000	1.1342 2500	1.1449 0000	1.1556 2500	1.1664 0000
3	1.1910 1600	1.2079 4963	1.2250 4300	1.2422 9688	1.2597 1200
4	1.2624 7696	1.2864 6635	1.3107 9601	1.3354 6914	1.3604 8896
5	1.3382 2558	1.3700 8666	1.4025 5173	1.4356 2933	1.4693 2808
6	1.4185 1911	1.4591 4230	1.5007 3035	1.5433 0153	1.5868 7432
7	1.5036 3026	1.5539 8655	1.6057 8148	1.6590 4914	1.7138 2427
8	1.5938 4807	1.6549 9567	1.7181 8618	1.7834 7783	1.8509 3021
9	1.6894 7896	1.7625 7039	1.8384 5921	1.9172 3866	1.9990 0463
10	1.7908 4770	1.8771 3747	1.9671 5136	2.0610 3156	2.1589 2500
11	1.8982 9856	1.9991 5140	2.1048 5195	2.2156 0893	2.3316 3900
12	2.0121 9647	2.1290 9624	2.2521 9159	2.3817 7960	2.5181 7012
13	2.1329 2826	2.2674 8750	2.4098 4500	2.5604 1307	2.7196 2373
14	2.2609 0396	2.4148 7418	2.5785 3415	2.7524 4405	2.9371 9362
15	2.3965 5819	2.5718 4101	2.7590 3154	2.9588 7735	3.1721 6911
16	2.5403 5168	2.7390 1067	2.9521 6375	3.1807 9315	3.4259 4264
17	2.6927 7279	2.9170 4637	3.1588 1521	3.4193 5264	3.7000 1805
18	2.8543 3915	3.1066 5438	3.3799 3228	3.6758 0409	3.9960 1950
19	3.0255 9950	3.3085 8691	3.6165 2754	3.9514 8940	4.3157 0106
20	3.2071 3547	3.5236 4506	3.8696 8446	4.2478 5110	4.6609 5714
21	3.3995 6360	3.7526 8199	4.1405 6237	4.5664 3993	5.0338 3372
22	3.6035 3742	3.9966 0632	4.4304 0174	4.9089 2293	5.4365 4041
23	3.8197 4966	4.2563 8573	4.7405 2986	5.2770 9215	5.8714 6365
24	4.0489 3464	4.5330 5081	5.0723 6695	5.6728 7406	6.3411 8074
25	4.2918 7072	4.8276 9911	5.4274 3264	6.0983 3961	6.8484 7520
26	4.5493 8296	5.1414 9955	5.8073 5292	6.5557 1508	7.3963 5321
27	4.8223 4594	5.4756 9702	6.2138 6763	7.0473 9371	7.9880 6147
28	5.1116 8670	5.8316 1733	6.6488 3836	7.5759 4824	8.6271 0639
29	5.4183 8790	6.2106 7245	7.1142 5705	8.1441 4436	9.3172 7490
30	5.7434 9117	6.6143 6616	7.6122 5504	8.7549 5519	10.0626 5689
31	6.0881 0064	7.0442 9996	8.1451 1290	9.4115 7683	10.8676 6944
32	6.4533 8668	7.5021 7946	8.7152 7080	10.1174 4509	11.7370 8300
33	6.8405 8988	7.9898 2113	9.3253 3975	10.8762 5347	12.6760 4964
34	7.2510 2528	8.5091 5950	9.9781 1354	11.6919 7248	13.6901 3361
35	7.6860 8679	9.0622 5487	10.6765 8148	12.5688 7042	14.7853 4429
36	8.1472 5200	9.6513 0143	11.4239 4219	13.5115 3570	15.9681 7184
37	8.6360 8712	10.2786 3603	12.2236 1814	14.5249 0088	17.2456 2558
38	9.1542 5235	10.9467 4737	13.0792 7141	15.6142 6844	18.6252 7563
39	9.7035 0749	11.6582 8595	13.9948 2041	16.7853 3858	20.1152 9768
40	10.2857 1794	12.4160 7453	14.9744 5784	18.0442 3897	21.7245 2150
41	10.9028 6101	13.2231 1938	16.0226 6989	19.3975 5689	23.4624 8322
42	11.5570 3267	14.0826 2214	17.1442 5678	20.8523 7366	25.3394 8187
43	12.2504 5463	14.9979 9258	18.3443 5475	22.4163 0168	27.3666 4042
44	12.9854 8191	15.9728 6209	19.6284 5959	24.0975 2431	29.5559 7166
45	13.7646 1083	17.0110 9813	21.0024 5176	25.9048 3863	31.9204 4939
46	14.5904 8748	18.1168 1951	22.4726 2338	27.8477 0153	34.4740 8534
47	15.4659 1673	19.2944 1278	24.0457 0702	29.9362 7915	37.2320 1217
48	16.3938 7173	20.5485 4961	25.7289 0651	32.1815 0008	40.2105 7314
49	17.3775 0403	21.8842 0533	27.5299 2997	34.5951 1259	43.4274 1899
50	18.4201 5427	23.3066 7868	29.4570 2506	37.1897 4603	46.9016 1251

AMOUNT OF 1 AT COMPOUND INTEREST

$$s = (1 + i)^n$$

n	6 %	$6\frac{1}{2}$ %	7 %	$7\frac{1}{2}$ %	8 %
51	19.5253 6353	24.8216 1279	31.5190 1682	39.9789 7698	50.6537 4151
52	20.6968 8534	26.4350 1762	33.7253 4799	42.9774 0026	54.7060 4084
53	21.9386 9846	28.1532 9377	36.0861 2235	46.2007 0528	59.0825 2410
54	23.2550 2037	29.9832 5786	38.6121 5092	49.6657 5817	63.8091 2603
55	24.6503 2159	31.9321 6963	41.3150 0148	53.3906 9004	68.9138 5611
56	26.1293 4089	34.0077 6065	44.2070 5159	57.3949 9179	74.4269 6460
57	27.6971 0134	36.2182 6509	47.3015 4520	61.6996 1617	80.3811 2177
58	29.3589 2742	38.5724 5233	50.6126 5336	66.3270 8739	86.8116 1151
59	31.1204 6307	41.0796 6173	54.1555 3910	71.3016 1894	93.7565 4043
60	32.9876 9085	43.7498 3974	57.9464 2683	76.6492 4036	101.2570 6367
61	34.9669 5230	46.5935 7932	62.0026 7671	82.3979 3339	109.3576 2876
62	37.0649 6944	49.6221 6198	66.3428 6408	88.5777 7839	118.1062 3906
63	39.2888 6761	52.8476 0251	70.9868 6457	95.2211 1177	127.5547 3819
64	41.6461 9967	56.2826 9667	75.9559 4509	102.3626 9515	137.7591 1724
65	44.1449 7165	59.9410 7195	81.2728 6124	110.0398 9729	148.7798 4662
66	46.7936 6994	63.8372 4163	86.9619 6153	118.2928 8959	160.6822 3435
67	49.6012 9014	67.9866 6234	93.0492 9884	127.1648 5631	173.5368 1310
68	52.5773 6755	72.4057 9539	99.5627 4976	136.7022 2053	187.4197 5815
69	55.7320 0960	77.1121 7209	106.5321 4224	146.9548 8707	202.4133 3880
70	59.0759 3018	82.1244 6327	113.9893 9220	157.9765 0360	218.6064 0590
71	62.6204 8599	87.4625 5339	121.9686 4965	169.8247 4137	236.0949 1837
72	66.3777 1515	93.1476 1936	130.5064 5513	182.5615 9697	254.9825 1184
73	70.3603 7806	99.2022 1461	139.6419 0699	196.2537 1675	275.3811 1279
74	74.5820 0074	105.6503 5856	149.4168 4047	210.9727 4550	297.4116 0181
75	79.0569 2079	112.5176 3187	159.8760 1931	226.7957 0141	321.2045 2996
76	83.8003 3603	119.8312 7794	171.0673 4066	243.8053 7902	346.9008 9236
77	88.8283 5620	127.6203 1101	183.0420 5451	262.0907 8245	374.6529 6374
78	94.1580 5757	135.9156 3122	195.8549 9832	281.7475 9113	404.6252 0084
79	99.8075 4102	144.7501 4725	209.5648 4820	302.8786 6046	436.9952 1691
80	105.7959 9348	154.1589 0683	224.2343 8758	325.5945 6000	471.9548 3426
81	112.1437 5309	164.1792 3577	239.9307 9471	350.0141 5200	509.7112 2101
82	118.8723 7828	174.8508 8609	256.7259 5034	376.2652 1340	550.4881 1869
83	126.0047 2097	186.2161 9369	274.6967 6686	404.4851 0440	594.5271 6818
84	133.5650 0423	198.3202 4628	293.9255 4054	434.8214 8723	642.0893 4164
85	141.5789 0449	211.2110 6229	314.5003 2838	467.4330 9878	693.4564 8897
86	150.0736 3875	224.9397 8134	336.5153 5137	502.4905 8119	748.9330 0808
87	159.0780 5708	239.5608 6712	360.0714 2596	540.1773 7477	808.8476 4873
88	168.6227 4050	255.1323 2349	385.2764 2578	580.6906 7788	873.5554 6063
89	178.7401 0493	271.7159 2451	412.2457 7558	624.2424 7872	943.4398 9748
90	189.4645 1123	289.3774 5961	441.1029 7988	671.0606 6463	1018.9150 8928
91	200.8323 8190	308.1869 9448	471.9801 8847	721.3902 1447	1100.4282 9642
92	212.8823 2482	328.2191 4912	505.0188 0166	775.4944 8056	1188.4625 6013
93	225.6552 6431	349.5533 9382	540.3701 1778	833.6565 6660	1283.5395 6494
94	239.1945 8017	372.2743 6441	578.1960 2602	896.1808 0910	1386.2227 3014
95	253.5462 5498	396.4721 9810	618.6697 4784	963.3943 6978	1497.1205 4855
96	268.7590 3028	422.2428 9098	661.9766 3019	1035.6489 4751	1616.8901 9244
97	284.8845 7209	449.6886 7889	708.3149 9430	1113.3226 1858	1746.2414 0783
98	301.9776 4642	478.9184 4302	757.8970 4390	1196.8218 1497	1885.9407 2046
99	320.0963 0520	510.0481 4181	810.9498 3698	1286.5834 5109	2036.8159 7809
100	339.3020 8351	543.2012 7103	867.7163 2557	1383.0772 0993	2199.7612 5634

PRESENT VALUE OF 1 AT COMPOUND INTEREST

$$v^n = \frac{1}{(1+i)^n}$$

n	$\frac{1}{4}\%$	$\frac{1}{3}\%$	$\frac{5}{12}\%$	$\frac{1}{2}\%$	$\frac{7}{12}\%$
1	0.9975 0623	0.9966 7774	0.9958 5062	0.9950 2488	0.9942 0050
2	0.9950 1869	0.9933 6652	0.9917 1846	0.9900 7450	0.9844 3463
3	0.9925 3734	0.9900 6630	0.9876 0345	0.9851 4876	0.9827 0220
4	0.9900 6219	0.9867 7704	0.9835 0551	0.9802 4752	0.9770 0302
5	0.9875 9321	0.9834 9871	0.9794 2457	0.9753 7067	0.9713 3688
6	0.9851 3038	0.9802 3127	0.9753 6057	0.9705 1808	0.9657 0361
7	0.9826 7370	0.9769 7469	0.9713 1343	0.9656 8963	0.9601 0301
8	0.9802 2314	0.9737 2893	0.9672 8308	0.9608 8520	0.9545 3489
9	0.9777 7869	0.9704 9395	0.9632 6946	0.9561 0468	0.9489 9907
10	0.9753 4034	0.9672 6972	0.9592 7249	0.9513 4794	0.9434 9534
11	0.9729 0807	0.9640 5620	0.9552 9211	0.9466 1489	0.9380 2354
12	0.9704 8187	0.9608 5335	0.9513 2824	0.9419 0534	0.9325 8347
13	0.9680 6171	0.9576 6115	0.9473 8082	0.9372 1924	0.9271 7495
14	0.9656 4759	0.9544 7955	0.9434 4978	0.9325 5646	0.9217 9780
15	0.9632 3949	0.9513 0852	0.9395 3505	0.9279 1688	0.9164 5183
16	0.9608 3740	0.9481 4803	0.9356 3656	0.9233 0037	0.9111 3686
17	0.9584 4130	0.9449 9803	0.9317 5425	0.9187 0684	0.9058 5272
18	0.9560 5117	0.9418 5851	0.9278 8805	0.9141 3616	0.9005 9923
19	0.9536 6700	0.9387 2941	0.9240 3789	0.9095 8822	0.8953 7620
20	0.9512 8878	0.9356 1071	0.9202 0371	0.9050 6290	0.8901 8346
21	0.9489 1649	0.9325 0236	0.9163 8544	0.9005 6010	0.8850 2084
22	0.9465 5011	0.9294 0435	0.9125 8301	0.8960 7971	0.8798 8816
23	0.9441 8964	0.9263 1663	0.9087 9636	0.8916 2160	0.8747 8525
24	0.9418 3505	0.9232 3916	0.9050 2542	0.8871 8565	0.8697 1193
25	0.9394 8634	0.9201 7192	0.9012 7012	0.8827 7181	0.8646 6803
26	0.9371 4348	0.9171 1487	0.8975 3041	0.8783 7991	0.8596 5339
27	0.9348 0646	0.9140 6798	0.8938 0622	0.8740 0986	0.8546 6782
28	0.9324 7527	0.9110 3121	0.8900 9748	0.8696 6155	0.8497 1118
29	0.9301 4990	0.9080 0453	0.8864 0413	0.8653 3488	0.8447 8327
30	0.9278 3032	0.9049 8790	0.8827 2610	0.8610 2973	0.8398 8395
31	0.9255 1653	0.9019 8130	0.8790 6334	0.8567 4600	0.8350 1304
32	0.9232 0851	0.8989 8468	0.8754 1577	0.8524 8358	0.8301 7038
33	0.9209 0624	0.8959 9802	0.8717 8334	0.8482 4237	0.8253 5581
34	0.9186 0972	0.8930 2128	0.8681 6599	0.8440 2226	0.8205 6915
35	0.9163 1892	0.8900 5444	0.8645 6364	0.8398 2314	0.8158 1026
36	0.9140 3384	0.8870 9745	0.8609 7624	0.8356 4492	0.8110 7897
37	0.9117 5445	0.8841 5028	0.8574 0372	0.8314 8748	0.8063 7511
38	0.9094 8075	0.8812 1290	0.8538 4603	0.8273 5073	0.8016 9854
39	0.9072 1272	0.8782 8528	0.8503 0310	0.8232 3455	0.7970 4908
40	0.9049 5034	0.8753 6739	0.8467 7487	0.8191 3886	0.7924 2660
41	0.9026 9361	0.8724 5920	0.8432 6128	0.8150 6354	0.7878 3092
42	0.9004 4250	0.8695 6066	0.8397 6227	0.8110 0850	0.7832 6189
43	0.8981 9701	0.8666 7175	0.8362 7778	0.8069 7363	0.7787 1936
44	0.8959 5712	0.8637 9245	0.8328 0775	0.8029 5884	0.7742 0317
45	0.8937 2281	0.8609 2270	0.8293 5211	0.7989 6402	0.7697 1318
46	0.8914 9407	0.8580 6249	0.8259 1082	0.7949 8907	0.7652 4923
47	0.8892 7090	0.8552 1179	0.8224 8380	0.7910 3390	0.7608 1116
48	0.8870 5326	0.8523 7055	0.8190 7100	0.7870 9841	0.7563 9884
49	0.8848 4116	0.8495 3876	0.8156 7237	0.7831 8250	0.7520 1210
50	0.8826 3457	0.8467 1637	0.8122 8784	0.7792 8607	0.7476 5080

PRESENT VALUE OF 1 AT COMPOUND INTEREST

$$v^n = \frac{1}{(1 + i)^n}$$

n	$\frac{1}{4}\%$	$\frac{1}{3}\%$	$\frac{5}{12}\%$	$\frac{1}{2}\%$	$\frac{7}{12}\%$
51	0.8804 3349	0.8439 0336	0.8089 1735	0.7754 0902	0.7433 1480
52	0.8782 3790	0.8410 9969	0.8055 6084	0.7715 5127	0.7390 0394
53	0.8760 4778	0.8383 0534	0.8022 1827	0.7677 1270	0.7347 1809
54	0.8738 6312	0.8355 2027	0.7988 8956	0.7638 9324	0.7304 5709
55	0.8716 8391	0.8327 4446	0.7955 7467	0.7600 9277	0.7262 2080
56	0.8695 1013	0.8299 7787	0.7922 7353	0.7563 1122	0.7220 0908
57	0.8673 4178	0.8272 2047	0.7889 8608	0.7525 4847	0.7178 2179
58	0.8651 7883	0.8244 7222	0.7857 1228	0.7488 0445	0.7136 5878
59	0.8630 2128	0.8217 3311	0.7824 5207	0.7450 7906	0.7095 1991
60	0.8608 6911	0.8190 0310	0.7792 0538	0.7413 7220	0.7054 0505
61	0.8587 2230	0.8162 8216	0.7759 7216	0.7376 8378	0.7013 1405
62	0.8565 8085	0.8135 7026	0.7727 5236	0.7340 1371	0.6972 4678
63	0.8544 4474	0.8108 6737	0.7695 4591	0.7303 6190	0.6932 0310
64	0.8523 1395	0.8081 7346	0.7663 5278	0.7267 2826	0.6891 8286
65	0.8501 8848	0.8054 8850	0.7631 7289	0.7231 1269	0.6851 8594
66	0.8480 6831	0.8028 1246	0.7600 0620	0.7195 1512	0.6812 1221
67	0.8459 5343	0.8001 4531	0.7568 5265	0.7159 3544	0.6772 6151
68	0.8438 4382	0.7974 8702	0.7537 1218	0.7123 7357	0.6733 3373
69	0.8417 3947	0.7948 3756	0.7505 8474	0.7088 2943	0.6694 2873
70	0.8396 4037	0.7921 9690	0.7474 7028	0.7053 0291	0.6655 4638
71	0.8375 4650	0.7895 6502	0.7443 6874	0.7017 9394	0.6616 8654
72	0.8354 5786	0.7869 4188	0.7412 8008	0.6983 0243	0.6578 4909
73	0.8333 7442	0.7843 2745	0.7382 0423	0.6948 2829	0.6540 3389
74	0.8312 9618	0.7817 2171	0.7351 4114	0.6913 7143	0.6502 4082
75	0.8292 2312	0.7791 2463	0.7320 9076	0.6879 3177	0.6464 6975
76	0.8271 5523	0.7765 3618	0.7290 5304	0.6845 0923	0.6427 2054
77	0.8250 9250	0.7739 5632	0.7260 2792	0.6811 0371	0.6389 9308
78	0.8230 3491	0.7713 8504	0.7230 1536	0.6777 1513	0.6352 8724
79	0.8209 8246	0.7688 2230	0.7200 1529	0.6743 4342	0.6316 0289
80	0.8189 3512	0.7662 6807	0.7170 2768	0.6709 8847	0.6279 3991
81	0.8168 9289	0.7637 2233	0.7140 5246	0.6676 5022	0.6242 9817
82	0.8148 5575	0.7611 8505	0.7110 8959	0.6643 2858	0.6206 7755
83	0.8128 2369	0.7586 5619	0.7081 3901	0.6610 2346	0.6170 7793
84	0.8107 9670	0.7561 3574	0.7052 0067	0.6577 3479	0.6134 9919
85	0.8087 7476	0.7536 2366	0.7022 7453	0.6544 6248	0.6099 4120
86	0.8067 5787	0.7511 1993	0.6993 6052	0.6512 0644	0.6064 0384
87	0.8047 4600	0.7486 2451	0.6964 5861	0.6479 6661	0.6028 8700
88	0.8027 3915	0.7461 3739	0.6935 6874	0.6447 4290	0.5993 9056
89	0.8007 3731	0.7436 5853	0.6906 9086	0.6415 3522	0.5959 1439
90	0.7987 4046	0.7411 8790	0.6878 2493	0.6383 4350	0.5924 5838
91	0.7967 4859	0.7387 2548	0.6849 7088	0.6351 6766	0.5890 2242
92	0.7947 6168	0.7362 7125	0.6821 2868	0.6320 0763	0.5856 0638
93	0.7927 7973	0.7338 2516	0.6792 9827	0.6288 6331	0.5822 1015
94	0.7908 0273	0.7313 8720	0.6764 7960	0.6257 3464	0.5788 3363
95	0.7888 3065	0.7289 5735	0.6736 7263	0.6226 2153	0.5754 7668
96	0.7868 6349	0.7265 3556	0.6708 7731	0.6195 2391	0.5721 3920
97	0.7849 0124	0.7241 2182	0.6680 9359	0.6164 4170	0.5688 2108
98	0.7829 4388	0.7217 1610	0.6653 2141	0.6133 7483	0.5655 2220
99	0.7809 9140	0.7193 1837	0.6625 6074	0.6103 2321	0.5622 4245
100	0.7790 4379	0.7169 2861	0.6598 1153	0.6072 8678	0.5589 8172

PRESENT VALUE OF 1 AT COMPOUND INTEREST

$$v^n = \frac{1}{(1+i)^n}$$

n	$\frac{7}{8}$ %	1 %	$1\frac{1}{8}$ %	$1\frac{1}{4}$ %	$1\frac{3}{8}$ %
1	0.9913 2590	0.9900 9901	0.9888 7515	0.9876 5432	0.9864 3650
2	0.9827 2704	0.9802 9605	0.9778 7407	0.9754 6106	0.9730 5696
3	0.9742 0276	0.9705 9015	0.9669 9537	0.9634 1833	0.9598 5890
4	0.9657 5243	0.9609 8034	0.9562 3770	0.9515 2428	0.9468 3986
5	0.9573 7539	0.9514 6569	0.9455 9970	0.9397 7706	0.9339 9739
6	0.9490 7102	0.9420 4524	0.9350 8005	0.9281 7488	0.9213 2912
7	0.9408 3868	0.9327 1805	0.9246 7743	0.9167 1593	0.9088 3267
8	0.9326 7775	0.9234 8322	0.9143 9054	0.9053 9845	0.8965 0571
9	0.9245 8761	0.9143 3982	0.9042 1808	0.8942 2069	0.8843 4596
10	0.9165 6765	0.9052 8695	0.8941 5881	0.8831 8093	0.8723 5113
11	0.9086 1724	0.8963 2372	0.8842 1142	0.8722 7746	0.8605 1899
12	0.9007 3581	0.8874 4923	0.8743 7470	0.8615 0860	0.8488 4734
13	0.8929 2273	0.8786 6260	0.8646 4742	0.8508 7269	0.8373 3400
14	0.8851 7743	0.8699 6297	0.8550 2835	0.8403 6809	0.8259 7682
15	0.8774 9931	0.8613 4947	0.8455 1629	0.8299 9318	0.8147 7368
16	0.8698 8779	0.8528 2126	0.8361 1005	0.8197 4635	0.8037 2250
17	0.8623 4230	0.8443 7749	0.8268 0846	0.8096 2602	0.7928 2120
18	0.8548 6225	0.8360 1731	0.8176 1034	0.7996 3064	0.7820 6777
19	0.8474 4709	0.8277 3992	0.8085 1455	0.7897 5866	0.7714 6020
20	0.8400 9624	0.8195 4447	0.7995 1995	0.7800 0855	0.7609 9649
21	0.8328 0917	0.8114 3017	0.7906 2542	0.7703 7881	0.7506 7472
22	0.8255 8530	0.8033 9621	0.7818 2983	0.7608 6796	0.7404 9294
23	0.8184 2409	0.7954 4179	0.7731 3210	0.7514 7453	0.7304 4926
24	0.8113 2499	0.7875 6613	0.7645 3112	0.7421 9707	0.7205 4181
25	0.8042 8748	0.7797 6844	0.7560 2583	0.7330 3414	0.7107 6874
26	0.7973 1101	0.7720 4796	0.7476 1516	0.7239 8434	0.7011 2823
27	0.7903 9505	0.7644 0392	0.7392 9806	0.7150 4626	0.6916 1847
28	0.7835 3908	0.7568 3557	0.7310 7348	0.7062 1853	0.6822 3771
29	0.7767 4258	0.7493 4215	0.7229 4040	0.6974 9978	0.6729 8417
30	0.7700 0504	0.7419 2292	0.7148 9780	0.6888 8867	0.6638 5615
31	0.7633 2594	0.7345 7715	0.7069 4467	0.6803 8387	0.6548 5194
32	0.7567 0477	0.7273 0411	0.6990 8002	0.6719 8407	0.6459 6985
33	0.7501 4104	0.7201 0307	0.6913 0287	0.6636 8797	0.6372 0824
34	0.7436 3424	0.7129 7334	0.6836 1223	0.6554 9429	0.6285 6546
35	0.7371 8388	0.7059 1420	0.6760 0715	0.6474 0177	0.6200 3991
36	0.7307 8947	0.6989 2495	0.6684 8667	0.6394 0916	0.6116 3000
37	0.7244 5053	0.6920 0490	0.6610 4986	0.6315 1522	0.6033 3416
38	0.7181 6657	0.6851 5337	0.6536 9578	0.6237 1873	0.5951 5083
39	0.7119 3712	0.6783 6967	0.6464 2352	0.6160 1850	0.5870 7850
40	0.7057 6171	0.6716 5314	0.6392 3216	0.6084 1334	0.5791 1566
41	0.6996 3986	0.6650 0311	0.6321 2080	0.6009 0206	0.5712 6083
42	0.6935 7111	0.6584 1892	0.6250 8855	0.5934 8352	0.5635 1253
43	0.6875 5500	0.6518 9992	0.6181 3454	0.5861 5656	0.5558 6933
44	0.6815 9108	0.6454 4546	0.6112 5789	0.5789 2006	0.5483 2979
45	0.6756 7889	0.6390 5492	0.6044 5774	0.5717 7290	0.5408 9252
46	0.6698 1798	0.6327 2764	0.5977 3324	0.5647 1397	0.5335 5612
47	0.6640 0792	0.6264 6301	0.5910 8355	0.5577 4219	0.5263 1923
48	0.6582 4824	0.6202 6041	0.5845 0784	0.5508 5649	0.5191 8050
49	0.6525 3853	0.6141 1921	0.5780 0528	0.5440 5579	0.5121 3860
50	0.6468 7835	0.6080 3882	0.5715 7506	0.5373 3905	0.5051 9220

PRESENT VALUE OF 1 AT COMPOUND INTEREST

$$v^n = \frac{1}{(1+i)^n}$$

n	$\frac{7}{8}$ %	1 %	$1\frac{1}{8}$ %	$1\frac{1}{4}$ %	$1\frac{3}{8}$ %
51	0.6412 6726	0.6020 1864	0.5652 1637	0.5307 0524	0.4983 4003
52	0.6357 0484	0.5960 5806	0.5589 2843	0.5241 5332	0.4915 8079
53	0.6301 9067	0.5901 5649	0.5527 1044	0.5176 8229	0.4849 1323
54	0.6247 2433	0.5843 1336	0.5465 6162	0.5112 9115	0.4783 3611
55	0.6193 0541	0.5785 2808	0.5404 8120	0.5049 7892	0.4718 4820
56	0.6139 3349	0.5728 0008	0.5344 6843	0.4987 4461	0.4654 4829
57	0.6086 0817	0.5671 2879	0.5285 2256	0.4925 8727	0.4591 3518
58	0.6033 2904	0.5615 1365	0.5226 4282	0.4865 0594	0.4529 0770
59	0.5980 9571	0.5559 5411	0.5168 2850	0.4804 9970	0.4467 6468
60	0.5929 0776	0.5504 4962	0.5110 7887	0.4745 6760	0.4407 0499
61	0.5877 6482	0.5449 9962	0.5053 9319	0.4687 0874	0.4347 2749
62	0.5826 6649	0.5396 0358	0.4997 7077	0.4629 2222	0.4288 3106
63	0.5776 1238	0.5342 6097	0.4942 1090	0.4572 0713	0.4230 1461
64	0.5726 0211	0.5289 7126	0.4887 1288	0.4515 6259	0.4172 7705
65	0.5676 3530	0.5237 3392	0.4832 7602	0.4459 8775	0.4116 1731
66	0.5627 1158	0.5185 4844	0.4778 9965	0.4404 8173	0.4060 3434
67	0.5578 3056	0.5134 1429	0.4725 8309	0.4350 4368	0.4005 2709
68	0.5529 9188	0.5083 3099	0.4673 2568	0.4296 7277	0.3950 9454
69	0.5481 9517	0.5032 9801	0.4621 2675	0.4243 6817	0.3897 3568
70	0.5434 4007	0.4983 1486	0.4569 8566	0.4191 2905	0.3844 4949
71	0.5387 2622	0.4933 8105	0.4519 0177	0.4139 5462	0.3792 3501
72	0.5340 5325	0.4884 9609	0.4468 7443	0.4088 4407	0.3740 9126
73	0.5294 2082	0.4836 5949	0.4419 0302	0.4037 9661	0.3690 1727
74	0.5248 2857	0.4788 7078	0.4369 8692	0.3988 1147	0.3640 1210
75	0.5202 7615	0.4741 2949	0.4321 2551	0.3938 8787	0.3590 7483
76	0.5157 6322	0.4694 3514	0.4273 1818	0.3890 2506	0.3542 0451
77	0.5112 8944	0.4647 8726	0.4225 6433	0.3842 2228	0.3494 0026
78	0.5068 5447	0.4601 8541	0.4178 6337	0.3794 7879	0.3446 6117
79	0.5024 5796	0.4556 2912	0.4132 1470	0.3747 9387	0.3399 8636
80	0.4980 9959	0.4511 1794	0.4086 1775	0.3701 6679	0.3353 7495
81	0.4937 7902	0.4466 5142	0.4040 7194	0.3655 9683	0.3308 2609
82	0.4894 9593	0.4422 2913	0.3995 7670	0.3610 8329	0.3263 3893
83	0.4852 4999	0.4378 5063	0.3951 3148	0.3566 2547	0.3219 1263
84	0.4810 4089	0.4335 1547	0.3907 3570	0.3522 2268	0.3175 4637
85	0.4768 6829	0.4292 2324	0.3863 8882	0.3478 7426	0.3132 3933
86	0.4727 3188	0.4249 7350	0.3820 9031	0.3435 7951	0.3089 9071
87	0.4686 3136	0.4207 6585	0.3778 3961	0.3393 3779	0.3047 9971
88	0.4645 6640	0.4165 9985	0.3736 3621	0.3351 4843	0.3006 6556
89	0.4605 3671	0.4124 7510	0.3694 7956	0.3310 1080	0.2965 8748
90	0.4565 4197	0.4083 9119	0.3653 6916	0.3269 2425	0.2925 6472
91	0.4525 8187	0.4043 4771	0.3613 0448	0.3228 8814	0.2885 9652
92	0.4486 5613	0.4003 4427	0.3572 8503	0.3189 0187	0.2846 8214
93	0.4447 6444	0.3963 8046	0.3533 1029	0.3149 6481	0.2808 2085
94	0.4409 0651	0.3924 5590	0.3493 7976	0.3110 7636	0.2770 1194
95	0.4370 8204	0.3885 7020	0.3454 9297	0.3072 3591	0.2732 5468
96	0.4332 9075	0.3847 2297	0.3416 4941	0.3034 4287	0.2695 4839
97	0.4295 3234	0.3809 1383	0.3378 4861	0.2996 9666	0.2658 9237
98	0.4258 0654	0.3771 4241	0.3340 9010	0.2959 9670	0.2622 8594
99	0.4221 1305	0.3734 0832	0.3303 7340	0.2923 4242	0.2587 2843
100	0.4184 5159	0.3697 1121	0.3266 9805	0.2887 3326	0.2552 1916

PRESENT VALUE OF 1 AT COMPOUND INTEREST

$$v^n = \frac{1}{(1 + i)^n}$$

n	$1\frac{1}{2}\%$	$1\frac{3}{4}\%$	2%	$2\frac{1}{4}\%$	$2\frac{1}{2}\%$
1	0.9852 2167	0.9828 0098	0.9803 9216	0.9779 9511	0.9756 0976
2	0.9706 6175	0.9658 9777	0.9611 6878	0.9564 7444	0.9518 1440
3	0.9563 1699	0.9492 8528	0.9423 2233	0.9354 2732	0.9285 9941
4	0.9421 8423	0.9329 5851	0.9238 4543	0.9148 4335	0.9059 5064
5	0.9282 6033	0.9169 1254	0.9057 3081	0.8947 1232	0.8838 5429
6	0.9145 4219	0.9011 4254	0.8879 7138	0.8750 2427	0.8622 9687
7	0.9010 2679	0.8856 4378	0.8705 6018	0.8557 6946	0.8412 6524
8	0.8877 1112	0.8704 1157	0.8534 9037	0.8369 3835	0.8207 4657
9	0.8745 9224	0.8554 4135	0.8367 5527	0.8185 2161	0.8007 2836
10	0.8616 6723	0.8407 2860	0.8203 4830	0.8005 1013	0.7811 9840
11	0.8489 3323	0.8262 6889	0.8042 6304	0.7828 9499	0.7621 4478
12	0.8363 8742	0.8120 5788	0.7884 9318	0.7656 6748	0.7435 5589
13	0.8240 2702	0.7980 9128	0.7730 3253	0.7488 1905	0.7254 2038
14	0.8118 4928	0.7843 6490	0.7578 7502	0.7323 4137	0.7077 2720
15	0.7998 5150	0.7708 7459	0.7430 1473	0.7162 2628	0.6904 6556
16	0.7880 3104	0.7576 1631	0.7284 4581	0.7004 6580	0.6736 2493
17	0.7763 8526	0.7445 8605	0.7141 6256	0.6850 5212	0.6571 9506
18	0.7649 1159	0.7317 7990	0.7001 5937	0.6699 7763	0.6411 6591
19	0.7536 0747	0.7191 9401	0.6864 3076	0.6552 3484	0.6255 2772
20	0.7424 7042	0.7068 2458	0.6729 7133	0.6408 1647	0.6102 7094
21	0.7314 9795	0.6946 6789	0.6597 7582	0.6267 1538	0.5953 8629
22	0.7206 8763	0.6827 2028	0.6468 3904	0.6129 2457	0.5808 6467
23	0.7100 3708	0.6709 7817	0.6341 5592	0.5994 3724	0.5666 9724
24	0.6995 4392	0.6594 3800	0.6217 2149	0.5862 4668	0.5528 7535
25	0.6892 0583	0.6480 9632	0.6095 3087	0.5733 4639	0.5393 9059
26	0.6790 2052	0.6369 4970	0.5975 7928	0.5607 2997	0.5262 3472
27	0.6689 8574	0.6259 9479	0.5858 6204	0.5483 9117	0.5133 9973
28	0.6590 9925	0.6152 2829	0.5743 7455	0.5363 2388	0.5008 7778
29	0.6493 5887	0.6046 4697	0.5631 1231	0.5245 2213	0.4886 6125
30	0.6397 6243	0.5942 4764	0.5520 7089	0.5129 8008	0.4767 4269
31	0.6303 0781	0.5840 2716	0.5412 4597	0.5016 9201	0.4651 1481
32	0.6209 9292	0.5739 8247	0.5306 3330	0.4906 5233	0.4537 7055
33	0.6118 1568	0.5641 1053	0.5202 2873	0.4798 5558	0.4427 0298
34	0.6027 7407	0.5544 0839	0.5100 2817	0.4692 9641	0.4319 0534
35	0.5938 6608	0.5448 7311	0.5000 2761	0.4589 6960	0.4213 7107
36	0.5850 8974	0.5355 0183	0.4902 2315	0.4488 7002	0.4110 9372
37	0.5764 4309	0.5262 9172	0.4806 1093	0.4389 9268	0.4010 6705
38	0.5679 2423	0.5172 4002	0.4711 8719	0.4293 3270	0.3912 8492
39	0.5595 3126	0.5083 4400	0.4619 4822	0.4198 8528	0.3817 4139
40	0.5512 6232	0.4996 0098	0.4528 9042	0.4106 4575	0.3724 3062
41	0.5431 1559	0.4910 0834	0.4440 1021	0.4016 0954	0.3633 4695
42	0.5350 8925	0.4825 6348	0.4353 0413	0.3927 7216	0.3544 8483
43	0.5271 8153	0.4742 6386	0.4267 6875	0.3841 2925	0.3458 3886
44	0.5193 9067	0.4661 0699	0.4184 0074	0.3756 7653	0.3374 0376
45	0.5117 1494	0.4580 9040	0.4101 9680	0.3674 0981	0.3291 7440
46	0.5041 5265	0.4502 1170	0.4021 5373	0.3593 2500	0.3211 4576
47	0.4967 0212	0.4424 6850	0.3942 6836	0.3514 1809	0.3133 1294
48	0.4893 6170	0.4348 5848	0.3865 3761	0.3436 8518	0.3056 7116
49	0.4821 2975	0.4273 7934	0.3789 5844	0.3361 2242	0.2982 1576
50	0.4750 0468	0.4200 2883	0.3715 2788	0.3287 2608	0.2909 4221

PRESENT VALUE OF 1 AT COMPOUND INTEREST

$$v^n = \frac{1}{(1 + i)^n}$$

n	$1\frac{1}{2}\%$	$1\frac{3}{4}\%$	2%	$2\frac{1}{4}\%$	$2\frac{1}{2}\%$
51	0.4679 8491	0.4128 0475	0.3642 4302	0.3214 9250	0.2838 4606
52	0.4610 6887	0.4057 0492	0.3571 0100	0.3144 1810	0.2769 2298
53	0.4542 5505	0.3987 2719	0.3500 9902	0.3074 9936	0.2701 6876
54	0.4475 4192	0.3918 6947	0.3432 3433	0.3007 3287	0.2635 7928
55	0.4409 2800	0.3851 2970	0.3365 0425	0.2941 1528	0.2571 5052
56	0.4344 1182	0.3785 0585	0.3299 0613	0.2876 4330	0.2508 7855
57	0.4279 9194	0.3719 9592	0.3234 3738	0.2813 1374	0.2447 5956
58	0.4216 6694	0.3655 9796	0.3170 9547	0.2751 2347	0.2387 8982
59	0.4154 3541	0.3593 1003	0.3108 7791	0.2690 6940	0.2329 6568
60	0.4092 9597	0.3531 3025	0.3047 8227	0.2631 4856	0.2272 8359
61	0.4032 4726	0.3470 5676	0.2988 0614	0.2573 5801	0.2217 4009
62	0.3972 8794	0.3410 8772	0.2929 4720	0.2516 9487	0.2163 3179
63	0.3914 1669	0.3352 2135	0.2872 0314	0.2461 5635	0.2110 5541
64	0.3856 3221	0.3294 5587	0.2815 7170	0.2407 3971	0.2059 0771
65	0.3799 3321	0.3237 8956	0.2760 5069	0.2354 4226	0.2008 8557
66	0.3743 1843	0.3182 2069	0.2706 3793	0.2302 6138	0.1959 8593
67	0.3687 8663	0.3127 4761	0.2653 3130	0.2251 9450	0.1912 0578
68	0.3633 3658	0.3073 6866	0.2601 2873	0.2202 3912	0.1865 4223
69	0.3579 6708	0.3020 8222	0.2550 2817	0.2153 9278	0.1819 9241
70	0.3526 7692	0.2968 8670	0.2500 2761	0.2106 5309	0.1775 5358
71	0.3474 6495	0.2917 8054	0.2451 2511	0.2060 1769	0.1732 2300
72	0.3423 3000	0.2867 6221	0.2403 1874	0.2014 8429	0.1689 9805
73	0.3372 7093	0.2818 3018	0.2356 0661	0.1970 5065	0.1648 7615
74	0.3322 8663	0.2769 8298	0.2309 8687	0.1927 1458	0.1608 5478
75	0.3273 7599	0.2722 1914	0.2264 5771	0.1884 7391	0.1569 3149
76	0.3225 3793	0.2675 3724	0.2220 1737	0.1843 2657	0.1531 0389
77	0.3177 7136	0.2629 3586	0.2176 6408	0.1802 7048	0.1493 6965
78	0.3130 7523	0.2584 1362	0.2133 9616	0.1763 0365	0.1457 2649
79	0.3084 4850	0.2539 6916	0.2092 1192	0.1724 2411	0.1421 7218
80	0.3038 9015	0.2496 0114	0.2051 0973	0.1686 2993	0.1387 0457
81	0.2993 9916	0.2453 0825	0.2010 8797	0.1649 1925	0.1353 2153
82	0.2949 7454	0.2410 8919	0.1971 4507	0.1612 9022	0.1320 2101
83	0.2906 1531	0.2369 4269	0.1932 7948	0.1577 4105	0.1288 0098
84	0.2863 2050	0.2328 6751	0.1894 8968	0.1542 6997	0.1256 5949
85	0.2820 8917	0.2288 6242	0.1857 7420	0.1508 7528	0.1225 9463
86	0.2779 2036	0.2249 2621	0.1821 3157	0.1475 5528	0.1196 0452
87	0.2738 1316	0.2210 5770	0.1785 6036	0.1443 0835	0.1166 8733
88	0.2697 6666	0.2172 5572	0.1750 5918	0.1411 3286	0.1138 4130
89	0.2657 7997	0.2135 1914	0.1716 2665	0.1380 2724	0.1110 6468
90	0.2618 5218	0.2098 4682	0.1682 6142	0.1349 8997	0.1083 5579
91	0.2579 8245	0.2062 3766	0.1649 6217	0.1320 1953	0.1057 1296
92	0.2541 6990	0.2026 9057	0.1617 2762	0.1291 1445	0.1031 3460
93	0.2504 1369	0.1992 0450	0.1585 5649	0.1262 7331	0.1006 1912
94	0.2467 1300	0.1957 7837	0.1554 4754	0.1234 9468	0.0981 6500
95	0.2430 6699	0.1924 1118	0.1523 9955	0.1207 7719	0.0957 7073
96	0.2394 7487	0.1891 0190	0.1494 1132	0.1181 1950	0.0934 3486
97	0.2359 3583	0.1858 4953	0.1464 8169	0.1155 2029	0.0911 5596
98	0.2324 4909	0.1826 5310	0.1436 0950	0.1129 7828	0.0889 3264
99	0.2290 1389	0.1795 1165	0.1407 9363	0.1104 9221	0.0867 6355
100	0.2256 2944	0.1764 2422	0.1380 3297	0.1080 6084	0.0846 4737

PRESENT VALUE OF 1 AT COMPOUND INTEREST

$$v^n = \frac{1}{(1 + i)^n}$$

n	$2\frac{3}{4}\%$	3%	$3\frac{1}{2}\%$	4%	$4\frac{1}{2}\%$
1	0.9732 3601	0.9708 7379	0.9661 8357	0.9615 3846	0.9569 3780
2	0.9471 8833	0.9425 9591	0.9335 1070	0.9245 5621	0.9157 2995
3	0.9218 3779	0.9151 4166	0.9019 4271	0.8889 9636	0.8762 9660
4	0.8971 6573	0.8884 8705	0.8714 4223	0.8548 0419	0.8385 6134
5	0.8731 5400	0.8626 0878	0.8419 7317	0.8219 2711	0.8024 5105
6	0.8497 8491	0.8374 8426	0.8135 0064	0.7903 1453	0.7678 9574
7	0.8270 4128	0.8130 9151	0.7859 9096	0.7599 1781	0.7348 2846
8	0.8049 0635	0.7894 0923	0.7594 1156	0.7306 9021	0.7031 8513
9	0.7833 6385	0.7664 1673	0.7337 3097	0.7025 8674	0.6729 0443
10	0.7623 9791	0.7440 9391	0.7089 1881	0.6755 6417	0.6439 2768
11	0.7419 9310	0.7224 2128	0.6849 4571	0.6495 8093	0.6161 9874
12	0.7221 3440	0.7013 7988	0.6617 8330	0.6245 9705	0.5896 6386
13	0.7028 0720	0.6809 5134	0.6394 0415	0.6005 7409	0.5642 7164
14	0.6839 9728	0.6611 1781	0.6177 8179	0.5774 7508	0.5399 7286
15	0.6656 9078	0.6418 6195	0.5968 9062	0.5552 6450	0.5167 2044
16	0.6478 7424	0.6231 6694	0.5767 0591	0.5339 0818	0.4944 6932
17	0.6305 3454	0.6050 1645	0.5572 0378	0.5133 7325	0.4731 7639
18	0.6136 5892	0.5873 9461	0.5383 6114	0.4936 2812	0.4528 0037
19	0.5972 3496	0.5702 8603	0.5201 5569	0.4746 4242	0.4333 0179
20	0.5812 5057	0.5536 7575	0.5025 6588	0.4563 8695	0.4146 4286
21	0.5656 9398	0.5375 4928	0.4855 7090	0.4388 3360	0.3967 8743
22	0.5505 5375	0.5218 9250	0.4691 5063	0.4219 5539	0.3797 0089
23	0.5358 1874	0.5066 9175	0.4532 8563	0.4057 2633	0.3633 5013
24	0.5214 7809	0.4919 3374	0.4379 5713	0.3901 2147	0.3477 0347
25	0.5075 2126	0.4776 0557	0.4231 4699	0.3751 1680	0.3327 3060
26	0.4939 3796	0.4636 9473	0.4088 3767	0.3606 8923	0.3184 0248
27	0.4807 1821	0.4501 8906	0.3950 1224	0.3468 1657	0.3046 9137
28	0.4678 5227	0.4370 7675	0.3816 5434	0.3334 7747	0.2915 7069
29	0.4553 3068	0.4243 4636	0.3687 4815	0.3206 5141	0.2790 1502
30	0.4431 4421	0.4119 8676	0.3562 7841	0.3083 1867	0.2670 0002
31	0.4312 8391	0.3999 8715	0.3442 3035	0.2964 6026	0.2555 0241
32	0.4197 4103	0.3883 3703	0.3325 8971	0.2850 5794	0.2444 9991
33	0.4085 0708	0.3770 2625	0.3213 4271	0.2740 9417	0.2339 7121
34	0.3975 7380	0.3660 4490	0.3104 7605	0.2635 5209	0.2238 9589
35	0.3869 3314	0.3553 8340	0.2999 7686	0.2534 1547	0.2142 5444
36	0.3765 7727	0.3450 3243	0.2898 3272	0.2436 6872	0.2050 2817
37	0.3664 9856	0.3349 8294	0.2800 3161	0.2342 9685	0.1961 9921
38	0.3566 8959	0.3252 2615	0.2705 6194	0.2252 8543	0.1877 5044
39	0.3471 4316	0.3157 5355	0.2614 1250	0.2166 2061	0.1796 6549
40	0.3378 5222	0.3065 5684	0.2525 7247	0.2082 8904	0.1719 2870
41	0.3288 0995	0.2976 2800	0.2440 3137	0.2002 7793	0.1645 2507
42	0.3200 0968	0.2889 5922	0.2357 7910	0.1925 7493	0.1574 4026
43	0.3114 4495	0.2805 4294	0.2278 0590	0.1851 6820	0.1506 6054
44	0.3031 0944	0.2723 7178	0.2201 0231	0.1780 4635	0.1441 7276
45	0.2949 9702	0.2644 3862	0.2126 5924	0.1711 9841	0.1379 6437
46	0.2871 0172	0.2567 3653	0.2054 6787	0.1646 1386	0.1320 2332
47	0.2794 1773	0.2492 5876	0.1985 1968	0.1582 8256	0.1263 3810
48	0.2719 3940	0.2419 9880	0.1918 0645	0.1521 9476	0.1208 9771
49	0.2646 6122	0.2349 5029	0.1853 2024	0.1463 4112	0.1156 9158
50	0.2575 7783	0.2281 0708	0.1790 5337	0.1407 1262	0.1107 0965

PRESENT VALUE OF 1 AT COMPOUND INTEREST

$$v^n = \frac{1}{(1+i)^n}$$

n	$2\frac{3}{4}$ %	3 %	$3\frac{1}{2}$ %	4 %	$4\frac{1}{2}$ %
51	0.2506 8402	0.2214 6318	0.1729 9843	0.1353 0059	0.1059 4225
52	0.2439 7471	0.2150 1280	0.1671 4824	0.1300 9672	0.1013 8014
53	0.2374 4497	0.2087 5029	0.1614 9589	0.1250 9300	0.0970 1449
54	0.2310 9000	0.2026 7019	0.1560 3467	0.1202 8173	0.0928 3683
55	0.2249 0511	0.1967 6717	0.1507 5814	0.1156 5551	0.0888 3907
56	0.2188 8575	0.1910 3609	0.1456 6004	0.1112 0722	0.0850 1347
57	0.2130 2749	0.1854 7193	0.1407 3433	0.1069 3002	0.0813 5260
58	0.2073 2603	0.1800 6984	0.1359 7520	0.1028 1733	0.0778 4938
59	0.2017 7716	0.1748 2508	0.1313 7701	0.0988 6282	0.0744 9701
60	0.1963 7679	0.1697 3309	0.1269 3431	0.0950 6040	0.0712 8901
61	0.1911 2097	0.1647 8941	0.1226 4184	0.0914 0423	0.0682 1915
62	0.1860 0581	0.1599 8972	0.1184 9453	0.0878 8868	0.0652 8148
63	0.1810 2755	0.1553 2982	0.1144 8747	0.0845 0835	0.0624 7032
64	0.1761 8253	0.1508 0565	0.1106 1591	0.0812 5803	0.0597 8021
65	0.1714 6718	0.1464 1325	0.1068 7528	0.0781 3272	0.0572 0594
66	0.1668 7804	0.1421 4879	0.1032 6114	0.0751 2762	0.0547 4253
67	0.1624 1172	0.1380 0853	0.0997 6922	0.0722 3809	0.0523 8519
68	0.1580 6493	0.1339 8887	0.0963 9538	0.0694 5970	0.0501 2937
69	0.1538 3448	0.1300 8628	0.0931 3563	0.0667 8818	0.0479 7069
70	0.1497 1726	0.1262 9736	0.0899 8612	0.0642 1940	0.0459 0497
71	0.1457 1023	0.1226 1880	0.0869 4311	0.0617 4942	0.0439 2820
72	0.1418 1044	0.1190 4737	0.0840 0300	0.0593 7445	0.0420 3655
73	0.1380 1503	0.1155 7998	0.0811 6232	0.0570 9081	0.0402 2637
74	0.1343 2119	0.1122 1357	0.0784 1770	0.0548 9501	0.0384 9413
75	0.1307 2622	0.1089 4521	0.0757 6590	0.0527 8367	0.0368 3649
76	0.1272 2747	0.1057 7205	0.0732 0376	0.0507 5353	0.0352 5023
77	0.1238 2235	0.1026 9131	0.0707 2827	0.0488 0147	0.0337 3228
78	0.1205 0837	0.0997 0030	0.0683 3650	0.0469 2449	0.0322 7969
79	0.1172 8309	0.0967 9641	0.0660 2560	0.0451 1970	0.0308 8965
80	0.1141 4412	0.0939 7710	0.0637 9285	0.0433 8433	0.0295 5948
81	0.1110 8917	0.0912 3990	0.0616 3561	0.0417 1570	0.0282 8658
82	0.1081 1598	0.0885 8243	0.0595 5131	0.0401 1125	0.0270 6850
83	0.1052 2237	0.0860 0236	0.0575 3750	0.0385 6851	0.0259 0287
84	0.1024 0620	0.0834 9743	0.0555 9178	0.0370 8510	0.0247 8744
85	0.0996 6540	0.0810 6547	0.0537 1187	0.0356 5875	0.0237 2003
86	0.0969 9795	0.0787 0434	0.0518 9553	0.0342 8726	0.0226 9860
87	0.0944 0190	0.0764 1198	0.0501 4060	0.0329 6852	0.0217 2115
88	0.0918 7533	0.0741 8639	0.0484 4503	0.0317 0050	0.0207 8579
89	0.0894 1638	0.0720 2562	0.0468 0679	0.0304 8125	0.0198 9070
90	0.0870 2324	0.0699 2779	0.0452 2395	0.0293 0890	0.0190 3417
91	0.0846 9415	0.0678 9105	0.0436 9464	0.0281 8163	0.0182 1451
92	0.0824 2740	0.0659 1364	0.0422 1704	0.0270 9772	0.0174 3016
93	0.0802 2131	0.0639 9383	0.0407 8941	0.0260 5550	0.0166 7958
94	0.0780 7427	0.0621 2993	0.0394 1006	0.0250 5337	0.0159 6132
95	0.0759 8469	0.0603 2032	0.0380 7735	0.0240 8978	0.0152 7399
96	0.0739 5104	0.0585 6342	0.0367 8971	0.0231 6325	0.0146 1626
97	0.0719 7181	0.0568 5769	0.0355 4562	0.0222 7235	0.0139 8685
98	0.0700 4556	0.0552 0164	0.0343 4359	0.0214 1572	0.0133 8454
99	0.0681 7086	0.0535 9383	0.0331 8221	0.0205 9204	0.0128 0817
100	0.0663 4634	0.0520 3284	0.0320 6011	0.0198 0004	0.0122 5663

PRESENT VALUE OF 1 AT COMPOUND INTEREST

$$v^n = \frac{1}{(1 + i)^n}$$

n	5 %	$5\frac{1}{2}$ %	6 %	7 %	8 %
1	0.9523 8095	0.9478 6730	0.9433 9623	0.9345 7944	0.9259 2593
2	0.9070 2948	0.8984 5242	0.8899 9644	0.8734 3873	0.8573 3882
3	0.8638 3760	0.8516 1366	0.8396 1928	0.8162 9788	0.7938 3224
4	0.8227 0247	0.8072 1674	0.7920 9366	0.7628 9521	0.7350 2985
5	0.7835 2617	0.7651 3435	0.7472 5817	0.7129 8618	0.6805 8320
6	0.7462 1540	0.7252 4583	0.7049 6054	0.6663 4222	0.6301 6963
7	0.7106 8133	0.6874 3681	0.6650 5711	0.6227 4974	0.5834 9040
8	0.6768 3936	0.6515 9887	0.6274 1237	0.5820 0910	0.5402 6888
9	0.6446 0892	0.6176 2926	0.5918 9846	0.5439 3374	0.5002 4897
10	0.6139 1325	0.5854 3058	0.5583 9478	0.5083 4929	0.4631 9349
11	0.5846 7929	0.5549 1050	0.5267 8753	0.4750 9280	0.4288 8286
12	0.5568 3742	0.5259 8152	0.4969 6936	0.4440 1196	0.3971 1376
13	0.5303 2135	0.4985 6068	0.4688 3902	0.4149 6445	0.3676 9792
14	0.5050 6795	0.4725 6937	0.4423 0096	0.3878 1724	0.3404 6104
15	0.4810 1710	0.4479 3305	0.4172 6506	0.3624 4602	0.3152 4170
16	0.4581 1152	0.4245 8109	0.3936 4628	0.3387 3460	0.2918 9047
17	0.4362 9669	0.4024 4653	0.3713 6442	0.3165 7439	0.2702 6895
18	0.4155 2065	0.3814 6590	0.3503 4379	0.2958 6392	0.2502 4903
19	0.3957 3396	0.3615 7906	0.3305 1301	0.2765 0832	0.2317 1206
20	0.3768 8948	0.3427 2896	0.3118 0473	0.2584 1900	0.2145 4821
21	0.3589 4236	0.3248 6158	0.2941 5540	0.2415 1309	0.1986 5575
22	0.3418 4987	0.3079 2567	0.2775 0510	0.2257 1317	0.1839 4051
23	0.3255 7131	0.2918 7267	0.2617 9726	0.2109 4688	0.1703 1528
24	0.3100 6791	0.2766 5656	0.2469 7855	0.1971 4662	0.1576 9934
25	0.2953 0277	0.2622 3370	0.2329 9863	0.1842 4918	0.1460 1790
26	0.2812 4073	0.2485 6275	0.2198 1003	0.1721 9549	0.1352 0176
27	0.2678 4832	0.2356 0450	0.2073 6795	0.1609 3037	0.1251 8682
28	0.2550 9364	0.2233 2181	0.1956 3014	0.1504 0221	0.1159 1372
29	0.2429 4632	0.2116 7944	0.1845 5674	0.1405 6282	0.1073 2752
30	0.2313 7745	0.2006 4402	0.1741 1013	0.1313 6712	0.0993 7733
31	0.2203 5947	0.1901 8390	0.1642 5484	0.1227 7301	0.0920 1605
32	0.2098 6617	0.1802 6910	0.1549 5740	0.1147 4113	0.0852 0005
33	0.1998 7254	0.1708 7119	0.1461 8622	0.1072 3474	0.0788 8893
34	0.1903 5480	0.1619 6321	0.1379 1153	0.1002 1934	0.0730 4531
35	0.1812 9029	0.1535 1963	0.1301 0522	0.0936 6294	0.0676 3454
36	0.1726 5741	0.1455 1624	0.1227 4077	0.0875 3546	0.0626 2458
37	0.1644 3563	0.1379 3008	0.1157 9318	0.0818 0884	0.0579 8572
38	0.1566 0536	0.1307 3941	0.1092 3885	0.0764 5686	0.0536 9048
39	0.1491 4797	0.1239 2362	0.1030 5552	0.0714 5501	0.0497 1341
40	0.1420 4568	0.1174 6314	0.0972 2219	0.0667 8038	0.0460 3093
41	0.1352 8160	0.1113 3947	0.0917 1905	0.0624 1157	0.0426 2123
42	0.1288 3962	0.1055 3504	0.0865 2740	0.0583 2857	0.0394 6411
43	0.1227 0440	0.1000 3322	0.0816 2962	0.0545 1268	0.0365 4084
44	0.1168 6133	0.0948 1822	0.0770 0908	0.0509 4643	0.0338 3411
45	0.1112 9651	0.0898 7509	0.0726 5007	0.0476 1349	0.0313 2788
46	0.1059 9668	0.0851 8965	0.0685 3781	0.0444 9859	0.0290 0730
47	0.1009 4921	0.0807 4849	0.0646 5831	0.0415 8747	0.0268 5861
48	0.0961 4211	0.0765 3885	0.0609 9840	0.0388 6679	0.0248 6908
49	0.0915 6391	0.0725 4867	0.0575 4566	0.0363 2410	0.0230 2693
50	0.0872 0373	0.0687 6652	0.0542 8836	0.0339 4776	0.0213 2123

PRESENT VALUE OF 1 AT COMPOUND INTEREST

$$v^n = \frac{1}{(1+i)^n}$$

n	5 %	$5\frac{1}{2}$ %	6 %	7 %	8 %
51	0.0830 5117	0.0651 8153	0.0512 1544	0.0317 2688	0.0197 4188
52	0.0790 9635	0.0617 8344	0.0483 1645	0.0296 5129	0.0182 7952
53	0.0753 2986	0.0585 6250	0.0455 8156	0.0277 1148	0.0169 2548
54	0.0717 4272	0.0555 0948	0.0430 0147	0.0258 9858	0.0156 7174
55	0.0683 2640	0.0526 1562	0.0405 6742	0.0242 0428	0.0145 1087
56	0.0650 7276	0.0498 7263	0.0382 7115	0.0226 2083	0.0134 3599
57	0.0619 7406	0.0472 7263	0.0361 0486	0.0211 4096	0.0124 4073
58	0.0590 2291	0.0448 0818	0.0340 6119	0.0197 5791	0.0115 1920
59	0.0562 1230	0.0424 7221	0.0321 3320	0.0184 6533	0.0106 6592
60	0.0535 3552	0.0402 5802	0.0303 1434	0.0172 5732	0.0098 7585
61	0.0509 8621	0.0381 5926	0.0285 9843	0.0161 2834	0.0091 4431
62	0.0485 5830	0.0361 6992	0.0269 7965	0.0150 7321	0.0084 6695
63	0.0462 4600	0.0342 8428	0.0254 5250	0.0140 8711	0.0078 3977
64	0.0440 4381	0.0324 9695	0.0240 1179	0.0131 6553	0.0072 5905
65	0.0419 4648	0.0308 0279	0.0226 5264	0.0123 0423	0.0067 2134
66	0.0399 4903	0.0291 9696	0.0213 7041	0.0114 9928	0.0062 2346
67	0.0380 4670	0.0276 7485	0.0201 6077	0.0107 4699	0.0057 6247
68	0.0362 3495	0.0262 3208	0.0190 1959	0.0100 4392	0.0053 3562
69	0.0345 0948	0.0248 6453	0.0179 4301	0.0093 8684	0.0049 4039
70	0.0328 6617	0.0235 6828	0.0169 2737	0.0087 7275	0.0045 7443
71	0.0313 0111	0.0223 3960	0.0159 6921	0.0081 9883	0.0042 3558
72	0.0298 1058	0.0211 7498	0.0150 6530	0.0076 6246	0.0039 2184
73	0.0283 9103	0.0200 7107	0.0142 1254	0.0071 6117	0.0036 3133
74	0.0270 3908	0.0190 2471	0.0134 0806	0.0066 9269	0.0033 6234
75	0.0257 5150	0.0180 3290	0.0126 4911	0.0062 5485	0.0031 1328
76	0.0245 2524	0.0170 9279	0.0119 3313	0.0058 4565	0.0028 8267
77	0.0233 5737	0.0162 0170	0.0112 5767	0.0054 6323	0.0026 6914
78	0.0222 4512	0.0153 5706	0.0106 2044	0.0051 0582	0.0024 7142
79	0.0211 8582	0.0145 5646	0.0100 1928	0.0047 7179	0.0022 8835
80	0.0201 7698	0.0137 9759	0.0094 5215	0.0044 5962	0.0021 1885
81	0.0192 1617	0.0130 7828	0.0089 1713	0.0041 6787	0.0019 6190
82	0.0183 0111	0.0123 9648	0.0084 1238	0.0038 9520	0.0018 1657
83	0.0174 2963	0.0117 5022	0.0079 3621	0.0036 4038	0.0016 8201
84	0.0165 9965	0.0111 3765	0.0074 8699	0.0034 0222	0.0015 5742
85	0.0158 0919	0.0105 5701	0.0070 6320	0.0031 7965	0.0014 4205
86	0.0150 5637	0.0100 0664	0.0066 6340	0.0029 7163	0.0013 3523
87	0.0143 3940	0.0094 8497	0.0062 8622	0.0027 7723	0.0012 3633
88	0.0136 5657	0.0089 9049	0.0059 3040	0.0025 9554	0.0011 4475
89	0.0130 0626	0.0085 2180	0.0055 9472	0.0024 2574	0.0010 5995
90	0.0123 8691	0.0080 7753	0.0052 7803	0.0022 6704	0.0009 8144
91	0.0117 9706	0.0076 5643	0.0049 7928	0.0021 1873	0.0009 0874
92	0.0112 3530	0.0072 5728	0.0046 9743	0.0019 8012	0.0008 4142
93	0.0107 0028	0.0068 7894	0.0044 3154	0.0018 5058	0.0007 7910
94	0.0101 9074	0.0065 2032	0.0041 8070	0.0017 2952	0.0007 2138
95	0.0097 0547	0.0061 8040	0.0039 4405	0.0016 1637	0.0006 6795
96	0.0092 4331	0.0058 5820	0.0037 2081	0.0015 1063	0.0006 1847
97	0.0088 0315	0.0055 5279	0.0035 1019	0.0014 1180	0.0005 7266
98	0.0083 8395	0.0052 6331	0.0033 1150	0.0013 1944	0.0005 3024
99	0.0079 8471	0.0049 8892	0.0031 2406	0.0012 3312	0.0004 9096
100	0.0076 0449	0.0047 2883	0.0029 4723	0.0011 5245	0.0004 5459

ANNUITY WHICH 1 WILL BUY
(Annuity Whose Present Value, at Compound Interest, is 1)

$$\frac{1}{a_{\overline{n}|i}} = \frac{i}{1 - (1 + i)^{-n}}$$

n	$\frac{1}{4}\%$	$\frac{1}{3}\%$	$\frac{5}{12}\%$	$\frac{1}{2}\%$	$\frac{7}{12}\%$
1	1.0025 0000	1.0033 3333	1.0041 6667	1.0050 0000	1.0058 3333
2	0.5018 7578	0.5025 0139	0.5031 2717	0.5037 5312	0.5043 7924
3	0.3350 0139	0.3355 5802	0.3361 1496	0.3366 7221	0.3372 2976
4	0.2515 6445	0.2520 8680	0.2526 0958	0.2531 3279	0.2536 5644
5	0.2015 0250	0.2020 0444	0.2025 0693	0.2030 0997	0.2035 1357
6	0.1681 2803	0.1686 1650	0.1691 0564	0.1695 9546	0.1700 8594
7	0.1442 8928	0.1447 6824	0.1452 4800	0.1457 2854	0.1462 0986
8	0.1264 1035	0.1268 8228	0.1273 5512	0.1278 2886	0.1283 0351
9	0.1125 0462	0.1129 7118	0.1134 3876	0.1139 0736	0.1143 7698
10	0.1013 8015	0.1018 4248	0.1023 0596	0.1027 7057	0.1032 3632
11	0.0922 7840	0.0927 3736	0.0931 9757	0.0936 5903	0.0941 2175
12	0.0846 9370	0.0851 4990	0.0856 0748	0.0860 6643	0.0865 2675
13	0.0782 7595	0.0787 2989	0.0791 8532	0.0796 4224	0.0801 0064
14	0.0727 7510	0.0732 2716	0.0736 8082	0.0741 3609	0.0745 9295
15	0.0680 0777	0.0684 5825	0.0689 1045	0.0693 6436	0.0698 1999
16	0.0638 3642	0.0642 8557	0.0647 3655	0.0651 8937	0.0656 4401
17	0.0601 5587	0.0606 0389	0.0610 5387	0.0615 0579	0.0619 5966
18	0.0568 8433	0.0573 3140	0.0577 8053	0.0582 3173	0.0586 8499
19	0.0539 5722	0.0544 0348	0.0548 5191	0.0553 0253	0.0557 5532
20	0.0513 2288	0.0517 6844	0.0522 1630	0.0526 6645	0.0531 1889
21	0.0489 3947	0.0493 8445	0.0498 3183	0.0502 8163	0.0507 3383
22	0.0467 7278	0.0472 1726	0.0476 6427	0.0481 1380	0.0485 6585
23	0.0447 9455	0.0452 3861	0.0456 8531	0.0461 3465	0.0465 8663
24	0.0429 8121	0.0434 2492	0.0438 7139	0.0443 2061	0.0447 7258
25	0.0413 1298	0.0417 5640	0.0422 0270	0.0426 5186	0.0431 0388
26	0.0397 7312	0.0402 1630	0.0406 6247	0.0411 1163	0.0415 6376
27	0.0383 4736	0.0387 9035	0.0392 3645	0.0396 8565	0.0401 3793
28	0.0370 2347	0.0374 6632	0.0379 1239	0.0383 6167	0.0388 1415
29	0.0357 9093	0.0362 3367	0.0366 7974	0.0371 2914	0.0375 8186
30	0.0346 4059	0.0350 8325	0.0355 2936	0.0359 7892	0.0364 3191
31	0.0335 6449	0.0340 0712	0.0344 5330	0.0349 0304	0.0353 5633
32	0.0325 5569	0.0329 9830	0.0334 4458	0.0338 9453	0.0343 4815
33	0.0316 0806	0.0320 5067	0.0324 9708	0.0329 4727	0.0334 0124
34	0.0307 1620	0.0311 5885	0.0316 0540	0.0320 5586	0.0325 1020
35	0.0298 7533	0.0303 1803	0.0307 6476	0.0312 1550	0.0316 7024
36	0.0290 8121	0.0295 2399	0.0299 7090	0.0304 2194	0.0308 7710
37	0.0283 3004	0.0287 7291	0.0292 2003	0.0296 7139	0.0301 2698
38	0.0276 1843	0.0280 6141	0.0285 0875	0.0289 6045	0.0294 1649
39	0.0269 4335	0.0273 8644	0.0278 3402	0.0282 8607	0.0287 4258
40	0.0263 0204	0.0267 4527	0.0271 9310	0.0276 4552	0.0281 0251
41	0.0256 9204	0.0261 3543	0.0265 8352	0.0270 3631	0.0274 9379
42	0.0251 1112	0.0255 5466	0.0260 0303	0.0264 5622	0.0269 1420
43	0.0245 5724	0.0250 0095	0.0254 4961	0.0259 0320	0.0263 6170
44	0.0240 2855	0.0244 7246	0.0249 2141	0.0253 7541	0.0258 3443
45	0.0235 2339	0.0239 6749	0.0244 1675	0.0248 7117	0.0253 3073
46	0.0230 4022	0.0234 8451	0.0239 3409	0.0243 8894	0.0248 4905
47	0.0225 7762	0.0230 2213	0.0234 7204	0.0239 2733	0.0243 8798
48	0.0221 3433	0.0225 7905	0.0230 2929	0.0234 8503	0.0239 4624
49	0.0217 0915	0.0221 5410	0.0226 0468	0.0230 6087	0.0235 2265
50	0.0213 0099	0.0217 4618	0.0221 9711	0.0226 5376	0.0231 1611

ANNUITY WHICH 1 WILL BUY
(Annuity Whose Present Value, at Compound Interest, is 1)

$$\frac{1}{a_{\overline{n}|i}} = \frac{i}{1 - (1 + i)^{-n}}$$

n	$\frac{1}{4}\%$	$\frac{1}{3}\%$	$\frac{5}{12}\%$	$\frac{1}{2}\%$	$\frac{7}{12}\%$
51	0.0209 0886	0.0213 5429	0.0218 0557	0.0222 6269	0.0227 2563
52	0.0205 3184	0.0209 7751	0.0214 2916	0.0218 8675	0.0223 5027
53	0.0201 6906	0.0206 1499	0.0210 6700	0.0215 2507	0.0219 8919
54	0 0198 1974	0.0202 6592	0.0207 1830	0.0211 7686	0.0216 4157
55	0.0194 8314	0.0199 2958	0.0203 8234	0.0208 4139	0.0213 0671
56	0.0191 5858	0.0196 0529	0.0200 5843	0.0205 1797	0.0209 8390
57	0.0188 4542	0.0192 9241	0.0197 4593	0.0202 0598	0.0206 7251
58	0.0185 4308	0.0189 9035	0.0194 4426	0.0199 0481	0.0203 7196
59	0.0182 5101	0.0186 9856	0.0191 5287	0.0196 1392	0.0200 8170
60	0.0179 6869	0.0184 1652	0.0188 7123	0.0193 3280	0.0198 0120
61	0.0176 9564	0.0181 4377	0.0185 9888	0.0190 6096	0.0195 2999
62	0.0174 3142	0.0178 7984	0.0183 3536	0.0187 9796	0.0192 6762
63	0.0171 7561	0.0176 2432	0.0180 8025	0.0185 4337	0.0190 1366
64	0.0169 2780	0.0173 7681	0.0178 3315	0.0182 9681	0.0187 6773
65	0.0166 8764	0.0171 3695	0.0175 9371	0.0180 5789	0.0185 2946
66	0.0164 5476	0.0169 0438	0.0173 6156	0.0178 2627	0.0182 9848
67	0.0162 2886	0.0166 7878	0.0171 3639	0.0176 0163	0.0180 7449
68	0.0160 0961	0.0164 5985	0.0169 1788	0.0173 8366	0.0178 5716
69	0.0157 9674	0.0162 4729	0.0167 0574	0.0171 7206	0.0176 4622
70	0.0155 8996	0.0160 4083	0.0164 9971	0.0169 6657	0.0174 4138
71	0.0153 8902	0.0158 4021	0.0162 9952	0.0167 6693	0.0172 4239
72	0.0151 9368	0.0156 4518	0.0161 0493	0.0165 7289	0.0170 4901
73	0.0150 0370	0.0154 5553	0.0159 1572	0.0163 8422	0.0168 6100
74	0.0148 1887	0.0152 7103	0.0157 3165	0.0162 0070	0.0166 7814
75	0.0146 3898	0.0150 9147	0.0155 5253	0.0160 2214	0.0165 0024
76	0.0144 6385	0.0149 1666	0.0153 7816	0.0158 4832	0.0163 2709
77	0.0142 9327	0.0147 4641	0.0152 0836	0.0156 7908	0.0161 5851
78	0.0141 2708	0.0145 8056	0.0150 4295	0.0155 1423	0.0159 9432
79	0.0139 6511	0.0144 1892	0.0148 8177	0.0153 5360	0.0158 3436
80	0.0138 0721	0.0142 6135	0.0147 2464	0.0151 9704	0.0156 7847
81	0.0136 5321	0.0141 0770	0.0145 7144	0.0150 4439	0.0155 2650
82	0.0135 0298	0.0139 5781	0.0144 2200	0.0148 9552	0.0153 7830
83	0.0133 5639	0.0138 1156	0.0142 7620	0.0147 5028	0.0152 3373
84	0.0132 1330	0.0136 6881	0.0141 3391	0.0146 0855	0.0150 9268
85	0.0130 7359	0.0135 2944	0.0139 9500	0.0144 7021	0.0149 5501
86	0.0129 3714	0.0133 9333	0.0138 5935	0.0143 3513	0.0148 2060
87	0.0128 0384	0.0132 6038	0.0137 2685	0.0142 0320	0.0146 8935
88	0.0126 7357	0.0131 3046	0.0135 9740	0.0140 7431	0.0145 6115
89	0.0125 4625	0.0130 0349	0.0134 7088	0.0139 4837	0.0144 3588
90	0.0124 2177	0.0128 7936	0.0133 4721	0.0138 2527	0.0143 1347
91	0.0123 0004	0.0127 5797	0.0132 2629	0.0137 0493	0.0141 9380
92	0.0121 8096	0.0126 3925	0.0131 0803	0.0135 8724	0.0140 7679
93	0.0120 6446	0.0125 2310	0.0129 9234	0.0134 7213	0.0139 6236
94	0.0119 5044	0.0124 0944	0.0128 7915	0.0133 5950	0.0138 5042
95	0.0118 3884	0.0122 9819	0.0127 6837	0.0132 4930	0.0137 4090
96	0.0117 2957	0.0121 8928	0.0126 5992	0.0131 4143	0.0136 3372
97	0.0116 2257	0.0120 8263	0.0125 5374	0.0130 3583	0.0135 2880
98	0.0115 1776	0.0119 7818	0.0124 4976	0.0129 3242	0.0134 2608
99	0.0114 1508	0.0118 7585	0.0123 4790	0.0128 3115	0.0133 2549
100	0.0113 1446	0.0117 7559	0.0122 4811	0.0127 3194	0.0132 2696
∞	0.0025 0000	0.0033 3333	0.0041 6667	0.0050 0000	0.0058 3333

ANNUITY WHICH 1 WILL BUY
(Annuity Whose Present Value, at Compound Interest, is 1)

$$\frac{1}{a_{\overline{n}|i}} = \frac{i}{1 - (1 + i)^{-n}}$$

n	$\frac{7}{8}\%$	1%	$1\frac{1}{8}\%$	$1\frac{1}{4}\%$	$1\frac{3}{8}\%$
1	1.0087 5000	1.0100 0000	1.0112 5000	1.0125 0000	1.0137 5000
2	0.5065 7203	0.5075 1244	0.5084 5323	0.5093 9441	0.5103 3597
3	0.3391 8361	0.3400 2211	0.3408 6130	0.3417 0117	0.3425 4173
4	0.2554 9257	0.2562 8109	0.2570 7058	0.2578 6102	0.2586 5243
5	0.2052 8049	0.2060 3980	0.2068 0034	0.2075 6211	0.2083 2510
6	0.1718 0789	0.1725 4837	0.1732 9034	0.1740 3381	0.1747 7877
7	0.1479 0070	0.1486 2828	0.1493 5762	0.1500 8872	0.1508 2157
8	0.1299 7190	0.1306 9029	0.1314 1071	0.1321 3314	0.1328 5758
9	0.1160 2868	0.1167 4037	0.1174 5432	0.1181 7055	0.1188 8906
10	0.1048 7538	0.1055 8208	0.1062 9131	0.1070 0307	0.1077 1737
11	0.0957 5111	0.0964 5408	0.0971 5984	0.0978 6839	0.0985 7973
12	0.0881 4860	0.0888 4879	0.0895 5203	0.0902 5831	0.0909 6764
13	0.0817 1669	0.0824 1482	0.0831 1626	0.0838 2100	0.0845 2903
14	0.0762 0453	0.0769 0117	0.0776 0138	0.0783 0515	0.0790 1246
15	0.0714 2817	0.0721 2378	0.0728 2321	0.0735 2646	0.0742 3351
16	0.0672 4965	0.0679 4460	0.0686 4363	0.0693 4672	0.0700 5388
17	0.0635 6346	0.0642 5806	0.0649 5698	0.0656 6023	0.0663 6780
18	0.0602 8756	0.0609 8205	0.0616 8113	0.0623 8479	0.0630 9301
19	0.0573 5715	0.0580 5175	0.0587 5120	0.0594 5548	0.0601 6457
20	0.0547 2042	0.0554 1532	0.0561 1531	0.0568 2039	0.0575 3054
21	0.0523 3541	0.0530 3075	0.0537 3145	0.0544 3748	0.0551 4884
22	0.0501 6779	0.0508 6371	0.0515 6525	0.0522 7238	0.0529 8507
23	0.0481 8921	0.0488 8584	0.0495 8833	0.0502 9666	0.0510 1080
24	0.0463 7604	0.0470 7347	0.0477 7701	0.0484 8665	0.0492 0235
25	0.0447 0843	0.0454 0675	0.0461 1144	0.0468 2247	0.0475 3981
26	0.0431 6959	0.0438 6888	0.0445 7479	0.0452 8729	0.0460 0635
27	0.0417 4520	0.0424 4553	0.0431 5273	0.0438 6677	0.0445 8763
28	0.0404 2300	0.0411 2444	0.0418 3299	0.0425 4863	0.0432 7134
29	0.0391 9243	0.0398 9502	0.0406 0498	0.0413 2228	0.0420 4689
30	0.0380 4431	0.0387 4811	0.0394 5953	0.0401 7854	0.0409 0511
31	0.0369 7068	0.0376 7573	0.0383 8866	0.0391 0942	0.0398 3798
32	0.0359 6454	0.0366 7089	0.0373 8535	0.0381 0791	0.0388 3850
33	0.0350 1976	0.0357 2744	0.0364 4349	0.0371 6786	0.0379 0053
34	0.0341 3092	0.0348 3997	0.0355 5763	0.0362 8387	0.0370 1864
35	0.0332 9324	0.0340 0368	0.0347 2299	0.0354 5111	0.0361 8801
36	0.0325 0244	0.0332 1431	0.0339 3529	0.0346 6533	0.0354 0438
37	0.0317 5473	0.0324 6805	0.0331 9072	0.0339 2270	0.0346 6394
38	0.0310 4671	0.0317 6150	0.0324 8589	0.0332 1983	0.0339 6327
39	0.0303 7531	0.0310 9160	0.0318 1773	0.0325 5365	0.0332 9931
40	0.0297 3780	0.0304 5560	0.0311 8349	0.0319 2141	0.0326 6931
41	0.0291 3169	0.0298 5102	0.0305 8069	0.0313 2063	0.0320 7078
42	0.0285 5475	0.0292 7563	0.0300 0709	0.0307 4906	0.0315 0148
43	0.0280 0493	0.0287 2737	0.0294 6064	0.0302 0466	0.0309 5936
44	0.0274 8039	0.0282 0441	0.0289 3949	0.0296 8557	0.0304 4257
45	0.0269 7943	0.0277 0505	0.0284 4197	0.0291 9012	0.0299 4941
46	0.0265 0053	0.0272 2775	0.0279 6652	0.0287 1675	0.0294 7836
47	0.0260 4228	0.0267 7111	0.0275 1173	0.0282 6406	0.0290 2799
48	0.0256 0338	0.0263 3384	0.0270 7632	0.0278 3075	0.0285 9701
49	0.0251 8265	0.0259 1474	0.0266 5910	0.0274 1563	0.0281 8424
50	0.0247 7900	0.0255 1273	0.0262 5898	0.0270 1763	0.0277 8857

ANNUITY WHICH 1 WILL BUY
(Annuity Whose Present Value, at Compound Interest, is 1)

$$\frac{1}{a_{\overline{n}|i}} = \frac{i}{1 - (1 + i)^{-n}}$$

n	$\frac{7}{8}\%$	1%	$1\frac{1}{8}\%$	$1\frac{1}{4}\%$	$1\frac{3}{8}\%$
51	0.0243 9142	0.0251 2680	0.0258 7494	0.0266 3571	0.0274 0900
52	0.0240 1899	0.0247 5603	0.0255 0606	0.0262 6897	0.0270 4461
53	0.0236 6084	0.0243 9956	0.0251 5149	0.0259 1653	0.0266 9453
54	0.0233 1619	0.0240 5658	0.0248 1043	0.0255 7760	0.0263 5797
55	0.0229 8430	0.0237 2637	0.0244 8213	0.0252 5145	0.0260 3418
56	0.0226 6449	0.0234 0823	0.0241 6592	0.0249 3739	0.0257 2249
57	0.0223 5611	0.0231 0156	0.0238 6116	0.0246 3478	0.0254 2225
58	0.0220 5858	0.0228 0573	0.0235 6726	0.0243 4303	0.0251 3287
59	0.0217 7135	0.0225 2020	0.0232 8366	0.0240 6158	0.0248 5380
60	0.0214 9390	0.0222 4445	0.0230 0985	0.0237 8993	0.0245 8452
61	0.0212 2575	0.0219 7800	0.0227 4534	0.0235 2758	0.0243 2455
62	0.0209 6644	0.0217 2041	0.0224 8969	0.0232 7410	0.0240 7344
63	0.0207 1557	0.0214 7125	0.0222 4247	0.0230 2904	0.0238 3076
64	0.0204 7273	0.0212 3013	0.0220 0329	0.0227 9203	0.0235 9612
65	0.0202 3754	0.0209 9667	0.0217 7178	0.0225 6268	0.0233 6914
66	0.0200 0968	0.0207 7052	0.0215 4758	0.0223 4065	0.0231 4949
67	0.0197 8879	0.0205 5136	0.0213 3037	0.0221 2560	0.0229 3682
68	0.0195 7459	0.0203 3888	0.0211 1985	0.0219 1724	0.0227 3082
69	0.0193 6677	0.0201 3280	0.0209 1571	0.0217 1527	0.0225 3122
70	0.0191 6506	0.0199 3282	0.0207 1769	0.0215 1941	0.0223 3773
71	0.0189 6921	0.0197 3870	0.0205 2552	0.0213 2941	0.0221 5009
72	0.0187 7897	0.0195 5019	0.0203 3896	0.0211 4501	0.0219 6806
73	0.0185 9411	0.0193 6706	0.0201 5779	0.0209 6600	0.0217 9140
74	0.0184 1441	0.0191 8910	0.0199 8177	0.0207 9215	0.0216 1991
75	0.0182 3966	0.0190 1609	0.0198 1072	0.0206 2325	0.0214 5336
76	0.0180 6967	0.0188 4784	0.0196 4442	0.0204 5910	0.0212 9157
77	0.0179 0426	0.0186 8416	0.0194 8269	0.0202 9953	0.0211 3435
78	0.0177 4324	0.0185 2488	0.0193 2536	0.0201 4435	0.0209 8151
79	0.0175 8645	0.0183 6984	0.0191 7226	0.0199 9341	0.0208 3290
80	0.0174 3374	0.0182 1885	0.0190 2323	0.0198 4652	0.0206 8836
81	0.0172 8494	0.0180 7180 ′	0.0188 7812	0.0197 0356	0.0205 4772
82	0.0171 3992	0.0179 2851	0.0187 3678	0.0195 6437	0.0204 1086
83	0.0169 9854	0.0177 8886	0.0185 9908	0.0194 2881	0.0202 7762
84	0.0168 6067	0.0176 5273	0.0184 6489	0.0192 9675	0.0201 4789
85	0.0167 2619	0.0175 1998	0.0183 3409	0.0191 6808	0.0200 2153
86	0.0165 9497	0.0173 9050	0.0182 0654	0.0190 4267	0.0198 9843
87	0.0164 6691	0.0172 6417	0.0180 8215	0.0189 2041	0.0197 7847
88	0.0163 4190	0.0171 4089	0.0179 6081	0.0188 0119	0.0196 6155
89	0.0162 1982	0.0170 2056	0.0178 4240	0.0186 8490	0.0195 4756
90	0.0161 0060	0.0169 0306	0.0177 2684	0.0185 7146	0.0194 3641
91	0.0159 8413	0.0167 8832	0.0176 1403	0.0184 6076	0.0193 2799
92	0.0158 7031	0.0166 7624	0.0175 0387	0.0183 5271	0.0192 2222
93	0.0157 5908	0.0165 6673	0.0173 9629	0.0182 4724	0.0191 1902
94	0.0156 5033	0.0164 5971	0.0172 9119	0.0181 4425	0.0190 1829
95	0.0155 4401	0.0163 5511	0.0171 8851	0.0180 4366	0.0189 1997
96	0.0154 4002	0.0162 5284	0.0170 8816	0.0179 4540	0.0188 2397
97	0.0153 3829	0.0161 5284	0.0169 9007	0.0178 4941	0.0187 3022
98	0.0152 3877	0.0160 5503	0.0168 9418	0.0177 5560	0.0186 3866
99	0.0151 4137	0.0159 5936	0.0168 0041	0.0176 6391	0.0185 4921
100	0.0150 4604	0.0158 6574	0.0167 0870	0.0175 7428	0.0184 6181
∞	0.0087 5000	0.0100 0000	0.0112 5000	0.0125 0000	0.0137 5000

ANNUITY WHICH 1 WILL BUY
(Annuity Whose Present Value, at Compound Interest, is 1)

$$\frac{1}{a_{\overline{n}|i}} = \frac{i}{1 - (1 + i)^{-n}}$$

n	$1\frac{1}{2}\%$	$1\frac{3}{4}\%$	2%	$2\frac{1}{4}\%$	$2\frac{1}{2}\%$
1	1.0150 0000	1.0175 0000	1.0200 0000	1.0225 0000	1.0250 0000
2	0.5112 7792	0.5131 6295	0.5150 4950	0.5169 3758	0.5188 2716
3	0.3433 8296	0.3450 6746	0.3467 5467	0.3484 4458	0.3501 3717
4	0.2594 4478	0.2610 3237	0.2626 2375	0.2642 1893	0.2658 1788
5	0.2090 8932	0.2106 2142	0.2121 5839	0.2137 0021	0.2152 4686
6	0.1755 2521	0.1770 2256	0.1785 2581	0.1800 3496	0.1815 4997
7	0.1515 5616	0.1530 3059	0.1545 1196	0.1560 0025	0.1574 9543
8	0.1335 8402	0.1350 4292	0.1365 0980	0.1379 8462	0.1394 6735
9	0.1196 0982	0.1210 5813	0.1225 1544	0.1239 8170	0.1254 5689
10	0.1084 3418	0.1098 7534	0.1113 2653	0.1127 8768	0.1142 5876
11	0.0992 9384	0.1007 3038	0.1021 7794	0.1036 3649	0.1051 0596
12	0.0916 7999	0.0931 1377	0.0945 5960	0.0960 1740	0.0974 8713
13	0.0852 4036	0.0866 7283	0.0881 1835	0.0895 7686	0.0910 4827
14	0.0797 2332	0.0811 5562	0.0826 0197	0.0840 6230	0.0855 3653
15	0.0749 4436	0.0763 7739	0.0778 2547	0.0792 8852	0.0807 6646
16	0.0707 6508	0.0721 9958	0.0736 5013	0.0751 1663	0.0765 9899
17	0.0670 7966	0.0685 1623	0.0699 6984	0.0714 4039	0.0729 2777
18	0.0638 0578	0.0652 4492	0.0667 0210	0.0681 7720	0.0696 7008
19	0.0608 7847	0.0623 2061	0.0637 8177	0.0652 6182	0.0667 6062
20	0.0582 4574	0.0596 9122	0.0611 5672	0.0626 4207	0.0641 4713
21	0.0558 6550	0.0573 1464	0.0587 8477	0.0602 7572	0.0617 8733
22	0.0537 0331	0.0551 5638	0.0566 3140	0.0581 2821	0.0596 4661
23	0.0517 3075	0.0531 8796	0.0546 6810	0.0561 7097	0.0576 9638
24	0.0499 2410	0.0513 8565	0.0528 7110	0.0543 8023	0.0559 1282
25	0.0482 6345	0.0497 2952	0.0512 2044	0.0527 3599	0.0542 7592
26	0.0467 3196	0.0482 0269	0.0496 9923	0.0512 2134	0.0527 6875
27	0.0453 1527	0.0467 9079	0.0482 9309	0.0498 2188	0.0513 7687
28	0.0440 0108	0.0454 8151	0.0469 8967	0.0485 2525	0.0500 8793
29	0.0427 7878	0.0442 6424	0.0457 7836	0.0473 2081	0.0488 9127
30	0.0416 3919	0.0431 2975	0.0446 4992	0.0461 9934	0.0477 7764
31	0.0405 7430	0.0420 7005	0.0435 9635	0.0451 5280	0.0467 3900
32	0.0395 7710	0.0410 7812	0.0426 1061	0.0441 7415	0.0457 6831
33	0.0386 4144	0.0401 4779	0.0416 8653	0.0432 5722	0.0448 5938
34	0.0377 6189	0.0392 7363	0.0408 1867	0.0423 9655	0.0440 0675
35	0.0369 3363	0.0384 5082	0.0400 0221	0.0415 8731	0.0432 0558
36	0.0361 5240	0.0376 7507	0.0392 3285	0.0408 2522	0.0424 5158
37	0.0354 1437	0.0369 4257	0.0385 0678	0.0401 0643	0.0417 4090
38	0.0347 1613	0.0362 4990	0.0378 2057	0.0394 2753	0.0410 7012
39	0.0340 5463	0.0355 9399	0.0371 7114	0.0387 8543	0.0404 3615
40	0.0334 2710	0.0349 7209	0.0365 5575	0.0381 7738	0.0398 3623
41	0.0328 3106	0.0343 8170	0.0359 7188	0.0376 0087	0.0392 6786
42	0.0322 6426	0.0338 2057	0.0354 1729	0.0370 5364	0.0387 3876
43	0.0317 2465	0.0332 8666	0.0348 8993	0.0365 3364	0.0382 1688
44	0.0312 1038	0.0327 7810	0.0343 8794	0.0360 3901	0.0377 3037
45	0.0307 1976	0.0322 9321	0.0339 0962	0.0355 6805	0.0372 6752
46	0.0302 5125	0.0318 3043	0.0334 5342	0.0351 1921	0.0368 2676
47	0.0298 0342	0.0313 8836	0.0330 1792	0.0346 9107	0.0364 0669
48	0.0293 7500	0.0309 6569	0.0326 0184	0.0342 8233	0.0360 0599
49	0.0289 6478	0.0305 6124	0.0322 0396	0.0338 9179	0.0356 2348
50	0.0285 7168	0.0301 7391	0.0318 2321	0.0335 1836	0.0352 5806

ANNUITY WHICH 1 WILL BUY
(Annuity Whose Present Value, at Compound Interest, is 1)

$$\frac{1}{a_{\overline{n}|i}} = \frac{i}{1 - (1 + i)^{-n}}$$

n	$1\frac{1}{2}\%$	$1\frac{3}{4}\%$	2%	$2\frac{1}{4}\%$	$2\frac{1}{2}\%$
51	0.0281 9469	0.0298 0269	0.0314 5856	0.0331 6102	0.0349 0870
52	0.0278 3287	0.0294 4665	0.0311 0909	0.0328 1884	0.0345 7446
53	0.0274 8537	0.0291 0492	0.0307 7392	0.0324 9094	0.0342 5449
54	0.0271 5138	0.0287 7672	0.0304 5226	0.0321 7654	0.0339 4799
55	0.0268 3018	0.0284 6129	0.0301 4337	0.0318 7489	0.0336 5419
56	0.0265 2106	0.0281 5795	0.0298 4656	0.0315 8530	0.0333 7243
57	0.0262 2341	0.0278 6606	0.0295 6120	0.0313 0712	0.0331 0204
58	0.0259 3661	0.0275 8503	0.0292 8667	0.0310 3977	0.0328 4244
59	0.0256 6012	0.0273 1430	0.0290 2243	0.0307 8268	0.0325 9307
60	0.0253 9343	0.0270 5336	0.0287 6797	0.0305 3533	0.0323 5340
61	0.0251 3604	0.0268 0172	0.0285 2278	0.0302 9724	0.0321 2294
62	0.0248 8751	0.0265 5892	0.0282 8643	0.0300 6795	0.0319 0126
63	0.0246 4741	0.0263 2455	0.0280 5848	0.0298 4704	0.0316 8790
64	0.0244 1534	0.0260 9821	0.0278 3855	0.0296 3411	0.0314 8249
65	0.0241 9094	0.0258 7952	0.0276 2624	0.0294 2878	0.0312 8463
66	0.0239 7386	0.0256 6813	0.0274 2122	0.0292 3070	0.0310 9398
67	0.0237 6376	0.0254 6372	0.0272 2316	0.0290 3955	0.0309 1021
68	0.0235 6033	0.0252 6596	0.0270 3173	0.0288 5500	0.0307 3300
69	0.0233 6329	0.0250 7459	0.0268 4665	0.0286 7677	0.0305 6206
70	0.0231 7235	0.0248 8930	0.0266 6765	0.0285 0458	0.0303 9712
71	0.0229 8727	0.0247 0985	0.0264 9446	0.0283 3816	0.0302 3790
72	0.0228 0779	0.0245 3600	0.0263 2683	0.0281 7728	0.0300 8417
73	0.0226 3368	0.0243 6750	0.0261 6454	0.0280 2169	0.0299 3568
74	0.0224 6473	0.0242 0413	0.0260 0736	0.0278 7118	0.0297 9222
75	0.0223 0072	0.0240 4570	0.0258 5508	0.0277 2554	0.0296 5358
76	0.0221 4146	0.0238 9200	0.0257 0751	0.0275 8457	0.0295 1956
77	0.0219 8676	0.0237 4284	0.0255 6447	0.0274 4808	0.0293 8997
78	0.0218 3645	0.0235 9806	0.0254 2576	0.0273 1589	0.0292 6463
79	0.0216 9036	0.0234 5748	0.0252 9123	0.0271 8784	0.0291 4338
80	0.0215 4832	0.0233 2093	0.0251 6071	0.0270 6376	0.0290 2605
81	0.0214 1019	0.0231 8828	0.0250 3405	0.0269 4350	0.0289 1248
82	0.0212 7583	0.0230 5936	0.0249 1110	0.0268 2692	0.0288 0254
83	0.0211 4509	0.0229 3406	0.0247 9173	0.0267 1387	0.0286 9608
84	0.0210 1784	0.0228 1223	0.0246 7581	0.0266 0423	0.0285 9298
85	0.0208 9396	0.0226 9375	0.0245 6321	0.0264 9787	0.0284 9310
86	0.0207 7333	0.0225 7850	0.0244 5381	0.0263 9467	0.0283 9633
87	0.0206 5584	0.0224 6636	0.0243 4750	0.0262 9452	0.0283 0255
88	0.0205 4138	0.0223 5724	0.0242 4416	0.0261 9730	0.0282 1165
89	0.0204 2984	0.0222 5102	0.0241 4370	0.0261 0291	0.0281 2353
90	0.0203 2113	0.0221 4760	0.0240 4602	0.0260 1126	0.0280 3809
91	0.0202 1516	0.0220 4690	0.0239 5101	0.0259 2224	0.0279 5523
92	0.0201 1182	0.0219 4882	0.0238 5859	0.0258 3577	0.0278 7486
93	0.0200 1104	0.0218 5327	0.0237 6868	0.0257 5176	0.0277 9690
94	0.0199 1273	0.0217 6017	0.0236 8118	0.0256 7012	0.0277 2126
95	0.0198 1681	0.0216 6944	0.0235 9602	0.0255 9078	0.0276 4786
96	0.0197 2321	0.0215 8101	0.0235 1313	0.0255 1366	0.0275 7662
97	0.0196 3186	0.0214 9480	0.0234 3242	0.0254 3868	0.0275 0747
98	0.0195 4268	0.0214 1074	0.0233 5383	0.0253 6578	0.0274 4034
99	0.0194 5560	0.0213 2876	0.0232 7729	0.0252 9489	0.0273 7517
100	0.0193 7057	0.0212 4880	0.0232 0274	0.0252 2594	0.0273 1188
∞	0.0150 0000	0.0175 0000	0.0200 0000	0.0225 0000	0.0250 0000

ANNUITY WHICH 1 WILL BUY
(Annuity Whose Present Value, at Compound Interest, is 1)

$$\frac{1}{a_{\overline{n}|i}} = \frac{i}{1 - (1 + i)^{-n}}$$

n	$2\frac{3}{4}$ %	3 %	$3\frac{1}{2}$ %	4 %	$4\frac{1}{2}$ %
1	1.0275 0000	1.0300 0000	1.0350 0000	1.0400 0000	1.0450 0000
2	0.5207 1825	0.5226 1084	0.5264 0049	0.5301 9608	0.5339 9756
3	0.3518 3243	0.3535 3036	0.3569 3418	0.3603 4854	0.3637 7336
4	0.2674 2059	0.2690 2705	0.2722 5114	0.2754 9005	0.2787 4365
5	0.2167 9832	0.2183 5457	0.2214 8137	0.2246 2711	0.2277 9164
6	0.1830 7083	0.1845 9750	0.1876 6821	0.1907 6190	0.1938 7839
7	0.1589 9747	0.1605 0635	0.1635 4449	0.1666 0961	0.1697 0147
8	0.1409 5795	0.1424 5639	0.1454 7665	0.1485 2783	0.1516 0965
9	0.1269 4095	0.1284 3386	0.1314 4601	0.1344 9299	0.1375 7447
10	0.1157 3972	0.1172 3051	0.1202 4137	0.1232 9094	0.1263 7882
11	0.1065 8629	0.1080 7745	0.1110 9197	0.1141 4904	0.1172 4818
12	0.0989 6871	0.1004 6209	0.1034 8395	0.1065 5217	0.1096 6619
13	0.0925 3252	0.0940 2954	0.0970 6157	0.1001 4373	0.1032 7535
14	0.0870 2457	0.0885 2634	0.0915 7073	0.0946 6897	0.0978 2032
15	0.0822 5917	0.0837 6658	0.0868 2507	0.0899 4110	0.0931 1381
16	0.0780 9710	0.0796 1085	0.0826 8483	0.0858 2000	0.0890 1537
17	0.0744 3186	0.0759 5253	0.0790 4313	0.0821 9852	0.0854 1758
18	0.0711 8063	0.0727 0870	0.0758 1684	0.0789 9333	0.0822 3690
19	0.0682 7802	0.0698 1388	0.0729 4033	0.0761 3862	0.0794 0734
20	0.0656 7173	0.0672 1571	0.0703 6108	0.0735 8175	0.0768 7614
21	0.0633 1941	0.0648 7178	0.0680 3659	0.0712 8011	0.0746 0057
22	0.0611 8640	0.0627 4739	0.0659 3207	0.0691 9881	0.0725 4565
23	0.0592 4410	0.0608 1390	0.0640 1880	0.0673 0906	0.0706 8249
24	0.0574 6863	0.0590 4742	0.0622 7283	0.0655 8683	0.0689 8703
25	0.0558 3997	0.0574 2787	0.0606 7404	0.0640 1196	0.0674 3903
26	0.0543 4116	0.0559 3829	0.0592 0540	0.0625 6738	0.0660 2137
27	0.0529 5776	0.0545 6421	0.0578 5241	0.0612 3854	0.0647 1946
28	0.0516 7738	0.0532 9323	0.0566 0265	0.0600 1298	0.0635 2081
29	0.0504 8935	0.0521 1467	0.0554 4538	0.0588 7993	0.0624 1461
30	0.0493 8442	0.0510 1926	0.0543 7133	0.0578 3010	0.0613 9154
31	0.0483 5453	0.0499 9893	0.0533 7240	0.0568 5535	0.0604 4345
32	0.0473 9263	0.0490 4662	0.0524 4150	0.0559 4859	0.0595 6320
33	0.0464 9253	0.0481 5612	0.0515 7242	0.0551 0357	0.0587 4453
34	0.0456 4875	0.0473 2196	0.0507 5966	0.0543 1477	0.0579 8191
35	0.0448 5645	0.0465 3929	0.0499 9835	0.0535 7732	0.0572 7045
36	0.0441 1132	0.0458 0379	0.0492 8416	0.0528 8688	0.0566 0578
37	0.0434 0953	0.0451 1162	0.0486 1325	0.0522 3957	0.0559 8402
38	0.0427 4764	0.0444 5934	0.0479 8214	0.0516 3192	0.0554 0169
39	0.0421 2256	0.0438 4385	0.0473 8775	0.0510 6083	0.0548 5567
40	0.0415 3151	0.0432 6238	0.0468 2728	0.0505 2349	0.0543 4315
41	0.0409 7200	0.0427 1241	0.0462 9822	0.0500 1738	0.0538 6158
42	0.0404 4175	0.0421 9167	0.0457 9828	0.0495 4020	0.0534 0868
43	0.0399 3871	0.0416 9811	0.0453 2539	0.0490 8989	0.0529 8235
44	0.0394 6100	0.0412 2985	0.0448 7768	0.0486 6454	0.0525 8071
45	0.0390 0693	0.0407 8518	0.0444 5343	0.0482 6246	0.0522 0202
46	0.0385 7493	0.0403 6254	0.0440 5108	0.0478 8205	0.0518 4471
47	0.0381 6358	0.0399 6051	0.0436 6919	0.0475 2189	0.0515 0734
48	0.0377 7158	0.0395 7777	0.0433 0646	0.0471 8065	0.0511 8858
49	0.0373 9773	0.0392 1314	0.0429 6167	0.0468 5712	0.0508 8722
50	0.0370 4092	0.0388 6550	0.0426 3371	0.0465 5020	0.0506 0215

ANNUITY WHICH 1 WILL BUY
(Annuity Whose Present Value, at Compound Interest, is 1)

$$\frac{1}{a_{\overline{n}|i}} = \frac{i}{1 - (1 + i)^{-n}}$$

n	$2\frac{3}{4}\%$	3%	$3\frac{1}{2}\%$	4%	$4\frac{1}{2}\%$
51	0.0367 0014	0.0385 3382	0.0423 2156	0.0462 5885	0.0503 3232
52	0.0363 7444	0.0382 1718	0.0420 2429	0.0459 8212	0.0500 7679
53	0.0360 6297	0.0379 1471	0.0417 4100	0.0457 1915	0.0498 3469
54	0.0357 6491	0.0376 2558	0.0414 7090	0.0454 6910	0.0496 0519
55	0.0354 7953	0.0373 4907	0.0412 1323	0.0452 3124	0.0493 8754
56	0.0352 0612	0.0370 8447	0.0409 6730	0.0450 0487	0.0491 8105
57	0.0349 4404	0.0368 3114	0.0407 3245	0.0447 8932	0.0489 8506
58	0.0346 9270	0.0365 8848	0.0405 0810	0.0445 8401	0.0487 9897
59	0.0344 5153	0.0363 5593	0.0402 9366	0.0443 8836	0.0486 2221
60	0.0342 2002	0.0361 3296	0.0400 8862	0.0442 0185	0.0484 5426
61	0.0339 9767	0.0359 1908	0.0398 9249	0.0440 2398	0.0482 9462
62	0.0337 8402	0.0357 1385	0.0397 0480	0.0438 5430	0.0481 4284
63	0.0335 7866	0.0355 1682	0.0395 2513	0.0436 9237	0.0479 9848
64	0.0333 8118	0.0353 2760	0.0393 5308	0.0435 3780	0.0478 6115
65	0.0331 9120	0.0351 4581	0.0391 8826	0.0433 9019	0.0477 3047
66	0.0330 0837	0.0349 7110	0.0390 3031	0.0432 4921	0.0476 0608
67	0.0328 3236	0.0348 0313	0.0388 7892	0.0431 1451	0.0474 8765
68	0.0326 6285	0.0346 4159	0.0387 3375	0.0429 8578	0.0473 7487
69	0.0324 9955	0.0344 8618	0.0385 9453	0.0428 6272	0.0472 6745
70	0.0323 4218	0.0343 3663	0.0384 6095	0.0427 4506	0.0471 6511
71	0.0321 9048	0.0341 9266	0.0383 3277	0.0426 3253	0.0470 6759
72	0.0320 4420	0.0340 5404	0.0382 0973	0.0425 2489	0.0469 7465
73	0.0319 0311	0.0339 2053	0.0380 9160	0.0424 2190	0.0468 8606
74	0.0317 6698	0.0337 9191	0.0379 7816	0.0423 2334	0.0468 0159
75	0.0316 3560	0.0336 6796	0.0378 6919	0.0422 2900	0.0467 2104
76	0.0315 0878	0.0335 4849	0.0377 6450	0.0421 3869	0.0466 4422
77	0.0313 8633	0.0334 3331	0.0376 6390	0.0420 5221	0.0465 7094
78	0.0312 6806	0.0333 2224	0.0375 6721	0.0419 6939	0.0465 0104
79	0.0311 5382	0.0332 1510	0.0374 7426	0.0418 9007	0.0464 3434
80	0.0310 4342	0.0331 1175	0.0373 8489	0.0418 1408	0.0463 7069
81	0.0309 3674	0.0330 1201	0.0372 9894	0.0417 4127	0.0463 0995
82	0.0308 3361	0.0329 1576	0.0372 1628	0.0416 7150	0.0462 5197
83	0.0307 3389	0.0328 2284	0.0371 3676	0.0416 0463	0.0461 9663
84	0.0306 3747	0.0327 3313	0.0370 6025	0.0415 4054	0.0461 4379
85	0.0305 4420	0.0326 4650	0.0369 8662	0.0414 7909	0.0460 9334
86	0.0304 5397	0.0325 6284	0.0369 1576	0.0414 2018	0.0460 4516
87	0.0303 6667	0.0324 8202	0.0368 4756	0.0413 6370	0.0459 9915
88	0.0302 8219	0.0324 0393	0.0367 8190	0.0413 0953	0.0459 5522
89	0.0302 0041	0.0323 2848	0.0367 1868	0.0412 5758	0.0459 1325
90	0.0301 2125	0.0322 5556	0.0366 5781	0.0412 0775	0.0458 7316
91	0.0300 4460	0.0321 8508	0.0365 9919	0.0411 5995	0.0458 3486
92	0.0299 7038	0.0321 1694	0.0365 4273	0.0411 1410	0.0457 9827
93	0.0298 9850	0.0320 5107	0.0364 8834	0.0410 7010	0.0457 6331
94	0.0298 2887	0.0319 8737	0.0364 3594	0.0410 2789	0.0457 2991
95	0.0297 6141	0.0319 2577	0.0363 8546	0.0409 8738	0.0456 9799
96	0.0296 9605	0.0318 6619	0.0363 3682	0.0409 4850	0.0456 6749
97	0.0296 3272	0.0318 0856	0.0362 8995	0.0409 1119	0.0456 3834
98	0.0295 7134	0.0317 5281	0.0362 4478	0.0408 7538	0.0456 1048
99	0.0295 1185	0.0316 9886	0.0362 0124	0.0408 4100	0.0455 8385
100	0.0294 5418	0.0316 4667	0.0361 5927	0.0408 0800	0.0455 5839
∞	0.0275 0000	0.0300 0000	0.0350 0000	0.0400 0000	0.0450 0000

ANNUITY WHICH 1 WILL BUY
(Annuity Whose Present Value, at Compound Interest, is 1)

$$\frac{1}{a_{\overline{n}|i}} = \frac{i}{1 - (1 + i)^{-n}}$$

n	5 %	$5\frac{1}{2}$ %	6 %	7 %	8 %
1	1.0500 0000	1.0550 0000	1.0600 0000	1.0700 0000	1.0800 0000
2	0.5378 0488	0.5416 1800	0.5454 3689	0.5530 9179	0.5607 6923
3	0.3672 0856	0.3706 5407	0.3741 0981	0.3810 5166	0.3880 3351
4	0.2820 1183	0.2852 9449	0.2885 9149	0.2952 2812	0.3019 2080
5	0.2309 7480	0.2341 7644	0.2373 9640	0.2438 9069	0.2504 5645
6	0.1970 1747	0.2001 7895	0.2033 6263	0.2097 9580	0.2163 1539
7	0.1728 1982	0.1759 6442	0.1791 3502	0.1855 5322	0.1920 7240
8	0.1547 2181	0.1578 6401	0.1610 3594	0.1674 6776	0.1740 1476
9	0.1406 9008	0.1438 3946	0.1470 2224	0.1534 8647	0.1600 7971
10	0.1295 0458	0.1326 6777	0.1358 6796	0.1423 7750	0.1490 2949
11	0.1203 8889	0.1235 7065	0.1267 9294	0.1333 5690	0.1400 7634
12	0.1128 2541	0.1160 2923	0.1192 7703	0.1259 0199	0.1326 9502
13	0.1064 5577	0.1096 8426	0.1129 6011	0.1196 5085	0.1265 2181
14	0.1010 2397	0.1042 7912	0.1075 8491	0.1143 4494	0.1212 9685
15	0.0963 4229	0.0996 2560	0.1029 6276	0.1097 9462	0.1168 2954
16	0.0922 6991	0.0955 8254	0.0989 5214	0.1058 5765	0.1129 7687
17	0.0886 9914	0.0920 4197	0.0954 4480	0.1024 2519	0.1096 2943
18	0.0855 4622	0.0889 1992	0.0923 5654	0.0994 1260	0.1067 0210
19	0.0827 4501	0.0861 5006	0.0896 2086	0.0967 5301	0.1041 2763
20	0.0802 4259	0.0836 7933	0.0871 8456	0.0943 9293	0.1018 5221
21	0.0779 9611	0.0814 6478	0.0850 0455	0.0922 8900	0.0998 3225
22	0.0759 7051	0.0794 7123	0.0830 4557	0.0904 0577	0.0980 3207
23	0.0741 3682	0.0776 6965	0.0812 7848	0.0887 1393	0.0964 2217
24	0.0724 7090	0.0760 3580	0.0796 7900	0.0871 8902	0.0949 7796
25	0.0709 5246	0.0745 4935	0.0782 2672	0.0858 1052	0.0936 7878
26	0.0695 6432	0.0731 9307	0.0769 0435	0.0845 6103	0.0925 0713
27	0.0682 9186	0.0719 5228	0.0756 9717	0.0834 2573	0.0914 4809
28	0.0671 2253	0.0708 1440	0.0745 9255	0.0823 9193	0.0904 8891
29	0.0660 4551	0.0697 6857	0.0735 7961	0.0814 4865	0.0896 1854
30	0.0650 5144	0.0688 0539	0.0726 4891	0.0805 8640	0.0888 2743
31	0.0641 3212	0.0679 1665	0.0717 9222	0.0797 9691	0.0881 0728
32	0.0632 8042	0.0670 9519	0.0710 0234	0.0790 7292	0.0874 5081
33	0.0624 9004	0.0663 3469	0.0702 7293	0.0784 0807	0.0868 5163
34	0.0617 5545	0.0656 2958	0.0695 9843	0.0777 9674	0.0863 0411
35	0.0610 7171	0.0649 7493	0.0689 7386	0.0772 3396	0.0858 0326
36	0.0604 3446	0.0643 6635	0.0683 9483	0.0767 1531	0.0853 4467
37	0.0598 3979	0.0637 9993	0.0678 5743	0.0762 3685	0.0849 2440
38	0.0592 8423	0.0632 7217	0.0673 5812	0.0757 9505	0.0845 3894
39	0.0587 6462	0.0627 7991	0.0668 9377	0.0753 8676	0.0841 8513
40	0.0582 7816	0.0623 2034	0.0664 6154	0.0750 0914	0.0838 6016
41	0.0578 2229	0.0618 9090	0.0660 5886	0.0746 5962	0.0835 6149
42	0.0573 9471	0.0614 8927	0.0656 8342	0.0743 3591	0.0832 8684
43	0.0569 9333	0.0611 1337	0.0653 3312	0.0740 3590	0.0830 3414
44	0.0566 1625	0.0607 6128	0.0650 0606	0.0737 5769	0.0828 0152
45	0.0562 6173	0.0604 3127	0.0647 0050	0.0734 9957	0.0825 8728
46	0.0559 2820	0.0601 2175	0.0644 1485	0.0732 5996	0.0823 8991
47	0.0556 1421	0.0598 3129	0.0641 4768	0.0730 3744	0.0822 0799
48	0.0553 1843	0.0595 5854	0.0638 9766	0.0728 3070	0.0820 4027
49	0.0550 3965	0.0593 0230	0.0636 6356	0.0726 3853	0.0818 8557
50	0.0547 7674	0.0590 6145	0.0634 4429	0.0724 5985	0.0817 4286

ANNUITY WHICH 1 WILL BUY
(Annuity Whose Present Value, at Compound Interest, is 1)

$$\frac{1}{a_{\overline{n}|i}} = \frac{i}{1 - (1 + i)^{-n}}$$

n	5 %	$5\frac{1}{2}$ %	6 %	7 %	8 %
51	0.0545 2867	0.0588 3495	0.0632 3880	0.0722 9365	0.0816 1116
52	0.0542 9450	0.0586 2186	0.0630 4617	0.0721 3901	0.0814 8959
53	0.0540 7334	0.0584 2130	0.0628 6551	0.0719 9509	0.0813 7735
54	0.0538 6438	0.0582 3245	0.0626 9602	0.0718 6110	0.0812 7370
55	0.0536 6686	0.0580 5458	0.0625 3696	0.0717 3633	0.0811 7796
56	0.0534 8010	0.0578 8698	0.0623 8765	0.0716 2011	0.0810 8952
57	0.0533 0343	0.0577 2900	0.0622 4744	0.0715 1183	0.0810 0780
58	0.0531 3626	0.0575 8006	0.0621 1574	0.0714 1093	0.0809 3227
59	0.0529 7802	0.0574 3959	0.0619 9200	0.0713 1689	0.0808 6247
60	0.0528 2818	0.0573 0707	0.0618 7572	0.0712 2923	0.0807 9795
61	0.0526 8627	0.0571 8202	0.0617 6642	0.0711 4749	0.0807 3830
62	0.0525 5183	0.0570 6400	0.0616 6366	0.0710 7127	0.0806 8314
63	0.0524 2442	0.0569 5258	0.0615 6704	0.0710 0019	0.0806 3214
64	0.0523 0365	0.0568 4737	0.0614 7615	0.0709 3388	0.0805 8497
65	0.0521 8915	0.0567 4800	0.0613 9066	0.0708 7203	0.0805 4135
66	0.0520 8057	0.0566 5413	0.0613 1022	0.0708 1431	0.0805 0100
67	0.0519 7757	0.0565 6544	0.0612 3454	0.0707 6046	0.0804 6367
68	0.0518 7986	0.0564 8163	0.0611 6330	0.0707 1021	0.0804 2914
69	0.0517 8715	0.0564 0242	0.0610 9625	0.0706 6331	0.0803 9719
70	0.0516 9915	0.0563 2754	0.0610 3313	0.0706 1953	0.0803 6764
71	0.0516 1563	0.0562 5675	0.0609 7370	0.0705 7866	0.0803 4029
72	0.0515 3633	0.0561 8982	0.0609 1774	0.0705 4051	0.0803 1498
73	0.0514 6103	0.0561 2652	0.0608 6505	0.0705 0490	0.0802 9157
74	0.0513 8953	0.0560 6665	0.0608 1542	0.0704 7164	0.0802 6989
75	0.0513 2161	0.0560 1002	0.0607 6867	0.0704 4060	0.0802 4984
76	0.0512 5709	0.0559 5645	0.0607 2463	0.0704 1160	0.0802 3128
77	0.0511 9580	0.0559 0577	0.0606 8315	0.0703 8453	0.0802 1410
78	0.0511 3756	0.0558 5781	0.0606 4407	0.0703 5924	0.0801 9820
79	0.0510 8222	0.0558 1243	0.0606 0724	0.0703 3563	0.0801 8349
80	0.0510 2962	0.0557 6948	0.0605 7254	0.0703 1357	0.0801 6987
81	0.0509 7963	0.0557 2884	0.0605 3984	0.0702 9297	0.0801 5726
82	0.0509 3211	0.0556 9036	0.0605 0903	0.0702 7373	0.0801 4559
83	0.0508 8694	0.0556 5395	0.0604 7998	0.0702 5576	0.0801 3479
84	0.0508 4399	0.0556 1947	0.0604 5261	0.0702 3897	0.0801 2479
85	0.0508 0316	0.0555 8683	0.0604 2681	0.0702 2329	0.0801 1553
86	0.0507 6433	0.0555 5593	0.0604 0249	0.0702 0863	0.0801 0696
87	0.0507 2740	0.0555 2667	0.0603 7956	0.0701 9495	0.0800 9903
88	0.0506 9228	0.0554 9896	0.0603 5795	0.0701 8216	0.0800 9168
89	0.0506 5888	0.0554 7273	0.0603 3757	0.0701 7021	0.0800 8489
90	0.0506 2711	0.0554 4788	0.0603 1836	0.0701 5905	0.0800 7859
91	0.0505 9689	0.0554 2435	0.0603 0025	0.0701 4863	0.0800 7277
92	0.0505 6815	0.0554 0207	0.0602 8318	0.0701 3888	0.0800 6737
93	0.0505 4080	0.0553 8096	0.0602 6708	0.0701 2978	0.0800 6238
94	0.0505 1478	0.0553 6097	0.0602 5190	0.0701 2128	0.0800 5775
95	0.0504 9003	0.0553 4204	0.0602 3758	0.0701 1333	0.0800 5347
96	0.0504 6648	0.0553 2410	0.0602 2408	0.0701 0590	0.0800 4951
97	0.0504 4407	0.0553 0711	0.0602 1135	0.0700 9897	0.0800 4584
98	0.0504 2274	0.0552 9101	0.0601 9935	0.0700 9248	0.0800 4244
99	0.0504 0245	0.0552 7577	0.0601 8803	0.0700 8643	0.0800 3930
100	0.0503 8314	0.0552 6132	0.0601 7736	0.0700 8076	0.0800 3638
∞	0.0500 0000	0.0550 0000	0.0600 0000	0.0700 0000	0.0800 0000

INDEX